Dossier on Jam

Name: James Bond

Occupation: British Agent. Code Number: to kill.

D1539200

Personality: Sophistic id. Addicted to good food, good women, and good spying. Fulfills his Government assignments with speed and ruthlessness. As an antidote to danger, frankly enjoys the softer side of life.

Assignments:

—*Casino Royale* (1954): A formidable Communist agent called "Le Chiffre" must recoup some funds embezzled from his party, or be liquidated. Bond's mission: break Le Chiffre's bankroll. In some of the most excruciatingly tense gaming scenes ever recorded, Bond faces his adversary across the baccarat table of a famous French casino.

—*From Russia, with Love* (1957): SMERSH, the murder organization of the Soviet, has given orders to kill Bond "with ignominy." The deadly snare, set for Bond in Istanbul, is baited with a virginal young Russian Garbo and directed by a malevolent female executioner whose methods make even the Kremlin cringe. Other essential ingredients: a mad Irish gunman who kills by the light of the moon and a maximum of violence in the cozy compartments of the Orient Express.

—*Doctor No* (1958): When Bond nearly loses his life through negligence, his superior reprimands him by handing him a seemingly shabby little case in the Caribbean. No pushover after all, the case involves a maniacal genius who looks like "a giant venomous worm wrapped in grey tin-foil." Dr. No's goal? World power. His hobby? Torture.

Summing up: In the words of Paul Gallico: "Mr. Fleming's books cannot hurt you, but with a little imagination on your part, they can scare the hell out of you."

GILT-EDGED BONDS

gilt-edged bonds

CASINO ROYALE
FROM RUSSIA, WITH LOVE
DOCTOR NO

Ian Fleming

With an Introduction by Paul Gallico

THE MACMILLAN COMPANY
NEW YORK 1961

INTRODUCTION

IT WOULD seem that at least once in every generation there appears on the horizon of the literary world a writer of spy thrillers who creates and presents a character who manages wholly to capture the imagination of a large portion of the reading public.

The spy is older than recorded history. The secret service is a game that has fascinated man from the very beginning of that time when the incurable predilection of the human race for aggression and violence made it a necessity to know what the other fellow was up to. Intelligence, counterintelligence, and security came into being the moment that man ceased to fight as an individual and banded together as a group for invasion or defense.

Out of the exploits of the undercover men who risk their lives to obtain the secrets of the enemy, storytellers have woven romantic tales that have never failed to fascinate the reader. Latest and last in the line of these is James Bond of the British Secret Service, created one day out of the blue by a colleague of mine, Mr. Ian Fleming, with whom I was associated when he was Foreign Manager for the Kemsley newspapers in London and who, up to 1953, had given no indication whatsoever that within him there lurked a James Bond waiting to be born.

In seven years Fleming has produced eight James Bond novels, of which three of the best, including the first one to spring practically whole-panoplied from his brain, are presented in this omnibus.

All these novels were not only best sellers (if you are impressed by figures, more than two million copies have been sold in England, the United States, and foreign territory as far as Japan) but have also managed to kick up a fine dust of controversy. In the brief space of time between the appearance of *Casino Royale* and the present day, James Bond has taken his place as a living fictional character, as surely as have Bulldog Drummond, Raffles, Richard Hannay, and the Scarlet Pimpernel. Bond has made his mark upon the public consciousness, and exists now as truly as if he had been born of woman, filled with the breath of life. He has already lived long enough to haunt and turn upon his creator, Mr. Fleming, to ride his shoulders like the Old Man of the Sea or, like the ventriloquist's dummy, to threaten to become his alter ego. He has in this brief span suffered all the duplications and reproductions of popularity. He has appeared between hard covers, in paperbacks, in serial form, as a cartoon strip, and now in an omnibus. Moving pictures featuring him are in production, and no doubt he will eventually tread the boards in a play.

Analysts, journalists, literary critics, not to mention viewers-with-alarm, have tried to ascertain reasons for the popularity of Bond. Mr. Fleming himself, in a lecture delivered before a group of adoring ladies at one of those literary teas perpetrated by a great London department store to stimulate book sales, made an attempt to untangle those elements that entered into the writing of a successful thriller. Shattered, in all probability, by facing an all-female audience, Mr. Fleming put it down to his meticulousness of detail, which included such items as identifying the nature of the cotton that went into the shirts worn by James Bond.

Undoubtedly the publishers will take credit for astuteness; the publisher's promotion department will not be averse to taking a bow for helping to create a demand, but none of these, not even the author himself, is in the main truly responsible for the sudden popularity of a fictional character. Praise or blame for this must be laid at the door of the public.

In *Casino Royale* Ian Fleming offered a new and fascinating Secret Service operative involved in equally fascinating and thrilling adventures. The public fell in love with him, and demanded more. Thereafter Ian Fleming ceased to work for himself and became instead the marriage broker between his character and the demanding public. The love affair is still going on.

The James Bond stories are filled with violence, torture, sex, cruelty, and other of the less admirable attributes of humanity, and Mr. Fleming has been assailed by the critics for being a sadist delighting in the recounting of the agonies that may be inflicted upon the human body. None of these critics, however, appears to have accused the readers of a like sadism for enjoying these books, or to suggest that really what Mr. Fleming has done with his character and his adventures is to keynote the times, the era in which we live, and the violences either perpetrated upon our fellow men or equally threatening us.

If one took the trouble to study the various heroes of thrillers who have captured the public since modern printing made cheap books available to all, one would find oneself unavoidably involved in the mood and history of the times. Every new, successful thriller hero has appeared at the very moment that the public was ready for him. The way to create a popular fiction character and write best sellers is to give the public what it craves at the very moment that it craves it.

It is a fair commentary upon the times and the mores that James Bond has entered the hero class in spite of the fact that his creator never intended him to be one, and Fleming himself has made it plain that Bond is not meant to be particularly virtuous. In fact the double "o" placed before his service number signalizes his antivirtue, for it means that Bond has killed and will kill to earn his salary.

Naturally this is no more wicked in Bond than in the soldier who likewise kills for pay, and on a wholesale scale. But human beings who enjoy paradox to the verge of idiocy insist upon making a distinction between the Government killer in peacetime and wartime. The author's approach to his creation is that he simply does an assigned Government job as well, as quickly, and as ruthlessly as he can and is not namby-pamby about enjoying the softer side of life, for, exactly like the soldier, he doesn't know how long he will be here to enjoy it. He regards himself as something of a blunt instrument in the hands of a Government department.

There is, it may be said, an almost attractive definiteness about the diplomacy of assassination; in fact, as one regards the number of unpleasant or dangerous specimens still permitted to remain on earth to disturb the peace, one is forced to the conclusion that this manner of settling matters with finality has fallen too much into neglect of late.

If the attempt to assassinate Hitler had succeeded, many thousands of better lives would have been saved.

A glance backward through history will show that the removal of monsters by violence, where nothing else would prevail, has in the main resulted in an improvement. It is true that there are always other monsters prepared to arise and take the place of the eliminated, but the example of a little corrective killing sometimes leads them to think twice.

The instruments of such sometimes necessary policy have never been regarded as admirable creatures, and James Bond has been attacked (as though indeed he were a living person) as no better than a thug, but the fact is that he is far better than that. Secret Service pay is never high; public kudos there is none; recognition and medals there are never, and so the Service hardly attracts the really bloody-minded killer-for-pay. Your genuine operative, of which Bond is a fair and accurate example, is always an odd ball of one kind or another, and in his odd ballness there is always more than a little touch of romantic patriotism. He may be playing a dangerous game for the game's sake, or the salary, but the fact is that he is playing it for *his* side and he sticks to that side under both temptation and torture. This is what willy-nilly, and Ian Fleming to the contrary notwithstanding, turns James Bond into a hero, or at least into a hero of our way of thinking *anno Domini* 1961.

Or one can, if one wishes, read some of the disillusionment and cynicism of our times into the adventures of Agent 007, James Bond. He is not like the fictional operatives and heroes of a generation ago, wholly indestructible. He doesn't always win, and when his enemies damage him it hurts loudly and violently. Likewise, he stays damaged and doesn't offend public intelligence by bouncing up off the floor after excruciating beatings and tortures to ride off unharmed in all directions. Mr. Bond decently goes to hospital.

Similarly, his encounters or connections with the female

sex are in the modern manner. Sooner or later he unites with them in the full meaning of the word. This may not be admirable or ideal, but then who ever said the times or human beings were either praiseworthy or idyllic?

Quite possibly one of the things that attracts the male reader to James Bond is the fact that the heroines of these stories are only "temporaries." Eventually, you may rest assured, Bond and the heroine will be in bed, with no kind of permanence threatened, thus injecting an entirely new meaning into "boy gets girl."

This combination of sex and battle, copulation and gunfire, comes, I am told, as a shock to the more sheltered, but is easily understood by men of the present generation, with a war no more than fifteen years behind them, who went from sex to battle or battle to sex, or sometimes even found an opportunity during battle.

In my day there was a middleweight prize fighter from Pittsburgh, the late Harry Greb, one of the most destructive humans ever to lace on a pair of red leather mittens. Dated up for an evening contest in which his opponent was not expected to provoke him too greatly, Greb was known to leap from the downy in his hotel circa nine-thirty, the bout being scheduled to begin at ten, and cover the maiden remaining there tenderly with the sheet, remarking, "Don't go 'way, baby; I'll be back in about an hour." He would then repair to the arena, flail his opponent into a state of coma, grab a fast shower, and return to the more delectable battleground. I quote this anecdote only to show that it can be done, a point likewise made by Mr. Fleming when booed by the Nice Nellies.

The modern gambit in literary criticism, or even extended reader interest, is to refuse to give the author credit for a vivid imagination or a true storytelling gift, and hence to try to search beyond the character or characters in a novel into the life and background of the writer for clues to explain this, that, and the other that one has just read.

The only occasion upon which Mr. Fleming was compelled to submit to torture doesn't exactly form a basis for the trials through which he has put his James Bond in the three volumes you are about to encounter, but you had best have the affair nevertheless for whatever you wish to make of it.

Ian Fleming, the second son among four, and under the shadow of a brilliant elder brother Peter who preceded him at Eton, in an effort to shine against this darkness became Victor Ludorum of Britain's great public school at the age of sixteen, which means that he won the individual track and field championship. The following year he was well on his way on points to win this championship a second consecutive time, a feat unique in Eton's history. There remained only the Eton steeplechase in which, if young Fleming placed, he would win the title again.

Unfortunately, bad marks for various scholastic failures and misdemeanors had been piling up against our hero to such a degree that he found himself facing an appointment with the headmaster to be birched, or in plain, simple English beaten on his posterior, a form of punishment considered salutary at that institution.

Birching at Eton takes place at midday, which was also the time of the start of the steeplechase. Yet once again the young Fleming broke historic precedent. He petitioned the headmaster that he should be birched at 11:45 to allow him to reach the starting line at noon. This request was graciously acceded to, and promptly at 11:45 the seventeen-year-old Fleming was properly tanned. He thereupon ran the steeplechase, his shanks and running shorts stained by his own gore, and duly came in second with Victor Ludorum in his grasp. This incident, among others, left Mr. Fleming with a mysterious affection for Eton that has lasted to this day. So much for torture.

Ian Fleming was born in 1908 of Scottish parents. His father, Major Valentine Fleming, D.S.O., M.P., was killed in 1916 serving with the Oxfordshire Hussars, which was also Winston Churchill's regiment. Major Fleming was a great friend of Churchill's, and the latter wrote his obituary in *The Times*.

Fleming's brilliant brother Peter was sent to Oxford. Ian, the second son, was consigned to Sandhurst (the English West Point) as being fit only for army fodder. Perhaps the ardent searcher here will find one explanation of Ian Fleming's turning himself into a hot bomb to explode beneath the chairs of the literati.

At Sandhurst, besides continuing as a track and field star, Fleming confesses that he distinguished himself by acquiring the heaviest punishment ever meted out there short of dismissal—a month confined to barracks and six months' stoppage of leave. This was imposed for arriving late from a visit to the London night clubs with a beautiful girl and bribing a friend to sign in for him in order that he might return her to her home at nearby Aldershot. He then climbed in the window of his company headquarters only to hear the shuffling of feet of the sentry already posted outside his door to keep him under close arrest.

Nevertheless he took the final exams for his commission and was due to be gazetted to the Black Watch, but states that at this time the terrible rumor ran through Sandhurst that the army was about to be mechanized, and he and a number of his pals decided they didn't wish to be "garage hands" for the rest of their lives. Hence they declined their commissions, and Fleming went abroad to study at the universities of Munich and Geneva, after which he joined Reuters and worked in London, Berlin, and Moscow. It was during this time that Fleming learned to write quick, hard-hitting prose, and likewise to be sure of his facts. For these were the days when Reuter's was engaged in its great battle against the Associated Press and the United Press of the U.S.A.

Thereafter Fleming tried a spell of stockbroking, but confesses he found that kind of money-making less than enjoyable, and in 1939 persuaded *The Times* of London to send him to Moscow as their special correspondent, where he remained until June of that year when, via the application of the Director of Naval Intelligence to the Governor of the Bank of England for a young man who had foreign languages and international experience, Fleming found himself in the uniform of a lieutenant in the Special Branch of the R.N.V.R., and heavily involved with secret services and the like as personal assistant to the Director of Naval Intelligence. Within eighteen months he was a full commander.

Like all diffident Englishmen, nothing about Fleming's war can be pried out of him beyond the mere statement that he survived it; but there are facts to indicate that there were some nervous moments at Dieppe when he and his friends, anxious to abstract German naval ciphers, ran into some irritable enemy soldiery, as well as various other foolish or hazardous engagements.

Upon being demobbed, Fleming was commissioned by Lord Kemsley to reorganize the foreign service of the *Sunday Times* and the rest of his group of newspapers, and was named Foreign Manager to the Kemsley string, where he remained until the end of 1959. One of the conditions made by Fleming was that he should have January and February of each year to himself to retire to a small house he had built on the north shore of Jamaica and named Goldeneye, since Fleming had always loved sunshine, the sea, and things beneath the sea. It was this house, incidentally, that was borrowed by Sir Anthony Eden when his health collapsed after Suez.

If so far you have encountered no clue as to the making of a best-selling thriller writer, what follows will baffle you still further; nevertheless you are entitled to the facts.

Up to 1952 Fleming had remained a bachelor; in that year the step toward matrimony had become to him terrifyingly inevitable. Horrified by the prospect, but equally hypnotized and unable to resist it, he attempted to anesthetize his nerves one day at Goldeneye by threading a piece of paper into his battered Royal portable and writing: "The scent and smoke and sweat of a casino are nauseating at three in the morning. . . . James Bond suddenly knew that he was tired. . . ." These are two of the opening sentences of *Casino Royale*. Having crossed that first fearful chasm that separates blank white paper from becoming a book, other sentences followed in due and logical course.

When Fleming returned from Jamaica that spring, he had the manuscript with him, and one day found himself lunching as he did once a month with his close friend William Plomer, the poet and author, who is also a reader for Jonathan Cape.

At this luncheon Fleming said to Plomer, "How do you get smoke out of a woman once you have got it into her?"

"What do you mean?"

"Well, a woman inhales a cigarette. In due course she has to get the smoke out of her. You can't say 'exhales' because that is an O.K. word, and she can't puff, blow, or dribble it out, as this doesn't sound feminine. How do you get it out of her?"

Plomer looked at him. "You've written a book!"

"Well, not exactly a book; it's a sort of thriller thing."

Plomer insisted upon seeing it, and shortly afterward a contract with Jonathan Cape was signed.

Fleming is probably the only author who ever perpetrated the sequel to his first novel before that novel was published, which courageous gamble was due to Michael Arlen to whom Fleming showed page proofs of *Casino Royale*. Arlen said, "Write your second book before you see reviews of your first; otherwise your literary heart may be broken."

Fleming did so, and wrote *Live and Let Die* in January and February of 1953 at Jamaica, which turned out to be money for jam, since Arlen was wrong. *Casino Royale* was an instantaneous hit.

Ian Fleming today is married and is the father of a son. His hobby is spear fishing beneath the Caribbean for barracuda, bonita, grouper, or whatever comes along, and his idea of a truly splendid day is a closely contested round of golf on a taxing course, followed by a game of bridge for high stakes.

Yet if there are no direct clues to James Bond to be found in the foregoing, there is no gainsaying that Fleming is a product of his era and a reflector of the times. The newspapers are filled daily with accounts of violences and horrors taking place on far continents, many of them far more agonizing and shocking than those presented in these books. Fleming simply puts this grist through the mill of his experience and his fictional mind and brings them a little closer to us.

Psychologists have analyzed the cat lovers as keepers of miniature tigers fully equipped with claws and teeth; so dangerous if they were larger, so safe because they are small. Mr. Fleming's books are something like this. They cannot hurt you, but with a little imagination on your part they can scare the hell out of you.

PAUL GALLICO

CASINO ROYALE

i. THE SECRET AGENT

THE SCENT and smoke and sweat of a casino are nauseating at three in the morning. Then the soul-erosion produced by high gambling—a compost of greed and fear and nervous tension—becomes unbearable, and the senses awake and revolt from it.

James Bond suddenly knew that he was tired. He always knew when his body or his mind had had enough, and he always acted on the knowledge. This helped him to avoid staleness and the sensual bluntness that breeds mistakes.

He shifted himself unobtrusively away from the roulette he had been playing and went to stand for a moment at the brass rail which surrounded breast-high the top table in the salle privée.

Le Chiffre was still playing and still, apparently, winning. There was an untidy pile of flecked hundred-mille plaques in front of him. In the shadow of his thick left arm there nestled a discreet stack of the big yellow ones worth half a million francs each.

Bond watched the curious, impressive profile for a time, and then he shrugged his shoulders to lighten his thoughts and moved away.

The barrier surrounding the caisse comes as high as your chin, and the caissier, who is generally nothing more than a minor bank clerk, sits on a stool and dips into his piles of notes and plaques. These are ranged on shelves. They are

9

on a level, behind the protecting barrier, with your groin. The caissier has a cosh and a gun to protect him, and to heave over the barrier and steal some notes and then vault back and get out of the Casino through the passages and doors would be impossible. And the caissiers generally work in pairs.

Bond reflected on the problem as he collected the sheaf of hundred-thousand and then the sheaves of ten-thousand-franc notes. With another part of his mind, he had a vision of tomorrow's regular morning meeting of the Casino committee.

'Monsieur Le Chiffre made two million. He played his usual game. Miss Fairchild made a million an hour and then left. She executed three bancos of Monsieur Le Chiffre within an hour and then left. She played with coolness. Monsieur le Vicomte de Villorin made one million two at roulette. He was playing the maximum on the first and last dozens. He was lucky. Then the Englishman, Mister Bond, increased his winnings to exactly three million over the two days. He was playing a progressive system on red at table five. Duclos, the chef de partie, has the details. It seems that he is persevering and pays in maximums. He has luck. His nerves seem good. On the soirée, the chemin-de-fer won x, the baccarat won y and the roulette won z. The boule, which was again badly frequented, still makes its expenses.'

'Merci, Monsieur Xavier.'

'Merci, Monsieur le Président.'

Or something like that, thought Bond as he pushed his way through the swing doors of the salle privée and nodded to the bored man in evening clothes whose job it is to bar your entry and your exit with the electric foot-switch which can lock the doors at any hint of trouble.

And the Casino committee would balance its books and break up to its homes or cafés for lunch.

As for robbing the caisse, in which Bond himself was not personally concerned, but only interested, he reflected that it would take ten good men, that they would certainly have to kill one or two employees, and that anyway you probably couldn't find ten non-squeal killers in France, or in any other country for the matter of that.

As he gave a thousand francs to the 'vestiaire' and walked down the steps of the Casino, Bond made up his mind that Le Chiffre would in no circumstances try to rob the caisse; and he put the contingency out of his mind. Instead he explored his present physical sensations. He felt the dry, uncomfortable gravel under his evening shoes, the bad, harsh taste in his mouth, and the slight sweat under his arms. He could feel his eyes filling their sockets. The front of his face, his nose and antrum, were congested. He breathed the sweet night air deeply and focused his senses and his wits. He wanted to know if anyone had searched his room since he had left it before dinner.

He walked across the broad boulevard and through the gardens to the Hotel Splendide. He smiled at the concierge who gave him his key—No. 45 on the first floor—and took the cable.

It was from Jamaica and read:

KINGSTONJA XXXX XXXXXX XXXX XXX

BOND SPLENDIDE ROYALE-LES-EAUX SEINE INFERIEURE HAVANA CIGAR PRODUCTION ALL CUBAN FACTORIES 1915 TEN MILLION REPEAT TEN MILLION STOP HOPE THIS FIGURE YOU REQUIRE REGARDS

DASILVA

This meant that ten million francs was on the way to him. It was the reply to a request Bond had sent that afternoon through Paris to his headquarters in London asking for more funds. Paris had spoken to London where Clements, the head of Bond's department, had spoken to M. who had smiled wryly and told 'The Broker' to fix it with the Treasury.

Bond had once worked in Jamaica, and his cover on the Royale assignment was that of a very rich client of Messrs. Caffery, the principal import and export firm of Jamaica. So he was being controlled through Jamaica, through a taciturn man who was head of the picture desk on the *Daily Gleaner*, the famous newspaper of the Caribbean.

This man on the *Gleaner*, whose name was Fawcett, had been bookkeeper for one of the leading turtle-fisheries on the Cayman Islands. One of the men from the Caymans who had volunteered on the outbreak of war, he had ended up as a Paymaster's clerk in a small naval intelligence organization in Malta. At the end of the war, when, with a heavy heart, he was about to return to the Caymans, he was spotted by the section of the Secret Service concerned with the Caribbean. He was strenuously trained in photography and in some other arts and, with the quiet connivance of an influential man in Jamaica, found his way to the picture desk of the *Gleaner*.

In the intervals between sifting photographs submitted by the great agencies—Keystone, Wide World, Universal, I.N.P., and Reuter-Photo—he would get peremptory instructions by telephone from a man he had never met to carry out certain simple operations requiring nothing but absolute discretion, speed, and accuracy. For these occasional services he received twenty pounds a month paid into his account with the Royal Bank of Canada by a fictitious relative in England.

Fawcett's present assignment was to relay immediately to

Bond, full rates, the text of messages which he received at home by telephone from his anonymous contact. He had been told by this contact that nothing he would be asked to send would arouse the suspicion of the Jamaican post office. So he was not surprised to find himself suddenly appointed string correspondent for the 'Maritime Press and Photo Agency,' with press-collect facilities to France and England, on a further monthly retainer of ten pounds.

He felt secure and, encouraged, had visions of a B.E.M. and made the first payment on a Morris Minor. He also bought a green eyeshade which he had long coveted, and which helped him to impose his personality on the picture desk.

Some of this background to his cable passed through Bond's mind. He was used to oblique control and rather liked it. He felt it featherbedded him a little, allowed him to give or take an hour or two in his communications with M. He knew that this was probably a fallacy, that probably there was another member of the Service at Royale-les-Eaux who was reporting independently, but it did give the illusion that he wasn't only 150 miles across the Channel from that deadly office building near Regent's Park, being watched and judged by those few cold brains that made the whole show work. Just as Fawcett, the Cayman Islander in Kingston, knew that if he bought that Morris Minor outright instead of signing the hire-purchase agreement, someone in London would probably know and want to know where the money had come from.

Bond read the cable twice. He tore a telegraph form off the pad on the desk (why give them carbon copies?) and wrote his reply in capital letters:

THANKS INFORMATION SHOULD SUFFICE

BOND.

He handed this to the concierge and put the cable signed 'Dasilva' in his pocket. The employers (if any) of the concierge could bribe a copy out of the local post office, if the concierge hadn't already steamed the envelope open or read the cable upside down in Bond's hands.

He took his key and said good night and turned to the stairs, shaking his head at the liftman. Bond knew what an obliging danger-signal a lift could be. He didn't expect any-one to be moving on the first floor, but he preferred to be prudent.

Walking quietly up on the balls of his feet, he regretted the hubris of his reply to M. via Jamaica. As a gambler he knew it was a mistake to rely on too small a capital. Anyway, M. probably wouldn't let him have any more. He shrugged his shoulders and turned off the stairs into the corridor and walked softly to the door of his room.

Bond knew exactly where the switch was, and it was with one flow of motion that he stood on the threshold with the door full open, the light on and a gun in his hand. The safe, empty room sneered at him. He ignored the half-open door of the bathroom and, after locking himself in, he turned up the bed-light and the mirror-light and threw his gun on the settee beside the window. Then he bent down and inspected one of his own black hairs which still lay undisturbed where he had left it before dinner, wedged into the drawer of the writing-desk.

Next he examined a faint trace of talcum powder on the inner rim of the porcelain handle of the clothes cupboard. It appeared immaculate. He went into the bathroom, lifted the cover of the lavatory cistern and verified the level of the water against a small scratch on the copper ball-cock.

Doing all this, inspecting these minute burglar-alarms, did not make him feel foolish or self-conscious. He was a secret agent, and still alive thanks to his exact attention to the detail of his profession. Routine precautions were to him no more unreasonable than they would be to a deep-sea diver or a test pilot, or to any man earning danger-money.

Satisfied that his room had not been searched while he was at the Casino, Bond undressed and took a cold shower. Then he lit his seventieth cigarette of the day and sat down at the writing-table with the thick wad of his stake money and winnings beside him and entered some figures in a small notebook. Over the two days' play, he was up exactly three million francs. In London he had been issued with ten million, and he had asked London for a further ten. With this on its way to the local branch of the Crédit Lyonnais, his working capital amounted to twenty-three million francs, or some twenty-three thousand pounds.

For a few moments Bond sat motionless, gazing out of the window across the dark sea; then he shoved the bundle of banknotes under the pillow of the ornate single bed, cleaned his teeth, turned out the lights and climbed with relief between the harsh French sheets. For ten minutes he lay on his left side reflecting on the events of the day. Then he turned over and focused his mind towards the tunnel of sleep.

His last action was to slip his right hand under the pillow until it rested under the butt of the .38 Colt Police Positive with the sawn barrel. Then he slept, and with the warmth and humour of his eyes extinguished his features relapsed into a taciturn mask, ironical, brutal, and cold.

TWO WEEKS before, this memorandum had gone from Station S. of the Secret Service to M., who was then and is today head of this adjunct to the British defence ministries:

To: M.

From: Head of S.

Subject: A project for the destruction of Monsieur Le Chiffre (alias 'The Number,' 'Herr Nummer,' 'Herr Ziffer,' etc.), one of the Opposition's chief agents in France and undercover Paymaster of the 'Syndicat des Ouvriers d'Alsace,' the communist-controlled trade union in the heavy and transport industries of Alsace and, as we know, an important fifth column in the event of war with Redland.

Documentation: Head of Archives' biography of Le Chiffre is attached at *Appendix A.* Also, *Appendix B,* a note on SMERSH.

We have been feeling for some time that Le Chiffre is getting into deep water. In nearly all respects he is an admirable agent of the U.S.S.R.; but his gross physical habits and predilections are an Achilles heel of which we have been able to take advantage from time to time, and one of his mistresses is a Eurasian (No. 1860) controlled by Station F., who has recently been able to obtain some insight into his private affairs.

Briefly, it seems that Le Chiffre is on the brink of a financial crisis. Certain straws in the wind were noticed by 1860 —some discreet sales of jewellery, the disposal of a villa at Antibes, and a general tendency to check the loose spending which has always been a feature of his way of life. Further inquiries were made with the help of our friends of the Deuxième Bureau (with whom we have been working jointly on this case) and a curious story has come to light.

In January 1946 Le Chiffre bought control of a chain of brothels, known as the 'Cordon Jaune,' operating in Normandy and Brittany. He was foolish enough to employ for this purpose some fifty million francs of the moneys entrusted to him by Leningrad Section III for the financing of S.O.D.A., the trade union mentioned above.

Normally the Cordon Jaune would have proved a most excellent investment; and it is possible that Le Chiffre was motivated more by a desire to increase his union funds than by the hope of lining his own pocket by speculating with his employers' money. However that may be, it is clear that he could have found many investments more savoury than prostitution, if he had not been tempted by the by-product of unlimited women for his personal use.

Fate rebuked him with terrifying swiftness.

Barely three months later, on the 13th April, there was passed in France Law No. 46685 entitled *Loi Tendant à la Fermeture des Maisons de Tolérance et au Renforcement de la Lutte contre le Proxénitisme.*

(When M. came to this sentence he grunted and pressed a switch on the intercom.

'Head of S?'

'Sir.'

'What the hell does this word mean?' He spelt it out.

'Pimping, sir.'

'This is not the Berlitz School of Languages, Head of S. If you want to show off your knowledge of foreign jaw-breakers, be good enough to provide a crib. Better still, write in English.'

'Sorry, sir.'

M. released the switch and turned back to the memorandum.)

This law (he read), known popularly as 'La Loi Marthe Richard,' closing all houses of ill-fame and forbidding the sale of pornographic books and films, knocked the bottom out of his investment almost overnight, and suddenly Le Chiffre was faced with a serious deficit in his union funds. In desperation he turned his open houses into 'maisons de passe' where clandestine rendezvous could be arranged on the border-line of the law, and he continued to operate one or two 'cinemas bleus' underground; but these shifts in no way served to cover his overheads, and all attempts to sell his investment, even at a heavy loss, failed dismally. Meanwhile the Police des Mœurs were on his trail, and in a short while twenty or more of his establishments were closed down.

The police were, of course, only interested in this man as a big-time brothel-keeper, and it was not until we expressed an interest in his finances that the Deuxième Bureau unearthed the parallel dossier which was running with their colleagues of the police department.

The significance of the situation became apparent to us and to our French friends, and, in the past few months, a veritable rat-hunt has been operated by the police after the establishments of the Cordon Jaune, with the result that to-day nothing remains of Le Chiffre's original investment, and any routine inquiry would reveal a deficit of around fifty million francs in the trade-union funds of which he is the treasurer and paymaster.

It does not seem that the suspicions of Leningrad have been aroused yet; but, unfortunately for Le Chiffre, it is possible that at any rate SMERSH is on the scent. Last week a high-grade source of Station P. reported that a senior official of this efficient organ of Soviet vengeance had left Warsaw for Strasbourg via the Eastern sector of Berlin. There is no confirmation of this report from the Deuxième Bureau, nor from the authorities in Strasbourg (who are reliable and thorough) and there is also no news from Le Chiffre's headquarters there, which we have well covered by a double agent (in addition to 1860).

If Le Chiffre knew that SMERSH was on his tail or that they had the smallest suspicion of him, he would have no alternative to committing suicide or attempting to escape; but his present plans suggest that, while he is certainly desperate, he does not yet realize that his life may be at stake. It is these rather spectacular plans of his that have suggested to us a counter-operation which, though risky and unconventional, we submit at the end of this memorandum with confidence.

In brief, Le Chiffre plans, we believe, to follow the example of most other desperate till-robbers and make good the deficit in his accounts by gambling. The 'Bourse' is too slow. So are the various illicit traffics in drugs, or rare medicines, such as aureo- and streptomycin and cortisone. No race tracks could carry the sort of stakes he will have to play; and, if he won, he would more likely be killed than paid off.

In any case, we know that he has withdrawn the final twenty-five million francs from the treasury of his union, and that he has taken a small villa in the neighbourhood of Royale-les-Eaux, just north of Dieppe, for a week from a fortnight tomorrow.

Now, it is expected that the Casino at Royale will see the highest gambling in Europe this summer. In an effort to wrest the big money from Deauville and Le Touquet, the Société des Bains de Mers de Royale have leased the baccarat and the two top chemin-de-fer tables to the Mahomet Ali Syndicate, a group of émigré Egyptian bankers and business-men with, it is said, a call on certain royal funds, who have for years been trying to cut in on the profits of Zographos and his Greek associates resulting from their monopoly of the highest French baccarat banks.

With the help of discreet publicity, a considerable num-ber of the biggest operators in America and Europe have been encouraged to book at Royale this summer and it seems possible that this old-fashioned watering-place will regain some of its Victorian renown.

Be that as it may, it is here that Le Chiffre will, we are confident, endeavour on or after 15 June to make a profit at baccarat of fifty million francs on a working capital of twen-ty-five million. (And, incidentally, save his life.)

Proposed Counter-operation

It would be greatly in the interests of this country and of the other nations of the North Atlantic Treaty Organiza-tion that this powerful Soviet agent should be ridiculed and destroyed, that his communist trade union should be bank-rupted and brought into disrepute, and that this potential fifth column, with a strength of 50,000, capable in time of war of controlling a wide sector of France's northern fron-tier, should lose faith and cohesion. All this would result if Le Chiffre could be defeated at the tables. (N.B. Assassina-tion is pointless. Leningrad would quickly cover up his de-falcations and make him into a martyr.)

We therefore recommend that the finest gambler available

to the Service should be given the necessary funds and endeavour to outgamble this man.

The risks are obvious, and the possible loss to the Secret funds is high; but other operations on which large sums have been hazarded have had fewer chances of success, often for a smaller objective.

If the decision is unfavourable, the only alternative would be to place our information and our recommendations in the hands of the Deuxième Bureau or of our American colleagues of the Combined Intelligence Agency in Washington. Both of these organizations would doubtless be delighted to take over the scheme.

Signed: S.

Appendix A.
Name: Le Chiffre.
Aliases: Variations on the words 'cypher' or 'number' in different languages; e.g., 'Herr Ziffer.'
Origin: Unknown.

First encountered as a displaced person, inmate of Dachau D.P. camp in the U.S. Zone of Germany, June, 1945. Apparently suffering from amnesia and paralysis of vocal cords (? both feigned). Dumbness succumbed to therapy, but subject continued to claim total loss of memory except associations with Alsace Lorraine and Strasbourg whither he was transferred in September, 1945, on Stateless Passport No. 304-596. Adopted the name 'Le Chiffre' ('since I am only a number on a passport'). No Christian names.

Age: About 45.
Description: Height 5 ft. 8 in. Weight 18 stone. Complexion

very pale. Clean-shaven. Hair red-brown, 'en brosse.'
Eyes very dark brown with whites showing all round
iris. Small, rather feminine mouth. False teeth of expensive quality. Ears small, with large lobes, indicating
some Jewish blood. Hands small, well-tended, hirsute.
Feet small. Racially, subject is probably a mixture of
Mediterranean with Prussian or Polish strains. Dresses
well and meticulously, generally in dark double-
breasted suits. Smokes incessantly Caporals, using a de-
nicotinizing holder. At frequent intervals inhales from
benzedrine inhaler. Voice soft and even. Bilingual in
French and English. Good German. Traces of Mar-
seillais accent. Smiles infrequently. Does not laugh.

Habits: Mostly expensive, but discreet. Large sexual appetites. Flagellant. Expert driver of fast cars. Adept with
small arms and other forms of personal combat, including knives. Carries three Eversharp razor blades, in hat-
band, heel of left shoe, and cigarette case. Knowledge
of accountancy and mathematics. Fine gambler. Always accompanied by two armed guards, well-dressed,
one French, one German (details available).

Comment: A formidable and dangerous agent of the U.S.
S.R., controlled by Leningrad Section III through
Paris.

Signed: Archivist.

Appendix B.

Subject: SMERSH

Sources: Own archives and scanty material made available
by Deuxième Bureau and C.I.A. Washington.

SMERSH is a conjunction of two Russian words:
'Smyert Shpionam,' meaning roughly: 'Death to
Spies.'

Ranks above M.W.D. (formerly N.K.V.D.) and is

believed to come under the personal direction of Beria.

Headquarters: Leningrad (substation at Moscow).

Its task is the elimination of all forms of treachery and back-sliding within the various branches of the Soviet Secret Service and Secret Police at home and abroad. It is the most powerful and feared organization in the U.S.S.R. and is popularly believed never to have failed in a mission of vengeance.

It is thought that SMERSH was responsible for the assassination of Trotsky in Mexico (22 August 1940) and may indeed have made its name with this successful murder after attempts by other Russian individuals and organizations had failed.

SMERSH was next heard of when Hitler attacked Russia. It was then rapidly expanded to cope with treachery and double agents during the retreat of the Soviet forces in 1941. At that time it worked as an execution squad for the N.K.V.D., and its present selective mission was not so clearly defined.

The organization itself was thoroughly purged after the war and is now believed to consist of only a few hundred operatives of very high quality divided into five sections:

Department I: In charge of counterintelligence among Soviet organizations at home and abroad.

Department II: Operations, including executions.

Department III: Administration and Finance.

Department IV: Investigations and legal work. Personnel.

Department V: Prosecutions: the section which passes final judgment on all victims.

Only one SMERSH operative has come into our hands since the war: Goytchev, alias Garrad-Jones. He shot

Petchora, medical officer at the Yugoslav Embassy, in
Hyde Park, 7 August 1948. During interrogation he
committed suicide by swallowing a coat-button of
compressed potassium cyanide. He revealed nothing
beyond his membership of SMERSH, of which he was
arrogantly boastful.

We believe that the following British double agents
were victims of SMERSH: Donovan, Harthrop-Vane,
Elizabeth Dumont, Ventnor, Mace, Savarin. (For details see Morgue: Section Q.)

Conclusion: Every effort should be made to improve our
knowledge of this very powerful organization and destroy its operatives.

iii. NUMBER 007

HEAD OF S. (the section of the Secret Service concerned
with the Soviet Union) was so keen on his plan for the destruction of Le Chiffre, and it was basically his own plan,
that he took the memorandum himself and went up to the
top floor of the gloomy building overlooking Regent's Park
and through the green baize door and along the corridor to
the end room.

He walked belligerently up to M.'s chief of staff, a young
sapper who had earned his spurs as one of the secretariat to
the Chiefs of Staff committee after having been wounded
during a sabotage operation in 1944, and had kept his sense
of humour in spite of both experiences.

'Now look here, Bill. I want to sell something to the Chief. Is this a good moment?'

'What do you think, Penny?' The Chief of Staff turned to M.'s private secretary, who shared the room with him.

Miss Moneypenny would have been desirable but for her eyes, which were cool and direct and quizzical.

'Should be all right. He won a bit of a victory at the F.O. this morning and he's not got anyone for the next half an hour.' She smiled encouragingly at Head of S., whom she liked for himself and for the importance of his section.

'Well, here's the dope, Bill.' He handed over the black folder with the red star which stood for Top Secret. 'And for God's sake look enthusiastic when you give it him. And tell him I'll wait here and read a good code-book while he's considering it. He may want some more details, and anyway I want to see you two don't pester him with anything else until he's finished.'

'All right, sir.' The Chief of Staff pressed a switch and leant towards the intercom on his desk.

'Yes?' asked a quiet, flat voice.

'Head of S. has an urgent docket for you, sir.'

There was a pause.

'Bring it in,' said the voice.

The Chief of Staff released the switch and stood up.

'Thanks, Bill. I'll be next door,' said Head of S.

The Chief of Staff crossed his office and went through the double doors leading into M.'s room. In a moment he came out, and over the entrance a small blue light burned the warning that M. was not to be disturbed.

Later, a triumphant Head of S. said to his Number Two: 'We nearly cooked ourselves with that last paragraph. He said it was subversion and blackmail. He got pretty sharp about it. Anyway, he approves. Says the idea's crazy but worth trying if the Treasury will play, and he thinks they will. He's going to tell them it's a better gamble than the money we're putting into deserting Russian colonels who turn double after a few months' "asylum" here. And he's longing to get at Le Chiffre, and anyway he's got the right man and wants to try him out on the job.'

'Who is it?' asked Number Two.

'One of the Double O's—I guess 007. He's tough, and M. thinks there may be trouble with those gunmen of Le Chiffre's. He must be pretty good with the cards, or he wouldn't have sat in the Casino in Monte Carlo for two months before the war watching that Roumanian team work their stuff with the invisible ink and the dark glasses. He and the Deuxième bowled them out in the end, and 007 turned in a million francs he had won at shemmy. Good money in those days.'

James Bond's interview with M. had been short.

'What about it, Bond?' asked M. when Bond came back into his room after reading Head of S.'s memorandum and after gazing for ten minutes out of the waiting-room window at the distant trees in the park.

Bond looked across the desk into the shrewd, clear eyes.

'It's very kind of you, sir, I'd like to do it. But I can't promise to win. The odds at baccarat are the best after "trente et quarante"—evens except for the tiny "cagnotte"— but I might get a bad run against me and get cleaned out. Play's going to be pretty high—opening'll go up to half a million, I should think.'

Bond was stopped by the cold eyes. M. knew all this already, knew the odds at baccarat as well as Bond. That was his job—knowing the odds at everything, and knowing men, his own and the opposition's. Bond wished he had kept quiet about his misgivings.

'He can have a bad run too,' said M. 'You'll have plenty of capital. Up to twenty-five million, the same as him. We'll start you on ten and send you another ten when you've had a look round. You can make the extra five yourself.' He smiled. 'Go over a few days before the big game starts and get your hand in. Have a talk to Q. about rooms and trains, and any equipment you want. The Paymaster will fix the funds. I'm going to ask the Deuxième to stand by. It's their territory, and as it is we shall be lucky if they don't kick up rough. I'll try and persuade them to send Mathis. You seemed to get on well with him in Monte Carlo on that other Casino job. And I'm going to tell Washington because of the N.A.T.O. angle. C.I.A. have got one or two good men at Fontainebleau with the joint intelligence chaps there. Anything else?'

Bond shook his head. 'I'd certainly like to have Mathis, sir.'

'Well, we'll see. Try and bring it off. We're going to look pretty foolish if you don't. And watch out. This sounds an amusing job, but I don't think it's going to be. Le Chiffre is a good man. Well, best of luck.'

'Thank you, sir,' said Bond, and went to the door.

'Just a minute.'

Bond turned.

'I think I'll keep you covered, Bond. Two heads are better than one and you'll need someone to run your communications. I'll think it over. They'll get in touch with you at Royale. You needn't worry. It'll be someone good.'

Bond would have preferred to work alone, but one didn't argue with M. He left the room hoping that the man they sent would be loyal to him and neither stupid nor, worse still, ambitious.

AS, TWO weeks later, James Bond awoke in his room at the Hotel Splendide, some of this history passed through his mind.

He had arrived at Royale-les-Eaux in time for luncheon two days before. There had been no attempt to contact him, and there had been no flicker of curiosity when he had signed the register 'James Bond, Port Maria, Jamaica.'

M. had expressed no interest in his cover.

'Once you start to make a set at Le Chiffre at the tables you'll have had it,' he said. 'But wear a cover that will stick with the general public.'

Bond knew Jamaica well, so he asked to be controlled from there and to pass as a Jamaican plantocrat whose father had made his pile in tobacco and sugar and who chose to play it away on the stock markets and in casinos. If inquiries were made, he would quote Charles Dasilva of Caffery's, Kingston, as his attorney. Charles would make the story stick.

Bond had spent the last two afternoons and most of the nights at the Casino, playing complicated progression systems on the even chances at roulette. He made a high banco at chemin-de-fer whenever he heard one offered. If he lost, he would 'suivi' once and not chase it further if he lost the second time.

In this way he had made some three million francs and had given his nerves and card-sense a thorough workout. He had got the geography of the Casino clear in his mind. Above all, he had been able to observe Le Chiffre at the tables and to note ruefully that he was a faultless and lucky gambler.

Bond liked to make a good breakfast. After a cold shower, he sat at the writing-table in front of the window. He looked out at the beautiful day and consumed half a pint of iced orange juice, three scrambled eggs and bacon, and a double portion of coffee without sugar. He lit his first cigarette, a Balkan and Turkish mixture made for him by Morlands of Grosvenor Street, and watched the small waves lick the long seashore and the fishing fleet from Dieppe string out towards the June heat-haze followed by a paper-chase of herring-gulls.

He was lost in his thoughts when the telephone rang. It was the concierge announcing that a Director of Radio Stentor was waiting below with the wireless set he had ordered from Paris.

'Of course,' said Bond. 'Send him up.'

This was the cover fixed by the Deuxième Bureau for their liaison man with Bond. Bond watched the door, hoping that it would be Mathis.

When Mathis came in, a respectable businessman carrying a large square parcel by its leather handle, Bond smiled broadly and would have greeted him with warmth if Mathis had not frowned and held up his free hand after carefully closing the door.

'I have just arrived from Paris, monsieur, and here is the set you asked to have on approval—five valves, superhet, I think you call it in England, and you should be able to get most of the capitals of Europe from Royale. There are no mountains for forty miles in any direction.'

'It sounds all right,' said Bond, lifting his eyebrows at this mystery-making.

Mathis paid no attention. He placed the set, which he had unwrapped, on the floor beside the unlit panel electric fire below the mantelpiece.

'It is just past eleven,' he said, 'and I see that the Compagnons de la Chanson should now be on the medium wave from Rome. They are touring Europe. Let us see what the reception is like. It should be a fair test.'

He winked. Bond noticed that he had turned the volume on to full and that the red light indicating the long waveband was illuminated, though the set was still silent.

Mathis fiddled at the back of the set. Suddenly an appalling roar of static filled the small room. Mathis gazed at the set for a few seconds with benevolence and then turned it off, and his voice was full of dismay.

'My dear monsieur—forgive me, please—badly tuned.' And he again bent to the dials. After a few adjustments the close harmony of the French came over the air, and Mathis walked up and clapped Bond very hard on the back and wrung his hand until Bond's fingers ached.

Bond smiled back at him. 'Now what the hell?' he asked.

'My dear friend,' Mathis was delighted, 'you are blown, blown, blown. Up there,' he pointed at the ceiling, 'at this moment, either Monsieur Muntz or his alleged wife, allegedly bedridden with the grippe, is deafened, absolutely deafened, and I hope in agony.' He grinned with pleasure at Bond's frown of disbelief.

Mathis sat down on the bed and ripped open a packet of Caporal with his thumbnail. Bond waited.

Mathis was satisfied with the sensation his words had caused. He became serious.

'How it has happened, I don't know. They must have been on to you for several days before you arrived. The opposition is here in real strength. Above you is the Muntz family. He is German. She is from somewhere in Central Europe, perhaps a Czech. This is an old-fashioned hotel. There are disused chimneys behind these electric fires. Just here,' he pointed a few inches above the panel fire, 'is suspended a very powerful radio pick-up. The wires run up the chimney to behind the Muntzes' electric fire where there is an amplifier. In their room is a wire recorder and a pair of earphones on which the Muntzes listen in turn. That is why Madame Muntz has the grippe and takes all her meals in bed and why Monsieur Muntz has to be constantly at her side instead of enjoying the sunshine and the gambling of this delightful resort.

'Some of this we knew because in France we are very clever. The rest we confirmed by unscrewing your electric fire a few hours before you got here.'

Suspiciously Bond walked over and examined the screws which secured the panel to the wall. Their grooves showed minute scratches.

'Now it is time for a little more play-acting,' said Mathis. He walked over to the radio, which was still transmitting close harmony to its audience of three, and switched it off.

'Are you satisfied, monsieur?' he asked. 'You notice how clearly they come over. Are they not a wonderful team?' He made a winding motion with his right hand and raised his eyebrows.

'They are so good,' said Bond, 'that I would like to hear the rest of the programme.' He grinned at the thought of the angry glances which the Muntzes must be exchanging overhead. 'The machine itself seems splendid. Just what I was looking for to take back to Jamaica.'

Mathis made a sarcastic grimace and switched back to the Rome programme.

'You and your Jamaica,' he said, and sat down again on the bed.

Bond frowned at him. 'Well, it's no good crying over spilt milk,' he said. 'We didn't expect the cover to stick for long, but it's worrying that they bowled it out so soon.' He searched his mind in vain for a clue. Could the Russians have broken one of our ciphers? If so, he might just as well pack up and go home. He and his job would have been stripped naked.

Mathis seemed to read his mind. 'It can't have been a cipher,' he said. 'Anyway, we told London at once, and they will have changed them. A pretty flap we caused, I can tell you.' He smiled with the satisfaction of a friendly rival. 'And now to business, before our good Compagnons run out of breath.

'First of all'—he inhaled a thick lungful of Caporal—'you will be pleased with your Number Two. She is very beautiful (Bond frowned), very beautiful indeed.' Satisfied with Bond's reaction, Mathis continued: 'She has black hair, blue eyes, and splendid . . . er . . . protuberances. Back and front,' he added. 'And she is a wireless expert which, though sexually less interesting, makes her a perfect employee of Radio Stentor and assistant to myself in my capacity as wireless salesman for this rich summer season down here.' He grinned. 'We are both staying in the hotel, and my assistant will thus be on hand in case your new radio breaks down. All new machines, even French ones, are apt to have teething troubles in the first day or two. And occasionally at night,' he added with an exaggerated wink.

Bond was not amused. 'What the hell do they want to send me a woman for,' he said bitterly. 'Do they think this is a bloody picnic?'

Mathis interrupted. 'Calm yourself, my dear James. She

is as serious as you could wish and as cold as an icicle. She speaks French like a native and knows her job backwards. Her cover's perfect, and I have arranged for her to team up with you quite smoothly. What is more natural than that you should pick up a pretty girl here? As a Jamaican millionaire,' he coughed respectfully, 'what with your hot blood and all, you would look naked without one.'

Bond grunted dubiously.

'Any other surprises?' he asked suspiciously.

'Nothing very much,' answered Mathis. 'Le Chiffre is installed in his villa. It's about ten miles down the coast road. He has his two guards with him. They look pretty capable fellows. One of them has been seen visiting a little pension in the town where three mysterious and rather subhuman characters checked in two days ago. They may be part of the team. Their papers are in order—stateless Czechs apparently—but one of our men says the language they talk in their room is Bulgarian. We don't see many of those around. They're mostly used against the Turks and the Yugoslavs. They're stupid, but obedient. The Russians use them for simple killings or as fall-guys for more complicated ones.'

'Thanks very much. Which is mine to be?' asked Bond. 'Anything else?'

'No. Come to the bar of the Hermitage before lunch. I'll fix the introduction. Ask her to dinner this evening. Then it will be natural for her to come into the Casino with you. I'll be there too, but in the background. I've got one or two good chaps, and we'll keep an eye on you. Oh, and there's an American called Leiter here, staying in the hotel. Felix Leiter. He's the C.I.A. chap from Fontainebleau. London told me to tell you. He looks okay. May come in useful.'

A torrent of Italian burst from the wireless set on the floor. Mathis switched it off and they exchanged some phrases about the set and about how Bond should pay for it. Then with effusive farewells and a final wink Mathis bowed himself out.

Bond sat at the window and gathered his thoughts. Nothing that Mathis had told him was reassuring. He was completely blown and under really professional surveillance. An attempt might be made to put him away even before he had a chance to pit himself against Le Chiffre at the tables. The Russians had no stupid prejudices about murder. And then there was this pest of a girl. He sighed. Women were for recreation. On a job, they got in the way and fogged things up with sex and hurt feelings and all the emotional baggage they carried around. One had to look out for them and take care of them.

'Bitch,' said Bond, and then remembering the Muntzes, he said 'bitch' again more loudly and walked out of the room.

𝒱. THE GIRL FROM HEADQUARTERS

IT WAS twelve o'clock when Bond left the Splendide, and the clock on the mairie was stumbling through its midday carillon. There was a strong scent of pine and mimosa in the air, and the freshly watered gardens of the Casino opposite, interspersed with neat gravel parterres and paths, lent the scene a pretty formalism more appropriate to ballet than to melodrama.

The sun shone, and there was a gaiety and sparkle in the

air which seemed to promise well for the new era of fashion and prosperity for which the little seaside town, after many vicissitudes, was making its gallant bid.

Royale-les-Eaux, which lies near the mouth of the Somme before the flat coast-line soars up from the beaches of southern Picardy to the Brittany cliffs which run on to Le Havre, had experienced much the same fortunes as Trouville.

Royale (without the Eaux) also started as a small fishing-village, and its rise to fame as a fashionable watering-place during the Second Empire was as meteoric as that of Trouville. But as Deauville killed Trouville, so, after a long period of decline, did Le Touquet kill Royale.

At the turn of the century, when things were going badly for the little seaside town and when the fashion was to combine pleasure with a 'cure,' a natural spring in the hills behind Royale was discovered to contain enough diluted sulphur to have a beneficent effect on the liver. Since all French people suffer from liver complaints, Royale quickly became Royale-les-Eaux, and Eau Royale, in a torpedo-shaped bottle, grafted itself demurely on to the tail of the mineral-water lists in hotels and restaurant cars.

It did not long withstand the powerful combines of Vichy and Perrier and Vittel. There came a series of lawsuits; a number of people lost a lot of money, and very soon its sale was again entirely local. Royale fell back on the takings from French and English families during the summer, on its fishing-fleet in winter and on the crumbs which fell to its elegantly dilapidated Casino from the tables at Le Touquet.

But there was something splendid about the Negresco baroque of the Casino Royale, a strong whiff of Victorian elegance and luxury, and in 1950 Royale caught the fancy of a syndicate in Paris which disposed of large funds belonging to a group of expatriate Vichyites.

Brighton had been revived since the war, and Nice. Nostalgia for more spacious, golden times might be a source of revenue.

The Casino was repainted in its original white and gilt, and the rooms decorated in the palest grey with wine-red carpets and curtains. Vast chandeliers were suspended from the ceilings. The gardens were spruced, and the fountains played again, and the two main hotels, the Splendide and the Hermitage, were prinked and furbished and restaffed.

Even the small town and the vieux-port managed to fix welcoming smiles across their ravaged faces, and the main street became gay with the 'vitrines' of great Paris jewellers and couturiers, tempted down for a butterfly season by rent-free sites and lavish promises.

Then the Mahomet Ali Syndicate was cajoled into starting a high game in the Casino and the Société des Bains de Mer de Royale felt that now at last Le Touquet would have to yield up some of the treasure stolen over the years from its parent plage.

Against the background of this luminous and sparkling stage Bond stood in the sunshine and felt his mission to be incongruous and remote and his dark profession an affront to his fellow actors.

He shrugged away the momentary feeling of unease and walked round the back of his hotel and down the ramp to the garage. Before his rendezvous at the Hermitage he decided to take his car down the coast road and have a quick look at Le Chiffre's villa and then drive back by the inland road until it crossed the route nationale to Paris.

Bond's car was his only personal hobby. One of the last of the 4½-litre Bentleys with the supercharger by Amherst Villiers, he had bought it almost new in 1933 and had kept it in careful storage through the war. It was still serviced every year and, in London, a former Bentley mechanic, who worked in a garage near Bond's Chelsea flat, tended it with jealous care. Bond drove it hard and well and with an almost sensual pleasure. It was a battleship-grey convertible coupé, which really did convert, and it was capable of touring at ninety with thirty miles an hour in reserve.

Bond eased the car out of the garage and up the ramp, and soon the loitering drumbeat of the two-inch exhaust was echoing down the tree-lined boulevard, through the crowded main street of the little town, and off through the sand dunes to the south.

An hour later, Bond walked into the Hermitage bar and chose a table near one of the broad windows.

The room was sumptuous with those overmasculine trappings which, together with briar pipes and wire-haired terriers, spell luxury in France. Everything was brass-studded leather and polished mahogany. The curtains and carpets were in royal blue. The waiters wore striped waistcoats and green baize aprons. Bond ordered an Americano and examined the sprinkling of overdressed customers, mostly from Paris he guessed, who sat talking with focus and vivacity, creating that theatrically clubbable atmosphere of l'heure de l'apéritif.

The men were drinking inexhaustible quarter-bottles of champagne, the women dry Martinis.

'Moi, j'adore le "dry," ' a bright-faced girl at the next table said to her companion, too neat in his unseasonable tweeds, who gazed at her with moist brown eyes over the top of an expensive shooting-stick from Hermes, 'fait avec du Gordon's, bien entendu.'

'D'accord, Daisy. Mais tu sais, un zeste de citron . . .'

Bond's eye was caught by the tall figure of Mathis on the pavement outside, his face turned in animation to a dark-haired girl in grey. His arm was linked in hers, high up above the elbow, and yet there was a lack of intimacy in their appearance, an ironical chill in the girl's profile, which made them seem two separate people rather than a couple. Bond waited for them to come through the street-door into the bar, but for appearances' sake continued to stare out of the window at the passers-by.

'But surely it is Monsieur Bond?' Mathis's voice behind him was full of surprised delight. Bond, appropriately flustered, rose to his feet. 'Can it be that you are alone? Are you awaiting someone? May I present my colleague, Mademoiselle Lynd? My dear, this is the gentleman from Jamaica with whom I had the pleasure of doing business this morning.'

Bond inclined himself with a reserved friendliness. 'It would be a great pleasure,' he addressed himself to the girl. 'I am alone. Would you both care to join me?' He pulled out a chair, and while they sat down he beckoned to a waiter and despite Mathis's expostulations insisted on ordering the drinks—a fine à l'eau for Mathis and a Bacardi for the girl.

Mathis and Bond exchanged cheerful talk about the fine weather and the prospects of a revival in the fortunes of Royale-les-Eaux. The girl sat silent. She accepted one of Bond's cigarettes, examined it, and then smoked it appreciatively and without affectation, drawing the smoke deeply into her lungs with a little sigh and then exhaling it casually through her lips and nostrils. Her movements were economical and precise with no trace of self-consciousness.

Bond felt her presence strongly. While he and Mathis talked, he turned from time to time towards her, politely including her in the conversation, but adding up the impressions recorded by each glance.

Her hair was very black, and she wore it cut square and

low on the nape of the neck, framing her face to below the clear and beautiful line of her jaw. Although it was heavy and moved with the movements of her head, she did not constantly pat it back into place, but let it alone. Her eyes were wide apart and deep blue, and they gazed candidly back at Bond with a touch of ironical disinterest which, to his annoyance, he found he would like to shatter, roughly. Her skin was lightly sun-tanned and bore no trace of make-up except on her mouth, which was wide and sensual. Her bare arms and hands had a quality of repose, and the general impression of restraint in her appearance and movements was carried even to her fingernails, which were unpainted and cut short. Round her neck she wore a plain gold chain of wide flat links, and on the fourth finger of the right hand a broad topaz ring. Her medium-length dress was of grey soie sauvage with a square-cut bodice, lasciviously tight across her fine breasts. The skirt was closely pleated and flowered down from a narrow, but not a thin, waist. She wore a three-inch, hand-stitched black belt. A hand-stitched black sabre-tache rested on the chair beside her, together with a wide cartwheel hat of gold straw, its crown encircled by a thin black velvet ribbon which tied at the back in a short bow. Her shoes were square-toed of plain black leather.

Bond was excited by her beauty and intrigued by her composure. The prospect of working with her stimulated him. At the same time he felt a vague disquiet. On an impulse he touched wood.

Mathis had noticed Bond's preoccupation. After a time he rose.

'Forgive me,' he said to the girl, 'while I telephone to the Dubernes. I must arrange my rendezvous for dinner tonight. Are you sure you won't mind being left to your own devices this evening?'

She shook her head.

Bond took the cue and, as Mathis crossed the room to the telephone booth beside the bar, he said: 'If you are going to be alone tonight, would you care to have dinner with me?'

She smiled with the first hint of conspiracy she had shown. 'I would like to very much,' she said, 'and then perhaps you would chaperon me to the Casino where Monsieur Mathis tells me you are very much at home. Perhaps I will bring you luck.'

With Mathis gone, her attitude towards him showed a sudden warmth. She seemed to acknowledge that they were a team and, as they discussed the time and place of their meeting, Bond realized that it would be quite easy after all to plan the details of his project with her. He felt that after all she was interested and excited by her role and that she would work willingly with him. He had imagined many hurdles before establishing a rapport, but now he felt he could get straight down to professional details. He was quite honest to himself about the hypocrisy of his attitude towards her. As a woman, he wanted to sleep with her, but only when the job had been done.

When Mathis came back to the table Bond called for his bill. He explained that he was expected back at his hotel to have lunch with friends. When for a moment he held her hand in his he felt a warmth of affection and understanding pass between them that would have seemed impossible half an hour earlier.

The girl's eyes followed him out on to the boulevard.

Mathis moved his chair close to hers and said softly: 'That is a very good friend of mine. I am glad you have met each other. I can already feel the ice-floes on the two rivers breaking up.' He smiled. 'I don't think Bond has ever been melted. It will be a new experience for him. And for you.'

She did not answer him directly.

'He is very good-looking. He reminds me rather of Hoagy Carmichael, but there is something cold and ruthless in his . . .'

The sentence was never finished. Suddenly a few feet away the entire plate-glass window shivered into confetti. The blast of a terrific explosion, very near, hit them so that they were rocked back in their chairs. There was an instant of silence. Some objects pattered down on to the pavement outside. Bottles slowly toppled off the shelves behind the bar. Then there were screams and a stampede for the door.

'Stay there,' said Mathis.

He kicked back his chair and hurtled through the empty window-frame on to the pavement.

vi. TWO MEN IN STRAW HATS

WHEN BOND left the bar he walked purposefully along the pavement flanking the tree-lined boulevard towards his hotel a few hundred yards away. He was hungry.

The day was still beautiful, but by now the sun was very hot and the plane-trees, spaced about twenty feet apart on the grass verge between the pavement and the broad tarmac, gave a cool shade.

There were few people abroad and the two men standing quietly under a tree on the opposite side of the boulevard looked out of place.

Bond noticed them when he was still a hundred yards away and when the same distance separated them from the ornamental 'porte-cochère' of the Splendide.

There was something rather disquieting about their appearance. They were both small, and they were dressed alike in dark and, Bond reflected, rather hot-looking suits. They had the appearance of a variety turn waiting for a bus on the way to the theatre. Each wore a straw hat with a thick black ribbon as a concession, perhaps, to the holiday atmosphere of the resort, and the brims of these and the shadow from the tree under which they stood obscured their faces. Incongruously, each dark, squat little figure was illuminated by a touch of bright colour. They were both carrying square camera-cases slung from the shoulder.

And one case was bright red and the other case bright blue.

By the time Bond had taken in these details, he had come to within fifty yards of the two men. He was reflecting on the ranges of various types of weapon and the possibilities of cover when an extraordinary and terrible scene was enacted.

Red-man seemed to give a short nod to Blue-man. With a quick movement Blue-man unslung his blue camera case. Blue-man, and Bond could not see exactly as the trunk of a plane-tree beside him just then intervened to obscure his vision, bent forward and seemed to fiddle with the case. Then with a blinding flash of white light there was the ear-splitting crack of a monstrous explosion and Bond, despite the protection of the tree-trunk, was slammed down to the pavement by a solid bolt of hot air which dented his cheeks and stomach as if they had been made of paper. He lay, gazing up at the sun, while the air (or so it seemed to him) went on twanging with the explosion as if someone had hit the bass register of a piano with a sledge hammer.

When, dazed and half-conscious, he raised himself on one knee, a ghastly rain of pieces of flesh and shreds of blood-soaked clothing fell on him and around him, mingled with branches and gravel. Then a shower of small twigs and leaves. From all sides came the sharp tinkle of falling glass. Above in the sky hung a mushroom of black smoke which rose and dissolved as he drunkenly watched it. There was an obscene smell of high explosive, of burning wood, and of, yes, that was it—roast mutton. For fifty yards down the boulevard the trees were leafless and charred. Opposite, two of them had snapped off near the base and lay drunkenly across the road. Between them there was a still smoking crater. Of the two men in straw hats, there remained absolutely nothing. But there were red traces on the road, and on the pavements and against the trunks of the trees, and there were glittering shreds high up in the branches.

Bond felt himself starting to vomit.

It was Mathis who got to him first, and by that time Bond was standing with his arm round the tree which had saved his life.

Stupefied, but unharmed, he allowed Mathis to lead him off towards the Splendide from which guests and servants were pouring in chattering fright. As the distant clang of bells heralded the arrival of ambulances and fire-engines, they managed to push through the throng and up the short stairs and along the corridor to Bond's room.

Mathis paused only to turn on the radio in front of the fireplace, then, while Bond stripped off his blood-flecked clothes, Mathis sprayed him with questions.

When it came to the description of the two men, Mathis tore the telephone off its hook beside Bond's bed.

'. . . and tell the police,' he concluded, 'tell them that the Englishman from Jamaica who was knocked over by the blast is my affair. He is unhurt, and they are not to worry him. I will explain to them in half an hour. They should tell the Press that it was apparently a vendetta between two Bulgarian communists and that one killed the other with a bomb. They need say nothing of the third Bulgar who must have been hanging about somewhere, but they must get him at all costs. He will certainly head for Paris. Roadblocks everywhere. Understood? Alors, bonne chance.'

Mathis turned back to Bond and heard him to the end.

'Merde, but you were lucky,' he said when Bond had finished. 'Clearly the bomb was intended for you. It must have been faulty. They intended to throw it and then dodge behind their tree. But it all came out the other way round. Never mind. We will discover the facts.' He paused. 'But certainly it is a curious affair. And these people appear to be taking you seriously.' Mathis looked affronted. 'But how did these sacré Bulgars intend to escape capture? And what was the significance of the red and the blue cases? We must try and find some fragments of the red one.'

Mathis bit his nails. He was excited, and his eyes glittered. This was becoming a formidable and dramatic affair, in many aspects of which he was now involved personally. Certainly it was no longer just a case of holding Bond's coat while he had his private battle with Le Chiffre in the Casino. Mathis jumped up.

'Now get a drink and some lunch and a rest,' he ordered Bond. 'For me, I must get my nose quickly into this affair before the police have muddied the trail with their big black boots.'

Mathis turned off the radio and waved an affectionate farewell. The door slammed, and silence settled on the room. Bond sat for a while by the window and enjoyed being alive.

Later, as Bond was finishing his first straight whisky 'on

the rocks' and was contemplating the pâté de foie gras and cold langouste which the waiter had just laid out for him, the telephone rang.

'This is Mademoiselle Lynd.'

The voice was low and anxious.

'Are you all right?'

'Yes, quite.'

'I'm glad. Please take care of yourself.'

She rang off.

Bond shook himself, then he picked up his knife and selected the thickest of the pieces of hot toast.

He suddenly thought: two of them are dead, and I have got one more on my side. It's a start.

He dipped the knife into the glass of very hot water which stood beside the pot of Strasbourg porcelain and reminded himself to tip the waiter doubly for this particular meal.

vii. ROUGE ET NOIR

BOND WAS determined to be completely fit and relaxed for a gambling session which might last most of the night. He ordered a masseur for three o'clock. After the remains of his luncheon had been removed, he sat at his window gazing out to sea until there came a knock on the door as the masseur, a Swede, presented himself.

Silently he got to work on Bond from his feet to his neck, melting the tensions in his body and calming his still twanging nerves. Even the long purpling bruises down Bond's left shoulder and side ceased to throb, and when the Swede had gone Bond fell into a dreamless sleep.

He awoke in the evening completely refreshed.

After a cold shower, Bond walked over to the Casino. Since the night before he had lost the mood of the tables. He needed to reestablish that focus which is half mathematical and half intuitive and which, with a slow pulse and a sanguine temperament, he knew to be the essential equipment of any gambler who was set on winning.

Bond had always been a gambler. He loved the dry riffle of the cards and the constant unemphatic drama of the quiet figures round the green tables. He liked the solid, studied comfort of cardrooms and casinos, the well-padded arms of the chairs, the glass of champagne or whisky at the elbow, the quiet unhurried attention of good servants. He was amused by the impartiality of the roulette ball and of the playing cards—and their eternal bias. He liked being an actor and a spectator and from his chair to take part in other men's dramas and decisions, until it came to his own turn to say that vital 'yes' or 'no,' generally on a fifty-fifty chance.

Above all, he liked it that everything was one's own fault. There was only oneself to praise or blame. Luck was a servant and not a master. Luck had to be accepted with a shrug or taken advantage of up to the hilt. But it had to be understood and recognized for what it was and not confused with a faulty appreciation of the odds, for, at gambling, the deadly sin is to mistake bad play for bad luck. And luck in all its moods had to be loved and not feared. Bond saw luck as a woman, to be softly wooed or brutally ravaged, never pandered to or pursued. But he was honest enough to admit that he had never yet been made to suffer by cards or by women.

One day, and he accepted the fact, he would be brought to his knees by love or by luck. When that happened he knew that he too would be branded with the deadly question-mark he recognized so often in others, the promise to pay before you have lost: the acceptance of fallibility.

But on this June evening when Bond walked through the 'kitchen' into the salle privée, it was with a sensation of confidence and cheerful anticipation that he changed a million francs into plaques of fifty mille and took a seat next to the chef de partie at Roulette Table Number 1.

Bond borrowed the chef's card and studied the run of the ball since the session had started at three o'clock that afternoon. He always did this although he knew that each turn of the wheel, each fall of the ball into a numbered slot, had absolutely no connexion with its predecessor. He accepted that the game begins afresh each time the croupier picks up the ivory ball with his right hand, gives one of the four spokes of the wheel a controlled twist clockwise with the same hand and, with a third motion, also with the right hand, flicks the ball round the outer rim of the wheel anti-clockwise, against its spin.

It was obvious that all this ritual and all the mechanical minutiae of the wheel, of the numbered slots and the cylinder, had been devised and perfected over the years so that neither the skill of the croupier nor any bias in the wheel could affect the fall of the ball. And yet it is a convention among roulette players, and Bond rigidly adhered to it, to take careful note of the past history of each session and to be guided by any peculiarities in the run of the wheel. To note, for instance, and consider significant, sequences of more than two on a single number or of more than four at the other chances down to evens.

Bond didn't defend the practice. He simply maintained that the more effort and ingenuity you put into gambling, the more you took out.

On the record of that particular table, after about three hours' play, Bond could see little of interest except that the last dozen had been out of favour. It was his practice to play always with the wheel, and only to turn against its previous pattern and start on a new tack after a zero had turned up. So he decided to play one of his favourite gambits and back two—in this case the first two—dozens, each with the maximum—one hundred thousand francs. He thus had two-thirds of the board covered (less the zero) and, since the dozens pay odds of two to one, he stood to win a hundred thousand francs every time any number lower than 25 turned up.

After seven coups he had won six times. He lost on the seventh when 30 came up. His net profit was half a million francs. He kept off the table for the eighth throw. Zero turned up. This piece of luck cheered him further and, accepting the 30 as a finger-post to the last dozen, he decided to back the first and last dozens until he had lost twice. Ten throws later the middle dozen came up twice, costing him four hundred thousand francs, but he rose from the table eleven hundred thousand francs to the good.

Directly Bond had started playing in maximums, his game had become the centre of interest at the table. As he seemed to be in luck, one or two pilot fish started to swim with the shark. Sitting directly opposite, one of these, whom Bond took to be an American, had shown more than the usual friendliness and pleasure at his share of the winning streak. He had smiled once or twice across the table, and there was something pointed in the way he duplicated Bond's movements, placing his two modest plaques of ten mille exactly opposite Bond's larger ones. When Bond rose, he too pushed back his chair and called cheerfully across the table:

'Thanks for the ride. Guess I owe you a drink. Will you join me?'

Bond had a feeling that this might be the C.I.A. man. He knew he was right as they strolled off together towards the bar, after Bond had thrown a plaque of ten mille to the croupier and had given a mille to the huissier who drew back his chair.

'My name's Felix Leiter,' said the American. 'Glad to meet you.'

'Mine's Bond—James Bond.'

'Oh, yes,' said his companion, 'and now let's see. What shall we have to celebrate?'

Bond insisted on ordering Leiter's Haig-and-Haig 'on the rocks,' and then he looked carefully at the barman.

'A dry Martini,' he said. 'One. In a deep champagne goblet.'

'Oui, Monsieur.'

'Just a moment. Three measures of Gordon's, one of vodka, half a measure of Kina Lillet. Shake it very well until it's ice-cold, then add a large thin slice of lemon-peel. Got it?'

'Certainly, monsieur.' The barman seemed pleased with the idea.

'Gosh, that's certainly a drink,' said Leiter.

Bond laughed. 'When I'm—er—concentrating,' he explained, 'I never have more than one drink before dinner. But I do like that one to be large and very strong and very cold and very well-made. I hate small portions of anything, particularly when they taste bad. This drink's my own invention. I'm going to patent it when I can think of a good name.'

He watched carefully as the deep glass became frosted with the pale golden drink, slightly aerated by the bruising of the shaker. He reached for it and took a long sip.

'Excellent,' he said to the barman, 'but if you can get a vodka made with grain instead of potatoes, you will find it still better.'

'Mais n'enculons pas des mouches,' he added in an aside to the barman. The barman grinned.

'That's a vulgar way of saying "we won't split hairs," ' explained Bond.

But Leiter was still interested in Bond's drink. 'You certainly think things out,' he said with amusement as they carried their glasses to a corner of the room. He lowered his voice:

'You'd better call it the "Molotov Cocktail" after the one you tasted this afternoon.'

They sat down. Bond laughed.

'I see that the spot marked X has been roped off, and they're making cars take a detour over the pavement. I hope it hasn't frightened away any of the big money.'

'People are accepting the communist story or else they think it was a burst gas-main. All the burnt trees are coming down tonight and if they work things here like they do at Monte Carlo, there won't be a trace of the mess left in the morning.'

Leiter shook a Chesterfield out of his pack. 'I'm glad to be working with you on this job,' he said, looking into his drink, 'so I'm particularly glad you didn't get blown to glory. Our people are definitely interested. They think it's just as important as your friends do, and they don't think there's anything crazy about it at all. In fact, Washington's pretty sick we're not running the show, but you know what the big brass is like. I expect your fellows are much the same in London.'

Bond nodded. 'Apt to be a bit jealous of their scoops,' he admitted.

'Anyway, I'm under your orders and I'm to give you any help you ask for. With Mathis and his boys here, there may not be much that isn't taken care of already. But, anyway, here I am.'

'I'm delighted you are,' said Bond. 'The opposition has got me, and probably you and Mathis too, all weighed up, and it seems no holds are going to be barred. I'm glad Le Chiffre seems as desperate as we thought he was. I'm afraid I haven't got anything very specific for you to do, but I'd be grateful if you'd stick around the Casino this evening. I've got an assistant, a Miss Lynd, and I'd like to hand her over to you when I start playing. You won't be ashamed of her. She's a good-looking girl.' He smiled at Leiter. 'And you might mark his two gunmen. I can't imagine he'll try a roughhouse, but you never know.'

'I may be able to help,' said Leiter. 'I was a regular in our Marine Corps before I joined this racket, if that means anything to you.' He looked at Bond with a hint of self-deprecation.

'It does,' said Bond.

It turned out that Leiter was from Texas. While he talked on about his job with the Joint Intelligence Staff of N.A.T.O. and the difficulty of maintaining security in an organization where so many nationalities were represented, Bond reflected that good Americans were fine people and that most of them seemed to come from Texas.

Felix Leiter was about thirty-five. He was tall with a thin bony frame and his lightweight, tan-coloured suit hung loosely from his shoulders like the clothes of Frank Sinatra.

His movements and speech were slow, but one had the feeling that there was plenty of speed and strength in him, and that he would be a tough and cruel fighter. As he sat hunched over the table, he seemed to have some of the jackknife quality of a falcon. There was this impression also in his face, in the sharpness of his chin and cheekbones and the wide wry mouth. His grey eyes had a feline slant which was increased by his habit of screwing them up against the smoke of the Chesterfields which he tapped out of the pack in a chain. The permanent wrinkles which this habit had etched at the corners gave the impression that he smiled more with his eyes than with his mouth. A mop of straw-coloured hair lent his face a boyish look which closer examination contradicted. Although he seemed to talk quite openly about his duties in Paris, Bond soon noticed that he never spoke of his American colleagues in Europe or in Washington, and he guessed that Leiter held the interests of his own organization far above the mutual concerns of the North Atlantic Allies. Bond sympathized with him.

By the time Leiter had swallowed another whisky and Bond had told him about the Muntzes and his short reconnaissance trip down the coast that morning, it was seven-thirty, and they decided to stroll over to their hotel together. Before leaving the Casino, Bond deposited his total capital of twenty-four million at the caisse, keeping only a few notes of ten mille as pocket-money.

As they walked across to the Splendide, they saw that a team of workmen was already busy at the scene of the explosion. Several trees were uprooted and hoses from three municipal tank cars were washing down the boulevard and pavements. The bomb-crater had disappeared and only a few passers-by had paused to gape. Bond assumed that similar face-lifting had already been carried out at the Her-

mitage and to the shops and frontages which had lost their
windows.

In the warm blue dusk Royale-les-Eaux was once again
orderly and peaceful.

'Who's the concierge working for?' asked Leiter as they
approached the hotel. Bond was not sure, and said so.

Mathis had been unable to enlighten him. 'Unless you
have bought him yourself,' he had said, 'you must assume
that he has been bought by the other side. All concierges are
venal. It is not their fault. They are trained to regard all
hotel guests except maharajahs as potential cheats and
thieves. They have as much concern for your comfort or
well-being as crocodiles.'

Bond remembered Mathis's pronouncement when the
concierge hurried up to inquire whether he had recovered
from his most unfortunate experience of the afternoon.
Bond thought it well to say that he still felt a little bit shaky.
He hoped that if the intelligence were relayed, Le Chiffre
would at any rate start playing that evening with a basic
misinterpretation of his adversary's strength. The concierge
proffered glycerine hopes for Bond's recovery.

Leiter's room was on one of the upper floors and they
parted company at the lift after arranging to see each other
at the Casino at around half-past ten or eleven, the usual
hour for the high tables to begin play.

viii. PINK LIGHTS AND CHAMPAGNE

BOND WALKED up to his room, which again showed no sign of trespass, threw off his clothes, took a long hot bath followed by an ice-cold shower, and lay down on his bed. There remained an hour in which to rest and compose his thoughts before he met the girl in the Splendide bar, an hour to examine minutely the details of his plans for the game, and for after the game, in all the various circumstances of victory or defeat. He had to plan the attendant roles of Mathis, Leiter, and the girl and visualize the reactions of the enemy in various contingencies. He closed his eyes, and his thoughts pursued his imagination through a series of carefully constructed scenes as if he were watching the tumbling chips of coloured glass in a kaleidoscope.

At twenty minutes to nine he had exhausted all the permutations which might result from his duel with Le Chiffre. He rose and dressed, dismissing the future completely from his mind.

As he tied his thin, double-ended, black satin tie, he paused for a moment and examined himself levelly in the mirror. His grey-blue eyes looked calmly back with a hint of ironical inquiry and the short lock of black hair which would never stay in place slowly subsided to form a thick comma above his right eyebrow. With the thin vertical scar down his right cheek the general effect was faintly piratical. Not much of Hoagy Carmichael there, thought Bond, as he filled a flat, light gun-metal box with fifty of the Morland cigarettes with the triple gold band. Mathis had told him of the girl's comment.

He slipped the case into his hip pocket and snapped his black oxidized Ronson to see if it needed fuel. After pocketing the thin sheaf of ten-mille notes, he opened a drawer and took out a light chamois leather holster and slipped it over his left shoulder so that it hung about three inches below his armpit. He then took from under his shirts in another drawer a very flat .25 Beretta automatic with a skeleton grip, extracted the clip and the single round in the barrel and whipped the action to and fro several times, finally pulling the trigger on the empty chamber. He charged the weapon again, loaded it, put up the safety catch, and dropped it into the shallow pouch of the shoulder-holster. He looked carefully round the room to see if anything had been forgotten and slipped his single-breasted dinner-jacket coat over his heavy silk evening shirt. He felt cool and comfortable. He verified in the mirror that there was absolutely no sign of the flat gun under his left arm, gave a final pull at his narrow tie and walked out of the door and locked it.

When he turned at the foot of the short stairs towards the bar, he heard the lift-door open behind him and a cool voice call, 'Good evening.'

It was the girl. She stood and waited for him to come up to her.

He had remembered her beauty exactly. He was not surprised to be thrilled by it again.

Her dress was of black velvet, simple and yet with the touch of splendour that only half a dozen couturiers in the world can achieve. There was a thin necklace of diamonds at her throat and a diamond clip in the low vee which just exposed the jutting swell of her breasts. She carried a plain

black evening bag, a flat oblong which she now held, her arm
akimbo, at her waist. Her jet-black hair hung straight and
simply to the final inward curl below the chin.

She looked quite superb, and Bond's heart lifted.

'You look absolutely lovely. Business must be good in the
radio world!'

She put her arm through his. 'Do you mind if we go
straight in to dinner?' she asked. 'I want to make a grand
entrance, and the truth is there's a horrible secret about black
velvet. It marks when you sit down. And, by the way, if
you hear me scream tonight, I shall have sat on a cane chair.'

Bond laughed. 'Of course, let's go straight in. We'll have
a glass of vodka while we order our dinner.'

She gave him an amused glance, and he corrected himself:
'Or a cocktail, of course, if you prefer it. The food here's
the best in Royale.'

For an instant he felt nettled at the touch of irony, the
lightest shadow of a snub, with which she had met his de-
cisiveness, and at the way he had risen to her quick glance.

But it was only an infinitesimal clink of foils and as the
bowing maître d'hôtel led them through the crowded room,
it was forgotten as Bond in her wake watched the heads of
the diners turn to look at her.

The fashionable part of the restaurant was beside the wide
crescent of window built out like the broad stern of a ship
over the hotel gardens, but Bond had chosen a table in one
of the mirrored alcoves at the back of the great room. These
had survived from Edwardian days and they were secluded
and gay in white and gilt, with the red silk-shaded table and
wall lights of the late Empire.

As they deciphered the maze of purple ink which covered
the double folio menu, Bond beckoned to the sommelier. He
turned to his companion.

'Have you decided?'

'I would love a glass of vodka,' she said simply, and went back to her study of the menu.

'A small carafe of vodka, very cold,' ordered Bond. He said to her abruptly: 'I can't drink the health of your new frock without knowing your Christian name.'

'Vesper,' she said. 'Vesper Lynd.'

Bond gave her a look of inquiry.

'It's rather a bore always having to explain, but I was born in the evening, on a very stormy evening according to my parents. Apparently they wanted to remember it.' She smiled. 'Some people like it, others don't. I'm just used to it.'

'I think it's a fine name,' said Bond. An idea struck him. 'Can I borrow it?' He explained about the special Martini he had invented and his search for a name for it. 'The Vesper,' he said. 'It sounds perfect and it's very appropriate to the violet hour when my cocktail will now be drunk all over the world. Can I have it?'

'So long as I can try one first,' she promised. 'It sounds a drink to be proud of.'

'We'll have one together when all this is finished,' said Bond. 'Win or lose. And now have you decided what you would like to have for dinner? Please be expensive,' he added as he sensed her hesitation, 'or you'll let down that beautiful frock.'

'I'd made two choices,' she laughed, 'and either would have been delicious; but behaving like a millionaire occasionally is a wonderful treat, and if you're sure . . . well, I'd like to start with caviar and then have a plain grilled rognon de veau with pommes soufflés. And then I'd like to have fraises des bois with a lot of cream. Is it very shameless to be so certain and so expensive?' She smiled at him inquiringly.

'It's a virtue, and anyway it's only a good plain whole-some meal.' He turned to the maître d'hôtel. 'And bring plenty of toast.

'The trouble always is,' he explained to Vesper, 'not how to get enough caviar, but how to get enough toast with it.

'Now,' he turned back to the menu, 'I myself will ac-company Mademoiselle with the caviar; but then I would like a very small tournedos, underdone, with sauce Béarnaise and a cœur d'artichaut. While Mademoiselle is enjoying the strawberries, I will have an avocado pear with a little French dressing. Do you approve?'

The maître d'hôtel bowed.

'My compliments, mademoiselle and monsieur. Monsieur George . . .' He turned to the sommelier and repeated the two dinners for his benefit.

'Parfait,' said the sommelier, proffering the leather-bound wine list.

'If you agree,' said Bond, 'I would prefer to drink cham-pagne with you tonight. It is a cheerful wine, and it suits the occasion—I hope,' he added.

'Yes, I would like champagne,' she said.

With his finger on the page, Bond turned to the som-melier: 'The Taittinger 45?'

'A fine wine, monsieur,' said the sommelier. 'But if Mon-sieur will permit,' he pointed with his pencil, 'the Brut Blanc de Blanc 1943 of the same marque is without equal.'

Bond smiled. 'So be it,' he said.

'That is not a well-known brand,' Bond explained to his companion, 'but it is probably the finest champagne in the world.' He grinned suddenly at the touch of pretension in his remark.

'You must forgive me,' he said. 'I take a ridiculous pleasure in what I eat and drink. It comes partly from being a bachelor, but mostly from a habit of taking a lot of trouble over details. It's very pernickety and old-maidish really, but then when I'm working I generally have to eat my meals alone and it makes them more interesting when one takes trouble.'

Vesper smiled at him.

'I like it,' she said. 'I like doing everything fully, getting the most out of everything one does. I think that's the way to live. But it sounds rather schoolgirlish when one says it,' she added apologetically.

The little carafe of vodka had arrived in its bowl of crushed ice, and Bond filled their glasses.

'Well, I agree with you anyway,' he said, 'and now, here's luck for tonight, Vesper.'

'Yes,' said the girl quietly, as she held up her small glass and looked at him with a curious directness straight in the eyes. 'I hope all will go well tonight.'

She seemed to Bond to give a quick involuntary shrug of the shoulders as she spoke, but then she leant impulsively towards him.

'I have some news for you from Mathis. He was longing to tell you himself. It's about the bomb. It's a fantastic story.'

i.x. THE GAME IS BACCARAT

BOND LOOKED round; but there was no possibility of being overheard, and the caviar would be waiting for the hot toast from the kitchens.

'Tell me.' His eyes glittered with interest.

'They got the third Bulgar, on the road to Paris. He was in a Citroën, and he had picked up two English hikers as protective colouring. At the roadblock his French was so bad that they asked for his papers, and he brought out a gun and shot one of the motor-cycle patrol. But the other man got him, I don't know how, and managed to stop him committing suicide. Then they took him down to Rouen and extracted the story—in the usual French fashion, I suppose.

'Apparently they were part of a pool held in France for this sort of job—saboteurs, thugs, and so on—and Mathis's friends are already trying to round up the rest. They were to get two million francs for killing you, and the agent who briefed them told them there was absolutely no chance of being caught if they followed his instructions exactly.'

She took a sip of vodka. 'But this is the interesting part.'

'The agent gave them the two camera-cases you saw. He said the bright colours would make it easier for them. He told them that the blue case contained a very powerful smoke-bomb. The red case was the explosive. As one of them threw the red case the other was to press a switch on the blue case, and they would escape under cover of the smoke. In fact, the smoke bomb was a pure invention to make the Bulgars think they could get away. Both cases contained an identical high-explosive bomb. There was no difference between the blue and the red cases. The idea was to destroy you and the bomb-throwers without a trace. Presumably there were other plans for dealing with the third man.'

'Go on,' said Bond, full of admiration for the ingenuity of the double-cross.

'Well, apparently the Bulgars thought this sounded very fine, but cannily they decided to take no chances. It would be better, they thought, to touch off the smoke-bomb first and, from inside the cloud of smoke, hurl the explosive bomb at you. What you saw was the assistant bomb-thrower pressing down the lever on the phony smoke-bomb; and, of course, they both went up together.

'The third Bulgar was waiting behind the Splendide to pick his two friends up. When he saw what had happened, he assumed they had bungled. But the police picked up some fragments of the unexploded red bomb, and he was confronted with them. When he saw that they had been tricked and that his two friends were meant to be murdered with you, he started to talk. I expect he's still talking now. But there's nothing to link all this with Le Chiffre. They were given the job by some intermediary, perhaps one of Le Chiffre's guards, and Le Chiffre's name means absolutely nothing to the one who survived.'

She finished her story just as the waiters arrived with the caviar, a mound of hot toast, and small dishes containing finely chopped onion and grated hard-boiled egg, the white in one dish and the yolk in another.

The caviar was heaped on to their plates, and they ate for a time in silence.

After a while Bond said: 'It's very satisfactory to be a corpse who changes places with his murderers. For them it certainly was a case of being hoist with their own petard. Mathis must be very pleased with the day's work—five of the opposition neutralized in twenty-four hours.' And he told her how the Muntzes had been confounded.

'Incidentally,' he asked, 'how did you come to get mixed up in this affair? What section are you in?'

'I'm personal assistant to Head of S,' said Vesper. 'As it was his plan he wanted his section to have a hand in the operation, and he asked M. if I could go. It seemed only to be a liaison job, so M. said yes although he told my chief that you would be furious at being given a woman to work with.' She paused and, when Bond said nothing, continued: 'I had to meet Mathis in Paris and come down with him. I've got a friend who is a vendeuse with Dior, and somehow she managed to borrow me this and the frock I was wearing this morning; otherwise I couldn't possibly have competed with all these people.' She made a gesture towards the room. 'The office was very jealous although they didn't know what the job was. All they knew was that I was to work with a Double O. Of course you're our heroes. I was enchanted.'

Bond frowned. 'It's not difficult to get a Double O number if you're prepared to kill people,' he said. 'That's all the meaning it has. It's nothing to be particularly proud of. I've got the corpses of a Japanese cipher expert in New York and a Norwegian double agent in Stockholm to thank for being a Double O. Probably quite decent people. They just got caught up in the gale of the world like that Yugoslav that Tito bumped off. It's a confusing business; but if it's one's profession one does what one's told. How do you like the grated egg with your caviar?'

'It's a wonderful combination,' she said. 'I'm loving my dinner. It seems a shame—' She stopped, warned by a cold look in Bond's eye.

'If it wasn't for the job, we wouldn't be here,' he said.

Suddenly he regretted the intimacy of their dinner and of their talk. He felt that he had said too much and what was only a working relationship had become confused.

'Let's consider what has to be done,' he said in a matter-of-fact voice. 'I'd better explain what I'm going to try and do, and how you can help. Which isn't very much, I'm afraid,' he added. 'Now these are the basic facts.' He proceeded to sketch out the plan and enumerate the various contingencies which faced them.

The maître d'hôtel supervised the serving of the second

course, and then as they ate the delicious food Bond continued.

She listened to him coldly, but with attentive obedience. She felt thoroughly deflated by his harshness, while admitting to herself that she should have paid more heed to the warnings of Head of S.

'He's a dedicated man,' her chief had said when he gave her the assignment. 'Don't imagine this is going to be any fun. He thinks of nothing but the job on hand and, while it's on, he's absolute hell to work for. But he's an expert, and there aren't many about; so you won't be wasting your time. He's a good-looking chap—but don't fall for him. I don't think he's got much heart. Anyway, good luck, and don't get hurt.'

All this had been something of a challenge, and she was pleased when she felt she attracted and interested him, as she knew intuitively that she did. Then at a hint that they were finding pleasure together, a hint that was only the first words of a conventional phrase, he had suddenly turned to ice and had brutally veered away as if warmth were poison to him. She felt hurt and foolish. Then she gave a mental shrug and concentrated with all her attention on what he was saying. She would not make the same mistake again.

'. . . and the main hope is to pray for a run of luck for me, or against him.'

Bond was explaining just how baccarat is played.

'It's much the same as any other gambling game. The odds against the banker and the player are more or less even. Only a run against either can be decisive and "break the bank," or break the players.

'Tonight, Le Chiffre, we know, has bought the baccarat bank from the Egyptian syndicate which is running the high tables here. He paid a million francs for it, and his capital has been reduced to twenty-four million. I have about the same. There will be ten players, I expect, and we sit round the banker at a kidney-shaped table.

'Generally, this table is divided into two tableaux. The banker plays two games, one against each of the tableaux to left and right of him. In that game the banker should be able to win by playing off one tableau against the other and by first-class accountancy. But there aren't enough baccarat players yet at Royale, and Le Chiffre is just going to pit his luck against the other players at the single tableau. It's unusual because the odds in favour of the banker aren't so good; but they're a shade in his favour and, of course, he has control of the size of the stakes.

'Well, the banker sits there in the middle with a croupier to rake in the cards and call the amount of each bank and a chef de partie to umpire the game generally. I shall be sitting as near dead opposite Le Chiffre as I can get. In front of him he has a shoe containing six packs of cards, well shuffled. There's absolutely no chance of tampering with the shoe. The cards are shuffled by the croupier and cut by one of the players and put into the shoe in full view of the table. We've checked on the staff. and they're all okay. It would be useful, but almost impossible, to mark all the cards, and it would mean the connivance at least of the croupier. Anyway, we shall be watching for that too.'

Bond drank some champagne and continued.

'Now what happens at the game is this. The banker announces an opening bank of five hundred thousand francs, or five hundred pounds as it is now. Each seat is numbered from the right of the banker, and the player next to the banker, or Number 1, can accept this bet and push his money out on to the table, or pass it if it is too much or he doesn't want to take it. Then Number 2 has the right to take it; and if he refuses then Number 3, and so on round the table. If no single player takes it all, the bet is offered to the table as a whole and everyone chips in, including sometimes the spectators round the table, until the five hundred thousand is made up.

'That is a small bet which would immediately be met, but when it gets to a million or two, it's often difficult to find a taker or even, if the bank seems to be in luck, a group of takers to cover the bet. At that moment I shall always try and step in and accept the bet—in fact, I shall attack Le Chiffre's bank whenever I get a chance until either I've bust his bank or he's bust me. It may take some time, but in the end one of us two is bound to break the other, irrespective of the other players at the table, although they can, of course, make him richer or poorer in the meantime.

'Being the banker, he's got a slight advantage in the play; but knowing that I'm making a dead set at him and not knowing, I hope, my capital, is bound to play on his nerves a bit, so I'm hoping that we start about equal.'

He paused while the strawberries came, and the avocado pear.

For a while they ate in silence, then they talked of other things while the coffee was served. They smoked. Neither of them drank brandy or a liqueur. Finally, Bond felt it was time to explain the actual mechanics of the game.

'It's a simple affair,' he said, 'and you'll understand it at once if you've ever played vingt-et-un, where the object is to get cards from the banker which add up more closely to a count of twenty-one than his do. In this game I get two cards and the banker gets two; and, unless anyone wins outright, either or both of us can get one more card. The object of the game is to hold two, or three cards which together count nine points, or as nearly nine as possible. Court cards and tens count nothing; aces one each; any other card its face value. It is only the last figure of your count that signifies. So nine plus seven equals six—not sixteen.

'The winner is the one whose count is nearest to nine. Draws are played over again.'

Vesper listened attentively, but she also watched the look of abstract passion on Bond's face.

'Now,' Bond continued, 'when the banker deals me my two cards, if they add up to eight or nine, they're a "natural" and I turn them up and I win, unless he has an equal or a better natural. If I haven't got a natural, I can stand on a seven or a six, perhaps ask for a card or perhaps not, on a five, and certainly ask for a card if my count is lower than five. Five is the turning point of the game. According to the odds, the chances of bettering or worsening your hand if you hold a five are exactly even.

'Only when I ask for a card or tap mine to signify that I stand on what I have, can the banker look at his. If he has a natural, he turns them up and wins. Otherwise he is faced with the same problems as I was. But he is helped in his decision to draw or not to draw a third card by my actions. If I have stood he must assume that I have a five, six, or seven: if I have drawn, he will know that I had something less than a six and I may have improved my hand or not with the card he gave me. And this card was dealt to me face up. On its face value and a knowledge of the odds, he will know whether to take another card or to stand on his own.

'So he has a very slight advantage over me. He has a tiny help over his decision to draw or to stand. But there is always one problem card at this game: Shall one draw or stand on a five, and what will your opponent do with a five? Some players always draw or always stand. I follow my intuition.

'But in the end'—Bond stubbed out his cigarette and called for the bill—'it's the natural eights and nines that matter, and I must just see that I get more of them than he does.'

X. THE HIGH TABLE

WHILE TELLING the story of the game and anticipating the coming fight, Bond's face had lit up again. The prospect of at last getting to grips with Le Chiffre stimulated him and quickened his pulse. He seemed to have completely forgotten the brief coolness between them, and Vesper was relieved and entered into his mood.

He paid the bill and gave a handsome tip to the sommelier. Vesper rose and led the way out of the restaurant and out on to the steps of the hotel.

The big Bentley was waiting, and Bond drove Vesper over, parking as close to the entrance as he could. As they walked through the ornate anterooms, he hardly spoke. She looked at him and saw that his nostrils were slightly flared. In other respects he seemed completely at ease, acknowledging cheerfully the greetings of the Casino functionaries. At the door to the salle privée they were not asked for their membership cards. Bond's high gambling had already made him a favoured client, and any companion of his shared in the glory.

Before they had penetrated very far into the main room,

Felix Leiter detached himself from one of the roulette tables and greeted Bond as an old friend. After being introduced to Vesper Lynd and exchanging a few remarks, Leiter said: 'Well, since you're playing baccarat this evening, will you allow me to show Miss Lynd how to break the bank at roulette? I've got three lucky numbers that are bound to show soon, and I expect Miss Lynd has some too. Then perhaps we could come and watch you when your game starts to warm up.'

Bond looked inquiringly at Vesper.

'I should love that,' she said. 'But will you give me one of your lucky numbers to play on?'

'I have no lucky numbers,' said Bond unsmilingly. 'I only bet on even chances, or as near them as I can get. Well, I shall leave you then.' He excused himself. 'You will be in excellent hands with my friend Felix Leiter.' He gave a short smile which embraced them both and walked with an unhurried gait towards the caisse.

Leiter sensed the rebuff.

'He's a very serious gambler, Miss Lynd,' he said. 'And I guess he has to be. Now come with me and watch Number 17 obey my extrasensory perceptions. You'll find it quite a painless sensation being given plenty of money for nothing.'

Bond was relieved to be on his own again and to be able to clear his mind of everything but the task on hand. He stood at the caisse and took his twenty-four million francs against the receipt which had been given him that afternoon. He divided the notes into equal packets and put half the sum into his right-hand coat pocket and the other half into the left. Then he strolled slowly across the room between the thronged tables until he came to the top of the room where the broad baccarat table waited behind the brass rail.

The table was filling up, and the cards were spread face

down, being stirred and mixed slowly in what is known as the 'croupiers' shuffle'—supposedly the shuffle which is most effective and least susceptible to cheating.

The chef de partie lifted the velvet-covered chain which allowed entrance through the brass rail.

'I've kept Number 6 as you wished, Monsieur Bond.'

There were still three other empty places at the table. Bond moved inside the rail to which a huissier was holding out his chair. He sat down with a nod to the players on his right and left. He took out his wide gun-metal cigarette case and his black lighter and placed them on the green baize at his right elbow. The huissier wiped a thick glass ashtray with a cloth and put it beside them. Bond lit a cigarette and leant back in his chair.

Opposite him, the banker's chair was vacant. He glanced round the table. He knew most of the players by sight, but few of their names. At Number 7, on his right, there was a Monsieur Sixte, a weathy Belgian with metal interests in the Congo. At Number 9 there was Lord Danvers, a distinguished but weak-looking man whose francs were presumably provided by his rich American wife, a middle-aged woman with the predatory mouth of a barracuda, who sat at Number 3. Bond reflected that they would probably play a pawky and nervous game and be amongst the early casualties. At Number 1, to the right of the bank, was a well-known Greek gambler who owned, as in Bond's experience apparently everyone does in the eastern Mediterranean, a profitable shipping line. He would play coldly and well and would be a stayer.

Bond asked the hussier for a card and wrote on it, under a neat question mark, the remaining numbers, 2, 4, 5, 8, 10, and asked the huissier to give it to the chef de partie.

Soon it came back with the names filled in.

Number 2, still empty, was to be Carmel Delane, the American film star with alimony from three husbands to burn and, Bond assumed, a call on still more from whoever her present companion at Royale might be. With her sanguine temperament she would play gaily and with panache and might run into a vein of luck.

Then came Lady Danvers at Number 3 and Numbers 4 and 5 were a Mr. and Mrs. Du Pont, rich-looking, who might or might not have some of the real Du Pont money behind them. Bond guessed they would be stayers. They both had a businesslike look about them and were talking together easily and cheerfully as if they felt very much at home at the big game. Bond was quite happy to have them next to him— Mrs. Du Pont sat at Number 5—and he felt prepared to share with them or with Monsieur Sixte on his right, if they found themselves faced with too big a bank.

At Number 8 was the Maharajah of a small Indian state, probably with all his wartime sterling balances to play with. Bond's experience told him that few of the Asiatic races were courageous gamblers, even the much-vaunted Chinese being inclined to lose heart if the going was bad. But the Maharajah would probably stay late in the game and stand some heavy losses if they were gradual.

Number 10 was a prosperous-looking young Italian, Signor Tomelli, who possibly had plenty of money from rackrents in Milan and would probably play a dashing and foolish game. He might lose his temper and make a scene.

Bond had just finished his sketchy summing-up of the players when Le Chiffre, with the silence and economy of movement of a big fish, came through the opening in the brass rail and, with a cold smile of welcome for the table, took his place directly opposite Bond in the Banker's chair.

With the same economy of movement, he cut the thick

slab of cards which the croupier had placed on the table squarely between his blunt relaxed hands. Then, as the croupier fitted the six packs with one swift motion into the metal and wooden shoe, Le Chiffre said something quietly to him.

'Messieurs, mesdames, les jeux sont faits. Un banco de cinq cent mille.' And, as the Greek at Number 1 tapped the table in front of his fat pile of hundred-mille plaques: 'Le banco est fait.'

Le Chiffre crouched over the shoe. He gave it a short deliberate slap to settle the cards, the first of which showed its semicircular pale pink tongue through the slanting aluminum mouth of the shoe. Then, with a thick white forefinger he pressed gently on the pink tongue and slipped out the first card six inches or a foot towards the Greek on his right hand. Then he slipped out a card for himself, then another for the Greek, then one more for himself.

He sat immobile, not touching his own cards.

He looked at the Greek's face.

With his flat wooden spatula, like a long bricklayer's trowel, the croupier delicately lifted up the Greek's two cards and dropped them with a quick movement an extra few inches to the right so that they lay just before the Greek's pale hairy hands, which lay inert like two watchful pink crabs on the table.

The two pink crabs scuttled out together and the Greek gathered the cards into his wide left hand and cautiously bent his head so that he could see, in the shadow made by his cupped hand, the value of the bottom of the two cards. Then he slowly inserted the forefinger of his right hand and slipped the bottom card slightly sideways so that the value of the top card was also just perceptible.

His face was quite impassive. He flattened out his left

hand on the table and then withdrew it, leaving the two pink
cards face down before him, their secret unrevealed.

Then he lifted his head and looked Le Chiffre in the eye.
'Non,' said the Greek flatly.

From the decision to stand on his two cards and not to
ask for another, it was clear that the Greek had a five, or a
six, or a seven. To be certain of winning, the bank had to reveal an eight or a nine. If the banker failed to show either
figure, he also had the right to take another card which
might or might not improve his count.

Le Chiffre's hands were clasped in front of him, his two
cards three or four inches away. With his right hand he
picked up the two cards and turned them face upwards on
the table with a faint snap.

They were a four and a five, an undefeatable natural nine.
He had won.

'Neuf à la banque,' quietly said the croupier. With his
spatula he faced the Greek's two cards, 'Et le sept,' he said
unemotionally, lifting up gently the corpses of the seven
and queen and slipping them through the wide slot in the
table near his chair which leads into the big metal canister
to which all dead cards are consigned. Le Chiffre's two cards
followed them with the faint rattle which comes from the
canister at the beginning of each session before the discards
have made a cushion over the metal floor of their oubliette.

The Greek pushed forward five plaques of one hundred
thousand, and the croupier added these to Le Chiffre's half-
million plaque which lay in the centre of the table. From
each bet the Casino takes a tiny percentage, the cagnotte; but
it is usual at a big game for the banker to subscribe this himself either in a prearranged lump sum or by contributions at
the end of each hand, so that the amount of the bank's stake

can aways be a round figure. Le Chiffre had chosen the second course.

The croupier slipped some counters through the slot in the table which receives the cagnotte and announced quietly:

'Un banco d'un million.'

'Suivi,' murmured the Greek, meaning that he exercised his right to follow up his lost bet.

Bond lit a cigarette and settled himself in his chair. The long game was launched, and the sequence of these gestures and the reiteration of this subdued litany would continue until the end came and the players dispersed. Then the enigmatic cards would be burnt or defaced, a shroud would be draped over the table, and the grass-green baize battlefield would soak up the blood of its victims and refresh itself.

The Greek, after taking a third card, could achieve no better than a four to the bank's seven.

'Un banco de deux millions,' said the croupier.

The players on Bond's left remained silent.

'Banco,' said Bond.

xi. MOMENT OF TRUTH

LE CHIFFRE looked incuriously at him, the whites of his eyes, which showed all round the irises, lending something impassive and doll-like to his gaze.

He slowly removed one thick hand from the table and slipped it into the pocket of his dinner jacket. The hand came out holding a small metal cylinder with a cap which Le Chiffre unscrewed. He inserted the nozzle of the cylinder, with an obscene deliberation, twice into each black nostril in turn, and luxuriously inhaled the benzedrine vapour.

Unhurriedly he pocketed the inhaler; then his hand came quickly back above the level of the table and gave the shoe its usual hard, sharp slap.

During this offensive pantomime Bond had coldly held the banker's gaze, taking in the wide expanse of white face surmounted by the short abrupt cliff of reddish brown hair, the unsmiling wet red mouth, and the impressive width of the shoulders, loosely draped in a massively cut dinner-jacket.

But for the high-lights on the satin of the shawl-cut lapels, he might have been faced by the thick bust of a black-fleeced Minotaur rising out of a green grass field.

Bond slipped a packet of notes on to the table without counting them. If he lost, the croupier would extract what was necessary to cover the bet; but the easy gesture conveyed that Bond didn't expect to lose, and that this was only a token display from the deep funds at Bond's disposal.

The other players sensed a tension between the two gamblers, and there was silence as Le Chiffre fingered the four cards out of the shoe.

The croupier slipped Bond's two cards across to him with the tip of his spatula. Bond, still with his eyes holding Le Chiffre's, reached his right hand out a few inches, glanced down very swiftly, then as he looked up again impassively at Le Chiffre, with a disdainful gesture he tossed the cards face upwards on the table.

They were a four and a five—an unbeatable nine.

There was a little gasp of envy from the table, and the

players to the left of Bond exchanged rueful glances at their failure to accept the two-million-franc bet.

With the hint of a shrug, Le Chiffre slowly faced his own two cards and flicked them away with his fingernail. They were two valueless knaves.

'Le baccarat,' intoned the croupier as he spaded the thick chips over the table to Bond.

Bond slipped them into his right-hand pocket with the unused packet of notes. His face showed no emotion, but he was pleased with the success of his first coup and with the outcome of the silent clash of wills across the table.

The woman on his left, the American Mrs. Du Pont, turned to him with a wry smile.

'I shouldn't have let it come to you,' she said. 'Directly the cards were dealt I kicked myself.'

'It's only the beginning of the game,' said Bond. 'You may be right the next time you pass it.'

Mr. Du Pont leant forward from the other side of his wife: 'If one could be right every hand, none of us would be here,' he said philosophically.

'I would be,' his wife laughed. 'You don't think I do this for pleasure.'

As the game went on, Bond looked over the spectators leaning on the high brass rail round the table. He soon saw Le Chiffre's two gunmen. They stood behind and to either side of the banker. They looked respectable enough, but not sufficiently a part of the game to be unobtrusive.

The one more or less behind Le Chiffre's right arm was tall and funereal in his dinner-jacket. His face was wooden and grey, but his eyes flickered and gleamed like a conjurer's. His whole long body was restless, and his hands shifted often on the brass rail. Bond guessed that he would kill without interest or concern for what he killed, and that he would prefer strangling. He had something of Lennie in *Of Mice and Men*, but his inhumanity would not come from infantilism but from drugs. Marihuana, decided Bond.

The other man looked like a Corsican shopkeeper. He was short and very dark with a flat head covered with thickly greased hair. He seemed to be a cripple. A chunky Malacca cane with a rubber tip hung on the rail beside him. He must have had permission to bring the cane into the Casino with him, reflected Bond, who knew that neither sticks nor any other objects were allowed in the rooms as a precaution against acts of violence. He looked sleek and well fed. His mouth hung vacantly half open and revealed very bad teeth. He wore a heavy black moustache, and the backs of his hands on the rail were matted with black hair. Bond guessed that hair covered most of his squat body. Naked, Bond supposed, he would be an obscene object.

The game continued uneventfully, but with a slight bias against the bank.

The third coup is the 'sound barrier' at chemin-de-fer and baccarat. Your luck can defeat the first and second tests, but when the third deal comes along it most often spells disaster. Again and again at this point you find yourself being bounced back to earth. It was like that now. Neither the bank nor any of the players seemed to be able to get hot. But there was a steady and inexorable seepage against the bank, amounting after about two hours' play to ten million francs. Bond had no idea what profits Le Chiffre had made over the past two days. He estimated them at five million and guessed that now the banker's capital could not be more than twenty million.

In fact, Le Chiffre had lost heavily all that afternoon. At this moment he only had ten million left.

Bond, on the other hand, by one o'clock in the morning,

had won four million, bring his resources up to twenty-eight million.

Bond was cautiously pleased. Le Chiffre showed no trace of emotion. He continued to play like an automaton, never speaking except when he gave instructions in a low aside to the croupier at the opening of each new bank.

Outside the pool of silence round the high table, there was the constant hum of the other tables, chemin-de-fer, roulette, and trente-et-quarante, interspersed with the clear calls of the croupiers and occasional bursts of laughter or gasps of excitement from different corners of the huge salle.

In the background there thudded always the hidden metronome of the Casino, ticking up its little treasure of one-per-cents with each spin of a wheel and each turn of a card— a pulsing fat-cat with a zero for a heart.

It was at ten minutes past one by Bond's watch that, at the high table, the whole pattern of play suddenly altered.

The Greek at Number 1 was still having a bad time. He had lost the first coup of half a million francs and the second. He passed the third time, leaving a bank of two millions. Carmel Delane at Number 2 refused it. So did Lady Danvers at Number 3.

The Du Ponts looked at each other.

'Banco,' said Mrs. Du Pont, and promptly lost to the banker's natural eight.

'Un banco de quatre millions,' said the croupier.

'Banco,' said Bond, pushing out a wad of notes.

Again he fixed Le Chiffre with his eye. Again he gave only a cursory look at his two cards.

'No,' he said. He held a marginal five. The position was dangerous.

Le Chiffre turned up a knave and a four. He gave the shoe another slap. He drew a three.

'Sept à la banque,' said the croupier, 'et cinq,' he added as he tipped Bond's losing cards face upwards. He raked over Bond's money, extracted four million francs and returned the remainder to Bond.

'Un banco de huit millions.'

'Suivi,' said Bond.

And lost again, to a natural nine.

In two coups he had lost twelve million francs. By scraping the barrel, he had just sixteen million francs left, exactly the amount of the next banco.

Suddenly Bond felt the sweat on his palms. Like snow in sunshine his capital had melted. With the covetous deliberation of the winning gambler, Le Chiffre was tapping a light tattoo on the table with his right hand. Bond looked across into the eyes of murky basalt. They held an ironical question. 'Do you want the full treatment?' they seemed to ask.

'Suivi,' Bond said softly.

He took some notes and plaques out of his right-hand pocket and the entire stack of notes out of his left and pushed them forward. There was no hint in his movements that this would be his last stake.

His mouth felt suddenly as dry as flock wall-paper. He looked up and saw Vesper and Felix Leiter standing where the gunman with the stick had stood. He did not know how long they had been standing there. Leiter looked faintly worried, but Vesper smiled encouragement at him.

He heard a faint rattle on the rail behind him and turned his head. The battery of bad teeth under the black moustache gaped vacantly back at him.

'Le jeu est fait,' said the croupier, and the two cards came slithering towards him over the green baize—a green baize which was no longer smooth, but thick now, and furry and almost choking, its colour as livid as the grass on a fresh tomb.

The light from the broad satin-lined shades which had seemed so welcoming now seemed to take the colour out of his hand as he glanced at the cards. Then he looked again.

It was nearly as bad as it could have been—the king of hearts and an ace, the ace of spades. It squinted up at him like a black widow spider.

'A card.' He still kept all emotion out of his voice.

Le Chiffre faced his own two cards. He had a queen and a black five. He looked at Bond and pressed out another card with a wide forefinger. The table was absolutely silent. He faced it and flicked it away. The croupier lifted it delicately with his spatula and slipped it over to Bond. It was a good card, the five of hearts, but to Bond it was a difficult finger-print in dried blood. He now had a count of six and Le Chiffre a count of five, but the banker having a five and giving a five, would and must draw another card and try and improve with a one, two, three, or four. Drawing any other card he would be defeated.

The odds were on Bond's side, but now it was Le Chiffre who looked across into Bond's eyes and hardly glanced at the card as he flicked it face upwards on the table.

It was, unnecessarily, the best, a four, giving the bank a count of nine. He had won, almost slowing up.

Bond was beaten and cleaned out.

xii. THE DEADLY TUBE

BOND SAT silent, frozen with defeat. He opened his wide black case and took out a cigarette. He snapped open the tiny jaws of the Ronson and lit the cigarette and put the lighter back on the table. He took a deep lungful of smoke and expelled it between his teeth with a faint hiss.

What now? Back to the hotel and bed, avoiding the commiserating eyes of Mathis and Leiter and Vesper. Back to the telephone call to London, and then tomorrow the plane home, the taxi up to Regent's Park, the walk up the stairs and along the corridor, and M.'s cold face across the table, his forced sympathy, his 'Better luck next time'; and, of course, there couldn't be one, not another chance like this.

He looked round the table and up at the spectators. Few were looking at him. They were waiting while the croupier counted the money and piled up the chips in a neat stack in front of the banker, waiting to see if anyone would conceivably challenge this huge bank of thirty-two million francs, this wonderful run of banker's luck.

Leiter had vanished, not wishing to look Bond in the eye after the knock-out, he supposed. Yet Vesper looked curiously unmoved, she gave him a smile of encouragement. But then, Bond reflected, she knew nothing of the game. Had no notion, probably, of the bitterness of his defeat.

The huissier was coming towards Bond inside the rail. He stopped beside him. Bent over him. Placed a squat envelope beside Bond on the table. It was as thick as a dictionary. Said something about the caisse. Moved away again.

Bond's heart thumped. He took the heavy anonymous envelope below the level of the table and slit it open with his thumbnail, noticing that the gum was still wet on the flap.

Unbelieving and yet knowing it was true, he felt the broad wads of notes. He slipped them into his pockets, retaining the half-sheet of notepaper which was pinned to the topmost of them. He glanced at it in the shadow below the table. There was one line of writing in ink: 'Marshall Aid. Thirty-two million francs. With the compliments of the U.S.A.'

Bond swallowed. He looked over towards Vesper. Felix Leiter was again standing beside her. He grinned slightly, and Bond smiled back and raised his hand from the table in a small gesture of benediction. Then he set his mind to sweeping away all traces of the sense of complete defeat which had swamped him a few minutes before. This was a reprieve, but only a reprieve. There could be no more miracles. This time he had to win—if Le Chiffre had not already made his fifty million—if he was going to go on!

The croupier had completed his task of computing the cagnotte, changing Bond's notes into plaques, and making a pile of the giant stake in the middle of the table.

There lay thirty-two thousand pounds. Perhaps, thought Bond, Le Chiffre needed just one more coup, even a minor one of a few million francs, to achieve his object. Then he would have made his fifty million francs and would leave the table. By tomorrow his deficits would be covered and his position secure.

He showed no signs of moving, and Bond guessed with relief that somehow he must have overestimated Le Chiffre's resources.

Then the only hope, thought Bond, was to stamp on him now. Not to share the bank with the table, or to take some minor part of it, but to go the whole hog. This would really jolt Le Chiffre. He would hate to see more than ten or fifteen million of the stake covered, and he could not possibly expect anyone to banco the entire thirty-two millions. He might not know that Bond had been cleaned out, but he must imagine that Bond had by now only small reserves. He could not know of the contents of the envelope. If he did, he would probably withdraw the bank and start all over again on the wearisome journey up from the five hundred franc opening bet.

The analysis was right.

Le Chiffre needed another eight million.

At last he nodded.

'Un banco de trente-deux millions.'

The croupier's voice rang out. A silence built itself up round the table.

'Un banco de trente-deux millions.'

In a louder, prouder voice the chef de partie took up the cry, hoping to draw big money away from the neighbouring chemin-de-fer tables. Besides, this was wonderful publicity. The stake had only once been reached in the history of baccarat—at Deauville in 1950. The rival Casino de la Forêt at Le Touquet had never got near it.

It was then that Bond leant slightly forward.

'Suivi,' he said quietly.

There was an excited buzz round the table. The word ran through the Casino. People crowded in. Thirty-two million! For most of them it was more than they had earned all their lives. It was their savings and the savings of their families. It was, literally, a small fortune.

One of the Casino directors consulted with the chef de

partie. The chef de partie turned apologetically to Bond.

'Excusez moi, monsieur. La mise?'

It was an indication that Bond really must show he had the money to cover the bet. They knew, of course, that he was a very wealthy man, but after all, thirty-two millions! And it sometimes happened that desperate people would bet without a sou in the world and cheerfully go to prison if they lost.

'Mes excuses, Monsieur Bond,' added the chef de partie obsequiously.

It was when Bond shovelled the great wad of notes out on to the table and the croupier busied himself with the task of counting the pinned sheaves of ten thousand franc notes, the largest denomination issued in France, that he caught a swift exchange of glances between Le Chiffre and the gunman standing directly behind Bond.

Immediately he felt something hard press into the base of his spine, right into the cleft between his two buttocks on the padded chair.

At the same time a thick voice speaking southern French said softly, urgently, just behind his right ear:

'This is a gun, monsieur. It is absolutely silent. It can blow the base of your spine off without a sound. You will appear to have fainted. I shall be gone. Withdraw your bet before I count ten. If you call for help I shall fire.'

The voice was confident. Bond believed it. These people had shown they would unhesitatingly go the limit. The thick walking stick was explained. Bond knew the type of gun. The barrel a series of soft rubber baffles which absorbed the detonation, but allowed the passage of the bullet. They had been invented and used in the war for assassinations. Bond had tested them himself.

'Un,' said the voice.

Bond turned his head. There was the man, leaning forward close behind him, smiling broadly under his black moustache as if he were wishing Bond luck, completely secure in the noise and the crowd.

The discoloured teeth came together. 'Deux,' said the grinning mouth.

Bond looked across. Le Chiffre was watching him. His eyes glittered back at Bond. His mouth was open, and he was breathing fast. He was waiting, waiting for Bond's hand to gesture to the croupier, or else for Bond suddenly to slump backwards in his chair, his face grimacing with a scream.

'Trois.'

Bond looked over at Vesper and Felix Leiter. They were smiling and talking to each other. The fools. Where was Mathis? Where were those famous men of his?

'Quatre.'

And the other spectators. This crowd of jabbering idiots. Couldn't someone see what was happening? The chef de partie, the croupier, the huissier?

'Cinq.'

The croupier was tidying up the pile of notes. The chef de partie bowed smilingly towards Bond. Directly the stake was in order he would announce, 'Le jeux est fait,' and the gun would fire whether the gunman had reached ten or not.

'Six.'

Bond decided. It was a chance. He carefully moved his hands to the edge of the table, gripped it, edged his buttocks right back, feeling the sharp gun-sight grind into his coccyx.

'Sept.'

The chef de partie turned to Le Chiffre with his eyebrows lifted, waiting for the banker's nod that he was ready to play.

Suddenly Bond heaved backwards with all his strength.

His momentum tipped the crossbar of the chair-back down so quickly that it cracked across the Malacca tube and wrenched it from the gunman's hand before he could pull the trigger.

Bond went head-over-heels on to the ground amongst the spectators' feet, his legs in the air. The back of the chair splintered with a sharp crack. There were cries of dismay. The spectators cringed away and then, reassured, clustered back. Hands helped him to his feet and brushed him down. The huissier bustled up with the chef de partie. At all costs a scandal must be avoided.

Bond held on to the brass rail. He looked confused and embarrassed. He brushed his hand across his forehead. 'A momentary faintness,' he said. 'It is nothing—the excitement, the heat.'

There were expressions of sympathy. Naturally, with this tremendous game. Would Monsieur prefer to withdraw, to lie down, to go home? Should a doctor be fetched?

Bond shook his head. He was perfectly all right now. His excuses to the table. To the banker also.

A new chair was brought and he sat down. He looked across at Le Chiffre. Through his relief at being alive, he felt a moment of triumph at what he saw—some fear in the fat, pale face.

There was a buzz of speculation round the table. Bond's neighbours on both sides of him bent forward and spoke solicitously about the heat and the lateness of the hour and the smoke and the lack of air.

Bond replied politely. He turned to examine the crowd behind him. There was no trace of the gunman, but the huissier was looking for someone to claim the Malacca stick. It seemed undamaged. But it no longer carried a rubber tip. Bond beckoned to him.

'If you will give it to that gentleman over there'—he indicated Felix Leiter—'he will return it. It belongs to an acquaintance of his.'

The huissier bowed.

Bond grimly reflected that a short examination would reveal to Leiter why he had made such an embarrassing public display of himself.

He turned back to the table and tapped the green cloth in front of him to show that he was ready.

xiii. 'A WHISPER OF LOVE, A WHISPER OF HATE'

'LA PARTIE continue,' announced the chef impressively. 'Un banco de trente-deux millions.'

The spectators craned forward. Le Chiffre hit the shoe with a flat-handed slap that made it rattle. As an afterthought he took out his benzedrine inhaler and sucked the vapour up his nose.

'Filthy brute,' said Mrs. Du Pont on Bond's left.

Bond's mind was clear again. By a miracle he had survived a devastating wound. He could feel his armpits still wet with the fear of it. But the success of his gambit with the chair had wiped out all memories of the dreadful valley of defeat through which he had just passed.

He had made a fool of himself. The game had been inter-

rupted for at least ten minutes, a delay unheard of in a respectable casino, but now cards were waiting for him in the
shoe. They must not fail him. He felt his heart lift at the
prospect of what was to come.

It was two o'clock in the morning. Apart from the thick
crowd round the big game, play was still going on at three
of the chemin-de-fer games and at the same number of roulette tables.

In the silence round his own table, Bond suddenly heard
a distant croupier intone: 'Neuf. Le rouge gagne, impair
et manque.'

Was this an omen for him or for Le Chiffre?

The two cards slithered towards him across the green sea.

Like an octopus under a rock, Le Chiffre watched him
from the other side of the table.

Bond reached out a steady right hand and drew the cards
towards him. Would it be the lift of the heart which a nine
brings, or an eight brings?

He fanned the two cards under the curtain of his hand.
The muscles of his jaw rippled as he clenched his teeth. His
whole body stiffened in a reflex of self-defence.

He had two queens, two red queens.

They looked roguishly back at him from the shadows.
They were the worst. They were nothing. Zero. Baccarat.

'A card,' said Bond, fighting to keep hopelessness out of
his voice. He felt Le Chiffre's eyes boring into his brain.

The banker slowly turned his own two cards face up.

He had a count of three—a king and a black three.

Bond softly exhaled a cloud of tobacco smoke. He still
had a chance. Now he was really faced with the moment
of truth. Le Chiffre slapped the shoe, slipped out a card,
Bond's card, Bond's fate, and slowly turned it face up.

It was a nine, a wonderful nine of hearts the card known

in gipsy magic as 'a whisper of love, a whisper of hate,' the card that meant almost certain victory for Bond.

The croupier slipped it delicately across. To Le Chiffre it meant nothing. Bond might have had a one, in which case he now had ten points, or nothing, or baccarat, as it is called. Or he might have had a two, three, four, or even five. In which case, with nine, his maximum count would be four.

Holding a three and giving a nine is one of the moot situations at the game. The odds are so nearly divided between to draw or not to draw. Bond let the banker sweat it out. Since his nine could only be equalled by the banker drawing a six, he would normally have shown his count if it had been a friendly game.

Bond's cards lay on the table before him, the two impersonal pale pink-patterned backs and the faced nine of hearts. To Le Chiffre the nine might be telling the truth or many variations of lies.

The whole secret lay in the reverse of the two pink backs where the pair of queens kissed the green cloth.

The sweat was running down either side of the banker's beaky nose. His thick tongue came out slyly and licked a drop out of the corner of his red gash of a mouth. He looked at Bond's cards, and then at his own, and then back at Bond's.

Then his whole body shrugged and he slipped out a card for himself from the lisping shoe.

He faced it. The table craned. It was a wonderful card, a five.

'Huit à la banque,' said the croupier.

As Bond sat silent, Le Chiffre suddenly grinned wolfishly. He must have won.

The croupier's spatula reached almost apologetically across the table. There was not a man at the table who did not believe Bond was defeated.

The spatula flicked the two pink cards over on their backs. The gay red queens smiled up at the lights.

'Et le neuf.'

A great gasp went up round the table, and then a hubbub of talk.

Bond's eyes were on Le Chiffre. The big man fell back in his chair as if slugged above the heart. His mouth opened and shut once or twice in protest, and his right hand felt at his throat. Then he rocked back. His lips were grey.

As the huge stack of plaques was shunted across the table to Bond the banker reached into an inner pocket of his jacket and threw a wad of notes on to the table.

The croupier riffled through them.

'Un banco de dix millions,' he announced. He slapped down their equivalent in ten plaques of a million each.

This is the kill, thought Bond. This man has reached the point of no return. This is the last of his capital. He has come to where I stood an hour ago, and he is making the last gesture that I made. But if this man loses there is no one to come to his aid, no miracle to help him.

Bond sat back and lit a cigarette. On a small table beside him half a bottle of Clicquot and a glass had materialized. Without asking who the benefactor was, Bond filled the glass to the brim and drank it down in two long draughts.

Then he leant back with his arms curled forward on the table in front of him like the arms of a wrestler seeking a hold at the opening of a bout of ju-jitsu.

The players on his left remained silent.

'Banco,' he said, speaking straight at Le Chiffre.

Once more the two cards were borne over to him, and this time the croupier slipped them into the green lagoon between the outstretched arms.

· Bond curled his right hand in, glanced briefly down and

flipped the cards face up into the middle of the table.

'Le neuf,' said the croupier.

Le Chiffre was gazing down at his own two black kings.

'Et le baccarat,' and the croupier eased across the table the fat tide of plaques.

Le Chiffre watched them go to join the serried millions in the shadow of Bond's left arm; then he stood up slowly, and without a word he brushed past the players to the break in the rail. He unhooked the velvet-covered chain and let it fall. The spectators opened a way for him. They looked at him curiously and rather fearfully as if he carried the smell of death on him. Then he vanished from Bond's sight.

Bond stood up. He took a hundred-mille plaque from the stacks beside him and slipped it across the table to the chef de partie. He cut short the effusive thanks and asked the croupier to have his winnings carried to the caisse. The other players were leaving their seats. With no banker, there could be no game, and by now it was half-past two. He exchanged some pleasant words with his neighbours to right and left and then ducked under the rail to where Vesper and Felix Leiter were waiting for him.

Together they walked over to the caisse. Bond was invited to come into the private office of the Casino directors. On the desk lay his huge pile of chips. He added the contents of his pockets to it.

In all there was over seventy million francs.

Bond took Felix Leiter's money in notes and took a cheque to cash on the Crédit Lyonnais for the remaining forty-odd million. He was congratulated warmly on his winnings. The directors hoped that he would be playing again that evening.

Bond gave an evasive reply. He walked over to the bar and handed Leiter's money to him. For a few minutes they discussed the game over a bottle of champagne. Leiter took a .45 bullet out of his pocket and placed it on the table.

'I gave the gun to Mathis,' he said. 'He's taken it away. He was as puzzled as we were by the spill you took. He was standing at the back of the crowd with one of his men when it happened. The gunman got away without difficulty. You can imagine how they kicked themselves when they saw the gun. Mathis gave me this bullet to show you what you escaped. The nose has been cut with a dum-dum cross. You'd have been in a terrible mess. But they can't tie it on to Le Chiffre. The man came in alone. They've got the form he filled up to get his entrance card. Of course, it'll all be phony. He got permission to bring the stick in with him. He had a certificate for a war-wound pension. These people certainly get themselves well organized. They've got his prints and they're on the Belinograph to Paris, so we may hear more about him in the morning.' Felix Leiter tapped out another cigarette. 'Anyway, all's well that ends well. You certainly took Le Chiffre for a ride at the end, though we had some bad moments. I expect you did too.'

Bond smiled. 'That envelope was the most wonderful thing that ever happened to me. I thought I was really finished. It wasn't at all a pleasant feeling. Talk about a friend in need. One day I'll try and return the compliment.'

He rose. 'I'll just go over to the hotel and put this away,' he said, tapping his pocket. 'I don't like wandering around with Le Chiffre's death warrant on me. He might get ideas. Then I'd like to celebrate a bit. What do you think?'

He turned to Vesper. She had hardly said a word since the end of the game.

'Shall we have a glass of champagne in the night club before we go to bed? It's called the Roi Galant. You get to it through the public rooms. It looks quite cheerful.'

'I think I'd love to,' said Vesper. 'I'll tidy up while you

put your winnings away. I'll meet you in the entrance hall.'

'What about you, Felix?' Bond hoped he could be alone with Vesper.

Leiter looked at him and read his mind.

'I'd rather take a little rest before breakfast,' he said. 'It's been quite a day, and I expect Paris will want me to do a bit of mopping-up tomorrow. There are several loose ends you won't have to worry about. I shall. I'll walk over to the hotel with you. Might as well convoy the treasure ship right into port.'

They strolled over through the shadows cast by the full moon. Both had their hands on their guns. It was three o'clock in the morning, but there were several people about and the courtyard of the Casino was still lined with motor-cars.

The short walk was uneventful.

At the hotel, Leiter insisted on accompanying Bond to his room. It was as Bond had left it six hours before.

'No reception committee,' observed Leiter, 'but I wouldn't put it past them to try a last throw. Do you think I ought to stay up and keep you two company?'

'You get your sleep,' said Bond. 'Don't worry about us. They won't be interested in me without the money and I've got an idea for looking after that. Thanks for all you've done. I hope we get on a job again one day.'

'Suits me,' said Leiter, 'so long as you can draw a nine when it's needed—and bring Vesper along with you,' he added dryly. He went out and closed the door.

Bond turned back to the friendliness of his room.

After the crowded arena of the big table and the nervous strain of the three hours' play, he was glad to be alone for a moment and to be welcomed by his pyjamas on the bed and his hairbrushes on the dressing-table. He went into the bathroom and dashed cold water over his face and gargled with a sharp mouthwash. He felt the bruises on the back of his head and on his right shoulder. He reflected cheerfully how narrowly he had twice that day escaped being murdered. Would he have to sit up all that night and wait for them to come again, or was Le Chiffre even now on his way to Le Havre or Bordeaux to pick up a boat for some corner of the world where he could escape the eyes and the guns of SMERSH?

Bond shrugged his shoulders. Sufficient unto that day had been its evil. He gazed for a moment into the mirror and wondered about Vesper's morals. He wanted her cold and arrogant body. He wanted to see tears and desire in her remote blue eyes and to take the ropes of her black hair in his hands and bend her long body back under his. Bond's eyes narrowed, and his face in the mirror looked back at him with hunger.

He turned away and took out of his pocket the cheque for forty million francs. He folded this very small. Then he opened the door and looked up and down the corridor. He left the door wide open and with his ears cocked for footsteps or the sound of the lift, he set to work with a small screwdriver.

Five minutes later he gave a last-minute survey to his handiwork, put some fresh cigarettes in his case, closed and locked the door, and went off down the corridor and across the hall and out into the moonlight.

xiv. 'LA VIE EN ROSE?'

THE ENTRANCE to the Roi Galant was a seven-foot golden picture-frame which had once, perhaps, enclosed the vast portrait of a noble European. It was in a discreet corner of the 'kitchen'—the public roulette and boule room, where several tables were still busy. As Bond took Vesper's arm and led her over the gilded step, he fought back a hankering to borrow some money from the caisse and plaster maximums over the nearest table. But he knew that this would be a brash and cheap gesture 'pour épater la bourgeoisie.' Whether he won or lost, it would be a kick in the teeth to the luck which had been given him.

The night club was small and dark, lit only by candles in gilded candelabra whose warm light was repeated in wall mirrors set in more gold picture-frames. The walls were covered in dark red satin, and the chairs and banquettes in matching red plush. In the far corner, a trio, consisting of a piano, an electric guitar, and drums, was playing 'La Vie en Rose' with muted sweetness. Seduction dripped on the quietly throbbing air. It seemed to Bond that every couple must be touching with passion under the tables.

They were given a corner table near the door. Bond ordered a bottle of Veuve Clicquot and scrambled eggs and bacon.

They sat for a time listening to the music, and then Bond turned to Vesper: 'It's wonderful sitting here with you and knowing the job's finished. It's a lovely end to the day—the prize-giving.'

He expected her to smile. She said, 'Yes, isn't it?' in a rather brittle voice. She seemed to be listening carefully to the music. One elbow rested on the table, and her hand supported her chin, but on the back of her hand and not on the palm; and Bond noticed that her knuckles showed white as if her fist was tightly clenched.

Between the thumb and first two fingers of her right hand she held one of Bond's cigarettes, as an artist holds a crayon; and though she smoked with composure she tapped the cigarette occasionally into an ashtray when the cigarette had no ash.

Bond noticed these small things because he felt intensely aware of her and because he wanted to draw her into his own feeling of warmth and relaxed sensuality. But he accepted her reserve. He thought it came from a desire to protect herself from him, or else it was her reaction to his coolness to her earlier in the evening, his deliberate coolness, which he knew had been taken as a rebuff.

He was patient. He drank champagne and talked a little about the happenings of the day and about the personalities of Mathis and Leiter and about the possible consequences for Le Chiffre. He was discreet, and he only talked about the aspects of the case on which she must have been briefed by London.

She answered perfunctorily. She said that, of course, they had picked out the two gunmen, but had thought nothing of it when the man with the stick had gone to stand behind Bond's chair. They could not believe that anything would be attempted in the Casino itself. Directly Bond and Leiter had left to walk over to the hotel, she had telephoned Paris and told M.'s representative of the result of the game. She had

had to speak guardedly, and the agent had rung off without comment. She had been told to do this whatever the result. M. had asked for the information to be passed on to him personally at any time of the day or night.

This was all she said. She sipped at her champagne and rarely glanced at Bond. She didn't smile. Bond felt frustrated. He drank a lot of champagne and ordered another bottle. The scrambled eggs came, and they ate in silence.

At four o'clock Bond was about to call for the bill when the maître d'hôtel appeared at their table and inquired for Miss Lynd. He handed her a note which she took and read hastily.

'Oh, it's only Mathis,' she said. 'He says would I come to the entrance hall. He's got a message for you. Perhaps he's not in evening clothes or something. I won't be a minute. Then perhaps we could go home.'

She gave him a strained smile. 'I'm afraid I don't feel very good company this evening. It's been rather a nerve-racking day. I'm so sorry.'

Bond made a perfunctory reply and rose, pushing back the table. 'I'll get the bill,' he said, and watched her take the few steps to the entrance.

He sat down and lit a cigarette. He felt flat. He suddenly realized that he was tired. The stuffiness of the room hit him as it had hit him in the Casino in the early hours of the previous day. He called for the bill and took a last mouthful of champagne. It tasted bitter, as the first glass too many always does. He would have liked to see Mathis's cheerful face and hear his news, perhaps even a word of congratulation.

Suddenly the note to Vesper seemed odd to him. It was not the way Mathis would do things. He would have asked them both to join him at the bar of the Casino, or he would have joined them in the night club, whatever his clothes. They would have laughed together, and Mathis would have been excited. He had much to tell Bond, more than Bond had to tell him: the arrest of the Bulgarian, who had probably talked some more; the chase after the man with the stick; Le Chiffre's movements when he left the Casino.

Bond shook himself. He hastily paid the bill, not waiting for the change. He pushed back his table and walked quickly through the entrance without acknowledging the good-nights of the maître d'hôtel and the doorman.

He hurried through the gaming-room and looked carefully up and down the long entrance hall. He cursed and quickened his step. There were only one or two officials and two or three men and women in evening clothes getting their things at the vestiaire.

No Vesper. No Mathis.

He was almost running. He got to the entrance and looked along the steps to left and right down and amongst the few remaining cars.

The commissionaire came towards him.

'A taxi, monsieur?'

Bond waved him aside and started down the steps, his eyes staring into the shadows, the night air cold on his sweating temples.

He was halfway down when he heard a faint cry, then the slam of a door away to the right. With a harsh growl and stutter from the exhaust a beetle-browed Citroën shot out of the shadows into the light of the moon, its front-wheel drive dry-skidding through the loose pebbles of the forecourt.

Its tail rocked on its soft springs as if a violent struggle was taking place on the back seat.

With a snarl it raced out to the wide entrance gate in a

spray of gravel. A small black object shot out of an open
rear window and thudded into a flower-bed. There was a
scream of tortured rubber as the tyres caught the boulevard
in a harsh left-handed turn, the deafening echo of a Citroën's
exhaust in second gear, a crash into top, then a swiftly
diminishing crackle as the car hared off between the shops
on the main street towards the coast-road.

Bond knew he would find Vesper's evening bag among
the flowers.

He ran back with it across the gravel to the brightly lit
steps and scrabbled through its contents while the commissionaire hovered round him.

The crumpled note was there amongst the usual feminine
baggage:

'Can you come out to the entrance hall for a moment? I
have news for your companion.

RENÉ MATHIS.'

XV. BLACK HARE AND GREY HOUND

IT WAS the crudest possible forgery.

Bond leapt for the Bentley, blessing the impulse which
had made him drive it over after dinner. With the choke full
out the engine answered at once to the starter, and the roar
drowned the faltering words of the commissionaire who
jumped aside as the rear wheels whipped gravel at his piped
trouser-legs.

As the car rocked to the left outside the gate, Bond ruefully longed for the front-wheel drive and low chassis of the Citroën. Then he went fast through the gears and settled himself for the pursuit, briefly savouring the echo of the huge exhaust as it came back at him from either side of the short main street through the town.

Soon he was out on the coast-road, a broad highway through the sand-dunes which he knew from his morning's drive had an excellent surface and was well cat's-eyed on the bends. He pushed the revs up and up, hurrying the car to eighty then to ninety, his huge Marchal headlights boring a safe white tunnel, nearly half a mile long, between the walls of the night.

He knew the Citroën must have come this way. He had heard the exhaust penetrate beyond the town, and a little dust still hung on the bends. He hoped soon to see the distant shaft of its headlights. The night was still and clear. Only out at sea there must be a light summer mist, for at intervals he could hear the foghorns lowing like iron cattle down the coast.

As he drove, whipping the car faster and faster through the night, with the other half of his mind he cursed Vesper, and M. for having sent her on the job.

This was just what he had been afraid of. These blithering women who thought they could do a man's work. Why the hell couldn't they stay at home and mind their pots and pans and stick to their frocks and gossip and leave men's work to the men? And now for this to happen to him, just when the job had come off so beautifully: for Vesper to fall for an old trick like that and get herself snatched and probably held to ransom like some bloody heroine in a strip cartoon. The silly bitch.

Bond boiled at the thought of the fix he was in.

Of course. The idea was a straight swop. The girl against his cheque for forty million. Well, he wouldn't play: wouldn't think of playing. She was in the Service and knew what she was up against. He wouldn't even ask M. This job was more important than her. It was just too bad. She was a fine girl, but he wasn't going to fall for this childish trick. No dice. He would try and catch the Citroën and shoot it out with them; and if she got shot in the process that was too bad too. He would have done his stuff—tried to rescue her before they got her off to some hide-out—but if he didn't catch up with them he would get back to his hotel and go to sleep and say no more about it. The next morning he would ask Mathis what had happened to her and show him the note. If Le Chiffre put the touch on Bond for the money in exchange for the girl, Bond would do nothing and tell no one. The girl would just have to take it. If the commissionaire came along with the story of what he had seen, Bond would bluff it out by saying he had had a drunken row with the girl.

Bond's mind raged furiously on with the problem as he flung the great car down the coast-road, automatically taking the curves and watching out for carts or cyclists on their way to Royale. On straight stretches the Amherst Villiers supercharger dug spurs into the Bentley's twenty-five horses, and the engine sent a high-pitched scream of pain into the night. Then the revolutions mounted until he was past 110 and on to the 120 m.p.h. mark on the speedometer.

He knew he must be gaining fast. Loaded as she was, the Citroën could hardly better eighty even on this road. On an impulse he slowed down to seventy, turned on his fog-lights, and dowsed the twin Marchals. Sure enough, without the blinding curtain of his own lights, he could see the glow of another car a mile or two down the coast.

He felt under the dashboard and from a concealed holster took out a long-barrelled Colt Army Special .45 and laid it on the seat beside him. With this, if he was lucky with the surface of the road, he could hope to get their tyres or their petrol tank at anything up to a hundred yards.

Then he switched on the big lights again and screamed off in pursuit. He felt calm and at ease. The problem of Vesper's life was a problem no longer. His face in the blue light from the dashboard was grim but serene.

Ahead in the Citroën there were three men and the girl.

Le Chiffre was driving, his big fluid body hunched forward, his hands light and delicate on the wheel. Beside him sat the squat man who had carried the stick in the Casino. In his left hand he grasped a thick lever which protruded beside him almost level with the floor. It might have been a lever to adjust the driving-seat.

In the back seat was the tall thin gunman. He lay back relaxed, gazing at the ceiling, apparently uninterested in the wild speed of the car. His right hand lay caressingly on Vesper's left thigh which stretched out naked beside him.

Apart from her legs, which were naked to the hips, Vesper was only a parcel. Her long black velvet skirt had been lifted over her arms and head and tied above her head with a piece of rope. Where her face was, a small gap had been torn in the velvet so that she could breathe. She was not bound in any other way, and she lay quiet, her body moving sluggishly with the swaying of the car.

Le Chiffre was concentrating half on the road ahead and half on the onrushing glare of Bond's headlights in the driving mirror. He seemed undisturbed when not more than a mile separated the hare from the hounds, and he even brought the car down from eighty to sixty miles an hour. Now, as he swept round a bend he slowed down still further. A few hundred yards ahead a Michelin post showed where a small parochial road crossed with the highway.

'Attention,' he said sharply to the man beside him.

The man's hand tightened on the lever.

A hundred yards from the crossroads he slowed to thirty. In the mirror Bond's great headlights were lighting up the bend.

Le Chiffre seemed to make up his mind.

'Allez.'

The man beside him pulled the lever sharply upwards. The boot at the back of the car yawned open like a whale's mouth. There was a tinkling clatter on the road and then a rhythmic jangling as if the car was towing lengths of chain behind it.

'Coupez.'

The man depressed the lever sharply and the jangling stopped with a final clatter.

Le Chiffre glanced again in the mirror. Bond's car was just entering the bend. Le Chiffre made a racing change and threw the Citroën left-handed down the narrow side-road, at the same time dowsing his lights.

He stopped the car with a jerk, and all three men got swiftly out and doubled back under cover of a low hedge to the crossroads, now fiercely illuminated by the lights of the Bentley. Each of them carried a revolver, and the thin man also had what looked like a large egg in his right hand.

The Bentley screamed down towards them like an express train.

xvi. THE CRAWLING OF THE SKIN

AS BOND hurtled round the bend, caressing the great car against the camber with an easy sway of body and hands, he was working out his plan of action when the distance between the two cars should narrow still further. He imagined that the enemy driver would try to dodge off into a side-road if he got the chance. So when he had got round the bend and saw no lights ahead, it was a normal reflex to ease up on the accelerator and, when he saw the Michelin post, to prepare to brake.

He was only doing about sixty as he approached the black patch across the right-hand crown of the road which he assumed to be the shadow cast by a wayside tree. Even so, there was no time to save himself. There was suddenly a small carpet of glinting steel spikes right under his off-side wing. Then he was on top of it.

Bond automatically slammed the brakes full on and braced all his sinews against the wheel to correct the inevitable sharp slew to the left, but he only kept control for a split second. As the rubber was flayed from his off-side wheels and the rims for an instant tore up the tarmac, the heavy car whirled across the road in a tearing dry skid, slammed the left bank with a crash that knocked Bond out of the driving seat on to the floor; and then, facing back up the road, it reared slowly up, its front wheels spinning and its great headlights searching the sky. For a split second, resting on the petrol tank, it seemed to paw at the heavens like a giant praying-mantis. Then slowly it toppled over backwards and fell with a splintering crash of coachwork and glass.

In the deafening silence, the near-side front wheel whispered briefly on and then squeaked to a stop.

Le Chiffre and his two men only had to walk a few yards from their ambush.

'Put your guns away and get him out,' he ordered brusquely. 'I'll keep you covered. Be careful of him. I don't want a corpse. And hurry up, it's getting light.'

The two men got down on their knees. One of them took out a long knife and cut some of the fabric away from the side of the convertible hood and took hold of Bond's shoulders. He was unconscious and immovable. The other squeezed between the up-turned car and the bank and forced his way through the crumpled window-frame. He eased Bond's legs, pinned between the steering wheel and the fabric roof of the car. Then they inched him out through a hole in the hood.

They were sweating and filthy with dust and oil by the time they had him lying in the road.

The thin man felt his heart and then slapped his face hard on either side. Bond grunted and moved a hand. The thin man slapped him again.

'That's enough,' said Le Chiffre. 'Tie his arms, and put him in the car. Here.' He threw a roll of flex to the man. 'Empty his pockets first and give me his gun. He may have got some other weapons, but we can get them later.'

He took the objects the thin man handed him and stuffed them and Bond's Beretta into his wide pockets without examining them. He left the men to it and walked back to the car. His face showed neither pleasure nor excitement.

It was the sharp bite of the wire flex into his wrists that

brought Bond to himself. He was aching all over as if he had been thrashed with a wooden club; but when he was yanked to his feet and pushed towards the narrow side-road where the engine of the Citroën was already running softly, he found that no bones were broken. But he felt in no mood for desperate attempts to escape and allowed himself to be dragged into the back seat of the car without resisting.

He felt thoroughly dispirited and weak in resolve as well as in his body. He had had to take too much in the past twenty-four hours and now this last stroke by the enemy seemed almost too final. This time there could be no miracles. No one knew where he was and no one would miss him until well on into the morning. The wreck of his car would be found before very long, but it would take hours to trace the ownership to him.

And Vesper. He looked to the right, past the thin man who was lying back with his eyes closed. His first reaction was one of scorn. Damn fool girl getting herself trussed up like a chicken, having her skirt pulled over her head as if the whole of this business was some kind of dormitory rag. But then he felt sorry for her. Her naked legs looked so childlike and defenceless.

'Vesper,' he said softly.

There was no answer from the bundle in the corner, and Bond suddenly had a chill feeling; but then she stirred slightly.

At the same time the thin man caught him a hard back-handed blow over the heart.

'Silence.'

Bond doubled over with pain and to shield himself from another blow, only to get a rabbit punch on the back of the neck which made him arch back again, the breath whistling through his teeth.

The thin man had hit him a hard professional cutting blow with the edge of the hand. There was something rather deadly about his accuracy and his lack of effort. He was now again lying back, his eyes closed. He was a man to make you afraid, an evil man. Bond hoped he might get a chance of killing him.

Suddenly the boot of the car was thrown open, and there was a clanking crash. Bond guessed that they had been waiting for the third man to retrieve the carpet of spiked chain-mail. He assumed it must be an adaptation of the nail-studded devices used by the Resistance against German staff-cars.

Again he reflected on the efficiency of these people and the ingenuity of the equipment they used. Had M. under-estimated their resourcefulness? He stifled a desire to place the blame on London. It was he who should have known. He who should have been warned by small signs and taken infinitely more precautions. He squirmed as he thought of himself washing down champagne in the Roi Galant while the enemy was busy preparing his counterstroke. He cursed himself and cursed the hubris which had made him so sure that the battle was won and the enemy in flight.

All this time Le Chiffre had said nothing. Directly the boot was shut, the third man, whom Bond at once recognized, climbed in beside him, and Le Chiffre reversed furiously back on to the main road. Then he banged the gear lever through the gate and was soon doing seventy on down the coast.

By now it was dawn—about five o'clock, Bond guessed—and he reflected that a mile or two on was the turning to Le Chiffre's villa. He had not thought that they would take Vesper there. Now that he realized that Vesper had only been a sprat to catch a mackerel the whole picture became clear.

It was an extremely unpleasant picture. For the first time since his capture, fear came to Bond and crawled up his spine.

Ten minutes later the Citroën lurched to the left, ran on a few hundred yards up a small side road partly overgrown with grass and then between a pair of dilapidated stucco pillars into an unkempt forecourt surrounded by a high wall. They drew up in front of a peeling white door. Above a rusty bell-push in the doorframe, small zinc letters on a wooden base spelled out 'Les Noctambules' and, underneath 'Sonnez SVP.'

From what Bond could see of the cement frontage, the villa was typical of the French seaside style. He could imagine the dead bluebottles being hastily swept out for the summer let and the stale rooms briefly aired by a cleaning woman sent by the estate agent in Royale. Every five years one coat of whitewash would be slapped over the rooms and the outside woodwork, and for a few weeks the villa would present a smiling front to the world. Then the winter rains would get to work, and the imprisoned flies, and quickly the villa would take on again its abandoned look.

But, Bond reflected, it would admirably serve Le Chiffre's purpose this morning, if he was right in assuming what that was to be. They had passed no other house since his capture, and from his reconnaissance of the day before he knew there was only an occasional farm for several miles to the south.

As he was urged out of the car with a sharp crack in the ribs from the thin man's elbow, he knew that Le Chiffre could have them both to himself, undisturbed, for several hours. Again his skin crawled.

Le Chiffre opened the door with a key and disappeared inside. Vesper, looking incredibly indecent in the early light of day, was pushed in after him with a torrent of lewd

French from the man whom Bond knew to himself as 'the Corsican.' Bond followed without giving the thin man a chance to urge him.

The key of the front door turned in the lock.

Le Chiffre was standing in the doorway of a room on the right. He crooked a finger at Bond in a silent, spidery summons.

Vesper was being led down a passage towards the back of the house. Bond suddenly decided.

With a wild backward kick which connected with the thin man's shins and brought a whistle of pain from him, he hurled himself down the passage after her. With only his feet as weapons, there was no plan in his mind except to do as much damage as possible to the two gunmen and be able to exchange a few hurried words with the girl. No other plan was possible. He just wanted to tell her not to give in.

As the Corsican turned at the commotion Bond was on him and his right shoe was launched in a flying kick at the other man's groin.

Like lightning the Corsican slammed himself back against the wall of the passage and, as Bond's foot whistled past his hip, he very quickly, but somehow delicately, shot out his left hand, caught Bond's shoe at the top of its arc and twisted it sharply.

Completely off balance, Bond's other foot left the ground. In the air his whole body turned and with the momentum of his rush behind it crashed sideways and down on to the floor.

For a moment he lay there, all the breath knocked out of him. Then the thin man came and hauled him up against the wall by his collar. He had a gun in his hand. He looked Bond inquisitively in the eyes. Then unhurriedly he bent down and swiped the barrel viciously across Bond's shins. Bond grunted and caved at the knees.

'If there is a next time, it will be across your teeth,' said the thin man in bad French.

A door slammed. Vesper and the Corsican had disappeared. Bond turned his head to the right. Le Chiffre had moved a few feet out into the passage. He lifted his finger and crooked it again. Then for the first time he spoke.

'Come, my dear friend. We are wasting our time.'

He spoke in English with no accent. His voice was low and soft and unhurried. He showed no emotion. He might have been a doctor summoning the next patient from the waiting-room, a hysterical patient who had been expostulating feebly with a nurse.

Bond again felt puny and impotent. Nobody but an expert in ju-jitsu could have handled him with the Corsican's economy and lack of fuss. The cold precision with which the thin man had paid him back in his own coin had been equally unhurried, even artistic.

Almost docilely Bond walked back down the passage. He had nothing but a few more bruises to show for his clumsy gesture of resistance to these people.

As he preceded the thin man over the threshold he knew that he was utterly and absolutely in their power.

xvii. 'MY DEAR BOY'

IT WAS a large bare room, sparsely furnished in cheap French 'art nouveau' style. It was difficult to say whether it was intended as a living- or dining-room, for a flimsy-looking mirrored sideboard, sporting an orange crackleware fruit dish and two painted wooden candlesticks, took up most of the wall opposite the door and contradicted the faded pink sofa ranged against the other side of the room.

There was no table in the centre under the alabasterine ceiling light, only a small square of stained carpet with a futurist design in contrasting browns.

Over by the window was an incongruous-looking throne-like chair in carved oak with a red velvet seat, a low table on which stood an empty water carafe and two glasses, and a light armchair with a round cane seat and no cushion.

Half-closed Venetian blinds obscured the view from the window, but cast bars of early sunlight over the few pieces of furniture and over part of the brightly papered wall and the brown-stained floorboards.

Le Chiffre pointed at the cane chair.

'That will do excellently,' he said to the thin man. 'Prepare him quickly. If he resists, damage him only a little.'

He turned to Bond. There was no expression on his large face, and his round eyes were uninterested. 'Take off your clothes. For every effort to resist, Basil will break one of your fingers. We are serious people, and your good health is of no interest to us. Whether you live or die depends on the outcome of the talk we are about to have.'

He made a gesture toward the thin man and left the room.

The thin man's first action was a curious one. He opened the clasp-knife he had used on the hood of Bond's car, took the small armchair, and with a swift motion cut out its cane seat.

Then he came back to Bond, sticking the still open knife, like a fountain pen, in the vest pocket of his coat. He turned Bond round to the light and unwound the flex from his

wrists. Then he stood quickly aside, and the knife was back
in his right hand.

'Vite.'

Bond stood chafing his swollen wrists and debating with
himself how much time he could waste by resisting. He
only delayed an instant. With a swift step and a downward
sweep of his free hand, the thin man seized the collar of his
dinner jacket and dragged it down, pinning Bond's arms
back. Bond made the traditional counter to this old policeman's hold by dropping down on one knee; but as he
dropped the thin man dropped with him and at the same
time brought his knife round and down behind Bond's back.
Bond felt the back of the blade pass down his spine. There
was the hiss of a sharp knife through cloth and his arms were
suddenly free as the two halves of his coat fell forward.

He cursed and stood up. The thin man was back in his
previous position, his knife again at the ready in his relaxed
hand. Bond let the two halves of his dinner jacket fall off
his arms on to the floor.

'Allez,' said the thin man with a faint trace of impatience.

Bond looked him in the eye and then slowly started to
take off his shirt.

Le Chiffre came quietly back into the room. He carried
a pot of what smelt like coffee. He put it on the small table
near the window. He also placed beside it on the table two
other homely objects, a three-foot-long carpet-beater in
twisted cane and a carving-knife.

He settled himself comfortably on the thronelike chair
and poured some of the coffee into one of the glasses. With
one foot he hooked forward the small armchair, whose seat
was now an empty circular frame of wood, until it was directly opposite him.

Bond stood stark naked in the middle of the room, bruises showing livid on his white body, his face a grey mask of exhaustion and knowledge of what was to come.

'Sit down there.' Le Chiffre nodded at the chair in front of him.

Bond walked over and sat down.

The thin man produced some flex. With this he bound Bond's wrists to the arms of the chair and his ankles to the front legs. He passed a double strand across his chest, under the armpits and through the chair-back. He made no mistakes with the knots and left no play in any of the bindings. All of them bit sharply into Bond's flesh. The legs of the chair were broadly spaced and Bond could not even rock it.

He was utterly a prisoner, naked and defenceless.

His buttocks and the underpart of his body protruded through the seat of the chair towards the floor.

Le Chiffre nodded to the thin man, who quietly left the room and closed the door.

There was a packet of Gauloises on the table and a lighter. Le Chiffre lit a cigarette and swallowed a mouthful of coffee from the glass. Then he picked up the cane carpet-beater and, resting the handle comfortably on his knee, allowed the flat trefoil base to lie on the floor directly under Bond's chair.

He looked Bond carefully, almost caressingly, in the eyes. Then his wrist sprang suddenly upwards on his knee.

The result was startling.

Bond's whole body arched in an involuntary spasm. His face contracted in a soundless scream, and his lips drew right away from his teeth. At the same time his head flew back with a jerk showing the taut sinews of his neck. For an instant, muscles stood out in knots all over his body, and his toes and fingers clenched until they were quite white. Then his body sagged, and perspiration started to bead all over his skin. He uttered a deep groan.

Le Chiffre waited for his eyes to open.

'You see, dear boy?' He smiled a soft, fat smile. 'Is the position quite clear now?'

A drop of sweat fell off Bond's chin on to his naked chest.

'Now let us get down to business and see how soon we can be finished with this unfortunate mess you have got yourself into.' He puffed cheerfully at his cigarette and gave an admonitory tap on the floor beneath Bond's chair with his horrible and incongruous instrument.

'My dear boy'—Le Chiffre spoke like a father—'the game of Red Indians is over, quite over. You have stumbled by mischance into a game for grown-ups, and you have already found it a painful experience. You are not equipped, my dear boy, to play games with adults, and it was very foolish of your nanny in London to have sent you out here with your spade and bucket. Very foolish indeed, and most unfortunate for you.

'But we must stop joking, my dear fellow, although I am sure you would like to follow me in developing this amusing little cautionary tale.'

He suddenly dropped his bantering tone and looked at Bond sharply and venomously.

'Where is the money?'

Bond's bloodshot eyes looked emptily back at him.

Again the upward jerk of the wrist, and again Bond's whole body writhed and contorted.

Le Chiffre waited until the tortured heart eased down its laboured pumping and until Bond's eyes dully opened again.

'Perhaps I should explain,' said Le Chiffre. 'I intend to continue attacking the sensitive parts of your body until you answer my question. I am without mercy, and there will be no relenting. There is no one to stage a last-minute rescue, and there is no possibility of escape for you. This is not a romantic adventure story in which the villain is finally routed and the hero is given a medal and marries the girl. Unfortunately these things don't happen in real life. If you continue to be obstinate, you will be tortured to the edge of madness, and then the girl will be brought in and we will set about her in front of you. If that is still not enough, you will both be painfully killed, and I shall reluctantly leave your bodies and make my way abroad to a comfortable house which is waiting for me. There I shall take up a useful and profitable career and live to a ripe and peaceful old age in the bosom of the family I shall doubtless create. So you see, my dear boy, that I stand to lose nothing. If you hand the money over, so much the better. If not, I shall shrug my shoulders and be on my way.'

He paused, and his wrist lifted slightly on his knee. Bond's flesh cringed as the cane surface just touched him.

'But you, my dear fellow, can only hope that I shall spare you further pain and spare your life. There is no other hope for you but that. Absolutely none.

'Well?'

Bond closed his eyes and waited for the pain. He knew that the beginning of torture is the worst. There is a parabola of agony. A crescendo leading up to a peak, and then the nerves are blunted and react progressively less until unconsciousness and death. All he could do was to pray for the peak, pray that his spirit would hold out so long and then accept the long free-wheel down to the final blackout.

He had been told by colleagues who had survived torture by the Germans and the Japanese that towards the end there came a wonderful period of warmth and languor leading into a sort of sexual twilight where pain turned to pleasure and where hatred and fear of the tortures turned to a masochistic infatuation. It was the supreme test of will, he had learnt, to avoid showing this form of punch-drunkenness. Directly it was suspected they would either kill you at once and save themselves further useless effort, or let you recover sufficiently for your nerves to creep back to the other side of the parabola. Then they would start again.

He opened his eyes a fraction.

Le Chiffre had been waiting for this, and like a rattlesnake the cane instrument leapt up from the floor. It struck again and again so that Bond screamed and his body jangled in the chair like a marionette.

Le Chiffre desisted only when Bond's tortured spasms showed a trace of sluggishness. He sat for a while sipping his coffee and frowning slightly like a surgeon watching a cardiograph during a difficult operation.

When Bond's eyes flickered and opened he addressed him again, but now with a trace of impatience.

'We know that the money is somewhere in your room,' he said. 'You drew a cheque to cash for forty million francs, and I know that you went back to the hotel to hide it.'

For a moment Bond wondered how he had been so certain.

'Directly you left for the night club,' continued Le Chiffre, 'your room was searched by four of my people.'

The Muntzes must have helped, reflected Bond.

'We found a good deal in childish hiding-places. The ball-cock in the lavatory yielded an interesting little code-book, and we found some more of your papers taped to the back of a drawer. All the furniture has been taken to pieces, and your clothes and the curtains and bedclothes have been cut up. Every inch of the room has been searched, and all the fittings removed. It is most unfortunate for you that we didn't find the cheque. If we had, you would now be comfortably in bed, perhaps with the beautiful Miss Lynd, instead of this.' He lashed upwards.

Through the red mist of pain, Bond thought of Vesper. He could imagine how she was being used by the two gunmen. They would be making the most of her before she was sent for by Le Chiffre. He thought of the fat wet lips of the Corsican and the slow cruelty of the thin man. Poor wretch to have been dragged into this. Poor little beast.

Le Chiffre was talking again.

'Torture is a terrible thing,' he was saying as he puffed at a fresh cigarette, 'but it is a simple matter for the torturer, particularly when the patient'—he smiled at the word—'is a man. You see, my dear Bond, with a man it is quite unnecessary to indulge in refinements. With this simple instrument, or with almost any other object, one can cause a man as much pain as is possible or necessary. Do not believe what you read in novels or books about the war. There is nothing worse. It is not only the immediate agony, but also the thought that your manhood is being gradually destroyed and that at the end, if you will not yield, you will no longer be a man.

'That, my dear Bond, is a sad and terrible thought—a long chain of agony for the body and also for the mind, and then the final screaming moment when you will beg me to kill you. All that is inevitable unless you tell me where you hid the money.'

He poured some more coffee into the glass and drank it down, leaving brown corners to his mouth.

Bond's lips were writhing. He was trying to say something. At last he got the word out in a harsh croak: 'Drink,' he said and his tongue came out and swilled across his dry lips.

'Of course, my dear boy, how thoughtless of me!' Le Chiffre poured some coffee into the other glass. There was a ring of sweat drops on the floor all round Bond's chair.

'We must certainly keep your tongue lubricated.'

He laid the handle of the carpet-beater down on the floor between his thick legs and rose from his chair. He went behind Bond and taking a handful of his soaking hair in one hand, he wrenched Bond's head sharply back. He poured the coffee down Bond's throat in small mouthfuls so that he would not choke. Then he released his head so that it fell forward again on his chest. He went back to his chair and picked up the carpet-beater.

Bond raised his head and spoke thickly.

'Money no good to you.' His voice was a laborious croak. 'Police trace it to you.'

Exhausted by the effort, his head sank forward again. He was a little, but only a little, exaggerating the extent of his physical collapse. Anything to gain time, and anything to defer the next searing pain.

'Ah, my dear fellow, I had forgotten to tell you.' Le Chiffre smiled wolfishly. 'We met after our little game at the Casino, and you were such a sportsman that you agreed we would have one more run through the pack between the two of us. It was a gallant gesture. Typical of an English gentleman.

'Unfortunately you lost, and this upset you so much that you decided to leave Royale immediately for an unknown destination. Like the gentleman you are, you very kindly gave me a note explaining the circumstances so that I would have no difficulty in cashing your cheque. You see, dear boy, everything has been thought of, and you need have no fears on my account.' He chuckled fatly.

'Now shall we continue? I have all the time in the world,

and truth to tell I am rather interested to see how long a man can stand this particular form of—er—encouragement.' He rattled the harsh cane on the floor.

So that was the score, thought Bond, with a final sinking of the heart. The 'unknown destination' would be under the ground or under the sea, or perhaps, more simple, under the crashed Bentley. Well, if he had to die anyway, he might as well try it the hard way. He had no hope that Mathis or Leiter would get to him in time, but at least there was a chance that they would catch up with Le Chiffre before he could get away. It must be getting on for seven. The car might have been found by now. It was a choice of evils; but the longer Le Chiffre continued the torture the more likely he would be revenged.

Bond lifted his head and looked Le Chiffre in the eyes.

The china of the whites was now veined with red. It was like looking at two black currants poached in blood. The rest of the wide face was yellowish except where a thick black stubble covered the moist skin. The upward edges of black coffee at the corners of the mouth gave his expression a false smile and the whole face was faintly striped by the light through the venetian blinds.

'No,' he said flatly, '. . . you.'

Le Chiffre grunted and set to work again with savage fury. Occasionally he snarled like a wild beast.

After ten minutes Bond had fainted, blessedly.

Le Chiffre at once stopped. He wiped some sweat from his face with a circular motion of his disengaged hand. Then he looked at his watch and seemed to make up his mind.

He got up and stood behind the inert, dripping body. There was no colour in Bond's face or anywhere on his body above the waist. There was a faint flutter of his skin above the heart. Otherwise he might have been dead.

Le Chiffre seized Bond's ears and harshly twisted them. Then he leant forward and slapped his cheeks hard several times. Bond's head rolled from side to side with each blow. Slowly his breathing became deeper. An animal groan came from his lolling mouth.

Le Chiffre took a glass of coffee and poured some into Bond's mouth and threw the rest in his face. Bond's eyes slowly opened.

Le Chiffre returned to his chair and waited. He lit a cigarette and contemplated the spattered pool of blood on the floor beneath the inert body opposite.

Bond groaned again pitifully. It was an inhuman sound. His eyes opened wide, and he gazed dully at his torturer.

Le Chiffre spoke.

'That is all, Bond. We will now finish with you. You understand? Not kill you, but finish with you. And then we will have in the girl and see if something can be got out of the remains of the two of you.'

He reached towards the table.

'Say goodbye to it, Bond.'

xviii. A CRAGLIKE FACE

IT WAS extraordinary to hear the third voice. The hour's ritual had only demanded a duologue against the horrible noise of the torture. Bond's dimmed senses hardly took it in. Then suddenly he was halfway back to consciousness. He found he could see and hear again. He could hear the dead silence after the one quiet word from the doorway. He could see Le Chiffre's head slowly come up and the expression of blank astonishment, of innocent amazement, slowly give way to fear.

'Shtop,' had said the voice, quietly.

Bond heard slow steps approaching behind his chair.

'Dhrop it,' said the voice.

Bond saw Le Chiffre's hand open obediently and the knife fall with a clatter to the floor.

He tried desperately to read into Le Chiffre's face what was happening behind him, but all he saw was blind incomprehension and terror. Le Chiffre's mouth worked, but only a high-pitched 'eek' came from it. His heavy cheeks trembled as he tried to collect enough saliva in his mouth to say something, ask something. His hands fluttered vaguely in his lap. One of them made a slight movement towards his pocket, but instantly fell back. His round staring eyes had lowered for a split second, and Bond guessed there was a gun trained on him.

There was a moment's silence.

'SMERSH.'

The word came almost with a sigh. It came with a downward cadence as if nothing else had to be said. It was the final explanation. The last word of all.

'No,' said Le Chiffre. 'No. I . . .' His voice tailed off.

Perhaps he was going to explain, to apologize, but what he must have seen in the other's face made it all useless.

'Your two men. Both dead. You are a fool and a thief and a traitor. I have been sent from the Soviet Union to eliminate you. You are fortunate that I have only time to shoot you. If it was possible, I was instructed that you should die most painfully. We cannot see the end of the trouble you have caused.'

The thick voice stopped. There was silence in the room save for the rasping breath of Le Chiffre.

Somewhere outside, a bird began to sing and there were other small noises from the awakening countryside. The sweat on Le Chiffre's face glistened brightly.

'Do you plead guilty?'

Bond wrestled with his consciousness. He screwed up his eyes and tried to shake his head to clear it; but his whole nervous system was numbed, and no message was transmitted to his muscles. He could just keep his focus on the great pale face in front of him and on its bulging eyes.

A thin string of saliva crept from the open mouth and hung down from the chin.

'Yes,' said the mouth.

There was a sharp *phut*, no louder than a bubble of air escaping from a tube of toothpaste. No other noise at all, and suddenly Le Chiffre had grown another eye, a third eye on a level with the other two, right where the thick nose started to jut out below the forehead. It was a small black eye, without eyelashes or eyebrows.

For a second the three eyes looked out across the room, and then the whole face seemed to slip and go down on one knee. The two outer eyes turned trembling up towards the ceiling. Then the heavy head fell sideways and the right shoulder and finally the whole upper part of the body lurched over the arm of the chair as if Le Chiffre were going to be sick. But there was only a short rattle of his heels on the ground, and then no other movement.

The tall back of the chair looked impassively out across the dead body in its arms.

There was a faint movement behind Bond. A hand came from behind and grasped his chin and pulled it back.

For a moment Bond looked up into two glittering eyes

behind a narrow black mask. There was the impression of a craglike face under a hatbrim, the collar of a fawn mackintosh. He could take in nothing more before his head was pushed down again.

'You are fortunate,' said the voice. 'I have no orders to kill you. Your life has been saved twice in one day. But you can tell your organization that SMERSH is only merciful by chance or by mistake. In your case you were saved first by chance and now by mistake, for I should have had orders to kill any foreign spies who were hanging round this traitor like flies round a dog's-mess.

'But I shall leave you my visiting card. You are a gambler. You play at cards. One day perhaps you will play against one of us. It would be well that you should be known as a spy.'

Steps moved round to behind Bond's right shoulder. There was the click of a knife opening. An arm in some grey material came into Bond's line of vision. A broad hairy hand emerging from a dirty white shirt-cuff was holding a thin stiletto like a fountain-pen. It poised for a moment above the back of Bond's right hand, immovably bound with flex to the arm of the chair. The point of the stiletto executed three quick straight slashes. A fourth slash crossed them where they ended, just short of the knuckles. Blood in the shape of an inverted 'M' welled out and slowly started to drip on to the floor.

The pain was nothing to what Bond was already suffering, but it was enough to plunge him again into unconsciousness.

The steps moved quietly away across the room. The door was softly closed.

In the silence, the cheerful small sounds of the summer's day crept through the closed window. High on the left-hand wall hung two small patches of pink light. They were reflections cast upwards from the floor by the zebra stripes of June sunshine, cast upwards from two separate pools of blood a few feet apart.

As the day progressed the pink patches marched slowly along the wall. And slowly they grew larger.

xix. THE WHITE TENT

YOU ARE about to awake when you dream that you are dreaming.

During the next two days James Bond was permanently in this state without regaining consciousness. He watched the procession of his dreams go by without making any effort to disturb their sequence, although many of them were terrifying and all were painful. He knew that he was in a bed and that he was lying on his back and could not move and in one of his twilight moments he thought there were people round him; but he made no effort to open his eyes and reenter the world.

He felt safer in the darkness, and he hugged it to him.

On the morning of the third day a bloody nightmare shook him awake, trembling and sweating. There was a hand on his forehead which he associated with his dream. He tried to lift an arm and smash it sideways into the owner of the hand, but his arms were immovable, secured to the sides of his bed. His whole body was strapped down and

something like a large white coffin covered him from chest
to feet and obscured his view of the end of the bed. He
shouted a string of obscenities; but the effort took all his
strength, and the words tailed off into a sob. Tears of for-
lornness and self-pity welled out of his eyes.

A woman's voice was speaking, and the words gradually
penetrated to him. It seemed to be a kind voice, and it slowly
came to him that he was being comforted, and that this was
a friend and not an enemy. He could hardly believe it. He
had been so certain that he was still a captive, and that the
torture was about to begin again. He felt his face being softly
wiped with a cool cloth which smelt of lavender, and then
he sank back into his dreams.

When he awoke again some hours later all his terrors had
gone, and he felt warm and languorous. Sun was streaming
into the bright room, and garden sounds came through the
window. In the background there was the noise of small
waves on a beach. As he moved his head he heard a rustle,
and a nurse who had been sitting beside his pillow rose and
came into his line of vision. She was pretty, and she smiled
as she put her hand on his pulse.

'Well, I'm certainly glad you've woken up at last. I've
never heard such dreadful language in my life.'

Bond smiled back at her.

'Where am I?' he asked, and was surprised that his voice
sounded firm and clear.

'You're in a nursing home at Royale and I've been sent
over from England to look after you. There are two of us,
and I'm Nurse Gibson. Now just lie quiet, and I'll go and
tell doctor you're awake. You've been unconscious since
they brought you in, and we've been quite worried.'

Bond closed his eyes and mentally explored his body. The
worst pain was in his wrists and ankles and in his right hand

where the Russian had cut him. In the centre of the body there was no feeling. He assumed that he had been given a local anaesthetic. The rest of his body ached dully as if he had been beaten all over. He could feel the pressure of bandages everywhere, and his unshaven neck and chin prickled against the sheets. From the feel of the bristles he knew that he must have been at least three days without shaving. That meant two days since the morning of the torture.

He was preparing a short list of questions in his mind when the door opened and the doctor came in followed by the nurse and, in the background, the dear figure of Mathis, a Mathis looking anxious behind his broad smile, who put a finger to his lips and walked on tiptoe to the window and sat down.

The doctor, a Frenchman with a young and intelligent face, had been detached from his duties with the Deuxième Bureau to look after Bond's case. He came and stood beside Bond and put his hand on Bond's forehead while he looked at the temperature chart behind the bed.

When he spoke he was forthright.

'You have a lot of questions to ask, my dear Mr. Bond,' he said in excellent English, 'and I can tell you most of the answers. I do not want you to waste your strength, so I will give you the salient facts and then you may have a few minutes with Monsieur Mathis who wishes to obtain one or two details from you. It is really too early for this talk, but I wish to set your mind at rest so that we can proceed with the task of repairing your body without bothering too much about your mind.'

Nurse Gibson pulled up a chair for the doctor and left the room.

'You have been here about two days,' continued the doctor. 'Your car was found by a farmer on the way to market in Royale, and he informed the police. After some delay Monsieur Mathis heard that it was your car, and he immediately went to Les Noctambules with his men. You and Le Chiffre were found and also your friend, Miss Lynd, who was unharmed and according to her account suffered no molestation. She was prostrated with shock, but is now fully recovered and is at her hotel. She has been instructed by her superiors in London to stay at Royale under your orders until you are sufficiently recovered to go back to England.

'Le Chiffre's two gunmen are dead, each killed by a single .35 bullet in the back of the skull. From the lack of expression on their faces, they evidently never saw or heard their assailant. They were found in the same room as Miss Lynd. Le Chiffre is dead, shot with a similar weapon between the eyes. Did you witness his death?'

'Yes,' said Bond.

'Your own injuries are serious, but your life is not in danger though you have lost a lot of blood. If all goes well, you will recover completely and none of the functions of your body will be impaired.' The doctor smiled grimly. 'But I fear that you will continue to be in pain for several days, and it will be my endeavour to give you as much comfort as possible. Now that you have regained consciousness your arms will be freed, but you must not move your body; and when you sleep the nurse has orders to secure your arms again. Above all, it is important that you rest and regain your strength. At the moment you are suffering from a grave condition of mental and physical shock.' The doctor paused. 'For how long were you maltreated?'

'About an hour,' said Bond.

'Then it is remarkable that you are alive, and I congratulate you. Few men could have supported what you have been through. Perhaps that is some consolation. As Monsieur

Mathis can tell you, I have had in my time to treat a number of patients who have suffered similar handling, and not one has come through it as you have done.'

The doctor looked at Bond for a moment and then turned brusquely to Mathis.

'You may have ten minutes, and then you will be forcibly ejected. If you put the patient's temperature up, you will answer for it.'

He gave them both a broad smile and left the room.

Mathis came over and took the doctor's chair.

'That's a good man,' said Bond. 'I like him.'

'He's attached to the Bureau,' said Mathis. 'He is a very good man, and I will tell you about him one of these days. He thinks you are a prodigy—and so do I.

'However, that can wait. As you can imagine, there is much to clear up, and I am being pestered by Paris and, of course, London, and even by Washington via our good friend Leiter. Incidentally,' he broke off, 'I have a personal message from M. He spoke to me himself on the telephone. He simply said to tell you that he is much impressed. I asked if that was all, and he said: "Well, tell him that the Treasury is greatly relieved." Then he rang off.'

Bond grinned with pleasure. What most warmed him was that M. himself should have rung up Mathis. This was quite unheard of. The very existence of M., let alone his identity, was never admitted. He could imagine the flutter this must have caused in the ultra-security-minded organization in London.

'A tall thin man with one arm came over from London the same day we found you,' continued Mathis, knowing from his own experience that these shop details would interest Bond more than anything else and give him most pleasure, 'and he fixed up the nurses and looked after everything.

Even your car's being repaired for you. He seemed to be Vesper's boss. He spent a lot of time with her and gave her strict instructions to look after you.'

Head of S., thought Bond. They're certainly giving me the red-carpet treatment.

'Now,' said Mathis, 'to business. Who killed Le Chiffre?'

'SMERSH,' said Bond.

Mathis gave a low whistle.

'My God,' he said respectfully. 'So they *were* on to him. What did he look like?'

Bond explained briefly what had happened up to the moment of Le Chiffre's death, omitting all but the most essential details. It cost him an effort, and he was glad when it was done. Casting his mind back to the scene awoke the whole nightmare, and the sweat began to pour off his forehead and a deep throb of pain started up in his body.

Mathis realized that he was going too far. Bond's voice was getting feebler, and his eyes were clouding. Mathis snapped shut his shorthand book and laid a hand on Bond's shoulder.

'Forgive me, my friend,' he said. 'It is all over now, and you are in safe hands. All is well, and the whole plan has gone splendidly. We have announced that Le Chiffre shot his two accomplices and then committed suicide because he could not face an inquiry into the union funds. Strasbourg and the north are in an uproar. He was considered a great hero there and a pillar of the Communist Party in France. This story of brothels and casinos has absolutely knocked the bottom out of his organization, and they're all running around like scalded cats. At the moment the Communist Party is giving out that he was off his head. But that hasn't helped much after Thorez's breakdown not long ago.

They're just making it look as if all their big-shots were gaga. God knows how they're going to unscramble the whole business.'

Mathis saw that his enthusiasm had had the desired effect. Bond's eyes were brighter.

'One last mystery,' Mathis said, 'and then I promise I will go.' He looked at his watch. 'The doctor will be after my skin in a moment. Now, what about the money? Where is it? Where did you hide it? We too have been over your room with a toothcomb. It isn't there.'

Bond grinned.

'It is,' he said, 'more or less. On the door of each room there is a small square of black plastic with the number of the room on it. On the corridor side, of course. When Leiter left me that night, I simply opened the door and unscrewed my number plate and put the folded cheque underneath it and screwed the plate back. It'll still be there.' He smiled. 'I'm glad there's something the stupid English can teach the clever French.'

Mathis laughed delightedly.

'I suppose you think that's paid me back for knowing what the Muntzes were up to. Well, I'll call it quits. Incidentally, we've got them in the bag. They were just some minor fry hired for the occasion. We'll see they get a few years.'

He rose hastily as the doctor stormed into the room and took one look at Bond.

'Out,' he said to Mathis. 'Out, and don't come back.'

Mathis just had time to wave cheerfully to Bond and call some hasty words of farewell before he was hustled through the door. Bond heard a torrent of heated French diminishing down the corridor. He lay back exhausted, but heartened by all he had heard. He found himself thinking of Vesper as he quickly drifted off into a troubled sleep.

There were still questions to be answered, but they could wait.

X.X. THE NATURE OF EVIL

BOND MADE good progress. When Mathis came to see him three days later he was propped up in bed, and his arms were free. The lower half of his body was still shrouded in the oblong tent, but he looked cheerful and it was only occasionally that a twinge of pain narrowed his eyes.

Mathis looked crestfallen.

'Here's your cheque,' he said to Bond. 'I've rather enjoyed walking around with forty million francs in my pocket, but I suppose you'd better sign it and I'll put it to your account with the Crédit Lyonnais. There's no sign of our friend from SMERSH. Not a damn trace. He must have got to the villa on foot or on a bicycle because you heard nothing of his arrival and the two gunmen obviously didn't. It's pretty exasperating. We've got precious little on this SMERSH organization, and neither has London. Washington said they had; but it turned out to be the usual waffle from refugee interrogation, and you know that's about as much good as interrogating an English man-in-the-street about his own Secret Service, or a Frenchman about the Deuxième.'

'He probably came from Leningrad to Berlin via Warsaw,' said Bond. 'From Berlin they've got plenty of routes open to the rest of Europe. He's back home by now being told off for not shooting me too. I fancy they've got quite a file on me in view of one or two of the jobs M.'s given me since the war. He obviously thought he was being smart enough cutting his initial in my hand.'

'What's that?' asked Mathis. 'The doctor said the cuts looked like a square M with a tail to the top. He said they didn't mean anything.'

'Well, I only got a glimpse before I passed out, but I've seen the cuts several times while they were being dressed and I'm pretty certain they are the Russian letter for SH. It's rather like an inverted M with a tail. That would make sense. SMERSH is short for SMYERT SHPIONAM—Death to Spies —and he thinks he's labelled me as a SHPION. It's a nuisance because M. will probably say I've got to go to hospital again when I get back to London and have new skin grafted over the whole of the back of my hand. It doesn't matter much. I've decided to resign.'

Mathis looked at him with his mouth open.

'Resign?' he asked incredulously. 'What the hell for?'

Bond looked away from Mathis. He studied his bandaged hands.

'When I was being beaten up,' he said, 'I suddenly liked the idea of being alive. Before Le Chiffre began, he used a phrase which stuck in my mind: "playing Red Indians." He said that's what I had been doing. Well, I suddenly thought he might be right.

'You see,' he said, still looking down at his bandages, 'when one's young, it seems very easy to distinguish between right and wrong; but as one gets older it becomes more difficult. At school it's easy to pick out one's own villains and heroes, and one grows up wanting to be a hero and kill the villains.'

He looked obstinately at Mathis.

'Well, in the last few years I've killed two villains. The first was in New York—a Japanese cipher expert cracking our codes on the thirty-sixth floor of the R.C.A. Building in Rockefeller Center, where the Japs had their consulate. I took a room on the fortieth floor of the next-door sky-scraper, and I could look across the street into his room and see him working. Then I got a colleague from our organization in New York and a couple of Remington thirty-thirty's with telescopic sights and silencers. We smuggled them up to my room and sat for days waiting for our chance. He shot at the man a second before me. His job was only to blast a hole through the window so that I could shoot the Jap through it. They have tough windows at Rockefeller Center to keep the noise out. It worked very well. As I ex-pected, his bullet got deflected by the glass and went God knows where. But I shot immediately after him, through the hole he had made. I got the Jap in the mouth as he turned to gape at the broken window.'

Bond smoked for a minute.

'It was a pretty sound job. Nice and clean too. Three hun-dred yards away. No personal contact. The next time in Stockholm wasn't so pretty. I had to kill a Norwegian who was doubling against us for the Germans. He'd managed to get two of our men captured—probably bumped off for all I know. For various reasons it had to be an absolutely silent job. I chose the bedroom of his flat and a knife. And, well, he just didn't die very quickly.

'For those two jobs I was awarded a Double O number in the Service. Felt pretty clever and got a reputation for being good and tough. A Double O number in our Service means you've had to kill a chap in cold blood in the course of some job.

'Now,' he looked up again at Mathis, 'that's all very fine—the hero kills two villains; but when the hero Le Chiffre starts to kill the villain Bond and the villain Bond knows he isn't a villain at all, you see the other side of the medal. The villains and heroes get all mixed up.

'Of course,' he added, as Mathis started to expostulate, 'patriotism comes along and makes it seem fairly all right, but this country-right-or-wrong business is getting a little out of date. Today we are fighting communism. Okay. If I'd been alive fifty years ago, the brand of conservatism we have today would have been damn near called communism, and we should have been told to go and fight that. History is moving pretty quickly these days, and the heroes and villains keep on changing parts.'

Mathis stared at him aghast. Then he tapped his head and put a calming hand on Bond's arm.

'You mean to say that this precious Le Chiffre who did his best to turn you into a eunuch doesn't qualify as a villain?' he asked. 'Anyone would think from the rot you talk that he had been battering your head instead of your . . .' he gestured down the bed. 'You wait till M. tells you to get after another Le Chiffre. I bet you'll go after him all right. And what about SMERSH? I can tell you I don't like the idea of these chaps running around France killing anyone they feel has been a traitor to their precious political system. You're a bloody anarchist.'

He threw his arms in the air and let them fall helplessly to his sides.

Bond laughed.

'All right,' he said. 'Take our friend Le Chiffre. It's simple enough to say he was an evil man; at least it's simple enough for me, because he did evil things to me. If he was here now, I wouldn't hesitate to kill him—but out of personal revenge and not, I'm afraid, for some high moral reason or for the sake of my country.'

He looked up at Mathis to see how bored he was getting with these introspective refinements of what, to Mathis, was a simple question of his duty.

Mathis smiled back at him.

'Continue, my dear friend. It is interesting for me to see this new Bond. Englishmen are so odd. They are like a nest of Chinese boxes. It takes a very long time to get to the centre of them. When one gets there the result is unrewarding, but the process is instructive and entertaining. Continue. Develop your arguments. There may be something I can use to my own chief the next time I want to get out of an unpleasant job.' He grinned maliciously.

Bond ignored him.

'Now in order to tell the difference between good and evil, we have manufactured two images representing the extremes—representing the deepest black and the purest white —and we call them God and the Devil. But in doing so we have cheated a bit. God is a clear image, you can see every hair on His beard. But the Devil. What does he look like?' Bond looked triumphantly at Mathis.

Mathis laughed ironically.

'A woman.'

'It's all very fine,' said Bond; 'but I've been thinking about these things, and I'm wondering whose side I ought to be on. I'm getting very sorry for the Devil and his disciples, such as the good Le Chiffre. The Devil has a rotten time, and I always like to be on the side of the underdog. We don't give the poor chap a chance. There's a Good Book about goodness and how to be good and so forth, but there's no Evil Book about evil and how to be bad. The Devil had no prophets to write his Ten Commandments, and no team of authors to write his biography. His case has gone completely by default. We know nothing about him but a lot of fairy stories from our parents and schoolmasters. He has no book from which we can learn the nature of evil in all its forms, with parables about evil people, proverbs about evil people, folklore about evil people. All we have is the living example of the people who are least good, or our own intuition.

'So,' continued Bond, warming to his argument, 'Le Chiffre was serving a wonderful purpose, a really vital purpose, perhaps the best and highest purpose of all. By his evil existence, which foolishly I have helped to destroy, he was creating a norm of badness by which, and by which alone, an opposite norm of goodness could exist. We were privileged, in our short knowledge of him, to see and estimate his wickedness, and we emerge from the acquaintanceship better and more virtuous men.'

'Bravo,' said Mathis. 'I'm proud of you. You ought to be tortured every day. I really must remember to do something evil this evening. I must start at once. I have a few marks in my favour—only small ones, alas,' he added ruefully; 'but I shall work fast now that I have seen the light. What a splendid time I'm going to have! Now, let's see, where shall I start —murder, arson, rape? But no, these are peccadilloes. I must really consult the good Marquis de Sade. I am a child, an absolute child in these matters.'

His face fell.

'Ah, but our conscience, my dear Bond. What shall we do with him while we are committing some juicy sin? That is a problem. He is a crafty person this conscience and very old, as old as the first family of apes which gave birth to him. We must give that problem really careful thought, or we shall spoil our enjoyment. Of course, we should murder him first, but he is a tough bird. It will be difficult, but if we succeed we could be worse even than Le Chiffre.

'For you, dear James, it is easy. You can start off by resigning. That was a brilliant thought of yours, a splendid start to your new career. And so simple. Everyone has the revolver of resignation in his pocket. All you've got to do is pull the trigger, and you will have made a big hole in your country and your conscience at the same time. A murder and a suicide with one bullet! Splendid. What a difficult and glorious profession! As for me, I must start embracing the new cause at once.'

He looked at his watch.

'Good. I've started already. I'm half an hour late for a meeting with the chief of police.'

He rose to his feet, laughing.

'That was most enjoyable, my dear James. You really ought to go on the halls. Now about that little problem of yours, this business of not knowing good men from bad men and villains from heroes, and so forth. It is, of course, a difficult problem in the abstract. The secret lies in personal experience, whether you're a Chinaman or an Englishman.'

He paused at the door.

'You admit that Le Chiffre did you personal evil, and that you would kill him if he appeared in front of you now?

'Well, when you get back to London you will find there are other Le Chiffres seeking to destroy you and your friends and your country. M. will tell you about them. And now that you have seen a really evil man you will know how evil they can be, and you will go after them to destroy them in order to protect yourself and the people you love. You won't wait or argue about it. You know what they look like now and what they can do to people. You may be a bit more choosy about the jobs you take on. You may want to be certain that the target really is black; but there are plenty of really black targets around. There's still plenty for you to do. And you'll do it. And when you fall in love and have a mistress or a wife and children to look after, it will seem all the easier.'

Mathis opened the door and stopped on the threshold.

'Surround yourself with human beings, my dear James. They are easier to fight for than principles.'

He laughed. 'But don't let me down and become human yourself. We would lose such a wonderful machine.'

With a wave of the hand he shut the door.

'Hey,' shouted Bond.

But the footsteps went quickly off down the passage.

xxi. VESPER

IT WAS on the next day that Bond asked to see Vesper.

He had not wanted to see her before. He was told that every day she came to the nursing home and asked after him. Flowers had arrived from her. Bond didn't like flowers, and he told the nurse to give them to another patient. After this had happened twice, no more flowers came. Bond had not meant to offend her. He disliked having feminine things around him. Flowers seemed to ask for recognition of the person who had sent them, to be constantly transmitting a message of sympathy and affection. Bond found this irksome. He disliked being cosseted. It gave him claustrophobia.

Bond was bored at the idea of having to explain some of this to Vesper. And he was embarrassed at having to ask one or two questions which mystified him, questions about Vesper's behaviour. The answers would almost certainly make her out to be a fool. Then he had his full report to M. to think about. In this he didn't want to have to criticize Vesper. It might easily cost her her job.

But above all, he admitted to himself, he shirked the answer to a more painful question.

The doctor had talked often to Bond about his injuries. He had always told him that there would be no evil effects from the terrible battering his body had received. He had said that Bond's full health would return, and that none of his powers had been taken from him. But the evidence of Bond's eyes and his nerves refused these comforting assurances. He was still painfully swollen and bruised, and whenever the injections wore off he was in agony. Above all, his imagination had suffered. For an hour in that room with Le Chiffre the certainty of impotence had been beaten into him; and a scar had been left on his mind that could only be healed by experience.

From the day when Bond first met Vesper in the Hermitage bar, he had found her desirable; and he knew that if things had been different in the night club, if Vesper had responded in any way and if there had been no kidnapping, he would have tried to sleep with her that night. Even later, in the car and outside the villa when he had had other things to think about, his eroticism had been hotly aroused by the sight of her indecent nakedness.

And now, when he could see her again, he was afraid. Afraid that his senses and his body would not respond to her sensual beauty. Afraid that he would feel no stir of desire, and that his blood would stay cool. In his mind he had made this first meeting into a test, and he was shirking the answer. That was the real reason, he admitted, why he had waited to give his body a chance to respond, why he had put off their first meeting for over a week. He would have liked to put off the meeting still further, but he explained to himself that his report must be written, that any day an emissary from London would come over and want to hear the full story, that today was as good as tomorrow, that anyway he might as well know the worst.

So on the eighth day he asked for her, for the early morning when he was feeling refreshed and strong after the night's rest.

For no reason at all, he had expected that she would show some sign of her experiences, that she would look pale and even ill. He was not prepared for the tall bronzed girl in a cream tussore frock with a black belt who came happily through the door and stood smiling at him.

'Good heavens, Vesper,' he said with a wry gesture of welcome, 'you look absolutely splendid. You must thrive on disaster. How have you managed to get such a wonderful sunburn?'

'I feel very guilty,' she said sitting down beside him. 'But I've been bathing every day while you've been lying here. The doctor said I was to and Head of S. said I was to; so— well, I just thought it wouldn't help you for me to be moping away all day long in my room. I've found a wonderful stretch of sand down the coast, and I take my lunch and go there every day with a book, and I don't come back till the evening. There's a bus that takes me there and back with only a short walk over the dunes, and I've managed to get over the fact that it's on the way down that road to the villa.'

Her voice faltered.

The mention of the villa had made Bond's eyes flicker.

She continued bravely, refusing to be defeated by Bond's lack of response.

'The doctor says it won't be long before you're allowed up. I thought perhaps . . . I thought perhaps I could take you down to this beach later on. The doctor says that bathing would be very good for you.'

Bond grunted.

'God knows when I'll be able to bathe,' he said. 'The doctor's talking through his hat. And when I can bathe it would probably be better for me to bathe alone for a bit. I don't want to frighten anybody. Apart from anything else,' he glanced pointedly down the bed, 'my body's a mass of scars and bruises. But you enjoy yourself. There's no reason why you shouldn't enjoy yourself.'

Vesper was stung by the bitterness and injustice in his voice.

'I'm sorry,' she said. 'I just thought . . . I was just trying . . .'

Suddenly her eyes filled with tears. She swallowed.

'I wanted . . . I wanted to help you get well.'

Her voice strangled. She looked piteously at him, facing the accusation in his eyes and in his manner.

Then she broke down and buried her face in her hands and sobbed.

'I'm sorry,' she said in a muffled voice. 'I'm really sorry.' With one hand she searched for a handkerchief in her bag. 'It's all my fault,' she dabbed at her eyes. 'I know it's all my fault.'

Bond at once relented. He put out a bandaged hand and laid it on her knee.

'It's all right, Vesper. I'm sorry I was so rough. It's just that I was jealous of you in the sunshine while I'm stuck here. Directly I'm well enough I'll come with you, and you must show me your beach. Of course it's just what I want. It'll be wonderful to get out again.'

She pressed his hand and stood up and walked over to the window. After a moment she busied herself with her make-up. Then she came back to the bed.

Bond looked at her tenderly. Like all harsh, cold men, he was easily tipped over into sentiment. She was very beautiful, and he felt warm towards her. He decided to make his questions as easy as possible.

He gave her a cigarette, and for a time they talked of the visit of Head of S. and of the reactions in London to the rout of Le Chiffre.

From what she said it was clear that the final object of the plan had been more than fulfilled. The story was still being splashed all over the world, and correspondents of most of the English and American papers had been at Royale trying to trace the Jamaican millionaire who had defeated Le Chiffre at the tables. They had got on to Vesper, but she had covered up well. Her story was that Bond had told her he was going on to Cannes and Monte Carlo to gamble with his winnings. The hunt had moved down to the South of France. Mathis and the police had obliterated all other traces, and the papers were forced to concentrate on the Strasbourg angles and the chaos in the ranks of the French communists.

'By the way, Vesper,' said Bond after a time, 'what really happened to you after you left me in the night club? All I saw was the actual kidnapping.' He told her briefly of the scene outside the Casino.

'I'm afraid I must have lost my head,' said Vesper, avoiding Bond's eyes. 'When I couldn't see Mathis anywhere in the entrance hall I went outside, and the commissionaire asked me if I was Miss Lynd, and then told me the man who

had sent in the note was waiting in a car down on the right
of the steps. Somehow I wasn't particularly surprised. I'd
only known Mathis for a day or two, and I didn't know how
he worked, so I just walked down towards the car. It was
away on the right and more or less in the shadows. Just as I
was coming up to it, Le Chiffre's two men jumped out from
behind one of the other cars in the row and simply scooped
my skirt over my head.'

Vesper blushed.

'It sounds a childish trick,' she looked penitently at Bond,
'but it's really frightfully effective. One's a complete prisoner and although I screamed I don't expect any sound came
out from under my skirt. I kicked out as hard as I could; but
that was no use, as I couldn't see, and my arms were absolutely helpless. I was just a trussed chicken. They picked
me up between them and shoved me into the back of the
car. I went on struggling, of course, and when the car started
and while they were trying to tie a rope or something round
the top of my skirt over my head, I managed to get an arm
free and throw my bag through the window. I hope it was
some use.'

Bond nodded.

'It was really instinctive. I just thought you'd have no
idea what had happened to me, and I was terrified. I did the
first thing I could think of.'

Bond knew that it was him they had been after and that,
if Vesper hadn't thrown her bag out, they would probably
have thrown it out themselves directly they saw him appear
on the steps.

'It certainly helped,' said Bond. 'But why didn't you make
any sign when they finally got me after the car smash, when
I spoke to you? I was dreadfully worried. I thought they
might have knocked you out or something.'

'I'm afraid I must have been unconscious,' said Vesper. 'I fainted once from lack of air, and when I came to they had cut a hole in front of my face. I must have fainted again. I don't remember much until we got to the villa. I really only gathered you had been captured when I heard you try and come after me in the passage.'

'And they didn't touch you?' asked Bond. 'They didn't try and mess about with you while I was being beaten up?'

'No,' said Vesper. 'They just left me in an armchair. They drank and played cards—belotte, I think it was from what I heard—and then they went to sleep. I suppose that was how SMERSH got them. They bound my legs and put me on a chair in a corner facing the wall, and I saw nothing of SMERSH. I heard some odd noises. I expect they woke me up. And then what sounded like one of them falling off his chair. Then there were some soft footsteps, and a door closed; and then nothing happened until Mathis and the police burst in hours later. I slept most of the time. I had no idea what had happened to you, but'—she faltered—'I did once hear a terrible scream. It sounded very far away. At least, I think it must have been a scream. At the time I thought it might have been a nightmare.'

'I'm afraid that must have been me,' said Bond.

Vesper put out a hand and touched one of his. Her eyes filled with tears.

'It's horrible,' she said. 'The things they did to you. And it was all my fault. If only . . .'

She buried her face in her hands.

'That's all right,' said Bond comfortingly. 'It's no good crying over spilt milk. It's all over now, and thank heavens they let you alone.' He patted her knee. 'They were going to start on you when they'd got me really softened up. We've got a lot to thank SMERSH for. Now, come on, let's forget about it. It certainly wasn't anything to do with you. Anybody could have fallen for that note. Anyway, it's all water over the dam,' he added cheerfully.

Vesper looked at him gratefully through her tears. 'You really promise?' she asked. 'I thought you would never forgive me. I . . . I'll try and make it up to you. Somehow.' She looked at him.

Somehow? thought Bond to himself. He looked at her. She was smiling at him. He smiled back.

'You'd better look out,' he said. 'I may hold you to that.'

She looked into his eyes and said nothing, but the enigmatic challenge was back. She pressed his hand and rose. 'A promise is a promise,' she said.

This time they both knew what the promise was.

She picked up her bag from the bed and walked to the door.

'Shall I come tomorrow?' She looked at Bond gravely.

'Yes, please, Vesper,' said Bond. 'I'd like that. Please do some more exploring. It will be fun to think of what we can do when I get up. Will you think of some things?'

'Yes,' said Vesper. 'Please get well quickly.'

They gazed at each other for a second. Then she went out and closed the door, and Bond listened until the sound of her footsteps had died away.

xxii. THE HASTENING SALOON

FROM THAT day Bond's recovery was rapid.

He sat up in bed and wrote his report to M. He made light of what he still considered amateurish behaviour on the part of Vesper. By juggling with the emphasis, he made the kidnapping sound much more Machiavellian than it had been. He praised Vesper's coolness and composure throughout the whole episode without saying that he had found some of her actions unaccountable.

Every day Vesper came to see him, and he looked forward to these visits with excitement. She talked happily of her adventures of the day before, her explorations down the coast, and the restaurants where she had eaten. She had made friends with the chief of police and with one of the directors of the Casino, and it was they who took her out in the evening and occasionally lent her a car during the day. She kept an eye on the repairs to the Bentley which had been towed down to coachbuilders at Rouen, and she even arranged for some new clothes to be sent out from Bond's London flat. Nothing survived from his original wardrobe. Every stitch had been cut to ribbons in the search for the forty million francs.

The Le Chiffre affair was never mentioned between them. She occasionally told Bond amusing stories of Head of S.'s office. She had apparently transferred there from the W.R. N.S. And he told her of some of his adventures in the Service.

He found he could speak to her easily, and he was surprised.

With most women his manner was a mixture of taciturnity and passion. The lengthy approaches to a seduction bored him almost as much as the subsequent mess of disentanglement. He found something grisly in the inevitability of the pattern of each affair. The conventional parabola—sentiment, the touch of the hand, the kiss, the passionate kiss, the feel of the body, the climax in the bed, then more bed, then less bed, then the boredom, the tears, and the final bitterness—was to him shameful and hypocritical. Even more he shunned the mise-en-scène for each of these acts in the play—the meeting at a party, the restaurant, the taxi, his flat, her flat, then the week-end by the sea, then the flats again, then the furtive alibis and the final angry farewell on some doorstep in the rain.

But with Vesper there could be none of this.

In the dull room and the boredom of his treatment her presence was each day an oasis of pleasure, something to look forward to. In their talk there was nothing but companionship with a distant undertone of passion. In the background there was the unspoken zest of the promise which, in due course and in their own time, would be met. Over all there brooded the shadow of his injuries and the tantalus of their slow healing.

Whether Bond liked it or not, the branch had already escaped his knife and was ready to burst into flower.

With enjoyable steps Bond recovered. He was allowed up. Then he was allowed to sit in the garden. Then he could go for a short walk, then for a long drive. And then the afternoon came when the doctor appeared on a flying visit from Paris and pronounced him well again. His clothes were brought round by Vesper, farewells were exchanged with the nurses, and a hired car drove them away.

It was three weeks from the day when he had been on the edge of death, and now it was July and the hot summer shimmered down the coast and out at sea. Bond clasped the moment to him.

Their destination was to be a surprise for him. He had not wanted to go back to one of the big hotels in Royale, and Vesper said she would find somewhere away from the town. But she insisted on being mysterious about it and only said that she had found a place he would like. He was happy to be in her hands, but he covered up his surrender by referring to their destination as 'Trou sur Mer' (she admitted it was by the sea), and lauding the rustic delights of outside lavatories, bedbugs, and cockroaches.

Their drive was spoiled by a curious incident.

While they followed the coast-road in the direction of Les Noctambules, Bond described to her his wild chase in the Bentley, finally pointing out the curve he had taken before the crash and the exact place where the vicious carpet of spikes had been laid. He slowed the car down and leant out to show her the deep cuts in the tarmac made by the rims of the wheels and the broken branches in the hedge and the patch of oil where the car had come to rest.

But all the time she was distrait and fidgety and commented only in monosyllables. Once or twice he caught her glancing in the driving-mirror; but when he had a chance to look back through the rear window they had just rounded a bend, and he could see nothing.

Finally he took her hand.

'Something's on your mind, Vesper,' he said.

She gave him a taut, bright smile. 'It's nothing. Absolutely nothing. I had a silly idea we were being followed. It's just nerves, I suppose. This road is full of ghosts.'

Under cover of a short laugh she looked back again.

'Look.' There was an edge of panic in her voice.

Obediently Bond turned his head. Sure enough, a quarter of a mile away, a black saloon was coming after them at a good pace.

Bond laughed.

'We can't be the only people using this road,' he said. 'Anyway, who wants to follow us? We've done nothing wrong.' He patted her hand. 'It's a middle-aged commercial traveller in car-polish on his way to Le Havre. He's probably thinking of his lunch and his mistress in Paris. Really, Vesper, you mustn't think evil of the innocent.'

'I expect you're right,' she said nervously. 'Anyway, we're nearly there.'

She relapsed into silence and gazed out of the window.

Bond could still feel her tenseness. He smiled to himself at what he took to be simply a hangover from their recent adventures. But he decided to humour her, and when they came to a small lane leading towards the sea and slowed to turn down it, he told the driver to stop directly they were off the main road.

Hidden by the tall hedge, they watched together through the rear window.

Through the quiet hum of summer noises they could hear the car approaching. Vesper dug her fingers into his arm. The pace of the car did not alter as it approached their hiding-place and they had only a brief glimpse of a man's profile as a black saloon tore by.

It was true that he seemed to glance quickly towards them, but above them in the hedge there was a gaily painted sign pointing down the lane and announcing 'L'Auberge du

Fruit Défendu, crustaces, fritures.' It was obvious to Bond that it was this that had caught the driver's eye.

As the rattle of the car's exhaust diminished down the road, Vesper sank back into her corner. Her face was pale.

'He looked at us,' she said. 'I told you so. I knew we were being followed. Now they know where we are.'

Bond could not contain his impatience. 'Bunkum,' he said. 'He was looking at that sign.' He pointed it out to Vesper.

She looked slightly relieved. 'Do you really think so?' she asked. 'Yes. I see. Of course, you must be right. Come on. I'm sorry to be so stupid. I don't know what came over me.'

She leant forward and talked to the driver through the partition, and the car moved on. She sank back and turned a bright face towards Bond. The colour had almost come back to her cheeks. 'I really am sorry. It's just that—it's that I can't believe everything's over and there's no one to be frightened of any more.' She pressed his hand. 'You must think me very stupid.'

'Of course not,' said Bond. 'But really nobody could be interested in us now. Forget it all. The whole job's finished, wiped up. This is our holiday, and there's not a cloud in the sky. Is there?' he persisted.

'No, of course not.' She shook herself slightly. 'I'm mad. Now we'll be there in a second. I do hope you're going to like it.'

They both leant forward. Animation was back in her face, and the incident left only the smallest question-mark hanging in the air. Even that faded as they came through the dunes and saw the sea and the modest little inn amongst the pines.

'It's not very grand, I'm afraid,' said Vesper. 'But it's very

clean, and the food's wonderful.' She looked at him anxiously.

She need not have worried. Bond loved the place at first
sight—the terrace leading almost to the high-tide mark, the
low two-storied house with gay brick-red awnings over the
windows, and the crescent-shaped bay of blue water and
golden sand. How many times in his life would he have
given anything to have turned off a main road to find a lost
corner like this where he could let the world go by and live
in the sea from dawn to dusk! And now he was to have a
whole week of this. And of Vesper. In his mind he fingered
the necklace of the days to come.

They drew up in the courtyard behind the house, and the
proprietor and his wife came out to greet them.

Monsieur Versoix was a middle-aged man with one arm.
The other he had lost fighting with the Free French in
Madagascar. He was a friend of the chief of police of Royale,
and it was the Commissaire who had suggested the place to
Vesper and had spoken to the proprietor on the telephone.
As a result, nothing was going to be too good for them.

Madame Versoix had been interrupted in the middle of
preparing dinner. She wore an apron and held a wooden
spoon in one hand. She was younger than her husband,
chubby and handsome and warm-eyed. Instinctively Bond
guessed that they had no children and that they gave their
thwarted affection to their friends and some regular customers, and probably to some pets. He thought that their
life was probably something of a struggle, and that the inn
must be very lonely in wintertime with the big seas and the
noise of the wind in the pines.

The proprietor showed them to their rooms.

Vesper's was a double room, and Bond was next door, at
the corner of the house, with one window looking out to

sea and another with a view of the distant arm of the bay. There was a bathroom between them. Everything was spotless, and sparsely comfortable.

The proprietor was pleased when they both showed their delight. He said that dinner would be at seven-thirty and that Madame la patronne was preparing broiled lobsters with melted butter. He was sorry that they were so quiet just then. It was Tuesday. There would be more people at the week-end. The season had not been good. Generally they had plenty of English people staying, but times were difficult over there and the English just came for a week-end at Royale and then went home after losing their money at the Casino. It was not like the old days. He shrugged his shoulders philosophically. But then no day was like the day before, and no century like the previous one, and . . .

'Quite so,' said Bond.

xxiii. TIDE OF PASSION

THEY WERE talking on the threshold of Vesper's room. When the proprietor left them, Bond pushed her inside and closed the door. Then he put his hands on her shoulders and kissed her on both cheeks.

'This is heaven,' he said.

Then he saw that her eyes were shining. Her hands came up and rested on his forearms. He stepped right up against her, and his arms dropped round her waist. Her head went back, and her mouth opened beneath his.

'My darling,' he said. He plunged his mouth down onto hers and felt her respond, shyly at first, then more passionately. His hand slipped down her back and pressed her body fiercely to his. Panting, she slipped her mouth away and they clung together; he brushed her ear with his lips and felt the firm warmth of her breasts against him. Then he reached up and seized her hair and bent her head back until he could kiss her again. She pushed him away and sank back exhausted on to the bed. For a moment they looked at each other hungrily.

'I'm sorry, Vesper,' he said. 'I didn't mean to then.'

She shook her head, dumb with the storm which had passed through her.

He came and sat beside her, and they looked at each other with lingering tenderness as the tide of passion ebbed in their veins.

She leant over and kissed him on the corner of the mouth, then she brushed the black comma of hair back from his damp forehead.

'My darling,' she said. 'Give me a cigarette. I don't know where my bag is.' She looked vaguely round the room.

Bond lit one for her and put it between her lips. She took a deep lungful of smoke and let it pour out through her mouth with a slow sigh.

Bond put his arm round her, but she got up and walked over to the window. She stood there with her back to him.

Bond looked down at his hands and saw they were still trembling.

'It's going to take some time to get ready for dinner,' said Vesper, still not looking at him. 'Why don't you go and bathe? I'll unpack for you.'

Bond left the bed and came and stood close against her. He put his arms round her and put a hand over each breast.

They filled his hands and the nipples were hard against his fingers. She put her hands over his and pressed them into her, but she still looked away from him out of the window.

'Not now,' she said in a low voice.

Bond bent and burrowed his lips into the nape of her neck. For a moment he strained her hard to him, then he let her go.

'All right, Vesper,' he said.

He walked over to the door and looked back. She had not moved. For some reason he thought she was crying. He took a step towards her and then realized that there was nothing to say between them then.

'My love,' he said.

Then he went out and shut the door.

Bond walked along to his room and sat down on the bed. He felt weak from the passion which had swept through his body. He was torn between the desire to fall back full-length on the bed and his longing to be cooled and revived by the sea. He played with the choice for a moment, then he went over to his suitcase and took out white linen bathing-trunks and a dark blue pyjama-suit.

Bond had always disliked pyjamas and had slept naked until in Hong Kong at the end of the war he came across the perfect compromise. This was a pyjama-coat which came almost down to the knees. It had no buttons, but there was a loose belt round the waist. The sleeves were wide and short, ending just above the elbow. The result was cool and comfortable, and now when he slipped the coat on over his trunks, all his bruises and scars were hidden except the thin white bracelets on wrists and ankles and the mark of SMERSH on his right hand.

He slipped his feet into a pair of dark-blue leather sandals and went downstairs and out of the house and across the terrace to the beach. As he passed across the front of the house he thought of Vesper; but he refrained from looking up to see if she was still standing at the window. If she saw him, she gave no sign.

He walked along the water line on the hard golden sand until he was out of sight of the inn. Then he threw off his pyjama-coat and took a short run and a quick flat dive into the small waves. The beach shelved quickly and he kept under water as long as he could, swimming with powerful strokes and feeling the soft coolness all over him. Then he surfaced and brushed the hair out of his eyes. It was nearly seven, and the sun had lost much of its heat. Before long it would sink beneath the further arm of the bay; but now it was straight in his eyes, and he turned on his back and swam away from it so that he could keep it with him as long as possible.

When he came ashore nearly a mile down the bay the shadows had already engulfed his distant pyjamas; but he knew he had time to lie on the hard sand and dry before the tide of dusk reached him.

He took off his bathing trunks and looked down at his body. There were only a few traces left of his injuries. He shrugged his shoulders and lay down with his limbs spread out in a star and gazed up at the empty blue sky and thought of Vesper.

His feelings for her were confused, and he was impatient with the confusion. They had been so simple. He had intended to sleep with her as soon as he could, because he desired her and also because—he admitted it to himself—he wanted coldly to put the repairs to his body to the final test. He thought they would sleep together for a few days and then he might see something of her in London. Then would come the inevitable disengagement which would be all the easier because of their positions in the Service. If it was not easy, he could go off on an assignment abroad or—which was also in his mind—he could resign and travel to different parts of the world as he had always wanted.

But somehow she had crept under his skin, and over the last two weeks his feelings had gradually changed.

He found her companionship easy and unexacting. There was something enigmatic about her which was a constant stimulus. She gave little of her real personality away, and he felt that, however long they were together, there would always be a private room inside her which he could never invade. She was thoughtful and full of consideration without being slavish and without compromising her arrogant spirit. And now he knew that she was profoundly, excitingly sensual, but that the conquest of her body, because of the central privacy in her, would each time have the tang of rape. Loving her physically would each time be a thrilling voyage without the anticlimax of arrival. She would surrender herself avidly, he thought, and greedily enjoy all the intimacies of the bed without ever allowing herself to be possessed.

Naked, Bond lay and tried to push away the conclusions he read in the sky. He turned his head and looked down the beach and saw that the shadows of the headland were almost reaching for him.

He stood up and brushed off as much of the sand as he could reach. He reflected that he would have a bath when he got in and he absent-mindedly picked up his trunks and started walking back along the beach. It was only when he reached his pyjama-coat and bent to pick it up that he realized he was still naked. Without bothering about the trunks, he slipped on the light coat and walked on to the hotel.

At that moment his mind was made up.

xxiv. 'FRUIT DÉFENDU'

WHEN HE got back to his room he was touched to find all his belongings put away and in the bathroom his toothbrush and shaving things neatly arranged at one end of the glass shelf over the washbasin. At the other end were Vesper's toothbrush and one or two small bottles and a jar of face-cream.

He glanced at the bottles and was surprised to see that one contained Nembutal sleeping pills. Perhaps her nerves had been more shaken by the events at the villa than he had imagined.

The bath had been filled for him, and there was a new flask of some expensive pine bath-essence on a chair beside it with his towel.

'Vesper,' he called.

'Yes?'

'You really are the limit. You make me feel like an expensive gigolo.'

'I was told to look after you. I'm only doing what I was told.'

'Darling, the bath's absolutely right. Will you marry me?'

She snorted. 'You need a slave, not a wife.'

'I want you.'

'Well, I want my lobster and champagne, so hurry up.'

'All right, all right,' said Bond.

He dried himself and dressed in a white shirt and dark blue

slacks. He hoped that she would be dressed as simply, and he was pleased when, without knocking, she appeared in the doorway wearing a blue linen shirt which had faded to the colour of her eyes and a dark red skirt in pleated cotton.

'I couldn't wait. I was famished. My room's over the kitchen, and I've been tortured by the wonderful smells.'

He came over and put his arm round her.

She took his hand, and together they went downstairs and out on to the terrace where their table had been laid in the light cast by the empty dining-room.

The champagne which Bond had ordered on their arrival stood in a plated wine-cooler beside their table, and Bond poured out two full glasses. Vesper busied herself with a delicious homemade liver pâté and helped them both to the crisp French bread and the thick squares of deep yellow butter set in chips of ice.

They looked at each other and drank deeply, and Bond filled their glasses again to the rim.

While they ate Bond told her of his bathe, and they talked of what they would do in the morning. All through the meal they left unspoken their feelings for each other, but in Vesper's eyes as much as in Bond's there was excited anticipation of the night. They let their hands and their feet touch from time to time as if to ease the tension in their bodies.

When the lobster had come and gone and the second bottle of champagne was half empty and they had just ladled thick cream over their fraises des bois, Vesper gave a deep sigh of contentment.

'I'm behaving like a pig,' she said happily. 'You always give me all the things I like best. I've never been so spoiled before.' She gazed across the terrace at the moonlit bay. 'I wish I deserved it.' Her voice had a wry undertone.

'What do you mean?' asked Bond surprised.

'Oh, I don't know. I suppose people get what they deserve, so perhaps I do deserve it.'

She looked at him and smiled. Her eyes narrowed quizzically.

'You really don't know much about me,' she said suddenly.

Bond was surprised by the undertone of seriousness in her voice.

'Quite enough,' he said laughing. 'All I need until tomorrow and the next day and the next. You don't know much about me for the matter of that.' He poured out more champagne.

Vesper looked at him thoughtfully.

'People are islands,' she said. 'They don't really touch. However close they are, they're really quite separate. Even if they've been married for fifty years.'

Bond thought with dismay that she must be going into a 'vin triste.' Too much champagne had made her melancholy. But suddenly she gave a happy laugh.

'Don't look so worried.' She leaned forward and put her hand over his. 'I was only being sentimental. Anyway, my island feels very close to your island tonight.' She took a sip of champagne.

Bond laughed, relieved. 'Let's join up and make a peninsula,' he said. 'Now, directly we've finished the strawberries.'

'No,' she said, flirting. 'I must have coffee.'

'And brandy,' countered Bond.

The small shadow had passed. The second small shadow. This too left a tiny question-mark hanging in the air. It quickly dissolved as warmth and intimacy enclosed them again.

When they had had their coffee and Bond was sipping

his brandy, Vesper picked up her bag and came and stood behind him.

'I'm tired,' she said, resting a hand on his shoulder.

He reached up and held it there, and they stayed motionless for a moment. She bent down and lightly brushed his hair with her lips. Then she was gone, and a few seconds later the light came on in her room.

Bond smoked and waited until it had gone out. Then he followed her, pausing only to say good night to the proprietor and his wife and thank them for the dinner. They exchanged compliments, and he went upstairs.

It was only half-past nine when he stepped into her room from the bathroom and closed the door behind him.

The moonlight shone through the half-closed shutters and lapped at the secret shadows in the snow of her body on the broad bed.

Bond awoke in his own room at dawn, and for a time he lay and stroked his memories.

Then he got quietly out of bed, and in his pyjama-coat he crept past Vesper's door and out of the house to the beach.

The sea was smooth and quiet in the sunrise. The small pink waves idly licked the sand. It was cold, but he took off his jacket and wandered naked along the edge of the sea to the point where he had bathed the evening before, then he walked slowly and deliberately into the water until it was just below his chin. He took his feet off the bottom and sank, holding his nose with one hand and shutting his eyes, feeling the cold water comb his body and his hair.

The mirror of the bay was unbroken except where it seemed a fish had jumped. Under the water he imagined the tranquil scene and wished that Vesper could just then come through the pines and be astonished to see him suddenly erupt from the empty seascape.

When after a full minute he came to the surface in a froth of spray, he was disappointed. There was no one in sight. For a time he swam and drifted, and then when the sun seemed hot enough, he came in to the beach and lay on his back and revelled in the body which the night had given back to him.

As on the evening before, he stared up into the empty sky and saw the same answer there.

After a while he rose and walked back slowly along the beach to his pyjama-coat.

That day he would ask Vesper to marry him. He was quite certain. It was only a question of choosing the right moment.

XXV. 'BLACK-PATCH'

AS HE walked quietly from the terrace into the half-darkness of the still shuttered dining-room, he was surprised to see Vesper emerge from the glass-fronted telephone booth near the front door and softly turn up the stairs towards their rooms.

'Vesper,' he called, thinking she must have had some urgent message which might concern them both.

She turned quickly, a hand up to her mouth.

For a moment longer than necessary she stared at him, her eyes wide.

'What is it, darling?' he asked, vaguely troubled and fearing some crisis in their lives.

'Oh,' she said breathlessly, 'you made me jump. It was only . . . I was just telephoning to Mathis. To Mathis,' she repeated. 'I wondered if he could get me another frock. You know, from that girl-friend I told you about. The vendeuse. You see'—she talked quickly, her words coming out in a persuasive jumble—'I've really got nothing to wear. I thought I'd catch him at home before he went to the office. I don't know my friend's telephone number, and I thought it would be a surprise for you. I didn't want you to hear me moving and wake you up. Is the water nice? Have you bathed? You ought to have waited for me.'

'It's wonderful,' said Bond, deciding to relieve her mind, though irritated with her obvious guilt over this childish mystery. 'You must go in, and then we'll have breakfast on the terrace. I'm ravenous. I'm sorry I made you jump. I was just startled to see anyone about at this hour of the morning.'

He put his arm round her; but she disengaged herself, and moved quickly on up the stairs.

'It was such a surprise to see you,' she said, trying to cover the incident up with a light touch.

'You looked like a ghost, a drowned man, with the hair down over your eyes like that.' She laughed harshly. Hearing the harshness, she turned the laugh into a cough.

'I hope I haven't caught cold,' she said.

She kept on patching up the edifice of her deceit until Bond wanted to spank her and tell her to relax and tell the truth. Instead he just gave her a reassuring pat on the back outside her room and told her to hurry up and have her bathe.

Then he went on to his room.

That was the end of the integrity of their love. The succeeding days were a shambles of falseness and hypocrisy, mingled with her tears and moments of animal passion to which she abandoned herself with a greed made indecent by the hollowness of their days.

Several times Bond tried to break down the dreadful walls of mistrust. Again and again he brought up the subject of the telephone call; but she obstinately bolstered up her story with embellishments which Bond knew she had thought out afterwards. She even accused Bond of thinking she had another lover.

These scenes always ended in her bitter tears and in moments almost of hysteria.

Each day the atmosphere became more hateful.

It seemed fantastic to Bond that human relationships could collapse into dust overnight, and he searched his mind again and again for a reason.

He felt that Vesper was just as horrified as he was, and, if anything, her misery seemed greater than his. But the mystery of the telephone conversation which Vesper angrily, almost fearfully it seemed to Bond, refused to explain was a shadow which grew darker with other small mysteries and reticencies.

Already at luncheon on that day things got worse.

After a breakfast which was an effort for both of them, Vesper said she had a headache and would stay in her room out of the sun. Bond took a book and walked for miles down the beach. By the time he returned he had argued to himself that they would be able to sort the problem out over lunch.

Directly they sat down, he apologized gaily for having startled her at the telephone booth and then he dismissed the subject and went on to describe what he had seen on his walk. But Vesper was distrait and commented only in monosyllables. She toyed with her food, and she avoided Bond's eyes and gazed past him with an air of preoccupation.

When she had failed once or twice to respond to some conversational gambit or other, Bond also relapsed into silence and occupied himself with his own gloomy thoughts.

All of a sudden she stiffened. Her fork fell with a clatter on to the edge of her plate and then noisily off the table on to the terrace.

Bond looked up. She had gone as white as a sheet, and she was looking over his shoulder with terror in her face.

Bond turned his head and saw that a man had just taken his place at a table on the opposite side of the terrace, well away from them. He seemed ordinary enough, perhaps rather sombrely dressed; but in his first quick glance Bond put him down as some businessman on his way along the coast who had just happened on the inn or had picked it out of the Michelin.

'What is it, darling?' he asked anxiously.

Vesper's eyes never moved from the distant figure.

'It's the man in the car,' she said in a stifled voice. 'The man who was following us. I know it is.'

Bond looked again over his shoulder. The patron was discussing the menu with the new customer. It was a perfectly normal scene. They exchanged smiles over some item on the menu and apparently agreed that it would suit, for the patron took the card and with, Bond guessed, a final exchange about the wine, withdrew.

The man seemed to realize that he was being watched. He looked up and gazed incuriously at them for a moment. Then he reached for a brief-case on the chair beside him, extracted a newspaper, and started to read it, his elbows propped up on the table.

When the man had turned his face towards them, Bond

noticed that he had a black patch over one eye. It was not tied with a tape across the eye, but screwed in like a monocle. Otherwise he seemed a friendly middle-aged man, with dark brown hair brushed straight back and, as Bond had seen while he was talking to the patron, particularly large, white teeth.

He turned back to Vesper. 'Really, darling. He looks very innocent. Are you sure he's the same man? We can't expect to have this place entirely to ourselves.'

Vesper's face was still a white mask. She was clutching the edge of the table with both hands. He thought she was going to faint and almost rose to come round to her, but she made a gesture to stop him. Then she reached for a glass of wine and took a deep draught. The glass rattled on her teeth, and she brought up her other hand to help. Then she put the glass down.

She looked at him with dull eyes.

'I know it's the same.'

He tried to reason with her, but she paid no attention. After glancing once or twice over his shoulder with eyes that held a curious submissiveness, she said that her headache was still bad and that she would spend the afternoon in her room. She left the table and walked indoors without a backward glance.

Bond was determined to set her mind at rest. He ordered coffee to be brought to the table, and then he rose and walked swiftly through to the courtyard. The black Peugeot which stood there might indeed have been the saloon they had seen, but it might equally have been one of a million others on the French roads. He took a quick glance inside, but the interior was empty and when he tried the boot, it was locked. He made a note of the Paris number-plate; then he went quickly to the lavatory adjoining the dining-room, pulled the chain, and walked out on to the terrace.

The man was eating and didn't look up.

Bond sat down in Vesper's chair so that he could watch the other table.

A few minutes later the man asked for the bill, paid it, and left. Bond heard the Peugeot start up, and soon the noise of its exhaust had disappeared in the direction of the road to Royale.

When the patron came back to his table, Bond explained that Madame had unfortunately a slight touch of sunstroke. After the patron had expressed his regret and enlarged on the dangers of going out of doors in almost any weather, Bond casually asked about the other customer. 'He reminds me of a friend who also lost an eye. They wear similar black patches.'

The patron answered that the man was a stranger. He had been pleased with his lunch and had said that he would be passing that way again in a day or two and would take another meal at the auberge. Apparently he was Swiss, which could also be seen from his accent. He was a traveller in watches. It was shocking to have only one eye. The strain of keeping that patch in place all day long. He supposed one got used to it.

'It is indeed very sad,' said Bond. 'You also have been unlucky,' he gestured to the proprietor's empty sleeve. 'I myself was very fortunate.'

For a time they talked about the war. Then Bond rose.

'By the way,' he said, 'Madame had an early telephone call which I must remember to pay for. Paris. An Elysée number, I think,' he added, remembering that that was Mathis's exchange.

'Thank you, monsieur, but the matter is regulated. I was

speaking to Royale this morning and the exchange mentioned that one of my guests had put through a call to Paris
and that there had been no answer. They wanted to know if
Madame would like the call kept in. I'm afraid the matter escaped my mind. Perhaps Monsieur would mention it to
Madame. But, let me see, it was an Invalides number the exchange referred to.'

XXVi. 'SLEEP WELL, MY DARLING'

THE NEXT two days were much the same.

On the fourth day of their stay Vesper went off early to
Royale. A taxi came and fetched her and brought her back.
She said she needed some medicine.

That night she made a special effort to be gay. She drank
a lot, and when they went upstairs she led him into her bedroom and made passionate love to him. Bond's body responded; but afterwards she cried bitterly into her pillow,
and Bond went to his room in grim despair.

He could hardly sleep, and in the early hours he heard her
door open softly. Some small sounds came from downstairs.
He was sure she was in the telephone-booth. Very soon he
heard her door softly close, and he guessed that again there
had been no reply from Paris.

This was Saturday.

On Sunday the man with the black patch was back again.
Bond knew it directly he looked up from his lunch and saw

her face. He had told her all that the patron had told him, withholding only the man's statement that he might be back. He had thought it would worry her.

He had also telephoned Mathis in Paris and checked on the Peugeot. It had been hired from a respectable firm two weeks before. The customer had had a Swiss triptique. His name was Adolph Gettler. He had given a bank in Zurich as his address.

Mathis had got on to the Swiss police. Yes, the bank had an account in his name. It was little used. Herr Gettler was understood to be connected with the watch industry. Inquiries could be pursued if there was a charge against him.

Vesper had shrugged her shoulders at the information.

This time when the man appeared she left her lunch in the middle and went straight up to her room.

Bond made up his mind. When he had finished, he followed her. Both her doors were locked, and when he made her let him in he saw that she had been sitting in the shadows by the window—watching, he presumed.

Her face was of cold stone. He led her to the bed and drew her down beside him. They sat stiffly, like people in a railway carriage.

'Vesper,' he said, holding her cold hands in his, 'we can't go on like this. We must finish with it. We are torturing each other, and there is only one way of stopping it. Either you must tell me what all this is about or we must leave. At once.'

She said nothing, and her hands were lifeless in his.

'My darling,' he said. 'Won't you tell me? Do you know, that first morning I was coming back to ask you to marry me. Can't we go back to the beginning again? What is this dreadful nightmare that is killing us?'

At first she said nothing, then a tear rolled slowly down her cheek.

'You mean you would have married me?'

Bond nodded.

'Oh, my God!' she cried. 'My God!' She turned and clutched him, pressing her face against his chest.

He held her closely to him. 'Tell me, my love,' he said. 'Tell me what's hurting you.'

Her sobs became quieter.

'Leave me for a little,' she said. A new note had come into her voice: a note of resignation. 'Let me think for a little.' She kissed his face and held it between her hands. She looked at him with yearning. 'Darling, I'm trying to do what's best for us. Please believe me. But it's terrible. I'm in a frightful . . .' She wept again, clutching him like a child with nightmares.

He soothed her, stroking the long black hair and kissing her softly.

'Go away now,' she said. 'I must have time to think. We've got to do something.'

She took his handkerchief and dried her eyes.

She led him to the door, and there they held tightly to each other. Then he kissed her again, and she shut the door behind him.

That evening most of the gayness and intimacy of their first night came back. She was excited, and some of her laughter sounded brittle; but Bond was determined to fall in with her new mood, and it was only at the end of dinner that he had made a passing remark which made her pause.

She put her hand over his.

'Don't talk about it now,' she said. 'Forget it now. It's all past. I'll tell you about it in the morning.'

She looked at him, and suddenly her eyes were full of tears. She found a handkerchief in her bag and dabbed at them.

'Give me some more champagne,' she said. She gave a queer little laugh. 'I want a lot more. You drink much more than me. It's not fair.'

They sat and drank together until the bottle was finished. Then she got to her feet. She knocked against her chair and giggled.

'I do believe I'm tight, 'she said. 'How disgraceful! Please, James, don't be ashamed of me. I did so want to be gay. And I am gay.'

She stood behind him and ran her fingers through his black hair.

'Come up quickly,' she said.

She blew a kiss at him and was gone.

For two hours they made slow, sweet love in a mood of happy passion which, the day before, Bond would never have thought they could regain. The barriers of self-consciousness and mistrust seemed to have vanished; the words they spoke to each other were innocent and true again, and there was no shadow between them.

'You must go now,' said Vesper when Bond had slept for a while in her arms.

As if to take back her words she held him more closely to her, murmuring endearments and pressing her body down the whole length of his.

When he finally rose and bent to smooth back her hair and finally kiss her eyes and her mouth good night, she reached out and turned on the light.

'Look at me,' she said, 'and let me look at you.'

He knelt beside her.

She examined every line of his face as if she were seeing him for the first time. Then she reached up and put an arm round his neck. Her deep blue eyes were swimming with tears as she drew his head slowly towards her and kissed him gently on the lips. Then she let him go and turned off the light.

'Good night, my dearest love,' she said.

Bond bent and kissed her. He tasted the tears on her cheek. He went to the door and looked back.

'Sleep well, my darling,' he said. 'Don't worry, everything's all right now.'

He closed the door softly and walked to his room with a full heart.

xxvii. THE BLEEDING HEART

THE PATRON brought him the letter in the morning.

He burst into Bond's room, holding the envelope in front of him as if it were on fire.

'There has been a terrible accident. Madame—'

Bond hurled himself out of bed and through the bathroom, but the communicating door was locked. He dashed back and through his room and down the corridor past a shrinking, terrified maid.

Vesper's door was open. The sunlight through the shutters lit up the room. Only her black hair showed above the sheet, and her body under the bedclothes was straight and moulded like a stone effigy on a tomb.

Bond fell on his knees beside her and drew back the sheet.

She was asleep. She must be. Her eyes were closed. There was no change in the dear face. She was just as she would look, and yet, and yet she was so still—no movement, no pulse, no breath. That was it. There was no breath.

Later the patron came and touched him on the shoulder. He pointed at the empty glass on the table beside her. There were white dregs in the bottom of it. It stood beside her book and her cigarettes and matches and the small pathetic litter of her mirror and lipstick and handkerchief. And on the floor the empty bottle of sleeping-pills, the pills Bond had seen in the bathroom that first evening.

Bond rose to his feet and shook himself. The patron was still holding out the letter towards him. He took it.

'Please notify the Commissaire,' said Bond. 'I will be in my room when he wants me.'

He walked blindly away without a backward glance.

He sat on the edge of his bed and gazed out of the window at the peaceful sea. Then he stared dully at the envelope. It was addressed simply in a large round hand, 'Pour Lui.'

The thought passed through Bond's mind that she must have left orders to be called early, so that he would not be the one to find her.

He turned the envelope over. Not long ago her warm tongue had sealed the flap.

He gave a sudden shrug and opened it.

It was not long. After the first few words he read it quickly, the breath coming harshly through his nostrils.

Then he threw it down on the bed as if it had been a scorpion.

My darling James [the letter opened],

I love you with all my heart, and while you read these words I hope you still love me because, now, with these words, this is the last moment that your love will last. So goodbye, my sweet love, while we still love each other. Goodbye, my darling.

I am an agent of the M.W.D. Yes, I am a double agent for the Russians. I was taken on a year after the war, and I have worked for them ever since. I was in love with a Pole in the R.A.F. Until you, I still was. You can find out who he was. He had two D.S.O.'s, and after the war he was trained by M. and dropped back into Poland. They caught him, and by torturing him they found out a lot and also about me. They came after me and told me he could live if I would work for them. He knew nothing of this, but he was allowed to write to me. The letter arrived on the fifteenth of each month. I found I couldn't stop. I couldn't bear the idea of a fifteenth coming round without his letter. It would mean that I had killed him. I tried to give them as little as possible. You must believe me about this. Then it came to you. I told them you had been given this job at Royale, what your cover was, and so on. That is why they knew about you before you arrived, and why they had time to put the microphones in. They suspected Le Chiffre, but they didn't know what your assignment was except that it was something to do with him. That was all I told them.

Then I was told not to stand behind you in the Casino, and to see that neither Mathis nor Leiter did. That was why the gunman was nearly able to shoot you. Then I had to stage that kidnapping. You may have wondered why I was so quiet in the night club. They didn't hurt me because I was working for M.W.D.

But when I found out what had been done to you, even though it was Le Chiffre who did it and he turned out to be a traitor, I decided I couldn't go on. By that time I had begun to fall in love with you. They wanted me to find out things from you while you were recovering, but I refused. I was controlled from Paris. I had to ring up an Invalides number twice a day. They threatened me; and finally they withdrew my control, and I knew my lover in Poland would have to die. But they were afraid I would talk, I suppose, and I got a final warning that SMERSH would come for me if I didn't obey them. I took no notice. I was in love with you. Then I saw the man with the black patch in the Splendide, and I found he had been making inquiries about my movements. This was the day before we came down here. I hoped I could shake him off. I decided that we would have an affair and I would escape to South America from Le Havre. I hoped I would have a baby of yours and be able to start again somewhere. But they followed us. You can't get away from them.

I knew it would be the end of our love if I told you. I realized that I could either wait to be killed by SMERSH and perhaps get you killed too, or I could kill myself.

There it is, my darling love. You can't stop me calling you that or saying that I love you. I am taking that with me, and the memories of you.

I can't tell you much to help you. The Paris number was Invalides 55200. I never met any of them in London. Everything was done through an accommodation address, a newsagent's at 450 Charing Cross Place.

At our first dinner together you talked about that man in Yugoslavia who was found guilty of treason. He said: 'I was carried away by the gale of the world.' That's my only excuse. That, and for love of the man whose life I tried to save.

It's late now and I'm tired, and you're just through two doors. But I've got to be brave. You might save my life, but I couldn't bear the look in your dear eyes.

My love, my love.   V.

Bond threw the letter down. Mechanically he brushed his fingers together. Suddenly he banged his temples with his fists and stood up. For a moment he looked out towards the quiet sea, then he cursed aloud, one harsh obscenity.

His eyes were wet, and he dried them.

He pulled on a shirt and trousers, and with a set cold face he walked down and shut himself in the telephone-booth.

While he was getting through to London, he calmly reviewed the facts of Vesper's letter. They all fitted. The little shadows and question marks of the past four weeks, which his instinct had noted but his mind rejected, all stood out now like signposts.

He saw her now only as a spy. Their love and his grief were relegated to the boxroom of his mind. Later, perhaps they would be dragged out, dispassionately examined, and then bitterly thrust back with other sentimental baggage he would rather forget. Now he could only think of her treachery to the Service and to her country, and of the damage it had done. His professional mind was completely absorbed with the consequences—the covers which must have been blown over the years, the codes which the enemy must have broken, the secrets which must have leaked from the centre of the very section devoted to penetrating the Soviet Union.

It was ghastly. God knew how the mess would be cleared up.

He ground his teeth. Suddenly Mathis's words came back to him: 'There are plenty of really black targets around,' and, earlier, 'What about SMERSH? I don't like the idea of these chaps running around France killing anyone they feel has been a traitor to their precious political system.'

Bond grinned bitterly to himself.

How soon Mathis had been proved right, and how soon his own little sophistries had been exploded in his face!

While he, Bond, had been playing Red Indians through the years (yes, Le Chiffre's description was perfectly accurate), the real enemy had been working quietly, coldly, without heroics, right there at his elbow.

He suddenly had a vision of Vesper walking down a corridor with documents in her hand. On a tray. They just got it on a tray while the cool secret agent with a Double O number was gallivanting round the world—playing Red Indians.

His fingernails dug into the palms of his hands, and his body sweated with shame.

Well, it was not too late. Here was a target for him, right to hand. He would take on SMERSH and hunt it down. Without SMERSH, without this cold weapon of death and revenge, the M.W.D. would be just another bunch of civil servant spies, no better and no worse than any of the western services.

SMERSH was the spur. Be faithful, spy well, or you die. Inevitably and without any question, you will be hunted down and killed.

It was the same with the whole Russian machine. Fear was the impulse. For them it was always safer to advance than to retreat. Advance against the enemy, and the bullet might miss you. Retreat, evade, betray, and the bullet would never miss.

But now he would attack the arm that held the whip and the gun. The business of espionage could be left to the white-collar boys. They could spy and catch the spies. He would go after the threat behind the spies, the threat that made them spy.

The telephone rang, and Bond snatched up the receiver. He was on to 'the Link,' the outside liaison officer who was the only man in London he might telephone from abroad. Then only in dire necessity.

He spoke quietly into the receiver.

'This is 007 speaking. This is an open line. It's an emergency. Can you hear me? . . . Pass this on at once: 3030 was a double, working for Redland. . . .

'Yes, dammit, I said "was." The bitch is dead now.'

FROM RUSSIA, WITH LOVE

Author's Note

NOT that it matters, but a great deal of the background to this story is accurate.

SMERSH, a contraction of Smiert Spionam — Death to Spies — exists and remains today the most secret department of the Soviet government.

At the beginning of 1956, when this book was written, the strength of SMERSH at home and abroad was about 40,000 and General Grubozaboyschikov was its chief. My description of his appearance is correct.

Today, the headquarters of SMERSH are where, in Chapter 4, I have placed them — at No. 13 Sretenka Ulitsa, Moscow. The Conference Room is faithfully described and the Intelligence chiefs who meet round the table are real officials who are frequently summoned to that room for purposes similar to those I have recounted.

I. F.

March 1956

Part One

THE PLAN

———————————————

CHAPTER I

Roseland

THE naked man who lay splayed out on his face beside the swimming pool might have been dead.

He might have been drowned and fished out of the pool and laid out on the grass to dry while the police or the next-of-kin were summoned. Even the little pile of objects in the grass beside his head might have been his personal effects, meticulously assembled in full view so that no one should think that something had been stolen by his rescuers.

To judge by the glittering pile, this had been, or was, a rich man. It contained the typical membership badges of the rich man's club — a money clip, made of a Mexican fifty-dollar piece and holding a substantial wad of banknotes, a well-used gold Dunhill lighter, an oval gold cigarette case with the wavy ridges and discreet turquoise button that means Fabergé, and the sort of novel a rich man pulls out of the bookcase to take into the garden — *The Little Nugget* — an old P. G. Wodehouse. There was also a bulky gold wrist-watch on a well-used brown crocodile strap. It was a Girard-Perregaux model designed for people who like gadgets, and it had a sweep second-hand and two little windows in the face to tell the day of the month, and the month, and the phase of the moon. The story it now told was 2.30 on June 10th with the moon three-quarters full.

A blue and green dragon-fly flashed out from among the rose bushes at the end of the garden and hovered in mid-air a few inches above the base of the man's spine. It had been attracted by the golden shimmer of the June sunshine on the ridge of fine blond hairs above the coccyx. A puff of breeze came off the sea. The tiny field of hairs bent gently. The dragon-fly darted nervously side-ways and hung above the man's left shoulder, looking down. The young grass below the man's open mouth stirred. A large drop of sweat rolled down the side of the fleshy nose and dropped glittering into the grass. That was enough. The dragon-fly flashed away through the roses and over the jagged glass on top of the high garden wall. It might be good food, but it moved.

The garden in which the man lay was about an acre of well-kept lawn surrounded on three sides by thickly banked rose bushes from which came the steady murmur of bees. Behind the drowsy noise of the bees the sea boomed softly at the bottom of the cliff at the end of the garden.

There was no view of the sea from the garden — no view of anything except of the sky and the clouds above the twelve-foot wall. In fact you could only see out of the property from the two upstairs bedrooms of the villa that formed the fourth side of this very private enclosure. From them you could see a great expanse of blue water in front of you and, on either side, the upper windows of neighbouring villas and the tops of the trees in their gardens — Mediterranean-type evergreen oaks, stone pines, casuarinas and an occasional palm tree.

The villa was modern — a squat elongated box without ornament. On the garden side the flat pink-washed façade was pierced by four iron-framed windows and by a central glass door leading on to a small square of pale green glazed tiles. The tiles merged into the lawn. The other side of the villa, standing back a few yards from a dusty road, was almost identical. But on this side the four windows were barred, and the central door was of oak.

The villa had two medium-sized bedrooms on the upper floor and on the ground floor a sitting-room and a kitchen, part of which was walled off into a lavatory. There was no bathroom.

The drowsy luxurious silence of early afternoon was broken by the sound of a car coming down the road. It stopped in front of the villa. There was the tinny clang of a car door being slammed and the car drove on. The door bell rang twice. The naked man beside the swimming pool did not move, but, at the noise of the bell and of the departing car, his eyes had for an instant opened very wide. It was as if the eyelids had pricked up like an animal's ears. The man immediately remembered where he was and the day of the week and the time of the day. The noises were identified. The eyelids with their fringe of short sandy eyelashes drooped drowsily back over the very pale blue, opaque, inward-looking eyes. The small cruel lips opened in a wide jaw-breaking yawn which brought saliva into the mouth. The man spat the saliva into the grass and waited.

A young woman carrying a small string bag and dressed in a white cotton shirt and a short, unalluring blue skirt came through the glass door and strode mannishly across the glazed tiles and the stretch of lawn towards the naked man. A few yards away from him, she dropped her string bag on the grass and sat down and took off her cheap and rather dusty shoes. Then she stood up and unbuttoned her shirt and took it off and put it, neatly folded, beside the string bag.

The girl had nothing on under the shirt. Her skin was pleasantly sunburned and her shoulders and fine breasts shone with health. When she bent her arms to undo the side-buttons of her skirt, small tufts of fair hair showed in her armpits. The impression of a healthy animal peasant girl was heightened by the chunky hips in faded blue stockinet bathing trunks and the thick short thighs and legs that were revealed when she had stripped.

The girl put the skirt neatly beside her shirt, opened the string bag, took out an old soda-water bottle containing some heavy colourless liquid and went over to the man and knelt on the grass beside him. She poured some of the liquid, a light olive oil, scented, as was everything in that part of the world, with roses, between his shoulder blades and, after flexing her fingers like a pianist, began massaging the sterno-mastoid and the trapezius muscles at the back of the man's neck.

It was hard work. The man was immensely strong and the bulging muscles at the base of the neck hardly yielded to the girl's thumbs even when the downward weight of her shoulders was behind them. By the time she was finished with the man she would be soaked in perspiration and so utterly exhausted that she would fall into the swimming pool and then lie down in the shade and sleep until the car came for her. But that wasn't what she minded as her hands worked automatically on across the man's back. It was her instinctive horror for the finest body she had ever seen.

None of this horror showed in the flat, impassive face of the masseuse, and the upward-slanting black eyes under the fringe of short coarse black hair were as empty as oil slicks, but inside her the animal whimpered and cringed and her pulse-rate, if it had occurred to her to take it, would have been high.

Once again, as so often over the past two years, she wondered why she loathed this splendid body, and once again she vaguely tried to analyse her revulsion. Perhaps this time she would get rid of feelings which she felt guiltily certain were much more unprofessional than the sexual desire some of her patients awoke in her.

To take the small things first: his hair. She looked down at the round, smallish head on the sinewy neck. It was covered with tight red-gold curls that should have reminded her pleasantly of the formalized hair in the pictures she had seen of classical statues. But the curls were somehow too tight, too thickly pressed against each other and against the skull. They set her teeth on edge like finger-nails against pile carpet. And the golden curls came down so low into the back of the neck — almost (she thought in professional terms) to the fifth cervical vertebra. And there they stopped abruptly in a straight line of small stiff golden hairs.

The girl paused to give her hands a rest and sat back on her haunches. The beautiful upper half of her body was already shining with sweat. She wiped the back of her forearm across her forehead and reached for the bottle of oil. She poured about a tablespoonful on to the small furry plateau at the base of the man's spine, flexed her fingers and bent forward again.

This embryo tail of golden down above the cleft of the buttocks — in a lover it would have been gay, exciting, but on this man it was somehow bestial. No, reptilian. But snakes had no hair. Well, she couldn't help that. It seemed reptilian to her. She shifted her hands on down to the two mounds of the gluteal muscles. Now was the time when many of her patients, particularly the young ones on the football team, would start joking with her. Then, if she was not very careful, the suggestions would come. Sometimes she could silence these by digging sharply down towards the sciatic nerve. At other times, and particularly if she found the man attractive, there would be giggling arguments, a brief wrestling-match and a quick, delicious surrender.

With this man it was different, almost uncannily different. From the very first he had been like a lump of inanimate meat. In two years he had never said a word to her. When she had done his back and it was time for him to turn over, neither his eyes nor his body had once shown the smallest interest in her. When she tapped his shoulder, he would just roll over and gaze at the sky through half-closed lids and occasionally let out one of the long shuddering yawns that were the only sign that he had human reactions at all.

The girl shifted her position and slowly worked down the right leg towards the Achilles tendon. When she came to it, she looked back up the fine body. Was her revulsion *only* physical? Was it the reddish colour of the sunburn on the naturally milk-white skin, the sort of roast meat look? Was it the texture of the skin itself, the deep, widely spaced pores in the satiny surface? The thickly

scattered orange freckles on the shoulders? Or was it the asexuality
of the man? The indifference of these splendid, insolently bulging
muscles? Or was it spiritual — an animal instinct telling her that
inside this wonderful body there was an evil person?

The masseuse got to her feet and stood, twisting her head slowly
from side to side and flexing her shoulders. She stretched her
arms out sideways and then upwards and held them for a moment
to get the blood down out of them. She went to her string bag
and took out a hand-towel and wiped the perspiration off her face
and body.

When she turned back to the man, he had already rolled over
and now lay, his head resting on one open hand, gazing blankly
at the sky. The disengaged arm was flung out on the grass, waiting
for her. She walked over and knelt on the grass behind his head.
She rubbed some oil into her palms, picked up the limp half-open
hand and started kneading the short thick fingers.

The girl glanced nervously sideways at the red-brown face below
the crown of tight golden curls. Superficially it was all right —
handsome in a butcher's-boyish way, with its full pink cheeks, upturned nose and rounded chin. But, looked at closer, there was
something cruel about the thin-lipped rather pursed mouth,
a pigginess about the wide nostrils in the upturned nose, and the
blankness that veiled the very pale blue eyes communicated itself
over the whole face and made it look drowned and morgue-like. It
was, she reflected, as if someone had taken a china doll and painted
its face to frighten.

The masseuse worked up the arm to the huge biceps. Where had
the man got these fantastic muscles from? Was he a boxer? What
did he do with his formidable body? Rumour said this was a police
villa. The two men-servants were obviously guards of some sort,
although they did the cooking and the housework. Regularly every
month the man went away for a few days and she would be told not
to come. And from time to time she would be told to stay away for
a week, or two weeks, or a month. Once, after one of these absences,
the man's neck and the upper part of his body had been a mass of

bruises. On another occasion the red corner of a half-healed wound had shown under a foot of surgical plaster down the ribs over his heart. She had never dared to ask about him at the hospital or in the town. When she had first been sent to the house, one of the men-servants had told her that if she spoke about what she saw she would go to prison. Back at the hospital, the Chief Superintendent, who had never recognized her existence before, had sent for her and had said the same thing. She would go to prison. The girl's strong fingers gouged nervously into the big deltoid muscle on the point of the shoulder. She had always known it was a matter of State Security. Perhaps that was what revolted her about this splendid body. Perhaps it was just fear of the organization that had the body in custody. She squeezed her eyes shut at the thought of who he might be, of what he could order to be done to her. Quickly she opened them again. He might have noticed. But the eyes gazed blankly up at the sky.

Now — she reached for the oil — to do the face.

The girl's thumbs had scarcely pressed into the sockets of the man's closed eyes when the telephone in the house started ringing. The sound reached impatiently out into the quiet garden. At once the man was up on one knee like a runner waiting for the gun. But he didn't move forward. The ringing stopped. There was the mutter of a voice. The girl could not hear what it was saying, but it sounded humble, noting instructions. The voice stopped and one of the men-servants showed briefly at the door, made a gesture of summons, and went back into the house. Half way through the gesture, the naked man was already running. She watched the brown back flash through the open glass door. Better not let him find her here when he came out again — doing nothing, perhaps listening. She got to her feet, took two steps to the concrete edge of the pool and dived gracefully in.

Although it would have explained her instincts about the man whose body she massaged, it was as well for the girl's peace of mind that she did not know who he was.

His real name was Donovan Grant, or 'Red' Grant. But, for the past ten years, it had been Krassno Granitski, with the code-name of 'Granit'.

He was the Chief Executioner of SMERSH, the murder *apparat* of the M.G.B., and at this moment he was receiving his instructions on the M.G.B. direct line with Moscow.

CHAPTER 2

The Slaughterer

GRANT put the telephone softly back on its cradle and sat looking at it.

The bullet-headed guard standing over him said, 'You had better start moving.'

'Did they give you any idea of the task?' Grant spoke Russian excellently but with a thick accent. He could have passed for a national of any of the Soviet Baltic provinces. The voice was high and flat as if it was reciting something dull from a book.

'No. Only that you are wanted in Moscow. The plane is on its way. It will be here in about an hour. Half an hour for refuelling and then three or four hours, depending on whether you come down at Kharkov. You will be in Moscow by midnight. You had better pack. I will order the car.'

Grant got nervously to his feet. 'Yes. You are right. But they didn't even say if it was an operation? One likes to know. It was a secure line. They could have given a hint. They generally do.'

'This time they didn't.'

Grant walked slowly out through the glass door on to the lawn.

If he noticed the girl sitting on the far edge of the pool he made no sign. He bent and picked up his book, and the golden trophies of his profession, and walked back into the house and up the few stairs to his bedroom.

The room was bleak and furnished only with an iron bedstead, from which the rumpled sheets hung down on one side to the floor, a cane chair, an unpainted clothes cupboard and a cheap wash-stand with a tin basin. The floor was strewn with English and American magazines. Garish paper-backs and hard-cover thrillers were stacked against the wall below the window.

Grant bent down and pulled a battered Italian fibre suitcase from under the bed. He packed into it a selection of well-laundered cheap respectable clothes from the cupboard. Then he washed his body hurriedly with cold water, and the inevitably rose-scented soap, and dried himself on one of the sheets from the bed.

There was the noise of a car outside. Grant hastily dressed in clothes as drab and nondescript as those he had packed, put on his wrist-watch, pocketed his other belongings and picked up his suit-case and went down the stairs.

The front door was open. He could see his two guards talking to the driver of a battered ZIS saloon. 'Bloody fools,' he thought. (He still did most of his thinking in English.) 'Probably telling him to see I get on the plane all right. Probably can't imagine that a foreigner would want to live in their blasted country.' The cold eyes sneered as Grant put down his suitcase on the door-step and hunted among the bunch of coats that hung from pegs on the kitchen door. He found his 'uniform', the drab raincoat and black cloth cap of Soviet officialdom, put them on, picked up his suitcase and went out and climbed in beside the plain-clothes driver, roughly shouldering aside one of the guards as he did so.

The two men stood back, saying nothing, but looking at him with hard eyes. The driver took his foot off the clutch, and the car, already in gear, accelerated fast away down the dusty road.

The villa was on the south-eastern coast of the Crimea, about half way between Feodosiya and Yalta. It was one of many official holiday *datchas* along the favourite stretch of mountainous coastline that is part of the Russian Riviera. Red Grant knew that he was immensely privileged to be housed there instead of in some dreary villa on the outskirts of Moscow. As the car climbed up into the mountains, he thought that they certainly treated him as well as they knew how, even if their concern for his welfare had two faces.

The forty-mile drive to the airport at Simferopol took an hour. There were no other cars on the road and the occasional cart from the vineyards quickly pulled into the ditch at the sound of their horn. As everywhere in Russia, a car meant an official, and an official could only mean danger.

There were roses all the way, fields of them alternating with the vineyards, hedges of them along the road and, at the approach to the airport, a vast circular bed planted with red and white varieties to make a red star against a white background. Grant was sick of them and he longed to get to Moscow and away from their sweet stench.

They drove past the entrance to the Civil Airport and followed a high wall for about a mile to the military side of the aerodrome. At a tall wire gate the driver showed his pass to two tommy-gunned sentries and drove through on to the tarmac. Several planes stood about, big camouflaged military transports, small twin-engined trainers and two Navy helicopters. The driver stopped to ask a man in overalls where to find Grant's plane. At once a metallic twanging came from the observant control tower and a loudspeaker barked at them: 'To the left. Far down to the left. Number V-BO.'

The driver was obediently motoring on across the tarmac when the iron voice barked again. 'Stop!'

As the driver jammed on his brakes, there sounded a deafening scream above their heads. Both men instinctively ducked as a flight of four MIG 17s came out of the setting sun and skimmed over them, their squat wind-brakes right down for the landing. The planes hit the huge runway one after the other, puffs of blue smoke spurting from their nose-tyres, and, with jets howling, taxied to the distant boundary line and turned to come back to the control tower and the hangars.

'Proceed!'

A hundred yards further on they came to a plane with the recognition letters V-BO. It was a two-engined Ilyushin 12. A small aluminium ladder hung down from the cabin door and the car stopped beside it. One of the crew appeared at the door. He came down the ladder and carefully examined the driver's pass and Grant's identity papers and then waved the driver away and gestured Grant to follow him up the ladder. He didn't offer to help with the suitcase, but Grant carried it up the ladder as if it had been no heavier than a book. The crewman pulled the ladder up after him, banged the wide hatch shut and went forward to the cockpit.

There were twenty empty seats to choose from. Grant settled into the one nearest the hatch and fastened his seat-belt. A short crackle of talk with the control tower came through the open door to the cockpit, the two engines whined and coughed and fired and the plane turned quickly as if it had been a motor car, rolled out to the start of the north-south runway, and, without any further preliminaries, hurtled down it and up into the air.

Grant unbuckled his seat-belt, lit a gold-tipped Troika cigarette and settled back to reflect comfortably on his past career and to consider the immediate future.

Donovan Grant was the result of a midnight union between a German professional weight-lifter and a Southern Irish waitress. The union lasted for a quarter of an hour on the damp grass behind a circus tent outside Belfast. Afterwards the father gave the mother half-a-crown and the mother walked happily home to her bed in the kitchen of a café near the railway station. When the baby was expected, she went to live with an aunt in the small village of Aughmacloy that straddles the border, and there, six months later, she died of puerperal fever shortly after giving birth to a twelve-pound boy. Before she died, she said that the boy was to be called Donovan (the weight-lifter had styled himself 'The Mighty O' Donovan) and Grant, which was her own name.

The boy was reluctantly cared for by the aunt and grew up healthy and extremely strong, but very quiet. He had no friends. He refused to communicate with other children and when he wanted anything from them he took it with his fists. In the local school he continued to be feared and disliked, but he made a name for himself boxing and wrestling at local fairs where the bloodthirsty fury of his attack, combined with guile, gave him victory over much older and bigger boys.

It was through his fighting that he came to the notice of the Sinn-Feiners who used Aughmacloy as a principal pipeline for their comings and goings with the north, and also of the local smugglers who used the village for the same purpose. When he left school he became a strong-arm man for both these groups. They paid him well for his work but saw as little of him as they could.

It was about this time that his body began to feel strange and violent compulsions around the time of the full moon. When, in October of his sixteenth year, he first got 'The Feelings' as he called them to himself, he went out and strangled a cat. This made him 'feel better' for a whole month. In November, it was a big sheep-dog, and, for Christmas, he slit the throat of a cow, at midnight in a neighbour's shed. These actions made him 'feel good'. He had enough sense to see that the village would soon start wondering about the mysterious deaths, so he bought a bicycle and on one night every month he rode off into the countryside. Often he had to go very far to find what he wanted and, after two months of having to satisfy himself with geese and chickens, he took a chance and cut the throat of a sleeping tramp.

There were so few people abroad at night that soon he took to the roads earlier, bicycling far and wide so that he came to distant villages in the dusk when solitary people were coming home from the fields and girls were going out to their trysts.

When he killed the occasional girl he did not 'interfere' with her in any way. That side of things, which he had heard talked about, was quite incomprehensible to him. It was only the wonderful act of killing that made him 'feel better'. Nothing else.

By the end of his seventeenth year, ghastly rumours were spreading round the whole of Fermanagh, Tyrone and Armagh. When a woman was killed in broad daylight, strangled and thrust carelessly into a haystack, the rumours flared into panic. Groups of vigilantes were formed in the villages, police reinforcements were brought in with police dogs, and stories about the 'Moon Killer' brought journalists to the area. Several times Grant on his bicycle was stopped and questioned, but he had powerful protection in Aughmacloy and his story of training-spins to keep him fit for his boxing were always backed up, for he was now the pride of the village and contender for the North of Ireland light-heavyweight championship.

Again, before it was too late, instinct saved him from discovery and he left Aughmacloy and went to Belfast and put himself in the hands of a broken-down boxing promoter who wanted him to turn professional. Discipline in the sleazy gymnasium was strict. It was almost a prison and, when the blood first boiled again in Grant's veins, there was nothing for it but to half kill one of his sparring partners. After twice having to be pulled off a man in the ring, it was only by winning the championship that he was saved from being thrown out by the promoter.

Grant won the championship in 1945, on his eighteenth birthday, then they took him for National Service and he became a driver in the Royal Corps of Signals. The training period in England sobered him, or at least made him more careful when he had 'The Feelings'. Now, at the full moon, he took to drink instead. He would take a bottle of whisky into the woods round Aldershot and drink it all down as he watched his sensations, coldly, until unconsciousness came. Then, in the early hours of the morning, he would stagger back to camp, only half satisfied, but not dangerous any more. If a sentry caught him, it was only a day's C.B., because his commanding officer wanted to keep him happy for the Army championships.

But Grant's transport section was rushed to Berlin about the time of the Corridor trouble with the Russians and he missed the championships. In Berlin, the constant smell of danger intrigued

him and made him even more careful and cunning. He still got
dead drunk at the full moon, but all the rest of the time he was
watching and plotting. He liked all he heard about the Russians,
their brutality, their carelessness of human life, and their guile, and
he decided to go over to them. But how? What could be bring
them as a gift? What did they want?

It was the B.A.O.R. championships that finally told him to go
over. By chance they took place on a night of the full moon. Grant,
fighting for the Royal Corps, was warned for holding and hitting
low and was disqualified in the third round for persistent foul
fighting. The whole stadium hissed him as he left the ring — the
loudest demonstration came from his own regiment — and the
next morning the commanding officer sent for him and coldly said
he was a disgrace to the Royal Corps and would be sent home
with the next draft. His fellow drivers sent him to Coventry and,
since no one would drive transport with him, he had to be transferred to the coveted motor cycle dispatch service.

The transfer could not have suited Grant better. He waited a few
days and then, one evening when he had collected the day's outgoing mail from the Military Intelligence Headquarters on the
Reichskanzlerplatz, he made straight for the Russian Sector, waited
with his engine running until the British control gate was opened
to allow a taxi through, and then tore through the closing gate at
forty and skidded to a stop beside the concrete pillbox of the
Russian Frontier post.

They hauled him roughly into the guardroom. A wooden-faced
officer behind a desk asked him what he wanted.

'I want the Soviet Secret Service,' said Grant flatly. 'The Head
of it.'

The officer stared coldly at him. He said something in Russian.
The soldiers who had brought Grant in started to drag him out
again. Grant easily shook them off. One of them lifted his tommy-
gun.

Grant said, speaking patiently and distinctly, 'I have a lot of
secret papers. Outside. In the leather bags on the motor cycle.' He

had a brainwave. 'You will get into bad trouble if they don't get to your Secret Service.'

The officer said something to the soldiers and they stood back. 'We have no Secret Service,' he said in stilted English. 'Sit down and complete this form.'

Grant sat down at the desk and filled in a long form which asked questions about anyone who wanted to visit the Eastern zone — name, address, nature of business and so forth. Meanwhile the officer spoke softly and briefly into a telephone.

By the time Grant had finished, two more soldiers, non-commissioned officers wearing drab green forage caps and with green badges of rank on their khaki uniforms, had come into the room. The frontier officer handed the form, without looking at it, to one of them and they took Grant out and put him and his motor cycle into the back of a closed van and locked the door on him. After a fast drive lasting a quarter of an hour the van stopped, and when Grant got out he found himself in the courtyard behind a large new building. He was taken into the building and up in a lift and left alone in a cell without windows. It contained nothing but one iron bench. After an hour, during which, he supposed, they went through the secret papers, he was led into a comfortable office in which an officer with three rows of decorations and the gold tabs of a full colonel was sitting behind a desk.

The desk was bare except for a bowl of roses.

Ten years later, Grant, looking out of the window of the plane at a wide cluster of lights twenty thousand feet below, which he guessed was Kharkov, grinned mirthlessly at his reflection in the Perspex window.

Roses. From that moment his life had been nothing but roses. Roses, roses, all the way.

CHAPTER 3

Post-Graduate Studies

'So you would like to work in the Soviet Union, Mister Grant?'
It was half an hour later and the M.G.B. colonel was bored
with the interview. He thought that he had extracted from
this rather unpleasant British soldier every military detail that could
possibly be of interest. A few polite phrases to repay the man for
the rich haul of secrets his dispatch bags had yielded, and then the
man could go down to the cells and in due course be shipped off to
Vorkuta or some other labour camp.

'Yes, I would like to work for you.'

'And what work could you do, Mister Grant? We have plenty
of unskilled labour. We do not need truck-drivers and,' the colonel
smiled fleetingly, 'if there is any boxing to be done we have plenty
of men who can box. Two possible Olympic champions amongst
them, incidentally.'

'I am an expert at killing people. I do it very well. I like it.'

The colonel saw the red flame that flickered for an instant behind
the very pale blue eyes under the sandy lashes. He thought, the man
means it. He's mad as well as unpleasant. He looked coldly at

29

Grant, wondering if it was worth while wasting food on him at
Vorkuta. Better perhaps have him shot. Or throw him back into
the British Sector and let his own people worry about him.

'You don't believe me,' said Grant impatiently. This was
the wrong man, the wrong department. 'Who does the rough
stuff for you here?' He was certain the Russians had some sort of
a murder squad. Everybody said so. 'Let me talk to them. I'll kill
somebody for them. Anybody they like. Now.'

The colonel looked at him sourly. Perhaps he had better report
the matter. 'Wait here.' He got up and went out of the room,
leaving the door open. A guard came and stood in the doorway and
watched Grant's back, his hand on his pistol.

The colonel went into the next room. It was empty. There were
three telephones on the desk. He picked up the receiver of the
M.G.B. direct line to Moscow. When the military operator answered he said, 'SMERSH'. When SMERSH answered he asked for the
Chief of Operations.

Ten minutes later he put the receiver back. What luck! A
simple, constructive solution. Whichever way it went it would turn
out well. If the Englishman succeeded, it would be splendid. If he
failed, it would still cause a lot of trouble in the Western Sector —
trouble for the British because Grant was their man, trouble with the
Germans because the attempt would frighten a lot of their spies,
trouble with the Americans because they were supplying most of the
funds for the Baumgarten ring and would now think Baumgarten's
security was no good. Pleased with himself, the colonel walked
back into his office and sat down again opposite Grant.

'You mean what you say?'

'Of course I do.'

'Have you a good memory?'

'Yes.'

'In the British Sector there is a German called Dr. Baumgarten.
He lives in Flat 5 at No. 22 Kurfürstendamm. Do you know where
that is?'

'Yes.'

'Tonight, with your motor cycle, you will be put back into the British Sector. Your number plates will be changed. Your people will be on the lookout for you. You will take an envelope to Dr. Baumgarten. It will be marked to be delivered by hand. In your uniform, and with this envelope, you will have no difficulty. You will say that the message is so private that you must see Dr. Baumgarten alone. Then you will kill him.' The colonel paused. His eyebrows lifted. 'Yes?'

'Yes,' said Grant stolidly. 'And if I do, will you give me more of this work?'

'It is possible,' said the colonel indifferently. 'First you must show what you can do. When you have completed your task and returned to the Soviet Sector, you may ask for Colonel Boris.' He rang a bell and a man in plain clothes came in. The colonel gestured towards him. 'This man will give you food. Later he will give you the envelope and a sharp knife of American manufacture. It is an excellent weapon. Good luck.'

The colonel reached and picked a rose out of the bowl and sniffed it luxuriously.

Grant got to his feet. 'Thank you, sir,' he said warmly.

The colonel did not answer or look up from the rose. Grant followed the man in plain clothes out of the room.

The plane roared on across the Heartland of Russia. They had left behind them the blast furnaces flaming far away to the east around Stalino and, to the west, the silver thread of the Dnieper branching away at Dnepropetrovsk. The splash of light around Kharkov had marked the frontier of the Ukraine, and the smaller blaze of the phosphate town of Kursk had come and gone. Now Grant knew that the solid unbroken blackness below hid the great central Steppe where the billions of tons of Russia's grain were whispering and ripening in the darkness. There would be no more oases of light until, in another hour, they would have covered the last three hundred miles to Moscow.

For by now Grant knew a lot about Russia. After the quick, neat, sensational murder of a vital West German spy, Grant had no sooner slipped back over the frontier and somehow fumbled his way to 'Colonel Boris' than he was put into plain clothes, with a flying helmet to cover his hair, hustled into an empty M.G.B. plane and flown straight to Moscow.

Then began a year of semi-prison which Grant had devoted to keeping fit and to learning Russian while people came and went around him – interrogators, stool-pigeons, doctors. Meanwhile, Soviet spies in England and Northern Ireland had painstakingly investigated his past.

At the end of the year Grant was given as clean a bill of political health as any foreigner can get in Russia. The spies had confirmed his story. The English and American stool-pigeons reported that he was totally uninterested in the politics or social customs of any country in the world, and the doctors and psychologists agreed that he was an advanced manic depressive whose periods coincided with the full moon. They added that Grant was also a narcissist and asexual and that his tolerance of pain was high. These peculiarities apart, his physical health was superb and, though his educational standards were hopelessly low, he was as naturally cunning as a fox. Everyone agreed that Grant was an exceedingly dangerous member of society and that he should be put away.

When the dossier came before the Head of Personnel of the M.G.B., he was about to write 'Kill him' in the margin when he had second thoughts.

A great deal of killing has to be done in the U.S.S.R., not because the average Russian is a cruel man, although some of their races are among the cruellest peoples in the world, but as an instrument of policy. People who act against the State are enemies of the State, and the State has no room for enemies. There is too much to do for precious time to be allotted to them, and, if they are a persistent nuisance, they get killed. In a country with a population of 200,000,000, you can kill many thousands a year without missing them. If, as happened in the two biggest purges, a million people have to be killed in one year, that is also not a grave loss. The serious problem is the shortage of executioners. Executioners have a short 'life'. They get tired of the work. The soul sickens of it. After ten, twenty, a hundred death-rattles, the human being, however sub-human he may be, acquires, perhaps by a process of osmosis with death itself, a germ of death which enters his body and eats into him like a canker. Melancholy and drink take him, and a dreadful lassitude which brings a glaze to the eyes and slows up the movements and destroys accuracy. When the employer sees these signs he has no alternative but to execute the executioner and find another one.

The Head of Personnel of the M.G.B. was aware of the problem and of the constant search not only for the refined assassin, but also for the common butcher. And here at last was a man who appeared to be expert at both forms of killing, dedicated to his craft and indeed, if the doctors were to be believed, destined for it.

Head of Personnel wrote a short, pungent minute on Grant's papers, marked them 'SMERSH Otdyel II' and tossed them into his OUT tray.

Department 2 of SMERSH, in charge of Operations and Executions, took over the body of Donovan Grant, changed his name to Granitsky and put him on their books.

The next two years were hard for Grant. He had to go back to school, and to a school that made him long for the chipped deal desks in the corrugated iron shed, full of the smell of little boys and the hum of drowsy blue-bottles, that had been his only conception of what a school was like. Now, in the Intelligence School for Foreigners outside Leningrad, squashed tightly among the ranks of Germans, Czechs, Poles, Balts, Chinese and Negroes, all with serious dedicated faces and pens that raced across their notebooks, he struggled with subjects that were pure double-dutch to him.

There were courses in 'General Political Knowledge', which included the history of Labour movements, of the Communist Party and the Industrial Forces of the world, and the teachings of Marx, Lenin and Stalin, all dotted with foreign names which he could barely spell. There were lessons on 'The Class-enemy we are fighting', with lectures on Capitalism and Fascism; weeks spent on 'Tactics, Agitation and Propaganda' and more weeks on the problems of minority peoples, Colonial races, the Negroes, the Jews. Every month ended with examinations during which Grant sat and wrote illiterate nonsense, interspersed with scraps of half-forgotten English history and mis-spelled Communist slogans, and inevitably had his papers torn up, on one occasion, in front of the whole class.

But he stuck it out, and when they came to 'Technical Subjects' he did better. He was quick to understand the rudiments of Codes and Ciphers, because he wanted to understand them. He was good at Communications, and immediately grasped the maze of contacts, cut-outs, couriers and post-boxes, and he got excellent marks for Fieldwork in which each student had to plan and operate dummy assignments in the suburbs and countryside around Leningrad. Finally, when it came to tests of Vigilance, Discretion, 'Safety First', Presence of Mind, Courage and Coolness, he got top marks out of the whole school.

At the end of the year, the report that went back to SMERSH concluded 'Political value Nil. Operational value Excellent' — which was just what Otdyel II wanted to hear.

The next year was spent, with only two other foreign students among several hundred Russians, at the School for Terror and Diversion at Kuchino, outside Moscow. Here Grant went triumphantly through courses in judo, boxing, athletics, photography and radio under the general supervision of the famous Colonel Arkady Fotoyev, father of the modern Soviet spy, and completed his small-arms instruction at the hands of Lieutenant-Colonel Nikolai Godlovsky, the Soviet Rifle Champion.

Twice during this year, without warning, an M.G.B. car came for him on the night of the full moon and took him to one of the Moscow jails. There, with a black hood over his head, he was allowed to carry out executions with various weapons — the rope, the axe, the sub-machine gun. Electro-cardiograms, blood-pressure and various other medical tests were applied to him before, during and after these occasions, but their purpose and findings were not revealed to him.

It was a good year and he felt, and rightly, that he was giving satisfaction.

In 1949 and '50 Grant was allowed to go on minor operations with Mobile Groups or *Avanposts*, in the satellite countries. These were beatings-up and simple assassinations of Russian spies and intelligence workers suspected of treachery or other aberrations. Grant carried out these duties neatly, exactly and inconspicuously, and though he was carefully and constantly watched he never showed the smallest deviation from the standards required of him, and no weaknesses of character or technical skill. It might have been different if he had been required to kill when doing a solo task at the full-moon period, but his superiors, realizing that at that period he would be outside their control, or his own, chose safe dates for his operations. The moon period was reserved exclusively for butchery in the prisons, and from time to time this was arranged for him as a reward for a successful operation in cold blood.

In 1951 and '52 Grant's usefulness became more fully and more officially recognized. As a result of excellent work, notably in the Eastern Sector of Berlin, he was granted Soviet citizenship and increases in pay which by 1953 amounted to a handsome 5000 roubles a month. In 1953 he was given the rank of Major, with pension rights back-dated to the day of his first contact with 'Colonel Boris', and the villa in the Crimea was allotted to him. Two bodyguards were attached to him, partly to protect him and partly to guard against the outside chance of his 'going private', as defection is called in M.G.B. jargon, and, once a month, he was transported to the nearest jail and allowed as many executions as there were candidates available.

Naturally Grant had no friends. He was hated or feared or envied by everyone who came in contact with him. He did not even have any of those professional acquaintanceships that pass for friendship in the discreet and careful world of Soviet officialdom. But, if he noticed the fact, he didn't care. The only individuals he was interested in were his victims. The rest of his life was inside him. And it was richly and excitingly populated with his thoughts.

Then, of course, he had SMERSH. No one in the Soviet Union who has SMERSH on his side need worry about friends, or indeed about anything whatever except keeping the black wings of SMERSH over his head.

Grant was still thinking vaguely of how he stood with his employers when the plane started to lose altitude as it picked up the radar beam of Tushino Airport just south of the red glow that was Moscow.

He was at the top of his tree, the chief executioner of SMERSH, and therefore of the whole of the Soviet Union. What could he aim for now? Further promotion? More money? More gold nicknacks? More important targets? Better techniques?

There really didn't seem to be anything more to go for. Or was there perhaps some other man whom he had never heard of, in some other country, who would have to be set aside before absolute supremacy was his?

CHAPTER 4

The Moguls of Death

SMERSH is the official murder organization of the Soviet government. It operates both at home and abroad and, in 1955, it employed a total of 40,000 men and women. SMERSH is a contraction of 'Smiert Spionam', which means 'Death to Spies'. It is a name used only among its staff and among Soviet officials. No sane member of the public would dream of allowing the word to pass his lips.

The headquarters of SMERSH is a very large and ugly modern building on the Sretenka Ulitsa. It is No. 13 on this wide, dull street, and pedestrians keep their eyes to the ground as they pass the two sentries with sub-machine guns who stand on either side of the broad steps leading up to the big iron double door. If they remember in time, or can do so inconspicuously, they cross the street and pass by on the other side.

The direction of SMERSH is carried out from the 2nd floor. The most important room on the 2nd floor is a very large light room painted in the pale olive green that is the common denominator of government offices all over the world. Opposite the sound-proofed door, two wide windows look over the courtyard at the back of the building. The floor is close-fitted with a colourful Caucasian carpet of the finest quality. Across the far left-hand corner of the room stands a massive oak desk. The top of the desk is covered with red velvet under a thick sheet of plate glass.

On the left side of the desk are IN and OUT baskets and on the right four telephones.

From the centre of the desk, to form a T with it, a conference table stretches diagonally out across the room. Eight straight-backed red leather chairs are drawn up to it. This table is also covered with red velvet, but without protective glass. Ash-trays are on the table, and two heavy carafes of water with glasses.

On the walls are four large pictures in gold frames. In 1955, these were a portrait of Stalin over the door, one of Lenin between the two windows and, facing each other on the other two walls, portraits of Bulganin and, where until January 13th, 1954, a portrait of Beria had hung, a portrait of Army General Ivan Aleksandro-vitch Serov, Chief of the Committee of State Security.

On the left-hand wall, under the portrait of Bulganin, stands a large *Televisor*, or TV set, in a handsome polished oak cabinet. Concealed in this is a tape-recorder which can be switched on from the desk. The microphone for the recorder stretches under the whole area of the conference table and its leads are concealed in the legs of the table. Next to the *Televisor* is a small door leading into a personal lavatory and washroom and into a small projection room for showing secret films.

Under the portrait of General Serov is a bookcase containing, on the top shelves, the works of Marx, Engels, Lenin and Stalin, and more accessibly, books in all languages on espionage, counter-espionage, police methods and criminology. Next to the bookcase, against the wall, stands a long narrow table on which are a dozen large leather-bound albums with dates stamped in gold on the covers. These contain photographs of Soviet citizens and foreigners who have been assassinated by SMERSH.

About the time Grant was coming in to land at Tushino Airport, just before 11.30 at night, a tough-looking, thick-set man of about fifty was standing at this table leafing through the volume for 1954.

The Head of SMERSH, Colonel General Grubozaboyschikov, known in the building as ' G.', was dressed in a neat khaki tunic with a high collar, and dark blue cavalry trousers with two thin red stripes down the sides. The trousers ended in riding boots of soft, highly polished black leather. On the breast of the tunic were three rows of medal ribbons — two Orders of Lenin, Order of Suvorov, Order of Alexander Nevsky, Order of the Red Banner, two Orders of the Red Star, the Twenty Years Service medal and medals for the Defence of Moscow and the Capture of Berlin. At the tail of these came the rose-pink and grey ribbon of the British C.B.E. and the claret and white ribbon of the American Medal for Merit. Above the ribbons hung the gold star of a Hero of the Soviet Union.

Above the high collar of the tunic the face was narrow and sharp. There were flabby pouches under the eyes, which were round and brown and protruded like polished marbles below thick black brows. The skull was shaven clean and the tight white skin glittered in the light of the central chandelier. The mouth was broad and grim above a deeply cleft chin. It was a hard, unyielding face of formidable authority.

One of the telephones on the desk buzzed softly. The man walked with tight and precise steps to his tall chair behind the desk. He sat down and picked up the receiver of the telephone marked in white with the letters V.Ch. These letters are short for *Vysoko-chastoty*, or High Frequency. Only some fifty supreme officials are connected to the V.Ch. switchboard, and all are Ministers of State or Heads of selected Departments. It is served by a small exchange in the Kremlin operated by professional security officers. Even they cannot overhear conversations on it, but every word spoken over its lines is automatically recorded.

'Yes?'

'Serov speaking. What action has been taken since the meeting of the Praesidium this morning?'

'I have a meeting here in a few minutes' time, Comrade General

— R.U.M.I.D., G.R.U. and of course M.G.B. After that, if action is agreed, I shall have a meeting with my Head of Operations and Head of Plans. In case liquidation is decided upon, I have taken the precaution of bringing the necessary operative to Moscow. This time I shall myself supervise the preparations. We do not want another Khoklov affair.'

'The devil knows we don't. Telephone me after the first meeting. I wish to report to the Praesidium tomorrow morning.'

'Certainly, Comrade General.'

General G. put back the receiver and pressed a bell under his desk. At the same time he switched on the wire-recorder. His A.D.C., an M.G.B. captain, came in.

'Have they arrived?'

'Yes, Comrade General.'

'Bring them in.'

In a few minutes six men, five of them in uniform, filed in through the door and, with hardly a glance at the man behind the desk, took their places at the conference table. They were three senior officers, heads of their departments, and each was accompanied by an A.D.C. In the Soviet Union, no man goes alone to a conference. For his own protection, and for the reassurance of his department, he invariably takes a witness so that his department can have independent versions of what went on at the conference and, above all, of what was said on its behalf. This is important in case there is a subsequent investigation. No notes are taken at the conference and decisions are passed back to departments by word of mouth.

On the far side of the table sat Lieutenant-General Slavin, head of the G.R.U., the intelligence department of the General Staff of the Army, with a full colonel beside him. At the end of the table sat Lieutenant-General Vozdvishensky of R.U.M.I.D., the Intelligence Department of the Ministry of Foreign Affairs, with a middle-aged man in plain clothes. With his back to the door, sat Colonel of State Security Nikitin, Head of Intelligence for the M.G.B., the Soviet Secret Service, with a major at his side.

'Good evening, Comrades.'

A polite, careful murmur came from the three senior officers. Each one knew, and thought he was the only one to know, that the room was wired for sound, and each one, without telling his A.D.C., had decided to utter the bare minimum of words consonant with good discipline and the needs of the State.

'Let us smoke.' General G. took out a packet of Moskwa-Volga cigarettes and lit one with an American Zippo lighter. There was a clicking of lighters round the table. General G. pinched the long cardboard tube of his cigarette so that it was almost flat and put it between his teeth on the right side of his mouth. He stretched his lips back from his teeth and started talking in short clipped sentences that came out with something of a hiss from between the teeth and the uptilted cigarette.

'Comrades, we meet under instructions from Comrade General Serov. General Serov, on behalf of the Praesidium, has ordered me to make known to you certain matters of State Policy. We are then to confer and recommend a course of action which will be in line with this Policy and assist it. We have to reach our decision quickly. But our decision will be of supreme importance to the State. It will therefore have to be a correct decision.'

General G. paused to allow the significance of his words time to sink in. One by one, he slowly examined the faces of the three senior officers at the table. Their eyes looked stolidly back at him. Inside, these extremely important men were perturbed. They were about to look through the furnace door. They were about to learn a State secret, the knowledge of which might one day have most dangerous consequences for them. Sitting in the quiet room, they felt bathed in the dreadful incandescence that shines out from the centre of all power in the Soviet Union – the High Praesidium.

The final ash fell off the end of General G.'s cigarette on to his tunic. He brushed it off and threw the cardboard butt into the basket for secret waste beside his desk. He lit another cigarette and spoke through it.

'Our recommendation concerns a conspicuous act of terrorism to be carried out in enemy territory within three months.'

Six pairs of expressionless eyes stared at the head of SMERSH, waiting.

'Comrades,' General G. leant back in his chair and his voice became expository, 'the foreign policy of the U.S.S.R. has entered a new phase. Formerly, it was a "Hard" policy — a policy [he allowed himself the joke on Stalin's name] of steel. This policy, effective as it was, built up tensions in the West, notably in America, which were becoming dangerous. The Americans are unpredictable people. They are hysterical. The reports of our Intelligence began to indicate that we were pushing America to the brink of an undeclared atomic attack on the U.S.S.R. You have read these reports and you know what I say is true. We do not want such a war. If there is to be a war, it is we who will choose the time. Certain powerful Americans, notably the Pentagon Group led by Admiral Radford, were helped in their firebrand schemes by the very successes of our "Hard" policy. So it was decided that the time had come to change our methods, while maintaining our aims. A new policy was created — the "Hard-Soft" policy. Geneva was the beginning of this policy. We were "soft". China threatens Quemoy and Matsu. We are "hard". We open our frontiers to a lot of newspaper men and actors and artists although we know many of them to be spies. Our leaders laugh and make jokes at receptions in Moscow. In the middle of the jokes we drop the biggest test bomb of all time. Comrades Bulganin and Khrushchev and Comrade General Serov [General G. carefully included the names for the ears of the tape-recorder] visit India and the East and blackguard the English. When they get back, they have friendly discussions with the British Ambassador about their forthcoming goodwill visit to London. And so it goes on — the stick and then the carrot, the smile and then the frown. And the West is confused. Tensions are relaxed before they have time to harden. The reactions of our enemies are clumsy, their strategy disorganized. Meanwhile the common people laugh at our jokes, cheer our football teams and slobber with delight when we release a few prisoners of war whom we wish to feed no longer!'

There were smiles of pleasure and pride round the table. What a brilliant policy! What fools we are making of them in the West!

'At the same time,' continued General G., himself smiling thinly at the pleasure he had caused, 'we continue to forge everywhere stealthily ahead — revolution in Morocco, arms to Egypt, friendship with Yugoslavia, trouble in Cyprus, riots in Turkey, strikes in England, great political gains in France — there is no front in the world on which we are not quietly advancing.'

General G. saw the eyes shining greedily round the table. The men were softened up. Now it was time to be hard. Now it was time for them to feel the new policy on themselves. The Intelligence services would also have to pull their weight in this great game that was being played on their behalf. Smoothly General G. leaned forward. He planted his right elbow on the desk and raised his first in the air.

'But Comrades,' his voice was soft, 'where has there been failure in carrying out the State Policy of the U.S.S.R.? Who has all along been soft when we wished to be hard? Who has suffered defeats while victory was going to all other departments of the State? Who, with their stupid blunders, has made the Soviet Union look foolish and weak throughout the world? WHO?'

The voice had risen almost to a scream. General G. thought how well he was delivering the denunciation demanded by the Praesidium. How splendid it would sound when the tape was played back to Serov!

He glared down the conference table at the pale, expectant faces. General G.'s fist crashed forward on to the desk.

'The whole Intelligence *apparat* of the Soviet Union, Comrades.' The voice was now a furious bellow. 'It is we who are the sluggards, the saboteurs, the traitors! It is we who are failing the Soviet Union in its great and glorious struggle! We!' His arm swept round the room. 'All of us!' The voice came back to normal, became more reasonable. 'Comrades, look at the record. *Sookin Sin* [he allowed himself the peasant obscenity], son-of-a-bitch, look at the record! First we lose Gouzenko and the whole of the Canadian *apparat* and the scientist Fuchs, then the American *apparat* is cleaned up, then we lose men like Tokaev, then comes the scandalous Khoklov affair which did great damage to our country, then Petrov and his wife in Australia — a bungled business if ever there was one! The list is endless — defeat after defeat, and the devil knows I have not mentioned the half of it.'

General G. paused. He continued in his softest voice. 'Comrades, I have to tell you that unless tonight we make a recommendation for a great Intelligence victory, and unless we act correctly on that recommendation, if it is approved, there will be trouble.'

General G. sought for a final phrase to convey the threat without defining it. He found it. 'There will be,' he paused and looked, with artificial mildness, down the table, 'displeasure.'

CHAPTER 5

———————

Konspiratsia

THE moujiks had received the knout. General G. gave them a few minutes to lick their wounds and recover from the shock of the official lashing that had been meted out.

No one said a word for the defence. No one spoke up for his department or mentioned the countless victories of Soviet Intelligence that could be set against the few mistakes. And no one questioned the right of the Head of SMERSH, who shared the guilt with them, to deliver this terrible denunciation. The Word had gone out from the Throne, and General G. had been chosen as the mouthpiece for the Word. It was a great compliment to General G. that he had been thus chosen, a sign of grace, a sign of coming preferment, and everyone present made a careful note of the fact that, in the Intelligence hierarchy, General G., with SMERSH behind him, had come to the top of the pile.

At the end of the table, the representative of the Foreign Ministry, Lieutenant-General Vozdvishensky of R.U.M.I.D., watched the smoke curl up from the tip of his long Kazbek cigarette and remembered how Molotov had privately told him, when Beria was dead, that

45

General G. would go far. There had been no great foresight in thi prophecy, reflected Vozdvishensky. Beria had disliked G. and had constantly hindered his advancement, side-tracking him away from the main ladder of power into one of the minor departments of the then Ministry of State Security, which, on the death of Stalin, Beri had quickly abolished as a Ministry. Until 1952, G. had been deputy to one of the heads of this Ministry. When the post wa abolished, he devoted his energies to plotting the downfall of Beria working under the secret orders of the formidable General Serov whose record put him out of even Beria's reach.

Serov, a Hero of the Soviet Union and a veteran of the famou predecessors of the M.G.B. — the Cheka, the Ogpu, the N.K.V.D and the M.V.D. — was in every respect a bigger man than Beria He had been directly behind the mass executions of the 1930s when a million died, he had been *metteur en scène* of most of the grea Moscow show trials, he had organized the bloody genocide in the Central Caucasus in February 1944, and it was he who had inspired the mass deportations from the Baltic States and the kidnapping o the German atom and other scientists who had given Russia he great technical leap forward after the war.

And Beria and all his court had gone to the gallows, while General G. had been given SMERSH as his reward. As for Arm General Ivan Serov, he, with Bulganin and Khrushchev, now rule Russia. One day, he might even stand on the peak, alone. But guessed General Vozdvishensky, glancing up the table at the gleam ing billiard-ball skull, probably with General G. not far behind him

The skull lifted and the hard bulging brown eyes looked straigh down the table into the eyes of General Vozdvishensky. Genera Vozdvishensky managed to look back calmly and even with a hin of appraisal.

That is a deep one, thought General G. Let us put the spotligh on him and see how he shows up on the sound-track.

'Comrades,' gold flashed from both corners of his mouth as h stretched his lips in a chairman's smile, 'let us not be too dis mayed. Even the highest tree has an axe waiting at its foot. W have never thought that our departments were so successful as to be beyond criticism. What I have been instructed to say to you will not have come as a surprise to any of us. So let us take up the challenge with a good heart and get down to business.'

Round the table there was no answering smile to these platitudes. General G. had not expected that there would be. He lit a cigarette and continued.

'I said that we have at once to recommend an act of terrorism in the intelligence field, and one of our departments — no doubt my own — will be called upon to carry out this act.'

An inaudible sigh of relief went round the table. So at least SMERSH would be the responsible department! That was something.

'But the choice of a target will not be an easy matter, and our collective responsibility for the correct choice will be a heavy one.'

Soft-hard, hard-soft. The ball was now back with the conference.

'It is not just a question of blowing up a building or shooting a prime minister. Such bourgeois horseplay is not contemplated. Our operation must be delicate, refined and aimed at the heart of the Intelligence *apparat* of the West. It must do grave damage to the enemy *apparat* — hidden damage which the public will hear perhaps nothing of, but which will be the secret talk of government circles. But it must also cause a public scandal so devastating that the world will lick its lips and sneer at the shame and stupidity of our enemies. Naturally Governments will know that it is a Soviet *konspiratsia*. That is good. It will be a piece of "hard" policy. And the agents and spies of the West will know it, too, and they will marvel at our cleverness and they will tremble. Traitors and possible defectors will change their minds. Our own operatives will be stimulated. They will be encouraged to greater efforts by our display of strength and genius. But of course we shall deny any knowledge of the deed, whatever it may be, and it is desirable that the common people of the Soviet Union should remain in complete ignorance of our complicity.'

General G. paused and looked down the table at the representative of R.U.M.I.D., who again held his gaze impassively.

'And now to choose the organization at which we will strike, and then to decide on the specific target within that organization. Comrade Lieutenant-General Vozdvishensky, since you observe the foreign intelligence scene from a neutral standpoint [this was a jibe at the notorious jealousies that exist between the military intelligence of the G.R.U. and the Secret Service of the M.G.B.] perhaps you would survey the field for us. We wish to have your opinion of the relative importance of the Western Intelligence Services. We will then choose the one which is the most dangerous and which we would most wish to damage.'

General G. sat back in his tall chair. He rested his elbows on the arms and supported his chin on the interlaced fingers of his joined hands, like a teacher preparing to listen to a long construe.

General Vozdvishensky was not dismayed by his task. He had been in intelligence, mostly abroad, for thirty years. He had served as a 'doorman' at the Soviet Embassy in London under Litvinoff. He had worked with the Tass Agency in New York and had then gone back to London, to Amtorg, the Soviet Trade Organization. For five years he had been Military Attaché under the brilliant Madame Kollontai in the Stockholm Embassy. He had helped train Sorge, the Soviet master spy, before Sorge went to Tokyo. During the war, he had been for a while Resident Director in Switzerland, or 'Schmidtland', as it had been known in the spy-jargon, and there he had helped sow the seeds of the sensationally successful but tragically misused 'Lucy' network. He had even gone several times into Germany as a courier to the 'Rote Kapelle', and had narrowly escaped being cleaned up with it. And after the war, on transfer to the Foreign Ministry, he had been on the inside of the Burgess and Maclean operation and on countless other plots to penetrate the Foreign Ministries of the West. He was a professional spy to his finger-tips and he was perfectly prepared to put on record his opinions of the rivals with whom he had been crossing swords all his life.

The A.D.C. at his side was less comfortable. He was nervous at R.U.M.I.D. being pinned down in this way, and without a full departmental briefing. He scoured his brain clear and sharpened his ears to catch every word.

'In this matter,' said General Vozdvishensky carefully, 'one must not confuse the man with the office. Every country has good spies and it is not always the biggest countries that have the most or the best. But Secret Services are expensive, and small countries cannot afford the co-ordinated effort which produces good intelligence — the forgery departments, the radio network, the record department, the digestive apparatus that evaluates and compares the reports of the agents. There are individual agents serving Norway, Holland, Belgium and even Portugal who could be a great nuisance to us if these countries knew the value of their reports or made good use of them. But they do not. Instead of passing their information on to the larger powers, they prefer to sit on it and feel important. So we need not worry with these smaller countries,' he paused, 'until we come to Sweden. There they have been spying on us for centuries. They have always had better information on the Baltic than even Finland or Germany. They are dangerous. I would like to put a stop to their activities.'

General G. interrupted. 'Comrade, they are always having spy scandals in Sweden. One more scandal would not make the world look up. Please continue.'

'Italy can be dismissed,' went on General Vozdvishensky, without appearing to notice the interruption. 'They are clever and active, but they do us no harm. They are only interested in their own backyard, the Mediterranean. The same can be said of Spain, except that their counter-intelligence is a great hindrance to the Party. We have lost many good men to these Fascists. But to mount an operation against them would probably cost us more men. And little would be achieved. They are not yet ripe for revolution. In France, while we have penetrated most of their Services, the Deuxième Bureau is still clever and dangerous. There is a man called Mathis at the head of it. A Mendès-France appointment. He would be a tempting target and it would be easy to operate in France.'

'France is looking after herself,' commented General G.

'England is another matter altogether. I think we all have respect for her Intelligence Service,' General Vozdvishensky looked round the table. There were grudging nods from everyone present, including General G. 'Their Security Service is excellent. England, being an island, has great security advantages and their so-called M.I.5 employs men with good education and good brains. Their Secret Service is still better. They have notable successes. In certain types of operation, we are constantly finding that they have been there before us. Their agents are good. They pay them little money — only a thousand or two thousand roubles a month — but they serve with devotion. Yet these agents have no special privileges in England, no relief from taxation and no special shops such as we have, from which they can buy cheap goods. Their social standing abroad is not high, and their wives have to pass as the wives of secretaries. They are rarely awarded a decoration until they retire. And yet these men and women continue to do this dangerous work. It is curious. It is perhaps the Public School and University tradition. The love of adventure. But still it is odd that they play this game so well, for they are not natural conspirators.' General Vozdvishensky felt that his remarks might be taken as too laudatory. He hastily qualified them. 'Of course, most of their strength lies in the myth — in the myth of Scotland Yard, of Sherlock Holmes, of the Secret Service. We certainly have nothing to fear from these gentlemen. But this myth is a hindrance which it would be good to set aside.'

'And the Americans?' General G. wanted to put a stop to Vozdvishensky's attempts to qualify his praise of British Intelligence. One day that bit about the Public School and University tradition would sound well in court. Next, hoped General G., he will be saying that the Pentagon is stronger than the Kremlin.

'The Americans have the biggest and richest service among our enemies. Technically, in such matters as radio and weapons and equipment, they are the best. But they have no understanding for the work. They get enthusiastic about some Balkan spy who says he has a secret army in the Ukraine. They load him with money with which to buy boots for this army. Of course he goes at once to Paris and spends the money on women. Americans try to do everything with money. Good spies will not work for money alone — only bad ones, of which the Americans have several divisions.'

'They have successes, Comrade,' said General G. silkily. 'Perhaps you underestimate them.'

General Vozdvishensky shrugged. 'They must have successes, Comrade General. You cannot sow a million seeds without reaping one potato. Personally I do not think the Americans need engage the attention of this conference.' The head of R.U.M.I.D. sat back in his chair and stolidly took out his cigarette case.

'A very interesting exposition,' said General G. coldly. 'Comrade General Slavin?'

General Slavin of the G.R.U. had no intention of committing himself on behalf of the General Staff of the Army. 'I have listened with interest to the words of Comrade General Vozdvishensky. I have nothing to add.'

Colonel of State Security Nikitin of M.G.B. felt it would do no great harm to show up the G.R.U. as being too stupid to have any ideas at all, and at the same time to make a modest recommendation that would probably tally with the inner thoughts of those present — and that was certainly on the tip of General G.'s tongue. Colonel Nikitin also knew that, given the proposition that had been posed by the Praesidium, the Soviet Secret Service would back him up.

'I recommend the English Secret Service as the object of terrorist action,' he said decisively. 'The devil knows my department hardly finds them a worthy adversary, but they are the best of an indifferent lot.'

General G. was annoyed by the authority in the man's voice, and by having his thunder stolen, for he also had intended to sum up in favour of an operation against the British. He tapped his lighter softly on the desk to reimpose his chairmanship. 'Is it agreed then, Comrades? An act of terrorism against the British Secret Service?'

There were careful, slow nods all round the table.

'I agree. And now for the target within that organization. I remember Comrade General Vozdvishensky saying something about a myth upon which much of the alleged strength of this Secret Service depends. How can we help to destroy the myth and thus strike at the very motive force of this organization? Where does this myth reside? We cannot destroy all its personnel at one blow. Does it reside in the Head? Who is the Head of the British Secret Service?'

Colonel Nikitin's aide whispered in his ear. Colonel Nikitin decided that this was a question he could and perhaps should answer.

'He is an Admiral. He is known by the letter M. We have a *zapiska* on him, but it contains little. He does not drink very much. He is too old for women. The public does not know of his existence. It would be difficult to create a scandal round his death. And he would not be easy to kill. He rarely goes abroad. To shoot him in a London street would not be very refined.'

'There is much in what you say, Comrade,' said General G. 'But we are here to find a target who *will* fulfil our requirements. Have they no one who is a hero to the organization? Someone who is admired and whose ignominious destruction would cause dismay? Myths are built on heroic deeds and heroic people. Have they no such men?'

There was silence round the table while everyone searched his memory. So many names to remember, so many dossiers, so many operations going on every day all over the world. Who was there in the British Secret Service? Who was that man who . . . ?

It was Colonel Nikitin of the M.G.B. who broke the embarrassed silence.

He said hesitantly, 'There is a man called Bond.'

CHAPTER 6

Death Warrant

'Y*b**nna mat!' The gross obscenity was a favourite with General G. His hand slapped down on the desk. 'Comrade, there certainly is "a man called Bond" as you put it.' His voice was sarcastic. 'James Bond. [He pronounced it 'Shems'.] And nobody, myself included, could think of this spy's name! We are indeed forgetful. No wonder the Intelligence *apparat* is under criticism.'

General Vozdvishensky felt he should defend himself and his department. 'There are countless enemies of the Soviet Union, Comrade General,' he protested. 'If I want their names, I send to the Central Index for them. Certainly I know the name of this Bond. He has been a great trouble to us at different times. But to-day my mind is full of other names – names of people who are causing us trouble today, this week. I am interested in football, but I cannot remember the name of every foreigner who has scored a goal against the Dynamos.'

'You are pleased to joke, Comrade,' said General G. to underline this out-of-place comment. 'This is a serious matter. I for one admit my fault in not remembering the name of this notorious agent. Comrade Colonel Nikitin will no doubt refresh our memories further, but I recall that this Bond has at least twice frustrated the operations of SMERSH. That is,' he added, 'before I assumed control of the department. There was this affair in France, at that Casino town. The man Le Chiffre. An excellent leader of the Party in France. He foolishly got into some money troubles. But he would have got out of them if this Bond had not interfered. I recall that the Department had to act quickly and liquidate the Frenchman. The executioner should have dealt with the Englishman at the same time, but he did not. Then there was this Negro of ours in Harlem. A great man — one of the greatest foreign agents we have ever employed, and with a vast network behind him. There was some business about a treasure in the Caribbean. I forget the details. This Englishman was sent out by the Secret Service and smashed the whole organization and killed our man. It was a great reverse. Once again my predecessor should have proceeded ruthlessly against this English spy.'

Colonel Nikitin broke in. 'We had a similar experience in the case of the German, Drax, and the rocket. You will recall the matter, Comrade General. A most important *konspiratsia*. The General Staff were deeply involved. It was a matter of High Policy which could have borne decisive fruit. But again it was this Bond who frustrated the operation. The German was killed. There were grave consequences for the State. There followed a period of serious embarrassment which was only solved with difficulty.'

General Slavin of G.R.U. felt that he should say something. The rocket had been an Army operation and its failure had been laid at the door of G.R.U. Nikitin knew this perfectly well. As usual M.G.B. was trying to make trouble for G.R.U. — raking up old history in this manner. 'We asked for this man to be dealt with by your department, Comrade Colonel,' he said icily. 'I cannot recall that any action followed our request. If it had, we should not now be having to bother with him.'

Colonel Nikitin's temples throbbed with rage. He controlled

himself. 'With due respect, Comrade General,' he said in a loud, sarcastic voice, 'the request of G.R.U. was not confirmed by Higher Authority. Further embarrassment with England was not desired. Perhaps that detail has slipped your memory. In any case, if such a request had reached M.G.B., it would have been referred to SMERSH for action.'

'My department received no such request,' said General G. sharply. 'Or the execution of this man would have rapidly followed. However, this is no time for historical researches. The rocket affair was three years ago. Perhaps the M.G.B. could tell us of the more recent activities of this man.'

Colonel Nikitin whispered hurriedly with his aide. He turned back to the table. 'We have very little further information, Comrade General,' he said defensively. 'We believe that he was involved in some diamond smuggling affair. That was last year. Between Africa and America. The case did not concern us. Since then we have no further news of him. Perhaps there is more recent information on his file.'

General G. nodded. He picked up the receiver of the telephone nearest to him. This was the so-called *Kommandant Telefon* of the M.G.B. All lines were direct and there was no central switchboard. He dialled a number. 'Central Index? Here General Grubozaboyschikov. The *zapiska* of "Bond" — English spy. Emergency.' He listened for the immediate 'At once, Comrade General,' and put back the receiver. He looked down the table with authority. 'Comrades, from many points of view this spy sounds an appropriate target. He appears to be a dangerous enemy of the State. His liquidation will be of benefit to all departments of our Intelligence *apparat*. Is that so?'

The conference grunted.

'Also his loss will be felt by the Secret Service. But will it do more? Will it seriously wound them? Will it help to destroy this myth about which we have been speaking? Is this man a hero to his organization and his country?'

General Vozdvishensky decided that this question was intended for him. He spoke up. 'The English are not interested in heroes unless they are footballers or cricketers or jockeys. If a man climbs a mountain or runs very fast he also is a hero to some people, but not to the masses. The Queen of England is also a hero, and Churchill. But the English are not greatly interested in military heroes. This man Bond is unknown to the public. If he was known, he would still not be a hero. In England, neither open war nor secret war is a heroic matter. They do not like to think about war, and after a war the names of their war heroes are forgotten as quickly as possible. Within the Secret Service, this man may be a local hero or he may not. It will depend on his appearance and personal characteristics. Of these I know nothing. He may be fat and greasy and unpleasant. No one makes a hero out of such a man, however successful he is.'

Nikitin broke in. 'English spies we have captured speak highly of this man. He is certainly much admired in his Service. He is said to be a lone wolf, but a good looking one.'

The internal office telephone purred softly. General G. lifted the receiver, listened briefly and said, 'Bring it in.' There was a knock on the door. The A.D.C. came in carrying a bulky file in cardboard covers. He crossed the room and placed the file on the desk in front of the General and walked out, closing the door softly behind him.

The file had a shiny black cover. A thick white stripe ran diagonally across it from top right-hand corner to bottom left. In the top left-hand space there were the letters 'S.S.' in white, and under them 'SOVERSHENNOE SEKRETNO', the equivalent of 'Top Secret'. Across the centre was neatly painted in white letters 'JAMES BOND', and underneath 'Angliski Spion'.

General G. opened the file and took out a large envelope containing photographs which he emptied on to the glass surface of the desk. He picked them up one by one. He looked closely at them, sometimes through a magnifying glass which he took out of a drawer, and passed them across the desk to Nikitin who glanced at them and handed them on.

The first was dated 1946. It showed a dark young man sitting at a table outside a sunlit café. There was a tall glass beside him on the table and a soda-water siphon. The right forearm rested on the table and there was a cigarette between the fingers of the right hand that hung negligently down from the edge of the table. The legs were crossed in that attitude that only an Englishman adopts — with the right ankle resting on the left knee and the left hand grasping the ankle. It was a careless pose. The man didn't know that he was being photographed from a point about twenty feet away.

The next was dated 1950. It was a face and shoulders, blurred, but of the same man. It was a close-up and Bond was looking with careful, narrowed eyes at something, probably the photographer's face, just above the lens. A miniature button-hole camera, guessed General G.

The third was from 1951. Taken from the left flank, quite close, it showed the same man in a dark suit, without a hat, walking down a wide empty street. He was passing a shuttered shop whose sign said 'Charcuterie'. He looked as if he was going somewhere urgently. The clean-cut profile was pointing straight ahead and the crook of the right elbow suggested that his right hand was in the pocket of his coat. General G. reflected that it was probably taken from a car. He thought that the decisive look of the man, and the purposeful slant of his striding figure, looked dangerous, as if he was making quickly for something bad that was happening further down the street.

The fourth and last photograph was marked *Passe. 1953.* The corner of the Royal Seal and the letters '... REIGN OFFICE' in the segment of a circle showed in the bottom right-hand corner. The photograph, which had been blown up to cabinet size, must have been made at a frontier, or by the concierge of an hotel when Bond had surrendered his passport. General G. carefully went over the face with his magnifying glass.

It was a dark, clean-cut face, with a three-inch scar showing whitely down the sunburned skin of the right cheek. The eyes were wide and level under straight, rather long black brows. The hair was black, parted on the left, and carelessly brushed so that a thick black comma fell down over the right eyebrow. The longish straight nose ran down to a short upper lip below which was a wide and finely drawn but cruel mouth. The line of the jaw was straight and firm. A section of dark suit, white shirt and black knitted tie completed the picture.

General G. held the photograph out at arm's length. Decision, authority, ruthlessness — these qualities he could see. He didn't care what else went on inside the man. He passed the photograph down the table and turned to the file, glancing rapidly down each page and flipping brusquely on to the next.

The photographs came back to him. He kept his place with a finger and looked briefly up. 'He looks a nasty customer,' he said grimly. 'His story confirms it. I will read out some extracts. Then we must decide. It is getting late.' He turned back to the first page and began to rattle off the points that struck him.

'First name: JAMES. Height: 183 centimetres; weight: 76 kilograms; slim build; eyes: blue; hair: black; scar down right cheek and on left shoulder; signs of plastic surgery on back of right hand (see Appendix "A"); all-round athlete; expert pistol shot, boxer, knife-thrower; does not use disguises. Languages: French and German. Smokes heavily (N.B.: special cigarettes with three gold bands); vices: drink, but not to excess, and women. Not thought to accept bribes.'

General G. skipped a page and went on:

'This man is invariably armed with a .25 Beretta automatic carried in a holster under his left arm. Magazine holds eight rounds. Has been known to carry a knife strapped to his left forearm; has used steel-capped shoes; knows the basic holds of judo. In general, fights with tenacity and has a high tolerance of pain (see Appendix "B").'

General G. riffled through more pages giving extracts from agents' reports from which this data was drawn. He came to the last page before the Appendices which gave details of the cases on which Bond had been encountered. He ran his eye to the bottom and read out: 'Conclusion. This man is a dangerous professional terrorist and spy. He has worked for the British Secret Service since 1938 and now (see Highsmith file of December 1950) holds the secret number "007" in that Service. The double o numerals signify an agent who has killed and who is privileged to kill on active service. There are believed to be only two other British agents with this authority. The fact that this spy was decorated with the C.M.G. in 1953, an award usually given only on retirement from the Secret Service, is a measure of his worth. If encountered in the field, the fact and full details to be reported to headquarters (see SMERSH, M.G.B. and G.R.U. Standing Orders 1951 onwards).'

General G. shut the file and slapped his hand decisively on the cover. 'Well, Comrades. Are we agreed?'

'Yes,' said Colonel Nikitin, loudly.

'Yes,' said General Slavin in a bored voice.

General Vozdvishensky was looking down at his fingernails. He was sick of murder. He had enjoyed his time in England. 'Yes,' he said. 'I suppose so.'

General G.'s hand went to the internal office telephone. He spoke to his A.D.C. 'Death Warrant,' he said harshly. 'Made out in the name of "James Bond".' He spelled the names out. 'Description: *Angliski Spion*. Crime: Enemy of the State.' He put the receiver back and leant forward in his chair. 'And now it will be a question of devising an appropriate *konspiratsia*. And one that cannot fail!' He smiled grimly. 'We cannot have another of those Khoklov affairs.'

The door opened and the A.D.C. came in carrying a bright yellow sheet of paper. He put it in front of General G. and went out. General G. ran his eyes down the paper and wrote the words 'To be killed. Grubozaboyschikov' at the head of the large empty space at the bottom. He passed the paper to the M.G.B. man who read it and wrote 'Kill him. Nikitin' and handed it across to the head of G.R.U. who wrote 'Kill him. Slavin'. One of the A.D.C.s passed the paper to the plain-clothes man sitting beside the representative of R.U.M.I.D. The man put it in front of General Vozdvishensky and handed him a pen.

General Vozdvishensky read the paper carefully. He raised his eyes slowly to those of General G. who was watching him and, without looking down, scribbled the 'Kill him' more or less under the other signatures and scrawled his name after it. Then he took his hands away from the paper and got to his feet.

'If that is all, Comrade General?' he pushed his chair back.

General G. was pleased. His instincts about this man had been right. He would have to put a watch on him and pass on his suspicions to General Serov. 'One moment, Comrade General,' he said. 'I have something to add to the warrant.'

The paper was handed up to him. He took out his pen and scratched out what he had written. He wrote again, speaking the words slowly as he did so.

'To be killed WITH IGNOMINY. Grubozaboyschikov.'

He looked up and smiled pleasantly to the company. 'Thank you, Comrades. That is all. I shall advise you of the decision of the Praesidium on our recommendation. Good night.'

When the conference had filed out, General G. rose to his feet and stretched and gave a loud controlled yawn. He sat down again at his desk, switched off the wire-recorder and rang for his A.D.C. The man came in and stood beside his desk.

General G. handed him the yellow paper. 'Send this over to General Serov at once. Find out where Kronsteen is and have him fetched by car. I don't care if he's in bed. He will have to come. Otdyel II will know where to find him. And I will see Colonel Klebb in ten minutes.'

'Yes, Comrade General.' The man left the room.

General G. picked up the V.Ch. receiver and asked for General Serov. He spoke quietly for five minutes. At the end he concluded: 'And I am now about to give the task to Colonel Klebb and the Planner, Kronsteen. We will discuss the outlines of a suitable *konspiratsia* and they will give me detailed proposals tomorrow. Is that in order, Comrade General?'

'Yes,' came the quiet voice of General Serov of the High Praesidium. 'Kill him. But let it be excellently accomplished. The Praesidium will ratify the decision in the morning.'

The line went dead. The inter-office telephone rang. General G. said 'Yes' into the receiver and put it back.

A moment later the A.D.C. opened the big door and stood in the entrance. 'Comrade Colonel Klebb,' he announced.

A toad-like figure in an olive green uniform which bore the single red ribbon of the Order of Lenin came into the room and walked with quick short steps over to the desk.

General G. looked up and waved to the nearest chair at the conference table. 'Good evening, Comrade.'

The squat face split into a sugary smile. 'Good evening, Comrade General.'

The Head of Otdyel II, the department of SMERSH in charge of Operations and Executions, hitched up her skirts and sat down.

CHAPTER 7

The Wizard of Ice

THE two faces of the double clock in the shiny, domed case looked out across the chess-board like the eyes of some huge sea monster that had peered over the edge of the table to watch the game.

The two faces of the chess clock showed different times. Kronsteen's showed twenty minutes to one. The long red pendulum that ticked off the seconds was moving in its staccato sweep across the bottom half of his clock's face, while the enemy clock was silent and its pendulum motionless down the face. But Makharov's clock said five minutes to one. He had wasted time in the middle of the game and he now had only five minutes to go. He was in bad 'time-trouble' and unless Kronsteen made some lunatic mistake, which was unthinkable, he was beaten.

Kronsteen sat motionless and erect, as malevolently inscrutable as a parrot. His elbows were on the table and his big head rested on clenched fists that pressed into his cheeks, squashing the pursed lips into a pout of hauteur and disdain. Under the wide, bulging brow the rather slanting black eyes looked down with deadly calm on his winning board. But, behind the mask, the blood was throbbing in the dynamo of his brain, and a thick worm-like vein in his right temple pulsed at a beat of over ninety. He had sweated away a pound of weight in the last two hours and ten minutes, and the spectre of a false move still had one hand at his throat. But to Makharov, and to the spectators, he was still 'The Wizard of Ice' whose game had been compared to a man eating fish. First he stripped off the skin, then he picked out the bones, then he ate the fish. Kronsteen had been Champion of Moscow two years running, was now in the final for the third time and, if he won this game, would be a contender for Grand Mastership.

In the pool of silence round the roped-off top table there was no sound except the loud tripping feet of Kronsteen's clock. The two umpires sat motionless in their raised chairs. They knew, as did Makharov, that this was certainly the kill. Kronsteen had introduced a brilliant twist into the Meran Variation of the Queen's Gambit Declined. Makharov had kept up with him until the 28th move. He had lost time on that move. Perhaps he had made a mistake there, and perhaps again on the 31st and 33rd moves. Who could say? It would be a game to be debated all over Russia for weeks to come.

There came a sigh from the crowded tiers opposite the Championship game. Kronsteen had slowly removed the right hand from his cheek and had stretched it across the board. Like the pincers of a pink crab, his thumb and forefinger had opened, then they had descended. The hand, holding a piece, moved up and sideways and down. Then the hand was slowly brought back to the face.

The spectators buzzed and whispered as they saw, on the great wall map, the 41st move duplicated with a shift of one of the three-foot placards. R-Kt8. That must be the kill!

Kronsteen reached deliberately over and pressed down the lever at the bottom of his clock. His red pendulum went dead. His clock showed a quarter to one. At the same instant, Makharov's pendulum came to life and started its loud, inexorable beat.

Kronsteen sat back. He placed his hands flat on the table and looked coldly across at the glistening, lowered face of the man whose guts he knew, for he too had suffered defeat in his time, would be writhing in agony like an eel pierced with a spear. Makharov, Champion of Georgia. Well, tomorrow Comrade Makharov could go back to Georgia and stay there. At any rate this year he would not be moving with his family up to Moscow.

A man in plain clothes slipped under the ropes and whispered to one of the umpires. He handed him a white envelope. The umpire shook his head, pointing at Makharov's clock, which now said three minutes to one. The man in plain clothes whispered one short sentence which made the umpire sullenly bow his head. He pinged a handbell.

'There is an urgent personal message for Comrade Kronsteen,' he announced into the microphone. 'There will be a three minutes' pause.'

A mutter went round the hall. Even though Makharov now courteously raised his eyes from the board and sat immobile, gazing up into the recesses of the high, vaulted ceiling, the spectators knew that the position of the game was engraved on his brain. A three minutes' pause simply meant three extra minutes for Makharov.

Kronsteen felt the same stab of annoyance, but his face was expressionless as the umpire stepped down from his chair and handed him a plain, unaddressed envelope. Kronsteen ripped it open with his thumb and extracted the anonymous sheet of paper. It said, in the large typewritten characters he knew so well, 'YOU ARE REQUIRED THIS INSTANT'. No signature and no address.

Kronsteen folded the paper and carefully placed it in his inside breast pocket. Later it would be recovered from him and destroyed. He looked up at the face of the plain-clothes man standing beside the umpire. The eyes were watching him impatiently, command-ingly. To hell with these people, thought Kronsteen. He would *not* resign with only three minutes to go. It was unthinkable. It was an insult to the People's Sport. But, as he made a gesture to the umpire that the game could continue, he trembled inside, and he avoided the eyes of the plain-clothes man who remained standing, in coiled immobility, inside the ropes.

The bell pinged. 'The game proceeds.'

Makharov slowly bent down his head. The hand of his clock slipped past the hour and he was still alive.

Kronsteen continued to tremble inside. What he had done was unheard of in an employee of SMERSH, or of any other State agency. He would certainly be reported. Gross disobedience. Dereliction of duty. What might be the consequences? At the best a tongue-lashing from General G., and a black mark on his *ʒapiska*. At the worst? Kronsteen couldn't imagine. He didn't like to think. Whatever happened, the sweets of victory had turned bitter in his mouth.

But now it was the end. With five seconds to go on his clock, Makharov raised his whipped eyes no higher than the pouting lips of his opponent and bent his head in the brief, formal bow of surrender. At the double ping of the umpire's bell, the crowded hall rose to its feet with a thunder of applause.

Kronsteen stood up and bowed to his opponent, to the umpires, and finally, deeply, to the spectators. Then, with the plain-clothes man in his wake, he ducked under the ropes and fought his way coldly and rudely through the mass of his clamouring admirers towards the main exit.

Outside the Tournament Hall, in the middle of the wide Push-kin Ulitza, with its engine running, stood the usual anonymous black ZIK saloon. Kronsteen climbed into the back and shut the door. As the plain-clothes man jumped on to the running-board and squeezed into the front seat, the driver crashed his gears and the car tore off down the street.

Kronsteen knew it would be a waste of breath to apologize to the plain-clothes guard. It would also be contrary to discipline. After all, he was Head of the Planning Department of SMERSH, with the honorary rank of full Colonel. And his brain was worth diamonds to the organization. Perhaps he could argue his way out of the mess. He gazed out of the window at the dark streets, already wet with the work of the night cleaning squad, and bent his mind to his defence. Then there came a straight street at the end of which the moon rode fast between the onion spires of the Kremlin, and they were there.

When the guard handed Kronsteen over to the A.D.C., he also handed the A.D.C. a slip of paper. The A.D.C. glanced at it and looked coldly up at Kronsteen with half-raised eyebrows. Kronsteen looked calmly back without saying anything. The A.D.C. shrugged his shoulders and picked up the office telephone and announced him.

When they went into the big room and Kronsteen had been waved to a chair and had nodded acknowledgment of the brief pursed smile of Colonel Klebb, the A.D.C. went up to General G. and handed him the piece of paper. The General read it and looked hard across at Kronsteen. While the A.D.C. walked to the door and went out, the General went on looking at Kronsteen. When the door was shut, General G. opened his mouth and said softly, 'Well, Comrade?'

Kronsteen was calm. He knew the story that would appeal. He spoke quietly and with authority. 'To the public, Comrade General, I am a professional chess player. Tonight I became Champion of Moscow for the third year in succession. If, with only three minutes to go, I had received a message that my wife was being murdered outside the door of the Tournament Hall, I would not have raised a finger to save her. My public know that. They are as dedicated to the game as myself. Tonight, if I had resigned the game and had come immediately on receipt of that message, five thousand people would have known that it could only be on the orders of such a department as this. There would have been a storm of gossip. My future goings and comings would have been watched for clues. It would have been the end of my cover. In the interests of State Security, I waited three minutes before obeying the order. Even so, my hurried departure will be the subject of much comment. I shall have to say that one of my children is gravely ill. I shall have to put a child into hospital for a week to support the story. I deeply apologize for the delay in carrying out the order. But the decision was a difficult one. I did what I thought best in the interests of the Department.'

General G. looked thoughtfully into the dark slanting eyes. The man was guilty, but the defence was good. He read the paper again as if weighing up the size of the offence, then he took out his lighter and burned it. He dropped the last burning corner on to the glass top of his desk and blew the ashes sideways on to the floor. He said nothing to reveal his thoughts, but the burning of the evidence was all that mattered to Kronsteen. Now nothing could go on his *zapiska*. He was deeply relieved and grateful. He would bend all his ingenuity to the matter on hand. The General had performed an act of great clemency. Kronsteen would repay him with the full coin of his mind.

'Pass over the photographs, Comrade Colonel,' said General G., as if the brief court-martial had not occurred. 'The matter is as follows. . . .'

So it is another death, thought Kronsteen, as the General talked and he examined the dark ruthless face that gazed levelly at him from the blown-up passport photograph. While Kronsteen listened with half his mind to what the General was saying, he picked out the salient facts – English spy. Great scandal desired. No Soviet involvement. Expert killer. Weakness for women (therefore not homosexual, thought Kronsteen). Drinks (but nothing is said about drugs). Unbribable (who knows? There is a price for every man). No expense would be spared. All equipment and personnel available from all intelligence departments. Success to be achieved within three months. Broad ideas required now. Details to be worked out later.

General G. fastened his sharp eyes on Colonel Klebb. 'What are your immediate reactions, Comrade Colonel?'

The square-cut rimless glass of the spectacles flashed in the light of the chandelier as the woman straightened from her position of bowed concentration and looked across the desk at the General.

The pale moist lips below the sheen of nicotine-stained fur over the mouth parted and started moving rapidly up and down as the woman gave her views. To Kronsteen, watching the face across the table, the square, expressionless opening and shutting of the lips reminded him of the boxlike jabber of a puppet.

The voice was hoarse and flat and without emotion, '. . . resembles in some respects the case of Stolzenberg. If you remember, Comrade General, this also was a matter of destroying a reputation as well as a life. On that occasion the matter was simple. The spy was also a pervert. If you recall . . .'

Kronsteen stopped listening. He knew all these cases. He had handled the planning of most of them and they were filed away in his memory like so many chess gambits. Instead, with closed ears, he examined the face of this dreadful woman and wondered casually how much longer she would last in her job — how much longer he would have to work with her.

Dreadful? Kronsteen was not interested in human beings — not even in his own children. Nor did the categories of 'good' and 'bad' have a place in his vocabulary. To him all people were chess pieces. He was only interested in their reactions to the movements of other pieces. To foretell their reactions, which was the greater part of his job, one had to understand their individual characteristics. Their basic instincts were immutable. Self-preservation, sex and the instinct of the herd — in that order. Their temperaments could be sanguine, phlegmatic, choleric or melancholic. The temperament of an individual would largely decide the comparative strength of his emotions and his sentiments. Character would greatly depend on upbringing and, whatever Pavlov and the Behaviourists might say, to a certain extent on the character of the parents. And, of course, people's lives and behaviour would be partly conditioned by physical strengths and weaknesses.

It was with these basic classifications at the back of his mind that Kronsteen's cold brain considered the woman across the table. It was the hundredth time he had summed her up, but now they had weeks of joint work in front of them and it was as well to refresh the memory so that a sudden intrusion of the human element in their partnership should not come as a surprise.

Of course Rosa Klebb had a strong will to survive, or she would not have become one of the most powerful women in the State, and certainly the most feared. Her rise, Kronsteen remembered, had begun with the Spanish Civil War. Then, as a double agent inside P.O.U.M. – that is, working for the O.G.P.U. in Moscow as well as for Communist Intelligence in Spain – she had been the right hand, and some sort of a mistress, they said, of her chief, the famous Andreas Nin. She had worked with him from 1935-37. Then, on the orders of Moscow, he was murdered and, it was rumoured, murdered by her. Whether this was true or not, from then on she had progressed slowly but straight up the ladder of power, surviving setbacks, surviving wars, surviving, because she forged no allegiances and joined no factions, all the purges, until, in 1953, with the death of Beria, the bloodstained hands grasped the rung, so few from the very top, that was Head of the Operations Department of SMERSH.

And, reflected Kronsteen, much of her success was due to the peculiar nature of her next most important instinct, the Sex Instinct. For Rosa Klebb undoubtedly belonged to the rarest of all sexual types. She was a Neuter. Kronsteen was certain of it. The stories of men and, yes, of women, were too circumstantial to be doubted. She might enjoy the act physically, but the instrument was of no importance. For her, sex was nothing more than an itch. And this psychological and physiological neutrality of hers at once relieved her of so many human emotions and sentiments and desires. Sexual neutrality was the essence of coldness in an individual. It was a great and wonderful thing to be born with.

In her, the Herd instinct would also be dead. Her urge for power demanded that she should be a wolf and not a sheep. She was a lone operator, but never a lonely one, because the warmth of company was unnecessary to her. And, of course, temperamentally, she would be a phlegmatic – imperturbable, tolerant of pain, sluggish. Laziness would be her besetting vice, thought Kronsteen.

She would be difficult to get out of her warm, hoggish bed in the morning. Her private habits would be slovenly, even dirty. It would not be pleasant, thought Kronsteen, to look into the intimate side of her life, when she relaxed, out of uniform. Kronsteen's pouting lips curled away from the thought and his mind hastened on, skipping her character, which was certainly cunning and strong, to her appearance.

Rosa Klebb would be in her late forties, he assumed, placing her by the date of the Spanish War. She was short, about five foot four, and squat, and her dumpy arms and short neck, and the calves of the thick legs in the drab khaki stockings, were very strong for a woman. The devil knows, thought Kronsteen, what her breasts were like, but the bulge of uniform that rested on the table-top looked like a badly packed sandbag, and in general her figure, with its big pear-shaped hips, could only be likened to a 'cello.

The *tricoteuses* of the French Revolution must have had faces like hers, decided Kronsteen, sitting back in his chair and tilting his head slightly to one side. The thinning orange hair scraped back to the tight, obscene bun; the shiny yellow-brown eyes that stared so coldly at General G. through the sharp-edged squares of glass, the wedge of thickly powdered, large-pored nose; the wet trap of a mouth, that went on opening and shutting as if it was operated by wires under the chin. Those French women, as they sat and knitted and chatted while the guillotine clanged down, must have had the same pale, thick chicken's skin that scragged in little folds under the eyes and at the corners of the mouth and below the jaws, the same big peasant's ears, the same tight, hard dimpled fists, like knobkerries, that, in the case of the Russian woman, now lay tightly clenched on the red velvet table-top on either side of the big bundle of bosom. And their faces must have conveyed the same impression, concluded Kronsteen, of coldness and cruelty and strength as this, yes, he had to allow himself the emotive word, *dreadful* woman of SMERSH.

'Thank you, Comrade Colonel. Your review of the position is of value. And now, Comrade Kronsteen, have you anything to add? Please be short. It is two o'clock and we all have a heavy day before us.' General G.'s eyes, bloodshot with strain and lack of sleep, stared fixedly across the desk into the fathomless brown pools below the bulging forehead. There had been no need to tell this man to be brief. Kronsteen never had much to say, but each of his words was worth speeches from the rest of the staff.

Kronsteen had already made up his mind, or he would not have allowed his thoughts to concentrate for so long on the woman.

He slowly tilted back his head and gazed into the nothingness of the ceiling. His voice was extremely mild, but it had the authority that commands close attention.

'Comrade General, it was a Frenchman, in some respects a predecessor of yours, Fouché, who observed that it is no good killing a man unless you also destroy his reputation. It will, of course, be easy to kill this man Bond. Any paid Bulgarian assassin would do it, if properly instructed. The second part of the operation, the destruction of this man's character, is more important and more difficult. At this stage it is only clear to me that the deed must be done away from England, and in a country over whose press and radio we have influence. If you ask me how the man is to be got there, I can only say that if the bait is important enough, and its capture is open to this man alone, he will be sent to seize it from wherever he may happen to be. To avoid the appearance of a trap, I would consider giving the bait a touch of eccentricity, of the unusual. The English pride themselves on their eccentricity. They treat the eccentric proposition as a challenge. I would rely partly on this reading of their psychology to have them send this important operator after the bait.'

Kronsteen paused. He lowered his head so that he was looking just over General G.'s shoulder.

'I shall proceed to devise such a trap,' he said indifferently. 'For the present, I can only say that if the bait is successful in attracting its prey, we are then likely to require an assassin with a perfect command of the English language.'

Kronsteen's eyes moved to the red velvet table-top in front of him. Thoughtfully, as if this was the kernel of the problem, he added: 'We shall also require a reliable and extremely beautiful girl.'

CHAPTER 8

The Beautiful Lure

SITTING by the window of her one room and looking out at the serene June evening, at the first pink of the sunset reflected in the windows across the street, at the distant onion spire of a church that flamed like a torch above the ragged horizon of Moscow roofs, Corporal of State Security Tatiana Romanova thought that she was happier than she had ever been before.

Her happiness was not romantic. It had nothing to do with the rapturous start to a love affair — those days and weeks before the first tiny tear-clouds appear on the horizon. It was the quiet, settled happiness of security, of being able to look forward with confidence to the future, heightened by the immediate things, a word of praise she had had that afternoon from Professor Denikin, the smell of a good supper cooking on the electric stove, her favourite prelude to *Boris Goudonov* being played by the Moscow State Orchestra on the radio, and, over all, the beauty of the fact that the long winter and short spring were past and it was June.

The room was a tiny box in the huge modern apartment building on the Sadovaya-Chernogriazskay Ulitza that is the women's barracks of the State Security Departments. Built by prison labour, and finished in 1939, the fine eight-storey building contains two thousand rooms, some, like hers on the third floor, nothing but square boxes with a telephone, hot and cold water, a single electric light and a share of the central bathrooms and lavatories, others, on the two top floors, consisting of two- and three-room flats with bathrooms. These were for high-ranking women. Graduation up the building was strictly by rank, and Corporal Romanova had to rise through Sergeant, Lieutenant, Captain, Major and Lieutenant-Colonel before she would reach the paradise of the eighth and Colonels' floor.

But heaven knew she was content enough with her present lot. A salary of 1200 roubles a month (thirty per cent more than she could have earned in any other Ministry), a room to herself; cheap food and clothes from the 'closed shops' on the ground floor of the building; a monthly allocation of at least two Ministry tickets to the Ballet or the Opera, a full two weeks' paid holiday a year. And, above all, a steady job with good prospects in Moscow — not in one of those dreary provincial towns where nothing happened month after month, and where the arrival of a new film or the visit of a travelling circus was the only thing to keep one out of bed in the evening.

Of course, you had to pay for being in the M.G.B. The uniform put you apart from the world. People were afraid, which didn't suit the nature of most girls, and you were confined to the society of other M.G.B. girls and men, one of whom, when the time came, you would have to marry in order to stay with the Ministry. And they worked like the devil—eight to six, five and a half days a week, and only forty minutes off for lunch in the canteen. But it was a good lunch, a real meal, and you could do with little supper and save up for the sable coat that would one day take the place of the well-worn Siberian fox.

At the thought of her supper, Corporal Romanova left the chair by the window and went to examine the pot of thick soup, with a few shreds of meat and some powdered mushroom, that was to be her supper. It was nearly done and smelled delicious. She turned off the electricity and let the pot simmer while she washed and tidied, as, years before, she had been taught to do before meals.

While she dried her hands, she examined herself in the big oval looking-glass over the washstand.

One of her early boy-friends had said she looked like the young Greta Garbo. What nonsense! And yet tonight she did look rather well. Fine dark brown silken hair brushed straight back from a tall brow and falling heavily down almost to the shoulders, there to curl slightly up at the ends (Garbo had once done her hair like that and Corporal Romanova admitted to herself that she had copied it), a good, soft pale skin with an ivory sheen at the cheek-bones; wide apart, level eyes of the deepest blue under straight natural brows (she closed one eye after the other. Yes, her lashes were certainly long enough!) a straight, rather imperious nose — and then the mouth. What about the mouth? Was it too broad? It must look terribly wide when she smiled. She smiled at herself in the mirror. Yes, it was wide; but then so had Garbo's been. At least the lips were full and finely etched. There was the hint of a smile at the corners. No one could say it was a cold mouth! And the oval of her face. Was that too long? Was her chin a shade too sharp? She swung her head sideways to see it in profile. The heavy curtain of hair swung forward and across her right eye so that she had to brush it back. Well, the chin was pointed, but at least it wasn't sharp. She faced the mirror again and picked up a brush and started on the long, heavy hair. Greta Garbo! She was all right, or so many men wouldn't tell her that she was — let alone the girls who were always coming to her for advice about their faces. But a film star — a famous one! She made a face at herself in the glass and went to eat her supper.

In fact Corporal Tatiana Romanova was a very beautiful girl indeed. Apart from her face, the tall, firm body moved particularly well. She had been a year in the ballet school in Leningrad and had abandoned dancing as a career only when she grew an inch over the prescribed limit of five feet six. The school had taught her to hold herself well and to walk well. And she looked wonderfully healthy, thanks to her passion for figure-skating, which she practised all through the year at the Dynamo ice-stadium and which had already earned her a place on the first Dynamo women's team. Her arms and breasts were faultless. A purist would have disapproved of her behind. Its muscles were so hardened with exercise that it had lost the smooth downward feminine sweep, and now, round at the back and flat and hard at the sides, it jutted like a man's.

Corporal Romanova was admired far beyond the confines of the English translation section of the M.G.B. Central Index. Everyone agreed that it would not be long before one of the senior officers came across her and peremptorily hauled her out of her modest section to make her his mistress, or if absolutely necessary, his wife.

The girl poured the thick soup into a small china bowl, decorated with wolves chasing a galloping sleigh round the rim, broke some black bread into it and went and sat in her chair by the window and ate it slowly with a nice shiny spoon she had slipped into her bag not many weeks before after a gay evening at the Hotel Moskwa.

When she had finished, she washed up and went back to her chair and lit the first cigarette of the day (no respectable girl in Russia smokes in public, except in a restaurant, and it would have meant instant dismissal if she had smoked at her work) and listened impatiently to the whimpering discords of an orchestra from Turkmenistan. This dreadful oriental stuff they were always putting on to please the kulaks of one of those barbaric outlying states! Why couldn't they play something *kulturny*? Some of that modern jazz music, or something classical. This stuff was hideous. Worse, it was old fashioned.

The telephone rang harshly. She walked over and turned down the radio and picked up the receiver.

'Corporal Romanova?'

It was the voice of her dear Professor Denikin. But out of office hours he always called her Tatiana or even Tania. What did this mean?

The girl was wide-eyed and tense. 'Yes, Comrade Professor.'

The voice at the other end sounded strange and cold. 'In fifteen minutes, at 8.30, you are required for interview by Comrade Colonel Klebb, of Otdyel II. You will call on her in her apartment, No. 1875, on the eighth floor of your building. Is that clear?'

'But, Comrade, why? What is ... What is ...?'

The odd, strained voice of her beloved Professor cut her short. 'That is all, Comrade Corporal.'

The girl held the receiver away from her face. She stared at it with frenzied eyes as if she could wring more words out of the circles of little holes in the black ear-piece. 'Hullo! Hullo!' The empty mouthpiece yawned at her. She realized that her hand and her forearm were aching with the strength of her grip. She bent slowly forward and put the receiver down on the cradle.

She stood for a moment, frozen, gazing blindly at the black machine. Should she call him back? No, that was out of the question. He had spoken as he had because he knew, and she knew, that every call, in and out of the building, was listened to or recorded. That was why he had not wasted a word. This was a State matter. With a message of this sort, you got rid of it as quickly as you could, in as few words as possible, and wiped your hands of it. You had got the dreadful card out of your hand. You had passed the Queen of Spades to someone else. Your hands were clean again.

The girl put her knuckles up to her open mouth and bit on them, staring at the telephone. What did they want her for? What had she done? Desperately she cast her mind back, scrabbling through the days, the months, the years. Had she made some terrible mistake in her work and they had just discovered it? Had she made some remark against the State, some joke that had been reported back? That was always possible. But which remark? When? If it had been a bad remark, she would have felt a twinge of guilt or fear at the time. Her conscience was clear. Or was it? Suddenly she remembered. What about the spoon she had stolen? Was it that? Government property! She would throw it out of the window, now, far to one side or the other. But no, it couldn't be that. That was too small. She shrugged her shoulders resignedly and her hand dropped to her side. She got up and moved towards the clothes cupboard to get out her best uniform, and her eyes were misty with the tears of fright and bewilderment of a child. It could be none of those things. SMERSH didn't send for one for that sort of thing. It must be something much, much worse.

The girl glanced through her wet eyes at the cheap watch on her wrist. Only seven minutes to go! A new panic seized her. She brushed her forearm across her eyes and grabbed down her parade uniform. On top of it all, whatever it was, to be late! She tore at the buttons of her white cotton blouse.

As she dressed and washed her face and brushed her hair, her mind went on probing at the evil mystery like an inquisitive child poking into a snake's hole with a stick. From whatever angle she explored the hole, there came an angry hiss.

Leaving out the nature of her guilt, contact with any tentacle of SMERSH was unspeakable. The very name of the organization was abhorred and avoided. SMERSH, 'Smiert Spionam', 'Death to Spies'. It was an obscene word, a word from the tomb, the very whisper of death, a word never mentioned even in secret office gossip among friends. Worst of all, within this horrible organization, Otdyel II, the Department of Torture and Death, was the central horror.

And the Head of Otdyel II, the woman, Rosa Klebb! Unbelievable things were whispered about this woman, things that came to Tatiana in her nightmares, things she forgot again during the day, but that she now paraded.

It was said that Rosa Klebb would let no torturing take place without her. There was a blood-spattered smock in her office, and a low camp-stool, and they said that when she was seen scurrying through the basement passages dressed in the smock and with the stool in her hand, the word would go round, and even the workers in SMERSH would hush their words and bend low over their papers — perhaps even cross their fingers in their pockets — until she was reported back in her room.

For, or so they whispered, she would take the camp-stool and draw it up close below the face of the man or woman that hung down over the edge of the interrogation table. Then she would squat down on the stool and look into the face and quietly say 'No. 1' or 'No. 10' or 'No. 25' and the inquisitors would know what she meant and they would begin. And she would watch the eyes in the face a few inches away from hers and breathe in the screams as if they were perfume. And, depending on the eyes, she would quietly change the torture, and say 'Now No. 36' or 'Now No. 64' and the inquisitors would do something else. As the courage and resistance seeped out of the eyes, and they began to weaken and beseech, she would start cooing softly. 'There, there my dove. Talk to me, my pretty one, and it will stop. It hurts. Ah me, it hurts so, my child. And one is so tired of the pain. One would like it to stop, and to be able to lie down in peace, and for it never to begin again. Your mother is here beside you, only waiting to stop the pain. She has a nice soft cosy bed all ready for you to sleep on and forget, forget, forget. Speak,' she would whisper lovingly. 'You have only to speak and you will have peace and no more pain.' If the eyes still resisted, the cooing would start again. 'But you are foolish, my pretty one. Oh so foolish. This pain is nothing. Nothing! You don't believe me, my little dove? Well then, your mother must try a little, but only a very little, of No. 87.' And the interrogators would hear and change their instruments and their aim, and she would squat there and watch the life slowly ebbing from the eyes until she had to speak loudly into the ear of the person or the words would not reach the brain.

But it was seldom, so they said, that the person had the will to travel far along SMERSH's road of pain, let alone to the end, and, when the soft voice promised peace, it nearly always won, for somehow Rosa Klebb knew from the eyes the moment when the adult had been broken down into a child crying for its mother. And she provided the image of the mother and melted the spirit where the harsh words of a man would have toughened it.

Then, after yet another suspect had been broken, Rosa Klebb would go back down the passage with her camp-stool and take off her newly soiled smock and get back to her work and the word would go round that all was over and normal activity would come back to the basement.

Tatiana, frozen by her thoughts, looked again at her watch. Four minutes to go. She ran her hands down her uniform and gazed once more at her white face in the glass. She turned and said farewell to the dear, familiar little room. Would she ever see it again?

She walked straight down the long corridor and rang for the lift.

When it came, she squared her shoulders and lifted her chin and walked into the lift as if it was the platform of the guillotine.

'Eighth,' she said to the girl operator. She stood facing the doors. Inside her, remembering a word she had not used since childhood, she repeated over and over 'My God — My God — My God.'

CHAPTER 9

A Labour of Love

OUTSIDE the anonymous, cream painted door, Tatiana already smelled the inside of the room. When the voice told her curtly to come in, and she opened the door, it was the smell that filled her mind while she stood and stared into the eyes of the woman who sat behind the round table under the centre light.

It was the smell of the Metro on a hot evening — cheap scent concealing animal odours. People in Russia soak themselves in scent, whether they have had a bath or not, but mostly when they have not, and healthy, clean girls like Tatiana always walk home from the office, unless the rain or the snow is too bad, so as to avoid the stench in the trains and the Metro.

Now Tatiana was in a bath of the smell. Her nostrils twitched with disgust.

It was her disgust and her contempt for a person who could live in the middle of such a smell that helped her to look down into the yellowish eyes that stared at her through the square glass panes. Nothing could be read in them. They were receiving eyes, not giving eyes. They slowly moved all over her, like camera lenses, taking her in.

Colonel Klebb spoke:

'You are a fine-looking girl, Comrade Corporal. Walk across the room and back.'

What were these honeyed words? Taut with a new fear, fear of the notorious personal habits of the woman, Tatiana did as she was told.

'Take your jacket off. Put it down on the chair. Raise your hands above your head. Higher. Now bend and touch your toes. Upright. Good. Sit down.' The woman spoke like a doctor. She gestured to the chair across the table from her. Her staring, probing eyes hooded themselves as they bent over the file on the table.

It must be my *zapiska*, thought Tatiana. How interesting to see the actual instrument that ordered the whole of one's life. How thick it was — nearly two inches thick. What could be on all those pages? She looked across at the open folder with wide, fascinated eyes.

Colonel Klebb riffled through the last pages and shut down the cover. The cover was orange with a diagonal black stripe. What did those colours signify?

The woman looked up. Somehow Tatiana managed to look bravely back.

'Comrade Corporal Romanova.' It was the voice of authority, of the senior officer. 'I have good reports of your work. Your record is excellent, both in your duties and in sport. The State is pleased with you.'

Tatiana could not believe her ears. She felt faint with reaction. She blushed to the roots of her hair and then turned pale. She put out a hand to the table edge. She stammered in a weak voice, 'I am g-grateful, Comrade Colonel.'

'Because of your excellent services you have been singled out for a most important assignment. This is a great honour for you. Do you understand?'

Whatever it was, it was better than what might have been. 'Yes, indeed, Comrade Colonel.'

'This assignment carries much responsibility. It bears a higher rank. I congratulate you on your promotion, Comrade Corporal, on completion of the assignment, to the rank of Captain of State Security.'

This was unheard of for a girl of twenty-four! Tatiana sensed danger. She stiffened like an animal who sees the steel jaws beneath the meat. 'I am deeply honoured, Comrade Colonel.' She was unable to keep the wariness out of her voice.

Rosa Klebb grunted non-committally. She knew exactly what the girl must have thought when she got the summons. The effect of her kindly reception, her shock of relief at the good news, her re-awakening fears, had been transparent. This was a beautiful, guile-less, innocent girl. Just what the *konspiratsia* demanded. Now she must be loosened up. 'My dear,' she said smoothly. 'How remiss of me. This promotion should be celebrated in a glass of wine. You must not think we senior officers are inhuman. We will drink together. It will be a good excuse to open a bottle of French champagne.'

Rosa Klebb got up and went over to the sideboard where her batman had laid out what she had ordered.

'Try one of these chocolates while I wrestle with the cork. It is never easy getting out champagne corks. We girls really need a man to help us with that sort of work, don't we?'

The ghastly prattle went on as she put a spectacular box of choco-lates in front of Tatiana. She went back to the sideboard. 'They're from Switzerland. The very best. The soft centres are the round ones. The hard ones are square.'

Tatiana murmured her thanks. She reached out and chose a round one. It would be easier to swallow. Her mouth was dry with fear of the moment when she would finally see the trap and feel it snap round her neck. It must be something dreadful to need to be concealed under all this play-acting. The bite of chocolate stuck in her mouth like chewing-gum. Mercifully the glass of champagne was thrust into her hand.

Rosa Klebb stood over her. She lifted her glass merrily. 'Za *vashe zdarovie*, Comrade Tatiana. And my warmest congratulations!'

Tatiana stitched a ghastly smile on her face. She picked up her glass and gave a little bow. '*Za vashe zdarovie*, Comrade Colonel.' She drained the glass, as is the custom in Russian drinking, and put it down in front of her.

Rosa Klebb immediately filled it again, slopping some over the table-top. 'And now to the health of your new department, Comrade.' She raised her glass. The sugary smile tightened as she watched the girl's reactions.

'To SMERSH!'

Numbly, Tatiana got to her feet. She picked up the full glass. 'To SMERSH.' The word scarcely came out. She choked on the champagne and had to take two gulps. She sat heavily down.

Rosa Klebb gave her no time for reflection. She sat down opposite and laid her hands flat on the table. 'And now to business, Comrade.' Authority was back in the voice. 'There is much work to be done.' She leant forward. 'Have you ever wished to live abroad, Comrade? In a foreign country?'

The champagne was having its effect on Tatiana. Probably worse was to come, but now let it come quickly.

'No, Comrade. I am happy in Moscow.'

'You have never thought what it might be like living in the West — all those beautiful clothes, the jazz, the modern things?'

'No, Comrade.' She was truthful. She had never thought about it.

'And if the State required you to live in the West?'

'I would obey.'

'Willingly?'

Tatiana shrugged her shoulders with a hint of impatience. 'One does what one is told.'

The woman paused. There was girlish conspiracy in the next question.

'Are you a virgin, Comrade?'

Oh, my God, thought Tatiana. 'No, Comrade Colonel.'

The wet lips glinted in the light.

'How many men?'

Tatiana coloured to the roots of her hair. Russian girls are reticent and prudish about sex. In Russia the sexual climate is mid-Victorian. These questions from the Klebb woman were all the more revolting for being asked in this cold inquisitorial tone by a State official she had never met before in her life. Tatiana screwed up her courage. She stared defensively into the yellow eyes. 'What is the purpose of these intimate questions please, Comrade Colonel?'

Rosa Klebb straightened. Her voice cut back like a whip. 'Remember yourself, Comrade. You are not here to ask questions. You forget to whom you are speaking. Answer me!'

Tatiana shrank back. 'Three men, Comrade Colonel.'

'When. How old were you?' The hard yellow eyes looked across the table into the hunted blue eyes of the girl and held them and commanded.

Tatiana was on the edge of tears. 'At school. When I was seventeen. Then at the Institute of Foreign Languages. I was twenty-two. Then last year. I was twenty-three. It was a friend I met skating.'

'Their names, please, Comrade.' Rosa Klebb picked up a pencil and pulled a scribbling pad towards her.

Tatiana covered her face with her hands and burst into tears. 'No,' she cried between her sobs. 'No, never, whatever you do to me. You have no right.'

'Stop that nonsense.' The voice was a hiss. 'In five minutes I could have those names from you, or anything else I wish to know. You are playing a dangerous game with me, Comrade. My patience will not last for ever.' Rosa Klebb paused. She was being too rough. 'For the moment we will pass on. Tomorrow you will give me the names. No harm will come to these men. They will be asked one or two questions about you – simple technical questions, that is all. Now sit up and dry your tears. We cannot have any more of this foolishness.'

Rosa Klebb got up and came round the table. She stood looking down at Tatiana. The voice became oily and smooth. 'Come,

come, my dear. You must trust me. Your little secrets are safe with me. Here, drink some more champagne and forget this little unpleasantness. We must be friends. We have work to do together. You must learn, my dear Tania, to treat me as you would your mother. Here, drink this down.'

Tatiana pulled a handkerchief out of the waistband of her skirt and dabbed at her eyes. She reached out a trembling hand for the glass of champagne and sipped at it with bowed head.

'Drink it down, my dear.'

Rosa Klebb stood over the girl like some dreadful mother duck, clucking encouragement.

Obediently Tatiana emptied the glass. She felt drained of resistance, tired, willing to do anything to finish with this interview and get away somewhere and sleep. She thought, so this is what it is like on the interrogation table, and that is the voice the Klebb uses. Well, it was working. She was docile now. She would co-operate.

Rosa Klebb sat down. She observed the girl appraisingly from behind the motherly mask.

'And now, my dear, just one more intimate little question. As between girls. Do you enjoy making love? Does it give you pleasure? Much pleasure?'

Tatiana's hands came up again and covered her face. From behind them, in a muffled voice, she said, 'Well yes, Comrade Colonel. Naturally, when one is in love...' Her voice trailed away. What else could she say? What answer did this woman want?

'And supposing, my dear, you were not in love. Then would love-making with a man still give you pleasure?'

Tatiana shook her head indecisively. She took her hands down from her face and bowed her head. The hair fell down on either side in a heavy curtain. She was trying to think, to be helpful, but she couldn't imagine such a situation. She supposed ... 'I suppose it would would depend on the man, Comrade Colonel.'

'That is a sensible answer, my dear.' Rosa Klebb opened a drawer in the table. She took out a photograph and slipped it across to the girl. 'What about this man, for instance?'

Tatiana drew the photograph cautiously towards her as if it might catch fire. She looked down warily at the handsome, ruthless face. She tried to think, to imagine ... 'I cannot tell, Comrade Colonel. He is good-looking. Perhaps if he was gentle ...' She pushed the photograph anxiously away from her.

'No, keep it, my dear. Put it up beside your bed and think of this man. You will learn more about him later in your new work. And now,' the eyes glittered behind the square panes of glass, 'would you like to know what your new work is to be? The task for which you have been chosen from all the girls in Russia?'

'Yes, indeed, Comrade Colonel,' Tatiana looked obediently across at the intent face that was now pointing at her like a gun-dog.

The wet, rubbery lips parted enticingly. 'It is a simple, delightful duty you have been chosen for, Comrade Corporal – a real labour of love, as we say. It is a matter of falling in love. That is all. Nothing else. Just falling in love with this man.'

'But who is he? I don't even know him.'

Rosa Klebb's mouth revelled. This would give the silly chit of a girl something to think about.

'He is an English spy.'

'*Bogou moiou!*' Tatiana clapped a hand over her mouth as much to stifle the use of God's name as from terror. She sat, tense with the shock, and gazed at Rosa Klebb through wide, slightly drunk eyes.

'Yes,' said Rosa Klebb, pleased with the effect of her words. 'He is an English spy. Perhaps the most famous of them all. And from now on you are in love with him. So you had better get used to the idea. And no silliness, Comrade. We must be serious. This is an important State matter for which you have been chosen as the instrument. So no nonsense, please. Now for some practical details.' Rosa Klebb stopped. She said sharply, 'And take your hand away from your silly face. And stop looking like a frightened cow. Sit up in your chair and pay attention. Or it will be the worse for you. Understood?'

'Yes, Comrade Colonel.' Tatiana quickly straightened her back and sat up with her hands in her lap as if she was back at the Security

Officers' School. Her mind was in a ferment, but this was no time for personal things. Her whole training told her that this was an operation for the State. She was now working for her country. Somehow she had come to be chosen for an important *konspiratsia*. As an officer in the M.G.B., she must do her duty and do it well. She listened carefully and with her whole professional attention.

'For the moment,' Rosa Klebb put on her official voice, 'I will be brief. You will hear more later. For the next few weeks you will be most carefully trained for this operation until you know exactly what to do in all contingencies. You will be taught certain foreign customs. You will be equipped with beautiful clothes. You will be instructed in all the arts of allurement. Then you will be sent to a foreign country, somewhere in Europe. There you will meet this man. You will seduce him. In this matter you will have no silly compunctions. Your body belongs to the State. Since your birth, the State has nourished it. Now your body must work for the State. Is that understood?'

'Yes, Comrade Colonel.' The logic was inescapable.

'You will accompany this man to England. There, you will no doubt be questioned. The questioning will be easy. The English do not use harsh methods. You will give such answers as you can without endangering the State. We will supply you with certain answers which we would like to be given. You will probably be sent to Canada. That is where the English send a certain category of foreign prisoner. You will be rescued and brought back to Moscow.' Rosa Klebb peered at the girl. She seemed to be accepting all this without question. 'You see, it is a comparatively simple matter. Have you any questions at this stage?'

'What will happen to the man, Comrade Colonel?'

'That is a matter of indifference to us. We shall simply use him as a means to introduce you into England. The object of the operation is to give false information to the British. We shall, of course, Comrade, be very glad to have your own impressions of life in England. The reports of a highly trained and intelligent girl such as yourself will be of great value to the State.'

'Really, Comrade Colonel!' Tatiana felt important. Suddenly it all sounded exciting. If only she could do it well. She would assuredly do her very best. But supposing she could not make the English spy love her. She looked again at the photograph. She put her head on one side. It was an attractive face. What were these 'arts of allurement' that the woman had talked about? What could they be? Perhaps they would help.

Satisfied, Rosa Klebb got up from the table. 'And now we can relax, my dear. Work is over for the night. I will go and tidy up and we will have a friendly chat together. I shan't be a moment. Eat up those chocolates or they will go to waste.' Rosa Klebb made a vague gesture of the hand and disappeared with a preoccupied look into the next room.

Tatiana sat back in her chair. So that was what it was all about! It really wasn't so bad after all. What a relief! And what an honour to have been chosen. How silly to have been so frightened! Naturally the great leaders of the State would not allow harm to come to an innocent citizen who worked hard and had no black marks on her *zapiska*. Suddenly she felt immensely grateful to the father-figure that was the State, and proud that she would now have a chance to repay some of her debt. Even the Klebb woman wasn't really so bad after all.

Tatiana was still cheerfully reviewing the situation when the bedroom door opened and 'the Klebb woman' appeared in the opening. 'What do you think of this my dear?' Colonel Klebb opened her dumpy arms and twirled on her toes like a mannequin. She struck a pose with one arm outstretched and the other arm crooked at her waist.

Tatiana's mouth had fallen open. She shut it quickly. She searched for something to say.

Colonel Klebb of SMERSH was wearing a semi-transparent night-gown in orange *crêpe de chine*. It had scallops of the same material round the low square neckline and scallops at the wrists of the broadly flounced sleeves. Underneath could be seen a brassière consisting of two large pink satin roses. Below, she wore old-fashioned knickers of pink satin with elastic above the knees. One dimpled knee, like a yellowish coconut, appeared thrust forward between the half open folds of the nightgown in the classic stance of the modeller. The feet were enclosed in pink satin slippers with pompoms of ostrich feathers. Rosa Klebb had taken off her spectacles and her naked face was now thick with mascara and rouge and lipstick.

She looked like the oldest and ugliest whore in the world.

Tatiana stammered, 'It is very pretty.'

'Isn't it,' twittered the woman. She went over to a broad couch in the corner of the room. It was covered with a garish piece of peasant tapestry. At the back, against the wall, were rather grimy satin cushions in pastel colours.

With a squeak of pleasure, Rosa Klebb threw herself down in the caricature of a Recamier pose. She reached up an arm and turned on a pink shaded table-lamp whose stem was a naked woman in sham Lalique glass. She patted the couch beside her.

'Turn out the top light, my dear. The switch is by the door. Then come and sit beside me. We must get to know each other better.'

Tatiana walked to the door. She switched off the top light. Her hand dropped decisively to the door knob. She turned it and opened the door and stepped coolly out into the corridor. Suddenly her nerve broke. She banged the door shut behind her and ran wildly off down the corridor with her hands over her ears against the pursuing scream that never came.

CHAPTER 10

The Fuse Burns

IT was the morning of the next day.

Colonel Klebb sat at her desk in the roomy office that was her headquarters in the underground basement of SMERSH. It was more an operations room than an office. One wall was completely papered with a map of the Western Hemisphere. The opposite wall was covered with the Eastern Hemisphere. Behind her desk and within reach of her left hand, a Telekrypton occasionally chattered out a signal *en clair*, duplicating another machine in the Cipher Department under the tall radio masts on the roof of the building. From time to time, when Colonel Klebb thought of it, she tore off the lengthening strip of tape and read through the signals. This was a formality. If anything important happened, her telephone would ring. Every agent of SMERSH throughout the world was controlled from this room, and it was a vigilant and iron control.

The heavy face looked sullen and dissipated. The chicken-skin under the eyes was pouched and the whites of the eyes were veined with red.

One of the three telephones at her side purred softly. She picked up the receiver. 'Send him in.'

She turned to Kronsteen who sat, picking his teeth thoughtfully with an opened paper clip, in an armchair up against the left-hand wall, under the toe of Africa.

'Granitsky.'

Kronsteen slowly turned his head and looked at the door.

Red Grant came in and closed the door softly behind him. He walked up to the desk and stood looking down, obediently, almost hungrily, into the eyes of his Commanding Officer. Kronsteen thought that he looked like a powerful mastiff, waiting to be fed.

Rosa Klebb surveyed him coldly. 'Are you fit and ready for work?'

'Yes, Comrade Colonel.'

'Let's have a look at you. Take off your clothes.'

Red Grant showed no surprise. He took off his coat and, after looking around for somewhere to put it, dropped it on the floor. Then, unselfconsciously, he took off the rest of his clothes and kicked off his shoes. The great red-brown body with its golden hair lit up the drab room. Grant stood relaxed, his hands held loosely at his sides and one knee bent slightly forward, as if he was posing for an art class.

Rosa Klebb got to her feet and came round the desk. She studied the body minutely, prodding here, feeling there, as if she was buying a horse. She went behind the man and continued her minute inspection. Before she came back in front of him, Kronsteen saw her slip something out of her jacket pocket and fit it into her hand. There was a glint of metal.

The woman came round and stood close up to the man's gleaming stomach, her right arm behind her back. She held his eyes in hers.

Suddenly, with terrific speed and the whole weight of her shoulder behind the blow, she whipped her right fist, loaded with a heavy brass knuckle-duster, round and exactly into the solar plexus of the man.

Whuck!

Grant let out a snort of surprise and pain. His knees gave

slightly, and then straightened. For a flash the eyes closed tight with agony. Then they opened again and glared redly down into the cold yellow probing eyes behind the square glasses. Apart from an angry flush on the skin just below the breast bone, Grant showed no ill effects from a blow that would have sent any normal man writhing to the ground.

Rosa Klebb smiled grimly. She slipped the knuckle-duster back in her pocket and walked to her desk and sat down. She looked across at Kronsteen with a hint of pride. 'At least he is fit enough,' she said.

Kronsteen grunted.

The naked man grinned with sly satisfaction. He brought up one hand and rubbed his stomach.

Rosa Klebb sat back in her chair and watched him thoughtfully. Finally she said, 'Comrade Granitsky, there is work for you. An important task. More important than anything you have attempted. It is a task that will earn you a medal' — Grant's eyes gleamed — 'for the target is a difficult and dangerous one. You will be in a foreign country, and alone. Is that clear?'

'Yes, Comrade Colonel.' Grant was excited. Here was a chance for that big step forward. What would the medal be? The Order of Lenin? He listened carefully.

'The target is an English spy. You would like to kill an English spy?'

'Very much indeed, Comrade Colonel.' Grant's enthusiasm was genuine. He asked nothing better than to kill an Englishman. He had accounts to settle with the bastards.

'You will need many weeks of training and preparation. On this assignment you will be operating in the guise of an English agent. Your manners and appearance are uncouth. You will have to learn at least some of the tricks,' the voice sneered, 'of a *chentleman*. You will be placed in the hands of a certain Englishman we have here. A former *chentleman* of the Foreign Office in London. It will be his task to make you pass as some sort of an English spy. They employ many different kinds of men. It should not be difficult. And you will have to learn many other things. The operation will be at the end of August, but you will start your training at once. There is much to be done. Put on your clothes and report back to the A.D.C. Understood?'

'Yes, Comrade Colonel.' Grant knew not to ask any questions. He scrambled into his clothes, indifferent to the woman's eyes on him, and walked over to the door, buttoning his jacket. He turned. 'Thank you, Comrade Colonel.'

Rosa Klebb was writing up her note of the interview. She didn't answer or look up and Grant went out and closed the door softly behind him.

The woman threw down her pen and sat back.

'And now, Comrade Kronsteen. Are there any points to discuss before we put the full machinery in motion? I should mention that the Praesidium has approved the target and ratified the death warrant. I have reported the broad lines of your plan to Comrade General Grubozaboyschikov. He is in agreement. The detailed execution has been left entirely in my hands. The combined planning and operations staff has been selected and is waiting to begin work. Have you any last minute thoughts, Comrade?'

Kronsteen sat looking up at the ceiling, the tips of his fingers joined in front of him. He was indifferent to the condescension in the woman's voice. The pulse of concentration beat in his temples.

'This man Granitsky. He is reliable? You can trust him in a foreign country? He will not go private?'

'He has been tested for nearly ten years. He has had many opportunities to escape. He has been watched for signs of itching feet. There has never been a breath of suspicion. The man is in the position of a drug addict. He would no more abandon the Soviet Union than a drugger would abandon the source of his cocaine. He is my top executioner. There is no one better.'

'And this girl, Romanova. She was satisfactory?'

The woman said grudgingly, 'She is very beautiful. She will serve our purpose. She is not a virgin, but she is prudish and sexually unawakened. She will receive instruction. Her English is excellent.

I have given her a certain version of her task and its object. She is co-operative. If she should show signs of faltering, I have the addresses of certain relatives, including children. I shall also have the names of her previous lovers. If necessary, it would be explained to her that these people will be hostages until her task is completed. She has an affectionate nature. Such a hint would be sufficient. But I do not anticipate any trouble from her.'

'Romanova. That is the name of a *buivshi* — of one of the former people. It seems odd to be using a Romanov for such a delicate task.'

'Her grandparents were distantly related to the Imperial Family. But she does not frequent *buivshi* circles. Anyway, all our grandparents were former people. There is nothing one can do about it.'

'Our grandparents were not called Romanov,' said Kronsteen dryly. 'However, so long as you are satisfied.' He reflected a moment. 'And this man Bond. Have we discovered his whereabouts?'

'Yes. The M.G.B. English network reports him in London. During the day, he goes to his headquarters. At night he sleeps in his flat in a district of London called Chelsea.'

'That is good. Let us hope he stays there for the next few weeks. That will mean that he is not engaged on some operation. He will be available to go after our bait when they get the scent. Meanwhile,' Kronsteen's dark, pensive eyes continued to examine a particular point on the ceiling, 'I have been studying the suitability of centres abroad. I have decided on Istanbul for the first contact. We have a good *apparat* there. The Secret Service has only a small station. The head of the station is reported to be a good man. He will be liquidated. The centre is conveniently placed for us, with short lines of communication with Bulgaria and the Black Sea. It is relatively far from London. I am working out details of the point of assassination and the means of getting this Bond there, after he has contacted the girl. It will be either in France or very near it. We have excellent leverage on the French press. They will make the most of this kind of story, with its sensational disclosures of sex and espionage. It also remains to be decided when Granitsky shall enter the picture. These are minor details. We must choose the cameramen and the other operatives and move them quietly into Istanbul. There must be no crowding of our *apparat* there, no congestion, no unusual activity. We will warn all departments that wireless traffic with Turkey is to be kept absolutely normal before and during the operation. We don't want the British interceptors smelling a rat. The Cipher Department has agreed that there is no Security objection to handing over the outer case of a Spektor machine. That will be attractive. The machine will go to the Special Devices section. They will handle its preparation.'

Kronsteen stopped talking. His gaze slowly came down from the ceiling. He rose thoughtfully to his feet. He looked across and into the watchful, intent eyes of the woman.

'I can think of nothing else at the moment, Comrade,' he said. 'Many details will come up and have to be settled from day to day. But I think the operation can safely begin.'

'I agree, Comrade. The matter can now go forward. I will issue the necessary directives.' The harsh, authoritative voice unbent. 'I am grateful for your co-operation.'

Kronsteen lowered his head one inch in acknowledgment. He turned and walked softly out of the room.

In the silence, the Telekrypton gave a warning ping and started up its mechanical chatter. Rosa Klebb stirred in her chair and reached for one of the telephones. She dialled a number.

'Operations Room,' said a man's voice.

Rosa Klebb's pale eyes, gazing out across the room, lit on the pink shape on the wall-map that was England. Her wet lips parted.

'Colonel Klebb speaking. The *konspiratsia* against the English spy Bond. The operation will commence forthwith.'

Part Two

THE EXECUTION

CHAPTER 11

The Soft Life

THE blubbery arms of the soft life had Bond round the neck and they were slowly strangling him. He was a man of war and when, for a long period, there was no war, his spirit went into a decline.

In his particular line of business, peace had reigned for nearly a year. And peace was killing him.

At 7.30 on the morning of Thursday, August 12th, Bond awoke in his comfortable flat in the plane-tree'd square off the King's Road and was disgusted to find that he was thoroughly bored with the prospect of the day ahead. Just as, in at least one religion, *accidie* is the first of the cardinal sins, so boredom, and particularly the incredible circumstance of waking up bored, was the only vice Bond utterly condemned.

Bond reached out and gave two rings on the bell to show May, his treasured Scottish housekeeper, that he was ready for breakfast. Then he abruptly flung the single sheet off his naked body and swung his feet to the floor.

There was only one way to deal with boredom — kick oneself

out of it. Bond went down on his hands and did twenty slow press-ups, lingering over each one so that his muscles had no rest. When his arms could stand the pain no longer, he rolled over on his back and, with his hands at his sides, did the straight leg-lift until his stomach muscles screamed. He got to his feet and, after touching his toes twenty times, went over to arm and chest exercises combined with deep breathing until he was dizzy. Panting with the exertion, he went into the big white-tiled bathroom and stood in the glass shower cabinet under very hot and then cold hissing water for five minutes.

At last, after shaving and putting on a sleeveless dark blue Sea Island cotton shirt and navy blue tropical worsted trousers, he slipped his bare feet into black leather sandals and went through the bedroom into the long big-windowed sitting-room with the satisfaction of having sweated his boredom, at any rate for the time being, out of his body.

May, an elderly Scotswoman with iron grey hair and a handsome closed face, came in with the tray and put it on the table in the bay window together with *The Times*, the only paper Bond ever read.

Bond wished her good morning and sat down to breakfast.

'Good morning-s.' (To Bond, one of May's endearing qualities was that she would call no man 'sir' except — Bond had teased her about it years before — English kings and Winston Churchill. As a mark of exceptional regard, she accorded Bond an occasional hint of an 's' at the end of a word.)

She stood by the table while Bond folded his paper to the centre news page.

'Yon man was here again last night about the Televeesion.'

'What man was that?' Bond looked along the headlines.

'Yon man that's always coming. Six times he's been here pestering me since June. After what I said to him the first time about the sinful thing, you'd think he'd give up trying to sell us one. By hire purchase, too, if you please!'

'Persistent chaps these salesmen.' Bond put down his paper and reached for the coffee pot.

'I gave him a right piece of my mind last night. Disturbing folk at their supper. Asked him if he'd got any papers — anything to show who he was.'

'I expect that fixed him.' Bond filled his large coffee cup to the brim with black coffee.

'Not a bit of it. Flourished his union card. Said he had every right to earn his living. Electricians Union it was too. They're the Communist one, aren't they-s?'

'Yes, that's right,' said Bond vaguely. His mind sharpened. Was it possible *They* could be keeping an eye on him? He took a sip of the coffee and put the cup down. 'Exactly what did this man say, May?' he asked, keeping his voice indifferent, but looking up at her.

'He said he's selling Televeesion sets on commission in his spare time. And are we sure we don't want one. He says we're one of the only folk in the square that haven't got one. Sees there isn't one of those aerial things on the house, I dare say. He's always asking if you're at home so that he can have a word with you about it. Fancy his cheek! I'm surprised he hasn't thought to catch you coming in or going out. He's always asking if I'm expecting you home. Naturally I don't tell him anything about your movements. Respectable, quiet-spoken body, if he wasn't so persistent.'

Could be, thought Bond. There are many ways of checking up whether the owner's at home or away. A servant's appearance and reactions — a glance through the open door. 'Well, you're wasting your time because he's away,' would be the obvious reception if the flat was empty. Should he tell the Security Section? Bond shrugged his shoulders irritably. What the hell. There was probably nothing in it. Why would *They* be interested in him? And, if there was something in it, Security was quite capable of making him change his flat.

'I expect you've frightened him away this time.' Bond smiled up at May. 'I should think you've heard the last of him.'

'Yes-s,' said May doubtfully. At any rate she had carried out her orders to tell him if she saw anyone 'hanging about the place'.

She bustled off with a whisper of the old-fashioned black uniform she persisted in wearing even in the heat of August.

Bond went back to his breakfast. Normally it was little straws in the wind like this that would start a persistent intuitive ticking in his mind, and, on other days, he would not have been happy until he had solved the problem of the man from the Communist Union who kept on coming to the house. Now, from months of idleness and disuse, the sword was rusty in the scabbard and Bond's mental guard was down.

Breakfast was Bond's favourite meal of the day. When he was stationed in London it was always the same. It consisted of very strong coffee, from De Bry in New Oxford Street, brewed in an American *Chemex*, of which he drank two large cups, black and without sugar. The single egg, in the dark blue egg cup with a gold ring round the top, was boiled for three and a third minutes.

It was a very fresh, speckled brown egg from French *Marans* hens owned by some friend of May in the country. (Bond disliked white eggs and, faddish as he was in many small things, it amused him to maintain that there was such a thing as the perfect boiled egg.) Then there were two thick slices of wholewheat toast, a large pat of deep yellow Jersey butter and three squat glass jars containing Tiptree 'Little Scarlet' strawberry jam; Cooper's Vintage Oxford marmalade and Norwegian Heather Honey from Fortnum's. The coffee pot and the silver on the tray were Queen Anne, and the china was Minton, of the same dark blue and gold and white as the egg-cup.

That morning, while Bond finished his breakfast with honey, he pinpointed the immediate cause of his lethargy and of his low spirits. To begin with, Tiffany Case, his love for so many happy months, had left him and, after final painful weeks during which she had withdrawn to an hotel, had sailed for America at the end of July. He missed her badly and his mind still sheered away from the thought of her. And it was August, and London was hot and stale. He was due for leave, but he had not the energy or the desire to go off alone, or to try and find some temporary replacement for Tiffany to go with him. So he had stayed on in the half-empty headquarters of the Secret Service grinding away at the old routines, snapping at his secretary and rasping his colleagues.

Even M. had finally got impatient with the surly caged tiger on the floor below, and, on Monday of this particular week, he had sent Bond a sharp note appointing him to a Committee of Inquiry under Paymaster Captain Troop. The note said that it was time Bond, as a senior officer in the Service, took a hand in major administrative problems. Anyway, there was no one else available. Headquarters were short-handed and the oo Section was quiescent. Bond would pray report that afternoon, at 2.30, to Room 412.

It was Troop, reflected Bond, as he lit his first cigarette of the day, who was the most nagging and immediate cause of his discontent.

In every large business, there is one man who is the office tyrant and bugbear and who is cordially disliked by all the staff. This individual performs an unconsciously important role by acting as a kind of lightning conductor for the usual office hates and fears. In fact, he reduces their disruptive influence by providing them with a common target. The man is usually the general manager, or the Head of Admin. He is that indispensable man who is a watchdog over the small things — petty cash, heat and light, towels and soap in the lavatories, stationery supplies, the canteen, the holiday rota, the punctuality of the staff. He is the one man who has real impact on the office comforts and amenities and whose authority extends into the privacy and personal habits of the men and women of the organization. To want such a job, and to have the necessary qualifications for it, the man must have exactly those qualities which irritate and abrade. He must be parsimonious, observant, prying and meticulous. And he must be a strong disciplinarian and indifferent to opinion. He must be a little dictator. In all well-run businesses there is such a man. In the Secret Service, it is Paymaster Captain Troop, R.N. Retired, Head of Admin., whose job it is, in his own words, 'to keep the place shipshape and Bristol fashion'.

It was inevitable that Captain Troop's duties would bring him into conflict with most of the organization, but it was particularly unfortunate that M. could think of no one but Troop to spare as Chairman for this particular Committee.

For this was yet one more of those Committees of Inquiry dealing with the delicate intricacies of the Burgess and Maclean case, and with the lessons that could be learned from it. M. had dreamed it up, five years after he had closed his own particular file on that case, purely as a sop to the Privy Council Inquiry into the Security Services which the Prime Minister had ordered in 1955.

At once Bond had got into a hopeless wrangle with Troop over the employment of 'intellectuals' in the Secret Service.

Perversely, and knowing it would annoy, Bond had put forward the proposition that, if M.I.5 and the Secret Service were to concern themselves seriously with the atom age 'intellectual spy', they must employ a certain number of intellectuals to counter them. 'Retired officers of the Indian Army,' Bond had pronounced, 'can't possibly understand the thought processes of a Burgess or a Maclean. They won't even know such people exist — let alone be in a position to frequent their cliques and get to know their friends and their secrets. Once Burgess and Maclean went to Russia, the only way to make contact with them again and, perhaps, when they got tired of Russia, turn them into double agents against the Russians, would have been to send their closest friends to Moscow and Prague and Budapest with orders to wait until one of these chaps crept out of the masonry and made contact. And one of them, probably Burgess, would have been driven to make contact by his loneliness and by his ache to tell his story to someone.[1] But they certainly wouldn't take the risk of revealing themselves to some man with a trench-coat and a cavalry moustache and a beta minus mind.'

'Oh really,' Troop had said with icy calm. 'So you suggest we should staff the organization with long-haired perverts. That's quite an original notion. I thought we were all agreed that homo-

[1] Written in March 1956. I. F.

sexuals were about the worst security risk there is. I can't see the Americans handing over many atom secrets to a lot of pansies soaked in scent.'

'All intellectuals aren't homosexual. And many of them are bald. I'm just saying that . . . ,' and so the argument had gone on intermittently through the hearings of the past three days, and the other committee members had ranged themselves more or less with Troop. Now, today, they had to draw up their recommendations and Bond was wondering whether to take the unpopular step of entering a minority report.

How seriously did he feel about the whole question, Bond wondered as, at nine o'clock, he walked out of his flat and down the steps to his car? Was he just being petty and obstinate? Had he constituted himself into a one-man opposition only to give his teeth something to bite into? Was he so bored that he could find nothing better to do than make a nuisance of himself inside his own organization? Bond couldn't make up his mind. He felt restless and indecisive, and, behind it all, there was a nagging disquiet he couldn't put his finger on.

As he pressed the self-starter and the twin exhausts of the Bentley woke to their fluttering growl, a curious bastard quotation slipped from nowhere into Bond's mind.

'Those whom the Gods wish to destroy, they first make bored.'

CHAPTER 12

A Piece of Cake

As it turned out, Bond never had to make a decision on the Committee's final report.

He had complimented his secretary on a new summer frock, and was half way through the file of signals that had come in during the night, when the red telephone that could only mean M. or his Chief-of-Staff gave its soft, peremptory burr.

Bond picked up the receiver. '007.'

'Can you come up?' It was the Chief-of-Staff.

'M.?'

'Yes. And it looks like a long session. I've told Troop you won't be able to make the Committee.'

'Any idea what it's about?'

The Chief-of-Staff chuckled. 'Well, I have as a matter of fact. But you'd better hear about it from him. It'll make you sit up. There's quite a swerve on this one.'

As Bond put on his coat and went out into the corridor, banging the door behind him, he had a feeling of certainty that the starter's gun had fired and that the dog days had come to an end. Even the ride up to the top floor in the lift and the walk down the long quiet corridor to the door of M.'s staff office seemed to be charged with the significance of all those other occasions when the bell of the red telephone had been the signal that had fired him, like a loaded projectile, across the world towards some distant target of M.'s choosing. And the eyes of Miss Moneypenny, M.'s private secretary, had that old look of excitement and secret knowledge as she smiled up at him and pressed the switch on the intercom.

'007's here, sir.'

'Send him in,' said the metallic voice, and the red light of privacy went on above the door.

Bond went through the door and closed it softly behind him. The room was cool, or perhaps it was the venetian blinds that gave an impression of coolness. They threw bars of light and shadow across the dark green carpet up to the edge of the big central desk. There the sunshine stopped so that the quiet figure behind the desk sat in a pool of suffused greenish shade. In the ceiling directly above the desk, a big twin-bladed tropical fan, a recent addition to M.'s room, slowly revolved, shifting the thundery August air that, even high up above the Regent's Park, was heavy and stale after a week of heat-wave.

M. gestured to the chair opposite him across the red leather desk. Bond sat down and looked across into the tranquil, lined sailor's face that he loved, honoured and obeyed.

'Do you mind if I ask you a personal question, James?' M. never asked his staff personal questions and Bond couldn't imagine what was coming.

'No, sir.'

M. picked his pipe out of the big copper ash-tray and began to fill it, thoughtfully watching his fingers at work with the tobacco. He said harshly: 'You needn't answer, but it's to do with your, er, friend, Miss Case. As you know, I don't generally interest myself in these matters, but I did hear that you had been, er, seeing a lot of each other since that diamond business. Even some idea you might be going to get married.' M. glanced up at Bond and then down again. He put the loaded pipe into his mouth and set a match to it. Out of the corner of his mouth, as he drew at the jigging flame, he said: 'Care to tell me anything about it?'

Now what? wondered Bond. Damn these office gossips. He said gruffly, 'Well, sir, we did get on well. And there was some idea we might get married. But then she met some chap in the American Embassy. On the Military Attaché's staff. Marine Corps major. And I gather she's going to marry him. They've both gone back to the States, as a matter of fact. Probably better that way. Mixed marriages aren't often a success. I gather he's a nice enough fellow. Probably suit her better than living in London. She couldn't really settle down here. Fine girl, but she's a bit neurotic. We had too many rows. Probably my fault. Anyway it's over now.'

M. gave one of the brief smiles that lit up his eyes more than his mouth. 'I'm sorry if it went wrong, James,' he said. There was no sympathy in M.'s voice. He disapproved of Bond's 'womanizing', as he called it to himself, while recognizing that his prejudice was the relic of a Victorian upbringing. But, as Bond's chief, the last thing he wanted was for Bond to be permanently tied to one woman's skirts. 'Perhaps it's for the best. Doesn't do to get mixed up with neurotic women in this business. They hang on your gun-arm, if you know what I mean. Forgive me for asking about it. Had to know the answer before I told you what's come up. It's a pretty odd business. Be difficult to get you involved if you were on the edge of marrying or anything of that sort.'

Bond shook his head, waiting for the story.

'All right then,' said M. There was a note of relief in his voice. He leant back in his chair and gave several quick pulls on his pipe to get it going. 'This is what's happened. Yesterday there was a long signal in from Istanbul. Seems on Tuesday the Head of Station T got an anonymous typewritten message which told him to take a round ticket on the 8 p.m. ferry steamer from the Galata Bridge to the mouth of the Bosphorus and back. Nothing else. Head of T's an adventurous sort of chap, and of course he took the steamer. He stood up for'ard by the rail and waited. After about a quarter of an hour a girl came and stood beside him, a Russian girl, very good-looking, he says, and after they'd talked a bit about the view and so on, she suddenly switched and in the same sort of conversational voice she told him an extraordinary story.'

M. paused to put another match to his pipe. Bond interjected, 'Who is Head of T, sir? I've never worked in Turkey.'

'Man called Kerim, Darko Kerim. Turkish father and English mother. Remarkable fellow. Been Head of T since before the war. One of the best men we've got anywhere. Does a wonderful job. Loves it. Very intelligent and he knows all that part of the world like the back of his hand.' M. dismissed Kerim with a sideways jerk of his pipe. 'Anyway, the girl's story was that she was a Corporal in the M.G.B. Had been in the show since she left school and had just got transferred to the Istanbul centre as a cipher officer. She'd engineered the transfer because she wanted to get out of Russia and come over.'

'That's good,' said Bond. 'Might be useful to have one of their cipher girls. But why does she want to come over?'

M. looked across the table at Bond. 'Because she's in love.' He paused and added mildly, 'She says she's in love with you.'

'In love with *me*?'

'Yes, with you. That's what she says. Her name's Tatiana Romanova. Ever heard of her?'

'Good God, no! I mean, no, sir.' M. smiled at the mixture of expressions on Bond's face. 'But what the hell does she mean? Has she ever met me? How does she know I exist?'

'Well,' said M. 'The whole thing sounds absolutely ridiculous. But it's so crazy that it just might be true. This girl is twenty-four. Ever since she joined the M.G.B. she's been working in their Central Index, the same as our Records. And she's been working in the English section of it. She's been there six years. One of the files she had to deal with was yours.'

'I'd like to see that one,' commented Bond.

'Her story is that she first took a fancy to the photographs they've got of you. Admired your looks and so on.' M.'s mouth turned downwards at the corners as if he had just sucked at a lemon. 'She read up all your cases. Decided that you were the hell of a fellow.'

Bond looked down his nose. M.'s face was non-committal.

'She said you particularly appealed to her because you reminded her of the hero of a book by some Russian fellow called Lermontov. Apparently it was her favourite book. This hero chap liked gambling and spent his whole time getting in and out of scraps. Anyway, you reminded her of him. She says she came to think of nothing else, and one day the idea came to her that if only she could transfer to one of their foreign centres she could get in touch with you and you would come and rescue her.'

'I've never heard such a crazy story, sir. Surely Head of T didn't swallow it.'

'Now wait a moment,' M.'s voice was testy. 'Just don't be in too much of a hurry simply because something's turned up you've never come across before. Suppose you happened to be a film star instead of being in this particular trade. You'd get daft letters from girls all over the world stuffed with Heaven knows what sort of rot about not being able to live without you and so on. Here's a silly girl doing a secretary's job in Moscow. Probably the whole department is staffed by women, like our Records. Not a man in the room to look at, and here she is, faced with your, er, dashing features on a file that's constantly coming up for review. And she gets what I believe they call a 'crush' on these pictures just as secretaries all over the world get crushes on these dreadful faces in the magazines.' M. waved his pipe sideways to indicate his ignorance of these grisly female habits. 'The Lord knows I don't know much about these things, but you must admit that they happen.'

Bond smiled at the appeal for help. 'Well, as a matter of fact, sir, I'm beginning to see there is some sense in it. There's no reason why a Russian girl shouldn't be just as silly as an English one. But she must have got guts to do what she did. Does Head of T say if she realized the consequences if she was found out?'

'He said she was frightened out of her wits,' said M. 'Spent the whole time on the boat looking round to see if anybody was watching her. But it seems they were the usual peasants and commuters that take these boats, and as it was a late boat there weren't many passengers anyway. But wait a minute. You haven't heard half the story.' M. took a long pull at his pipe and blew a cloud of smoke up towards the slowly turning fan above his head. Bond watched the smoke get caught up in the blades and whirled into nothingness. 'She told Kerim that this passion for you gradually developed into a phobia. She got to hate the sight of Russian men. In time this turned into a dislike of the régime and particularly of the work she was doing for them and, so to speak, against you. So she applied for a transfer abroad, and since her languages were very good — English and French — in due course she was offered Istanbul if she would join the Cipher Department, which meant a cut in pay. To cut a long story short, after six months' training, she got to Istanbul about three weeks ago. Then she sniffed about and soon got hold of the name of our man, Kerim. He's been there so long that everybody in Turkey knows what he does by now. He doesn't mind, and it takes people's eyes off the special men we send in from time to time. There's no harm in having a front man in some of these places. Quite a lot of customers would come to us if they knew where to go and who to talk to.'

Bond commented: 'The public agent often does better than the man who has to spend a lot of time and energy keeping under cover.'

'So she sent Kerim the note. Now she wants to know if he can help her.' M. paused and sucked thoughtfully at his pipe. 'Of course Kerim's first reactions were exactly the same as yours, and he fished around looking for a trap. But he simply couldn't see what the Russians could gain from sending this girl over to us. All this time the steamer was getting further and further up the Bosphorus and soon it would be turning to come back to Istanbul. And the girl got more and more desperate as Kerim went on trying to break down her story. Then,' M.'s eyes glittered softly across at Bond, 'came the clincher.'

That glitter in M.'s eyes, thought Bond. How well he knew

those moments when M.'s cold grey eyes betrayed their excitement and their greed.

'She had a last card to play. And she knew it was the ace of trumps. If she could come over to us, she would bring her cipher machine with her. It's the brand new Spektor machine. The thing we'd give our eyes to have.'

'God,' said Bond softly, his mind boggling at the immensity of the prize. The Spektor! The machine that would allow them to decipher the Top Secret traffic of all. To have that, even if its loss was immediately discovered and the settings changed, or the machine taken out of service in Russian embassies and spy centres all over the world, would be a priceless victory. Bond didn't know much about cryptography, and, for security's sake, in case he was ever captured, wished to know as little as possible about its secrets, but at least he knew that, in the Russian secret service, loss of the Spektor would be counted a major disaster.

Bond was sold. At once he accepted all M.'s faith in the girl's story, however crazy it might be. For a Russian to bring them this gift, and take the appalling risk of bringing it, could only mean an act of desperation — of desperate infatuation if you liked. Whether the girl's story was true or not, the stakes were too high to turn down the gamble.

'You see, 007?' said M. softly. It was not difficult to read Bond's mind from the excitement in his eyes. 'You see what I mean?'

Bond hedged. 'But did she say how she could do it?'

'Not exactly. But Kerim says she was absolutely definite. Some business about night duty. Apparently she's on duty alone certain nights of the week and sleeps on a camp bed in the office. She seemed to have no doubts about it, although she realized that she would be shot out of hand if anyone even dreamed of her plan. She was even worried about Kerim reporting all this back to me. Made him promise he would encode the signal himself and send it on a one-time-only pad and keep no copy. Naturally he did as she asked. Directly she mentioned the Spektor, Kerim knew he might be on to the most important coup that's come our way since the war.'

'What happened then, sir?'

'The steamer was coming up to a place called Ortakoy. She said she was going to get off there. Kerim promised to get a signal off that night. She refused to make any arrangements for staying in touch. Just said that she would keep her end of the bargain if we would keep ours. She said good night and mixed in the crowd going down the gang-plank and that was the last Kerim saw of her.'

M. suddenly leant forward in his chair and looked hard at Bond. 'But of course he couldn't *guarantee* that we would make the bargain with her.'

Bond said nothing. He thought he could guess what was coming.

'This girl will only do these things on one condition.' M.'s eyes narrowed until they were fierce, significant slits. 'That you go out to Istanbul and bring her and the machine back to England.'

Bond shrugged his shoulders. That presented no difficulties. But . . . He looked candidly back at M. 'Should be a piece of cake, sir. As far as I can see there's only one snag. She's only seen photographs of me and read a lot of exciting stories. Suppose that when she sees me in the flesh, I don't come up to her expectations.'

'That's where the work comes in,' said M. grimly. 'That's why I asked those questions about Miss Case. It's up to you to see that you *do* come up to her expectations.'

CHAPTER 13

'B.E.A. Takes You There . . .'

THE four small, square-ended propellers turned slowly, one by one, and became four whizzing pools. The low hum of the turbo-jets rose to a shrill smooth whine. The quality of the noise, and the complete absence of vibration, were different from the stuttering roar and straining horsepower of all other aircraft Bond had flown in. As the Viscount wheeled easily out to the shimmering east-west runway of London Airport, Bond felt as if he was sitting in an expensive mechanical toy.

There was a pause as the chief pilot gunned up the four turbo-jets into a banshee scream and then, with a jerk of released brakes, the 10.30 B.E.A. Flight 130 to Rome, Athens and Istanbul gathered speed and hurtled down the runway and up into a quick, easy climb.

In ten minutes they had reached 20,000 feet and were heading south along the wide air-channel that takes the Mediterranean traffic from England. The scream of the jets died to a low, drowsy whistle. Bond unfastened his seat-belt and lit a cigarette. He reached for the slim, expensive-looking attaché case on the floor beside him and took out *The Mask of Dimitrios* by Eric Ambler and put the case, which was very heavy in spite of its size, on the seat beside him. He thought how surprised the ticket clerk at London Airport would have been if she had weighed the case instead of letting it go unchecked as an 'overnight bag'. And if, in their turn, Customs had been intrigued by its weight, how interested they would have been when it was slipped under the Inspectoscope.

Q Branch had put together this smart-looking little bag, ripping out the careful handiwork of Swaine and Adeney to pack fifty rounds of .25 ammunition, in two flat rows, between the leather and the lining of the spine. In each of the innocent sides there was a flat throwing knife, built by Wilkinsons, the sword makers, and the tops of their handles were concealed cleverly by the stitching at the corners. Despite Bond's efforts to laugh them out of it, Q's craftsmen had insisted on building a hidden compartment into the handle of the case, which, by pressure at a certain point, would deliver a cyanide death-pill into the palm of his hand. (Directly he had taken delivery of the case, Bond had washed this pill down the lavatory.) More important was the thick tube of Palmolive shaving cream in the otherwise guileless spongebag. The whole top of this unscrewed to reveal the silencer for the Beretta, packed in cotton wool. In case hard cash was needed, the lid of the attaché case contained fifty golden sovereigns. These could be poured out by slipping sideways one ridge of welting.

The complicated bag of tricks amused Bond, but he also had to admit that, despite its eight-pound weight, the bag was a convenient way of carrying the tools of his trade, which otherwise would have to be concealed about his body.

Only a dozen miscellaneous passengers were on the plane. Bond smiled at the thought of Loelia Ponsonby's horror if she knew that that made the load thirteen. The day before, when he had left M. and had gone back to his office to arrange the details of his flight, his secretary had protested violently at the idea of his travelling on Friday the thirteenth.

'But it's always best to travel on the thirteenth,' Bond had explained patiently. 'There are practically no passengers and it's more comfortable and you get better service. I always choose the thirteenth when I can.'

'Well,' she had said resignedly, 'it's your funeral. But I shall spend the day worrying about you. And for heaven's sake don't go walking under ladders or anything silly this afternoon. You oughtn't to overplay your luck like this. I don't know what you're going to Turkey for, and I don't want to know. But I have a feeling in my bones.'

'Ah, those beautiful bones!' Bond had teased her. 'I'll take them out to dinner the night I get back.'

'You'll do nothing of the sort,' she had said coldly. Later she had kissed him goodbye with a sudden warmth, and for the hundredth time Bond had wondered why he bothered with other women when the most darling of them all was his secretary.

The plane sang steadily on above the endless sea of whipped-cream clouds that looked solid enough to land on if the engines failed. The clouds broke up and a distant blue haze, far away to their left, was Paris. For an hour they flew high over the burned-up fields of France until, after Dijon, the land turned from a pale to a darker green as it sloped up into the Juras.

Lunch came. Bond put aside his book and the thoughts that kept coming between him and the printed page, and, while he ate, he gazed down at the cool mirror of the Lake of Geneva. As the pine forests began to climb towards the snow patches between the beautifully scoured teeth of the Alps, he remembered early skiing holidays. The plane skirted the great eye-tooth of Mont Blanc, a few hundred yards to port, and Bond looked down at the dirty grey elephant's skin of the glaciers and saw himself again, a young man in his teens, with the leading end of the rope round his waist, bracing himself against the top of a rock-chimney on the Aiguilles Rouges as his two companions from the University of Geneva inched up the smooth rock towards him.

And now? Bond smiled wryly at his reflection in the Perspex as the plane swung out of the mountains and over the grosgrained terazza of Lombardy. If that young James Bond came up to him in the street and talked to him, would he recognize the clean, eager youth that had been him at seventeen? And what would that youth think of him, the secret agent, the older James Bond? Would he recognize himself beneath the surface of this man who was tarnished with years of treachery and ruthlessness and fear — this man with the cold arrogant eyes and the scar down his cheek and the flat bulge beneath his left armpit? If the youth did recognize him what would his judgment be? What would he think of Bond's present assignment? What would he think of the dashing secret agent who was off across the world in a new and most romantic role — to pimp for England?

Bond put the thought of his dead youth out of his mind. Never job backwards. What-might-have-been was a waste of time. Follow your fate, and be satisfied with it, and be glad not to be a second-hand motor salesman, or a yellow-press journalist, pickled in gin and nicotine, or a cripple — or dead.

Gazing down on the sun-baked sprawl of Genoa and the gentle blue waters of the Mediterranean, Bond closed his mind to the past and focused it on the immediate future — on this business, as he sourly described it to himself, of 'pimping for England'.

For that, however else one might like to describe it, was what he was on his way to do — to seduce, and seduce very quickly, a girl whom he had never seen before, whose name he had heard yesterday for the first time. And all the while, however attractive she was — and Head of T had described her as 'very beautiful' — Bond's whole mind would have to be not on what she was, but on what she had — the dowry she was bringing with her. It would be like trying to marry a rich woman for her money. Would he be able to act the part? Perhaps he could make the right faces and say the right things, but would his body dissociate itself from his secret thoughts and effectively make the love he would declare? How did men behave credibly in bed when their whole minds were focused on a woman's bank balance? Perhaps there was an erotic stimulus in the notion that one was ravaging a sack of gold. But a cipher machine?

Elba passed below them and the plane slid into its fifty-mile glide towards Rome. Half an hour among the jabbering loudspeakers of Ciampino Airport, time to drink two excellent Americanos, and they were on their way again, flying steadily down towards the toe of Italy, and Bond's mind went back to sifting the minutest details of the rendezvous that was drawing closer at three hundred miles an hour.

Was it all a complicated M.G.B. plot of which he couldn't find the key? Was he walking into some trap that not even the tortuous mind of M. could fathom? God knew M. was worried about the possibility of such a trap. Every conceivable angle of the evidence, for and against, had been scrutinized — not only by M., but also by a full-dress operations meeting of Heads of Sections that had worked all through the afternoon and evening before. But, which ever way the case had been examined, no one had been able to suggest what the Russians might get out of it. They might want to kidnap Bond and interrogate him. But why Bond? He was an operating agent, unconcerned with the general working of the Service, carrying in his head nothing of use to the Russians except the details of his current duty and a certain amount of background information that could not possibly be vital. Or they might want to kill Bond, as an act of revenge. Yet he had not come up against them for two years. If they wanted to kill him, they had only to shoot him in the streets of London, or in his flat, or put a bomb in his car.

Bond's thoughts were interrupted by the stewardess. 'Fasten your seat-belts, please.' As she spoke the plane dropped sickeningly and soared up again with an ugly note of strain in the scream of the jets. The sky outside was suddenly black. Rain hammered on the windows. There came a blinding flash of blue and white light and a crash as if an anti-aircraft shell had hit them, and the plane heaved and bucketed in the belly of the electric storm that had ambushed them out of the mouth of the Adriatic.

Bond smelt the smell of danger. It is a real smell, something like the mixture of sweat and electricity you get in an amusement arcade. Again the lightning flung its hands across the windows. Crash! It felt as if they were the centre of the thunder clap. Suddenly the plane seemed incredibly small and frail. Thirteen passengers! Friday the Thirteenth! Bond thought of Loelia Ponsonby's words and his hands on the arms of his chair felt wet. How old is this plane, he wondered? How many flying hours has it done? Had the deathwatch beetle of metal fatigue got into the wings? How much of their strength had it eaten away? Perhaps he wouldn't get to Istanbul after all. Perhaps a plummeting crash into the Gulf of Corinth was going to be the destiny he had been scanning philosophically only an hour before.

In the centre of Bond was a hurricane-room, the kind of citadel found in old-fashioned houses in the tropics. These rooms are small, strongly built cells in the heart of the house, in the middle of the ground floor and sometimes dug down into its foundations. To this cell the owner and his family retire if the storm threatens to destroy the house, and they stay there until the danger is past. Bond went to his hurricane-room only when the situation was beyond his control and no other possible action could be taken. Now he retired to this citadel, closed his mind to the hell of noise and violent movement, and focused on a single stitch in the back of the seat in front of him, waiting with slackened nerves for whatever fate had decided for B.E.A. Flight No. 130.

Almost at once it got lighter in the cabin. The rain stopped crashing on the Perspex window and the noise of the jets settled back into their imperturbable whistle. Bond opened the door of his hurricane-room and stepped out. He slowly turned his head and looked curiously out of the window and watched the tiny shadow of the plane hastening far below across the quiet waters of the Gulf of Corinth. He heaved a deep sigh and reached into his hip-pocket for his gunmetal cigarette case. He was pleased to see his hands were dead steady as he took out his lighter and lit one of the Morland cigarettes with the three gold rings. Should he tell Lil that perhaps she had almost been right? He decided that if he could find a rude enough postcard in Istanbul he would.

The day outside faded through the colours of a dying dolphin and Mount Hymettus came at them, blue in the dusk. Down over the twinkling sprawl of Athens and then the Viscount was wheeling across the standard concrete air-strip with its drooping windsock and the notices in the strange dancing letters Bond had hardly seen since school.

Bond climbed out of the plane with the handful of pale, silent passengers and walked across to the transit lounge and up to the bar. He ordered a tumbler of Ouzo and drank it down and chased it with a mouthful of ice water. There was a strong bite under the sickly anisette taste and Bond felt the drink light a quick, small fire down his throat and in his stomach. He put down his glass and ordered another.

By the time the loudspeakers called him out again it was dusk and the half moon rode clear and high above the lights of the town. The air was soft with evening and the smell of flowers and there was the steady pulse-beat of the cicadas — zing-a-zing-a-zing — and the distant sound of a man singing. The voice was clear and sad and the song had a note of lament. Near the airport a dog barked excitedly at an unknown human smell. Bond suddenly realized that he had come into the East where the guard-dog howls all night. For some reason the realization sent a pang of pleasure and excitement into his heart.

They had only a ninety-minute flight to Istanbul, across the dark Aegean and the Sea of Marmara. An excellent dinner, with two dry Martinis and a half-bottle of Calvet claret, put Bond's reservations about flying on Friday the thirteenth, and his worries about his assignment, out of his mind and substituted a mood of pleased anticipation.

Then they were there and the plane's four propellers wheeled to a stop outside the fine modern airport of Yesilkoy, an hour's drive from Istanbul. Bond said goodbye and thank you for a good flight to the stewardess, carried the heavy little attaché case through the passport check into the customs, and waited for his suitcase to come off the plane.

So these dark, ugly, neat little officials were the modern Turks. He listened to their voices, full of broad vowels and quiet sibilants and modified u-sounds, and he watched the dark eyes that belied the soft, polite voices. They were bright, angry, cruel eyes that had only lately come down from the mountains. Bond thought he knew the history of those eyes. They were eyes that had been trained for centuries to watch over sheep and decipher small movements on far horizons. They were eyes that kept the knife-hand in sight without seeming to, that counted the grains of meal and the small fractions of coin and noted the flicker of the merchant's fingers. They were hard, untrusting, jealous eyes. Bond didn't take to them.

Outside the customs, a tall rangy man with drooping black moustaches stepped out of the shadows. He wore a smart dust-coat and a chauffeur's cap. He saluted and, without asking Bond his name, took his suitcase and led the way over to a gleaming aristocrat of a car — an old black basket-work Rolls Royce coupé-de-ville that Bond guessed must have been built for some millionaire of the '20s.

When the car was gliding out of the airport, the man turned and said politely over his shoulder, in excellent English, 'Kerim Bey thought you would prefer to rest tonight, sir. I am to call for you at nine tomorrow morning. What hotel are you staying at, sir?'

'The Kristal Palas.'

'Very good, sir.' The car sighed off down the wide modern road.

Behind them, in the dappled shadows of the airport parking place, Bond vaguely heard the crackle of a motor scooter starting up. The sound meant nothing to him and he settled back to enjoy the drive.

CHAPTER 14

Darko Kerim

J AMES BOND awoke early in his dingy room at the Kristal Palas on the heights of Pera and absent-mindedly reached down a hand to explore a sharp tickle on the outside of his right thigh. Something had bitten him during the night. Irritably he scratched the spot. He might have expected it.

When he had arrived the night before, to be greeted by a surly night-concierge in trousers and a collarless shirt, and had briefly inspected the entrance hall with the fly-blown palms in copper pots, and the floor and walls of discoloured Moorish tiles, he had known what he was in for. He had half thought of going to another hotel. Inertia, and a perverse liking for the sleazy romance that clings to old-fashioned Continental hotels, had decided him to stay, and he had signed in and followed the man up to the third floor in the old rope-and-gravity lift.

His room, with its few sticks of aged furniture and an iron bedstead, was what he had expected. He only looked to see if there were the blood spots of squashed bugs on the wall-paper behind the bedhead before dismissing the concierge.

He had been premature. When he went into the bathroom and turned on the hot tap it gave a deep sigh, then a deprecating cough, and finally ejected a small centipede into the basin. Bond morosely washed the centipede away with the thin stream of brownish water from the cold tap. So much, he had reflected wryly, for choosing an hotel because its name had amused him and because he had wanted to get away from the soft life of big hotels.

But he had slept well, and now, with the reservation that he must buy some insecticide, he decided to forget about his comforts and get on with the day.

Bond got out of bed, drew back the heavy red plush curtains and leant on the iron balustrade and looked out over one of the most famous views in the world — on his right the still waters of the Golden Horn, on his left the dancing waves of the unsheltered Bosphorus, and, in between, the tumbling roofs, soaring minarets and crouching mosques of Pera. After all, his choice had been good. The view made up for many bedbugs and much discomfort.

For ten minutes Bond stood and gazed out across the sparkling water barrier between Europe and Asia, then he turned back into the room, now bright with sunshine, and telephoned for his breakfast. His English was not understood, but his French at last got through. He turned on a cold bath and shaved patiently with cold water and hoped that the exotic breakfast he had ordered would not be a fiasco.

He was not disappointed. The yoghourt, in a blue china bowl, was deep yellow and with the consistency of thick cream. The green figs, ready peeled, were bursting with ripeness, and the Turkish coffee was jet black and with the burned taste that showed it had been freshly ground. Bond ate the delicious meal on a table drawn up beside the open window. He watched the steamers and the caïques criss-crossing the two seas spread out before him and wondered about Kerim and what fresh news there might be.

Punctually at nine, the elegant Rolls came for him and took him through Taksim square and down the crowded Istiklal and out of Asia. The thick black smoke of the waiting steamers, badged with

the graceful crossed anchors of the Merchant Marine, streamed across the first span of the Galata Bridge and hid the other shore towards which the Rolls nosed forward through the bicycles and trams, the well-bred snort of the ancient bulb horn just keeping the pedestrians from under its wheels. Then the way was clear and the old European section of Istanbul glittered at the end of the broad half-mile of bridge with the slim minarets lancing up into the sky and the domes of the mosques, crouching at their feet, looking like big firm breasts. It should have been the Arabian Nights, but to Bond, seeing it first above the tops of trams and above the great scars of modern advertising along the river frontage, it seemed a once beautiful theatre-set that modern Turkey had thrown aside in favour of the steel and concrete flat-iron of the Istanbul-Hilton Hotel, blankly glittering behind him on the heights of Pera.

Across the bridge, the car nosed to the right down a narrow cobbled street parallel with the waterfront and stopped outside a high wooden porte-cochère.

A tough-looking watchman with a chunky, smiling face, dressed in frayed khaki, came out of a porter's lodge and saluted. He opened the car door and gestured for Bond to follow him. He led the way back into his lodge and through a door into a small courtyard with a neatly raked gravel parterre. In the centre was a gnarled eucalyptus tree at whose foot two white ring-doves were pecking about. The noise of the town was a distant rumble and it was quiet and peaceful.

They walked across the gravel and through another small door and Bond found himself at one end of a great vaulted godown with high circular windows through which dusty bars of sunshine slanted across a vista of bundles and bales of merchandise. There was a cool, musty scent of spices and coffee and, as Bond followed the watchman down the central passage-way, a sudden strong wave of mint.

At the end of the long warehouse was a raised platform enclosed by a balustrade. On it half a dozen young men and girls sat on high stools and wrote busily in fat, old-fashioned ledgers. It was like a

Dickensian counting-house and Bond noticed that each high desk had a battered abacus beside the inkpot. Not one of the clerks looked up as Bond walked between them, but a tall, swarthy man with a lean face and unexpected blue eyes came forward from the furthest desk and took delivery of him from the watchman. He smiled warmly at Bond, showing a set of extremely white teeth, and led him to the back of the platform. He knocked on a fine mahogany door with a Yale lock and, without waiting for an answer, opened it and let Bond in and closed the door softly behind him.

'Ah, my friend. Come in. Come in.' A very large man in a beautifully cut cream tussore suit got up from a mahogany desk and came to meet him, holding out his hand.

A hint of authority behind the loud friendly voice reminded Bond that this was the Head of Station T, and that Bond was in another man's territory and juridically under his command. It was no more than a point of etiquette, but a point to remember.

Darko Kerim had a wonderfully warm dry handclasp. It was a strong Western handful of operative fingers — not the banana skin handshake of the East that makes you want to wipe your fingers on your coat-tails. And the big hand had a coiled power that said it could easily squeeze your hand tighter and tighter until finally it cracked your bones.

Bond was six feet tall, but this man was at least two inches taller and he gave the impression of being twice as broad and twice as thick as Bond. Bond looked up into two wide apart, smiling blue eyes in a large smooth brown face with a broken nose. The eyes were watery and veined with red, like the eyes of a hound who lies too often too close to the fire. Bond recognized them as the eyes of furious dissipation.

The face was vaguely gipsy-like in its fierce pride and in the heavy curling black hair and crooked nose, and the effect of a vagabond soldier of fortune was heightened by the small thin gold ring Kerim wore in the lobe of his right ear. It was a startlingly dramatic face, vital, cruel and debauched, but what one noticed more than its drama was that it radiated life. Bond thought he had never seen so much vitality and warmth in a human face. It was like being close to the sun, and Bond let go the strong dry hand and smiled back at Kerim with a friendliness he rarely felt for a stranger.

'Thanks for sending the car to meet me last night.'

'Ha!' Kerim was delighted. 'You must thank our friends too. You were met by both sides. They always follow my car when it goes to the airport.'

'Was it a Vespa or a Lambretta?'

'You noticed? A Lambretta. They have a whole fleet of them for their little men, the men I call "The Faceless Ones". They look so alike, we have never managed to sort them out. Little gangsters, mostly stinking Bulgars, who do their dirty work for them. But I expect this one kept well back. They don't get up close to the Rolls any more since the day my chauffeur stopped suddenly and then reversed back as hard as he could. Messed up the paintwork and bloodied the bottom of the chassis but it taught the rest of them manners.'

Kerim went to his chair and waved to an identical one across the desk. He pushed over a flat white box of cigarettes and Bond sat down and took a cigarette and lit it. It was the most wonderful cigarette he had ever tasted — the mildest and sweetest of Turkish tobacco in a slim long oval tube with an elegant gold crescent.

While Kerim was fitting one into a long nicotine-stained ivory holder, Bond took the opportunity to glance round the room, which smelled strongly of paint and varnish as if it had just been redecorated.

It was big and square and panelled in polished mahogany, except behind Kerim's chair where a length of Oriental tapestry hung down from the ceiling and gently moved in the breeze as if there was an open window behind it. But this seemed unlikely as light came from three circular windows high up in the walls. Perhaps, behind the tapestry, was a balcony looking out over the Golden Horn, whose waves Bond could hear lapping at the walls below. In the centre of the right-hand wall hung a gold-framed reproduction of Annigoni's portrait of the Queen. Opposite, also imposingly framed, was Cecil Beaton's war-time photograph of Winston Churchill looking up from his desk in the Cabinet Offices like a contemptuous bulldog. A broad bookcase stood against one wall and, opposite, a comfortably padded leather settee. In the centre of the room the big desk winked with polished brass handles. On the littered desk were three silver photograph frames, and Bond caught a sideways view of the copperplate script of two Mentions in Dispatches and the Military Division of the O.B.E.

Kerim lit his cigarette. He jerked his head back at the piece of tapestry. 'Our friends paid me a visit yesterday,' he said casually. 'Fixed a limpet bomb on the wall outside. Timed the fuse to catch me at my desk. By good luck, I had taken a few minutes off to relax on the couch over there with a young Rumanian girl who still believes that a man will tell secrets in exchange for love. The bomb went off at a vital moment. I refused to be disturbed, but I fear the experience was too much for the girl. When I released her, she had hysterics. I'm afraid she had decided that my love-making is altogether too violent.' He waved his cigarette holder apologetically. 'But it was a rush to get the room put to rights in time for your visit. New glass for the windows and my pictures, and the place stinks of paint. However.' Kerim sat back in his chair. There was a slight frown on his face. 'What I cannot understand is this sudden breach of the peace. We live together very amicably in Istanbul. We all have our work to do. It is unheard of that my *chers collègues* should suddenly declare war in this way. It is quite worrying. It can only lead to trouble for our Russian friends. I shall be forced to rebuke the man who did it when I have found out his name.' Kerim shook his head. 'It is most confusing. I am hoping it has nothing to do with this case of ours.'

'But was it necessary to make my arrival so public?' Bond asked mildly. 'The last thing I want is to get you involved in all this. Why send the Rolls to the airport? It only ties you in with me.'

Kerim's laugh was indulgent. 'My friend, I must explain something which you should know. We and the Russians and the Americans have a paid man in all the hotels. And we have all bribed an official of the Secret police at Headquarters and we receive a carbon copy of the list of all foreigners entering the country every day by air or train or sea. Given a few more days I could have smuggled you in through the Greek frontier. But for what purpose? Your existence here has to be known to the other side so that our friend can contact you. It is a condition she has laid down that she will make her own arrangements for the meeting. Perhaps she does not trust our security. Who knows? But she was definite about it and she said, as if I didn't know it, that her centre would immediately be advised of your arrival.' Kerim shrugged his broad shoulders. 'So why make things difficult for her? I am merely concerned with making things easy and comfortable for you so that you will at least enjoy your stay — even if it is fruitless.'

Bond laughed. 'I take it all back. I'd forgotten the Balkan formula. Anyway I'm under your orders here. You tell me what to do and I'll do it.'

Kerim waved the subject aside. 'And now, since we are talking of your comfort, how is your hotel? I was surprised you chose the Palas. It is little better than a disorderly house — what the French call a *baisodrome*. And it's quite a haunt of the Russians. Not that that matters.'

'It's not too bad. I just didn't want to stay at the Istanbul-Hilton or one of the other smart places.'

'Money?' Kerim reached into a drawer and took out a flat packet of new green notes. 'Here's a thousand Turkish pounds. Their real value, and their rate on the black market, is about twenty to the pound. The official rate is seven. Tell me when you've finished them and I'll give you as many more as you want. We can do our accounts after the game. It's muck, anyway. Ever since Croesus, the first millionaire, invented gold coins, money has depreciated. And the face of the coin has been debased as fast as its value. First the faces of gods were on the coins. Then the faces of kings. Then of presidents. Now there's no face at all. Look at this stuff!' Kerim tossed the money over to Bond. 'Today it's only paper, with a picture of a public building and the signature of a cashier. Muck! The miracle is that you can still buy things with it. However. What else? Cigarettes? Smoke only these. I will have a few hundred sent up to your hotel. They're the best. *Diplomates*. They're not easy to get. Most of them go to the Ministries and the Embassies. Anything else before we get down to business? Don't worry about your meals and your leisure. I will look after both. I shall enjoy it and, if you will forgive me, I wish to stay close to you while you are here.'

'Nothing else,' said Bond. 'Except that you must come over to London one day.'

'Never,' said Kerim definitely. 'The weather and the women are far too cold. And I am proud to have you here. It reminds me of the war. Now,' he rang a bell on his desk. 'Do you like your coffee plain or sweet? In Turkey we cannot talk seriously without coffee or raki and it is too early for raki.'

'Plain.'

The door behind Bond opened. Kerim barked an order. When the door was shut, Kerim unlocked a drawer and took out a file and put it in front of him. He smacked his hand down on it.

'My friend,' he said grimly, 'I do not know what to say about this case.' He leant back in his chair and linked his hands behind his neck. 'Has it ever occurred to you that our kind of work is rather like shooting a film? So often I have got everybody on location and I think I can start turning the handle. Then it's the weather, and then it's the actors, and then it's the accidents. And there is something else that also happens in the making of a film. Love appears in some shape or form, at the very worst, as it is now, between the two stars. To me that is the most confusing factor in this case, and the most inscrutable one. Does this girl really love her idea of you? Will she love you when she sees you? Will you be able to love her enough to make her come over?'

Bond made no comment. There was a knock on the door and the head clerk put a china eggshell, enclosed in gold filigree, in front of each of them and went out. Bond sipped his coffee and put it down. It was good, but thick with grains. Kerim swallowed his at a gulp and fitted a cigarette into his holder and lit it.

'But there is nothing we can do about this love matter,' Kerim continued, speaking half to himself. 'We can only wait and see. In the meantime there are other things.' He leant forward against the desk and looked across at Bond, his eyes suddenly very hard and shrewd.

'There is something going on in the enemy camp, my friend. It is not only this attempt to get rid of me. There are comings and goings. I have few facts,' he reached up a big index finger and laid it alongside his nose, 'but I have this.' He tapped the side of his nose as if he was patting a dog. 'But this is a good friend of mine and I trust him.' He brought his hand slowly and significantly down on to the desk and added softly, 'And if the stakes were not so big, I would say to you, "Go home my friend. Go home. There is something here to get away from".'

Kerim sat back. The tension went out of his voice. He barked out a harsh laugh. 'But we are not old women. And this is our work. So let us forget my nose and get on with the job. First of all, is there anything I can tell you that you do not know? The girl has made no sign of life since my signal and I have no other information. But perhaps you would like to ask me some questions about the meeting.'

'There's only one thing I want to know,' said Bond flatly. 'What do you think of this girl? Do you believe her story or not? Her story about me? Nothing else matters. If she hasn't got some sort of a hysterical crush on me, the whole business falls to the ground and it's some complicated M.G.B. plot we can't understand. Now. Did you believe the girl?' Bond's voice was urgent and his eyes searched the other man's face.

'Ah, my friend,' Kerim shook his head. He spread his arms wide. 'That is what I asked myself then, and it is what I ask myself the whole time since. But who can tell if a woman is lying about these things? Her eyes were bright — those beautiful innocent eyes.

Her lips were moist and parted in that heavenly mouth. Her voice was urgent and frightened at what she was doing and saying. Her knuckles were white on the guard rail of the ship. But what was in her heart?' Kerim raised his hands, 'God alone knows.' He brought his hands down resignedly. He placed them flat on the desk and looked straight at Bond. 'There is only one way of telling if a woman really loves you, and even that way can only be read by an expert.'

'Yes,' said Bond dubiously. 'I know what you mean. In bed.'

CHAPTER 15

Background to a Spy

COFFEE came again, and then more coffee, and the big room grew thick with cigarette smoke as the two men took each shred of evidence, dissected it and put it aside. At the end of an hour they were back where they had started. It was up to Bond to solve the problem of this girl and, if he was satisfied with her story, get her and the machine out of the country.

Kerim undertook to look after the administrative problems. As a first step he picked up the telephone and spoke to his travel agent and reserved two seats on every outgoing plane for the next week — by B.E.A., Air France, S.A.S. and Turkair.

'And now you must have a passport,' he said. 'One will be sufficient. She can travel as your wife. One of my men will take your photograph and he will find a photograph of some girl who looks more or less like her. As a matter of fact, an early picture of Garbo would serve. There is a certain resemblance. He can get one from the newspaper files. I will speak to the Consul General. He's an excellent fellow who likes my little cloak-and-dagger plots. The passport will be ready by this evening. What name would you like to have?'

'Take one out of a hat.'

'Somerset. My mother came from there. David Somerset. Profession, Company Director. That means nothing. And the girl? Let us say Caroline. She looks like a Caroline. A couple of clean-limbed young English people with a taste for travel. Finance Control Form? Leave that to me. It will show eighty pounds in travellers' cheques, let's say, and a receipt from the bank to show you changed fifty while you were in Turkey. Customs? They never look at anything. Only too glad if somebody has bought something in the country. You will declare some Turkish Delight — presents for your friends in London. If you have to get out quickly, leave your hotel bill and luggage to me. They know me well enough at the Palas. Anything else?'

'I can't think of anything.'

Kerim looked at his watch. 'Twelve o'clock. Just time for the car to take you back to your hotel. There might be a message. And have a good look at your things to see if anyone has been inquisitive.'

He rang the bell and fired instructions at the head clerk who stood with his sharp eyes on Kerim's and his lean head straining forward like a whippet's.

Kerim led Bond to the door. There came again the warm powerful handclasp. 'The car will bring you to lunch,' he said. 'A little place in the Spice Bazaar.' His eyes looked happily into Bond's. 'And I am glad to be working with you. We will do well together.' He let go of Bond's hand. 'And now I have a lot of things to do very quickly. They may be the wrong things, but at any rate,' he grinned broadly, '*jouons mal, mais jouons vite!*'

The head clerk, who seemed to be some sort of chief-of-staff to Kerim, led Bond through another door in the wall of the raised platform. The heads were still bowed over the ledgers. There was a short passage with rooms on either side. The man led the way into one of these and Bond found himself in an extremely well-equipped dark-room and laboratory. In ten minutes he was out again on the street. The Rolls edged out of the narrow alley and back again on to the Galata Bridge.

A new concierge was on duty at the Kristal Palas, a small obsequious man with guilty eyes in a yellow face. He came out from behind the desk, his hands spread in apology. 'Effendi, I greatly regret. My colleague showed you to an inadequate room. It was not realized that you are a friend of Kerim Bey. Your things have been moved to No. 12. It is the best room in the hotel. In fact,' the concierge leered, 'it is the room reserved for honeymoon couples. Every comfort. My apologies, Effendi. The other room is not intended for visitors of distinction.' The man executed an oily bow, washing his hands.

If there was one thing Bond couldn't stand it was the sound of his boots being licked. He looked the concierge in the eyes and said, 'Oh.' The eyes slid away. 'Let me see this room. I may not like it. I was quite comfortable where I was.'

'Certainly, Effendi,' the man bowed Bond to the lift. 'But alas the plumbers are in your former room. The water supply . . .' the voice trailed away. The lift rose about ten feet and stopped at the first floor.

Well, the story of the plumbers makes sense, reflected Bond. And, after all, there was no harm in having the best room in the hotel.

The concierge unlocked a high door and stood back.

Bond had to approve. The sun streamed in through wide double windows that gave on to a small balcony. The motif was pink and grey and the style was mock French Empire, battered by the years, but still with all the elegance of the turn of the century. There were fine Bokhara rugs on the parquet floor. A glittering chandelier hung from the ornate ceiling. The bed against the right-hand wall was huge. A large mirror in a gold frame covered most of the wall behind it. (Bond was amused. The honeymoon room! Surely there should be a mirror on the ceiling as well.) The adjoining bathroom was tiled and fitted with everything, including a bidet and a shower. Bond's shaving things were neatly laid out.

The concierge followed Bond back into the bedroom, and when Bond said he would take the room, bowed himself gratefully out.

Why not? Bond again walked round the room. This time he carefully inspected the walls and the neighbourhood of the bed and the telephone. Why not take the room? Why would there be microphones or secret doors? What would be the point of them?

His suitcase was on a bench near the chest-of-drawers. He knelt down. No scratches round the lock. The bit of fluff he had trapped in the clasp was still there. He unlocked the suitcase and took out the little attaché case. Again no signs of interference. Bond locked the case and got to his feet.

He washed and went out of the room and down the stairs. No, there had been no messages for the Effendi. The concierge bowed as he opened the door of the Rolls. Was there a hint of conspiracy behind the permanent guilt in those eyes? Bond decided not to care if there was. The game, whatever it was, had to be played out. If the change of rooms had been the opening gambit, so much the better. The game had to begin somewhere.

As the car sped back down the hill, Bond's thoughts turned to Darko Kerim. What a man for Head of Station T! His size alone, in this country of furtive, stunted little men, would give him authority, and his giant vitality and love of life would make everyone his friend. Where had this exuberant shrewd pirate come from? And how had he come to work for the Service? He was the rare type of man that Bond loved, and Bond already felt prepared to add Kerim to the half-dozen of those real friends whom Bond, who had no 'acquaintances', would be ready to take to his heart.

The car went back over the Galata Bridge and drew up outside the vaulted arcades of the Spice Bazaar. The chauffeur led the way up the shallow worn steps and into the fog of exotic scents, shouting curses at the beggars and sack-laden porters. Inside the entrance the chauffeur turned left out of the stream of shuffling, jabbering humanity and showed Bond a small arch in the thick wall. Turret-like stone steps curled upwards.

'Effendi, you will find Kerim Bey in the far room on the left. You have only to ask. He is known to all.'

Bond climbed the cool stairs to a small ante-room where a waiter, without asking his name, took charge and led him through a maze of small, colourfully tiled, vaulted rooms to where Kerim was sitting at a corner table over the entrance to the bazaar. Kerim greeted him boisterously, waving a glass of milky liquid in which ice tinkled.

'Here you are my friend! Now, at once, some raki. You must be exhausted after your sight-seeing.' He fired orders at the waiter.

Bond sat down in a comfortable-armed chair and took the small tumbler the waiter offered him. He lifted it towards Kerim and tasted it. It was identical with ouzo. He drank it down. At once the waiter refilled his glass.

'And now to order your lunch. They eat nothing but offal cooked in rancid olive oil in Turkey. At least the offal at the Misir Carsarsi is the best.'

The grinning waiter made suggestions.

'He says the Doner Kebab is very good today. I don't believe him, but it can be. It is very young lamb broiled over charcoal with savoury rice. Lots of onions in it. Or is there anything you prefer? A pilaff or some of those damned stuffed peppers they eat here? All right then. And you must start with a few sardines grilled *en papillotte*. They are just edible.' Kerim harangued the waiter. He sat back, smiling at Bond. 'That is the only way to treat these damned people. They love to be cursed and kicked. It is all they understand. It is in the blood. All this pretence of democracy is killing them. They want some sultans and wars and rape and fun. Poor brutes, in their striped suits and bowler hats. They are miserable. You've only got to look at them. However, to hell with them all. Any news?'

Bond shook his head. He told Kerim about the change of room and the untouched suitcase.

Kerim downed a glass of raki and wiped his mouth on the back of his hand. He echoed the thought Bond had had. 'Well, the game must begin sometime. I have made certain small moves. Now we can only wait and see. We will make a little foray into enemy territory after lunch. I think it will interest you. Oh, we shan't be seen. We shall move in the shadows, underground.' Kerim laughed delightedly at his cleverness. 'And now let us talk about other things. How do you like Turkey? No, I don't want to know. What else?'

They were interrupted by the arrival of their first course. Bond's sardines *en papillotte* tasted like any other fried sardines. Kerim set about a large plate of what appeared to be strips of raw fish. He saw Bond's look of interest. 'Raw fish,' he said. 'After this I shall have raw meat and lettuce and then I shall have a bowl of yoghourt. I am not a faddist, but I once trained to be a professional strong man. It is a good profession in Turkey. The public loves them. And my trainer insisted that I should eat only raw food. I got the habit. It is good for me, but,' he waved his fork, 'I do not pretend it is good for everyone. I don't care the hell what other people eat so long as they enjoy it. I can't stand sad eaters and sad drinkers.'

'Why did you decide not to be a strong man? How did you get into this racket?'

Kerim forked up a strip of fish and tore at it with his teeth. He drank down half a tumbler of raki. He lit a cigarette and sat back in his chair. 'Well,' he said with a sour grin, 'we might as well talk about me as about anything else. And you must be wondering "How did this big crazy man get into the Service?" I will tell you, but briefly, because it is a long story. You will stop me if you get bored. All right?'

'Fine.' Bond lit a *Diplomate*. He leant forward on his elbows.

'I come from Trebizond.' Kerim watched his cigarette smoke curl upwards. 'We were a huge family with many mothers. My father was the sort of man women can't resist. All women want to be swept off their feet. In their dreams they long to be slung over a man's shoulder and taken into a cave and raped. That was his way with them. My father was a great fisherman and his fame was spread all over the Black Sea. He went after the sword-fish. They are difficult to catch and hard to fight and he would always outdo all others after these fish. Women like their men to be heroes. He was a kind of hero in a corner of Turkey where it is a tradition for the men to be tough. He was a big, romantic sort of fellow. So he could have any woman he wanted. He wanted them all and sometimes killed other men to get them. Naturally he had many children. We all lived on top of each other in a great rambling old ruin of a house that our "aunts" made habitable. The aunts really amounted to a harem. One of them was an English governess from Istanbul my father had seen watching a circus. He took a fancy to her and she to him and that evening he put her on board his fishing boat and sailed up the Bosphorus and back to Trebizond. I don't think she ever regretted it. I think she forgot all the world except him. She died just after the war. She was sixty. The child before me had been by an Italian girl and the girl had called him Bianco. He was fair. I was dark. I got to be called Darko. There were fifteen of us children and we had a wonderful childhood. Our aunts fought often and so did we. It was like a gipsy encampment. It was held together by my father who thrashed us, women or children, when we were a nuisance. But he was good to us when we were peaceful and obedient. You cannot understand such a family?'

'The way you describe it I can.'

'Anyway so it was. I grew up to be nearly as big a man as my father, but better educated. My mother saw to that. My father only taught us to be clean and to go to the lavatory once a day and never to feel shame about anything in the world. My mother also taught me a regard for England, but that is by the way. By the time I was twenty, I had a boat of my own and I was making money. But I was wild. I left the big house and went to live in two small rooms on the waterfront. I wanted to have my women where my mother would not know. There was a stroke of bad luck. I had a little Bessarabian hell-cat. I had won her in a fight with some gipsies, here in the hills behind Istanbul. They came after me, but I got her on board the boat. I had to knock her unconscious first. She was still trying to kill me when we got back to Trebizond, so I got her to my place and took away all her clothes and kept her chained naked under the table. When I ate, I used to throw scraps to her under the table, like a dog. She had to learn who was master. Before that could happen, my mother did an unheard of thing. She visited my place without warning. She came to tell me that my father wanted to see me immediately. She found the girl. My mother was really angry with me for the first time in my life. Angry? She was beside herself. I was a cruel ne'er-do-well and she was ashamed to call me son. The girl must immediately be taken back to her people. My mother brought her some of her own clothes from the house. The girl put them on, but when the time came, she refused to leave me.' Darko Kerim laughed hugely. 'An interesting lesson in female psychology, my dear friend. However, the problem of the girl is another story. While my mother was fussing over her and getting nothing but gipsy curses for her pains, I was having an interview with my father, who had heard nothing of all this and who never did hear. My mother was like that. There was another man with my father, a tall, quiet Englishman with a black patch over one eye. They were talking about the Russians. The Englishman wanted to know what they were doing along their frontier, about what was going on at Batoum, their big oil and naval base only fifty miles away from Trebizond. He would pay good money for information. I knew English and I knew Russian. I had good eyes and ears. I had a boat. My father had decided that I would work for the Englishman. And that Englishman, my dear friend, was Major Dansey, my predecessor as Head of this Station. And the rest,' Kerim made a wide gesture with his cigarette holder, 'you can imagine.'

'But what about this training to be a professional strong man?'

'Ah,' said Kerim slyly, 'that was only a sideline. Our travelling circuses were almost the only Turks allowed through the frontier. The Russians cannot live without circuses. It is as simple as that. I was the man who broke chains and lifted weights by a rope between the teeth. I wrestled against the local strong men in the

Russian villages. And some of those Georgians are giants. Fortunately they are stupid giants and I nearly always won. Afterwards, at the drinking, there was always much talk and gossip. I would look foolish and pretend not to understand. Every now and then I would ask an innocent question and they would laugh at my stupidity and tell me the answer.'

The second course came, and with it a bottle of Kavaklidere, a rich coarse burgundy like any other Balkan wine. The Kebab was good and tasted of smoked bacon fat and onions. Kerim ate a kind of Steak Tartare — a large flat hamburger of finely minced raw meat laced with peppers and chives and bound together with yolk of egg. He made Bond try a forkful. It was delicious. Bond said so.

'You ought to eat it every day,' said Kerim earnestly. 'It is good for those who wish to make much love. There are certain exercises you should do for the same purpose. These things are important to men. Or at least they are to me. Like my father, I consume a large quantity of women. But, unlike him, I also drink and smoke too much, and these things do not go well with making love. Nor does this work I do. Too many tensions and too much thinking. It takes the blood to the head instead of to where it should be for making love. But I am greedy for life. I do too much of everything all the time. Suddenly one day my heart will fail. The Iron Crab will get me as it got my father. But I am not afraid of The Crab. At least I shall have died from an honourable disease. Perhaps they will put on my tombstone "This Man Died from Living Too Much".'

Bond laughed. 'Don't go too soon, Darko,' he said. 'M. would be very displeased. He thinks the world of you.'

'He does?' Kerim searched Bond's face to see if he was telling the truth. He laughed delightedly. 'In that case I will not let The Crab have my body yet.' He looked at his watch. 'Come, James,' he said. 'It is good that you reminded me of my duty. We will have coffee in the office. There is not much time to waste. Every day at 2.30 the Russians have their council of war. Today you and I will do them the honour of being present at their deliberations.'

CHAPTER 16

The Tunnel of Rats

BACK in the cool office, while they waited for the inevitable coffee, Kerim opened a cupboard in the wall and pulled out sets of engineers' blue overalls. Kerim stripped to his shorts and dressed himself in one of the suits and pulled on a pair of rubber boots. Bond picked out a suit and a pair of boots that more or less fitted him and put them on.

With the coffee, the head clerk brought in two powerful flashlights which he put on the desk.

When the clerk had left the room Kerim said, 'He is one of my sons — the eldest one. The others in there are all my children. The chauffeur and the watchman are uncles of mine. Common blood is the best security. And this spice business is good cover for us all. M. set me up in it. He spoke to friends of his in the City of London. I am now the leading spice merchant in Turkey. I have long ago repaid M. the money that was lent me. My children are shareholders in the business. They have a good life. When there is secret work to be done and I need help, I choose the child who will be most suitable. They all have training in different secret things.

They are clever and brave. Some have already killed for me. They would all die for me — and for M. I have taught them he is just below God.' Kerim made a deprecating wave. 'But that is just to tell you that you are in good hands.'

'I hadn't imagined anything different.'

'Ha!' said Kerim non-committally. He picked up the torches and handed one to Bond. 'And now to work.'

Kerim walked over to the wide glass-fronted bookcase and put his hand behind it. There was a click and the bookcase rolled silently and easily along the wall to the left. Behind it was a small door, flush with the wall. Kerim pressed one side of the door and it swung inwards to reveal a dark tunnel with stone steps leading straight down. A dank smell, mixed with a faint zoo stench, came out into the room.

'You go first,' said Kerim. 'Go down the steps to the bottom and wait. I must fix the door.'

Bond switched on his torch and stepped through the opening and went carefully down the stairs. The light of the torch showed fresh masonry, and, twenty feet below, a glimmer of water. When Bond got to the bottom he found that the glimmer was a small stream running down a central gutter in the floor of an ancient stone-walled tunnel that sloped steeply up to the right. To the left, the tunnel went on downwards and would, he guessed, come out below the surface of the Golden Horn.

Out of range of Bond's light there was a steady, quiet, scuttling sound, and in the blackness hundreds of pinpoints of red light flickered and moved. It was the same uphill and downhill. Twenty yards away on either side, a thousand rats were looking at Bond. They were sniffing at his scent. Bond imagined the whiskers lifting slightly from their teeth. He had a quick moment of wondering what action they would take if his torch went out.

Kerim was suddenly beside him. 'It is a long climb. A quarter of an hour. I hope you love animals,' Kerim's laugh boomed hugely away up the tunnel. The rats scuffled and stirred. 'Unfortunately there is not much choice. Rats and bats. Squadrons of them, divisions — a whole air force and army. And we have to drive them in front of us. Towards the end of the climb it becomes quite congested. Let's get started. The air is good. It is dry underfoot on both sides of the stream. But in winter the floods come and then we have to use frogmen's suits. Keep your torch on my feet. If a bat gets in your hair, brush him off. It will not be often. Their radar is very good.'

They set off up the steep slope. The smell of the rats and of the droppings of bats was thick — a mixture of monkey house and chicken battery. It occurred to Bond that it would be days before he got rid of it.

Clusters of bats hung like bunches of withered grapes from the roof and when, from time to time, either Kerim's head or Bond's brushed against them, they exploded twittering into the darkness. Ahead of them as they climbed there was the forest of squeaking, scuffling red pin-points that grew denser on both sides of the central gutter. Occasionally Kerim flashed his torch forward and the light shone on a grey field sown with glittering teeth and glinting whiskers. When this happened, an extra frenzy seized the rats, and those nearest jumped on the backs of the others to get away. All the while, fighting tumbling grey bodies came sweeping down the central gutter and, as the pressure of the mass higher up the tunnel grew heavier, the frothing rear-rank came closer.

The two men kept their torches levelled like guns on the rear ranks until, after a good quarter of an hour's climb, they reached their destination.

It was a deep alcove of newly faced brick in the side wall of the tunnel. There were two benches on each side of a thick tarpaulin-wrapped object that came down from the ceiling of the alcove.

They stepped inside. Another few yards' climb, Bond thought, and mass hysteria must have seized the distant thousands of rats further up the tunnel. The horde would have turned. Out of sheer pressure for space, the rats would have braved the lights and hurled themselves down on to the two intruders, in spite of the two glaring eyes and the threatening scent.

'Watch,' said Kerim.

There was a moment of silence. Further up the tunnel the squeaking had stopped, as if at a word of command. Then suddenly the tunnel was a foot deep in a great wave of hurtling, scrambling grey bodies as, with a continuous high-pitched squeal, the rats turned and pelted back down the slope.

For minutes the sleek grey river foamed by outside the alcove until at last the numbers thinned and only a trickle of sick or wounded rats came limping and probing their way down the tunnel floor.

The scream of the horde slowly vanished down towards the river, until there was silence except for the occasional twitter of a fleeing bat.

Kerim gave a non-committal grunt. 'One of these days those rats will start dying. Then we shall have the plague in Istanbul again. Sometimes I feel guilty for not telling the authorities of this tunnel so that they can clean the place up. But I can't so long as the Russians are up here.' He jerked his head at the roof. He looked at his watch. 'Five minutes to go. They will be pulling up their chairs and fiddling with their papers. There will be the three permanent men — M.G.B., or one of them may be from army intelligence, G.R.U. And there will probably be three others. Two came in a fortnight ago, one through Greece and another through Persia. Another one arrived on Monday. God knows who they are, or what they are here for. And sometimes the girl, Tatiana, comes in with a signal and goes out again. Let us hope we will see her today. You will be impressed. She is something.'

Kerim reached up and untied the tarpaulin cover and pulled it downwards. Bond understood. The cover protected the shining butt of a submarine periscope, fully withdrawn. The moisture glistened on the thick grease of the exposed bottom joint. Bond chuckled. 'Where the hell did you get that from, Darko?'

'Turkish Navy. War surplus.' Kerim's voice did not invite further questions. 'Now Q Branch in London is trying to fix some way of wiring the damn thing for sound. It's not going to be easy. The lens at the top of this is no bigger than a cigarette-lighter, end on. When I raise it, it comes up to floor level in their room. In the corner of the room where it comes up, we cut a small mousehole. We did it well. Once when I came to have a look, the first thing I saw was a big mousetrap with a piece of cheese on it. At least it looked big through the lens.' Kerim laughed briefly. 'But there's not much room to fit a sensitive pick-up alongside the lens. And there's no hope of getting in again to do any more fiddling about with their architecture. The only way I managed to install this thing was to get my friends in the Public Works Ministry to turn the Russians out for a few days. The story was that the trams going up the hill were shaking the foundations of the houses. There had to be a survey. It cost me a few hundred pounds for the right pockets. The Public Works inspected half a dozen houses on either side of this one and declared the place safe. By that time, I and the family had finished our construction work. The Russians were suspicious as hell. I gather they went over the place with a toothcomb when they got back, looking for microphones and bombs and so on. But we can't work that trick twice. Unless Q Branch can think up something very clever, I shall have to be content with keeping an eye on them. One of these days they'll give away something useful. They'll be interrogating someone we're interested in or something of that sort.'

Alongside the matrix of the periscope in the roof of the alcove there was a pendulous blister of metal, twice the size of a football. 'What's that?' said Bond.

'Bottom half of a bomb — a big bomb. If anything happens to me, or if war breaks out with Russia, that bomb will be set off by radio-control from my office. It is sad [Kerim didn't look sad] but I fear that many innocent people will get killed besides the Russians. When the blood is on the boil, man is as unselective as nature.'

Kerim had been polishing away at the hooded eyepieces between the two handle-bars that stuck out on both sides of the base of the periscope. Now he glanced at his watch and bent down and gripped the two handles and slowly brought them up level with his chin. There was a hiss of hydraulics as the glistening stem of the periscope slid up into its steel sheath in the roof of the alcove. Kerim bent his head and gazed into the eyepieces and slowly inched up the handles until he could stand upright. He twisted gently. He centred the lens and beckoned to Bond. 'Just the six of them.'

Bond moved over and took the handles.

'Have a good look at them,' said Kerim. 'I know them, but you'd better get their faces in your mind. Head of the table is their Resident Director. On his left are his two staff. Opposite them are the three new ones. The latest, who looks quite an important chap, is on the Director's right. Tell me if they do anything except talk.'

Bond's first impulse was to tell Kerim not to make so much noise. It was as if he was in the room with the Russians, as if he was sitting in a chair in the corner, a secretary perhaps, taking short-hand of the conference.

The wide, all-round lens, designed for spotting aircraft as well as surface ships, gave him a curious picture — a mouse's eye view of a forest of legs below the fore-edge of the table, and various aspects of the heads belonging to the legs. The Director and his two colleagues were clear — serious dull Russian faces whose charac-teristics Bond filed away. There was the studious, professorial face of the Director — thick spectacles, lantern jaw, big forehead and thin hair brushed back. On his left was a square wooden face with deep clefts on either side of the nose, fair hair *en brosse* and a nick out of the left ear. The third member of the permanent staff had a shifty Armenian face with clever bright almond eyes. He was talking now. His face wore a falsely humble look. Gold glinted in his mouth.

Bond could see less of the three visitors. Their backs were half towards him and only the profile of the nearest, and presumably most junior, showed clearly. This man's skin also was dark. He too would be from one of the southern republics. The jaw was badly shaved and the eye in profile was bovine and dull under a thick black brow. The nose was fleshy and porous. The upper lip was long over a sullen mouth and the beginning of a double chin. The tough black hair was cut very short so that most of the back of the neck looked blue to the level of the tips of the ears. It was a military haircut, done with mechanical clippers.

The only clues to the next man were an angry boil on the back of a fat bald neck, a shiny blue suit and rather bright brown shoes. The man was motionless during the whole period that Bond kept watch and apparently never spoke.

Now the senior visitor, on the right of the Resident Director, sat back and began talking. It was a strong, crag-like profile with big bones and a jutting chin under a heavy brown moustache of Stalin cut. Bond could see one cold grey eye under a bushy eyebrow and a low forehead topped by wiry grey-brown hair. This man was the only one who was smoking. He puffed busily at a tiny wooden pipe in the bowl of which stood half a cigarette. Every now and then he shook the pipe sideways so that the ash fell on the floor. His profile had more authority than any of the other faces and Bond guessed that he was a senior man sent down from Moscow.

Bond's eyes were getting tired. He twisted the handles gently and looked round the office as far as the blurring jagged edges of the mousehole would allow. He saw nothing of interest — two olive green filing cabinets, a hatstand by the door, on which he counted six more or less identical grey homburgs, and a sideboard with a heavy carafe of water and some glasses. Bond stood away from the eyepiece, rubbing his eyes.

'If only we could hear,' Kerim said, shaking his head sadly. It would be worth diamonds.'

'It would solve a lot of problems,' agreed Bond. Then, 'By the the way Darko, how did you come on this tunnel? What was it built for?'

Kerim bent and gave a quick glance into the eyepieces and straightened up.

'It's a lost drain from the Hall of Pillars,' he said. 'The Hall of Pillars is now a thing for tourists. It's up above us on the heights of Istanbul, near St. Sophia. A thousand years ago it was built as a reservoir in case of siege. It's a huge underground palace, a hundred yards long and about half as broad. It was made to hold millions of gallons of water. It was discovered again about four hundred years ago by a man called Gyllius. One day I was reading his account of finding it. He said it was filled in winter from "*a great pipe with a mighty noise*". It occurred to me that there might be another "*great pipe*" to empty it quickly if the city fell to the enemy. I went up to the Hall of Pillars and bribed the watchman and rowed about among the pillars all one night in a rubber dinghy with one of my boys. We went over the walls with a hammer and an echo-sounder. At one end, in the most likely spot, there was a hollow sound. I handed out more money to the Minister of Public Works and he closed the place for a week — "for cleaning". My little team got busy.' Kerim ducked down again for a look through the eyepieces and went on. 'We dug into the wall above water-level and came on the top of an arch. The arch was the beginning of a tunnel. We got into the tunnel and went down it. Quite exciting, not knowing where we were going to come out. And, of course, it went straight down the hill — under the Street of Books where the Russians have their place, and out into the Golden Horn, by the Galata Bridge, twenty yards away from my warehouse. So we filled in our hole in the Hall of Pillars and started digging from my end. That was two years ago. It took us a year and a lot of survey work to get directly under the Russians.' Kerim laughed. 'And now I suppose one of these days the Russians will decide to change their offices. By then I hope someone else will be Head of T.'

Kerim bent down to the rubber eyepieces. Bond saw him stiffen. Kerim said urgently. 'The door's opening. Quick. Take over. Here she comes.'

Killing Time

I T was seven o'clock on the same evening and James Bond was back in his hotel. He had had a hot bath and a cold shower. He thought that he had at last scoured the zoo smell out of his skin.

He was sitting, naked except for his shorts, at one of the windows of his room, sipping a vodka and tonic and looking out into the heart of the great tragic sunset over the Golden Horn. But his eyes didn't see the torn cloth of gold and blood that hung behind the minaretted stage beneath which he had caught his first glimpse of Tatiana Romanova.

He was thinking of the tall beautiful girl with the dancer's long gait who had walked through the drab door with a piece of paper in her hand. She had stood beside her Chief and handed him the paper. All the men had looked up at her. She had blushed and looked down. What had that expression on the men's faces meant? It was more than just the way some men look at a beautiful girl. They had shown curiosity. That was reasonable. They wanted to know what was in the signal, why they were being disturbed. But what else? There had been slyness and contempt — the way people stare at prostitutes.

It had been an odd, enigmatic scene. This was part of a highly disciplined para-military organization. These were serving officers, each of whom would be wary of the others. And this girl was just one of the staff, with a Corporal's rank, who was now going through a normal routine. Why had they all unguardedly looked at her with this inquisitive contempt — almost as if she was a spy who had been caught and was going to be executed? Did they suspect her? Had she given herself away? But that seemed less likely as the scene played itself out. The Resident Director read the signal and the other men's eyes turned away from the girl and on to him. He said something, presumably repeating the text of the signal, and the men looked glumly back at him as if the matter did not interest them. Then the Resident Director looked up at the girl and the other eyes followed his. He said something with a friendly, inquiring expression. The girl shook her head and answered briefly. The other men now only looked interested. The Director said one word with a question mark on the end. The girl blushed deeply, and nodded, holding his eyes obediently. The other men smiled encouragement, slyly perhaps, but with approval. No suspicion there. No condemnation. The scene ended with a few sentences from the Director to which the girl seemed to say the equivalent of 'Yes, sir' and turned and walked out of the room. When she had gone, the Director said something with an expression of irony on his face and the men laughed heartily and the sly expression was back on their faces, as if what he had said had been obscene. Then they went back to their work.

Ever since, on their way back down the tunnel, and later in Kerim's office while they discussed what Bond had seen, Bond had racked his brains for a solution to this maddening bit of dumb crambo and now, looking without focus at the dying sun, he was still mystified.

Bond finished his drink and lit another cigarette. He put the problem away and turned his mind to the girl.

Tatiana Romanova. A Romanov. Well, she certainly looked like a Russian princess, or the traditional idea of one. The tall, fine-boned body that moved so gracefully and stood so well. The thick sweep of hair down to the shoulders and the quiet authority of the profile. The wonderful Garbo-esque face with its curiously shy serenity. The contrast between the level innocence of the big, deep blue eyes and the passionate promise of the wide mouth. And the way she had blushed and the way the long eyelashes had come down over the lowered eyes. Had that been the prudery of a virgin? Bond thought not. There was the confidence of having been loved in the proud breasts and the insolently lilting behind — the assertion of a body that knows what it can be for.

On what Bond had seen, could he believe that she was the sort of girl to fall in love with a photograph and a file? How could one tell? Such a girl would have a deeply romantic nature. There were dreams in the eyes and in the mouth. At that age, twenty-four, the Soviet machine would not yet have ground the sentiment out of her. The Romanov blood might well have given her a yearning for men other than the type of modern Russian officer she would meet — stern, cold, mechanical, basically hysterical and, because of their Party education, infernally dull.

It could be true. There was nothing to disprove her story in her looks. Bond wanted it to be true.

The telephone rang. It was Kerim. 'Nothing new?'

'No.'

'Then I will pick you up at eight.'

'I'll be ready.'

Bond laid down the receiver and slowly started to put on his clothes.

Kerim had been firm about the evening. Bond had wanted to stay in his hotel room and wait for the first contact to be made — a note, a telephone call, whatever it might be. But Kerim had said no. The girl had been adamant that she would choose her own time and place. It would be wrong for Bond to seem a slave to her convenience. 'That is bad psychology, my friend,' Kerim had insisted.

'No girl likes a man to run when she whistles. She would despise you if you made yourself too available. From your face and your dossier she would expect you to behave with indifference — even with insolence. She would want that. She wishes to court you, to buy a kiss,' — Kerim had winked — 'from that cruel mouth. It is with an image she has fallen in love. Behave like the image. Act the part.'

Bond had shrugged his shoulders. 'All right, Darko. I daresay you're right. What do you suggest?'

'Live the life you would normally. Go home now and have a bath and a drink. The local vodka is all right if you drown it with tonic water. If nothing happens, I will pick you up at eight. We will have dinner at the place of a gipsy friend of mine. A man called Vavra. He is head of a tribe. I must anyway see him tonight. He is one of my best sources. He is finding out who tried to blow up my office. Some of his girls will dance for you. I will not suggest that they should entertain you more intimately. You must keep your sword sharp. There is a saying "Once a King, always a King. But once a Knight is enough!" '

Bond was smiling at the memory of Kerim's dictum when the telephone rang again. He picked up the receiver. It was only the car. As he went down the few stairs and out to Kerim in the waiting Rolls, Bond admitted to himself that he was disappointed.

They were climbing up the far hill through the poorer quarters above the Golden Horn when the chauffeur half turned his head and said something in a non-committal voice.

Kerim answered with a monosyllable. 'He says a Lambretta is on our tail. A Faceless One. It is of no importance. When I wish, I can make a secret of my movements. Often they have trailed this car for miles when there has been only a dummy in the back. A conspicuous car has its uses. They know this gipsy is a friend of mine, but I think they do not understand why. It will do no harm for them to know that we are having a night of relaxation. On a Saturday night, with a friend from England, anything else would be unusual.'

Bond looked back through the rear window and watched the crowded streets. From behind a stopped tram a motor scooter showed for a minute and then was hidden by a taxi. Bond turned away. He reflected briefly on the way the Russians ran their centres — with all the money and equipment in the world, while the Secret Service put against them a handful of adventurous, underpaid men, like this one, with his second-hand Rolls and his children to help him. Yet Kerim had the run of Turkey. Perhaps, after all, the right man was better than the right machine.

At half-past eight they stopped half way up a long hill on the outskirts of Istanbul at a dingy-looking open-air café with a few empty tables on the pavement. Behind it were the tops of trees over a high stone wall. They got out and the car drove off. They waited for the Lambretta, but its wasp-like buzz had stopped and at once it was on its way back down the hill. All they saw of the driver was a glimpse of a short squat man wearing goggles.

Kerim led the way through the tables and into the café. It seemed empty, but a man rose up quickly from behind the till. He kept one hand below the counter. When he saw who it was, he gave Kerim a nervous white smile. Something clanged to the floor. He stepped from behind the counter and led them out through the back and across a stretch of gravel to a door in the high wall and, after knocking once, unlocked it and waved them through.

There was an orchard with plank tables dotted about under the trees. In the centre was a circle of terrazza dancing floor. Round it were strung fairy lights, now dead, on poles planted in the ground. On the far side, at a long table, about twenty people of all ages had been sitting eating, but they had put down their knives and now looked towards the door. Some children had been playing in the grass behind the table. They also were now quiet and watching. The three-quarter moon showed everything up brightly and made pools of membraned shadow under the trees.

Kerim and Bond walked forward. The man at the head of the table said something to the others. He got up and came to meet them. The rest returned to their dinner and the children to their games.

The man greeted Kerim with reserve. He stood for a few moments making a long explanation to which Kerim listened attentively, occasionally asking a question.

The gipsy was an imposing, theatrical figure in Macedonian dress — white shirt with full sleeves, baggy trousers and laced soft leather top-boots. His hair was a tangle of black snakes. A large downward-drooping black moustache almost hid the full red lips. The eyes were fierce and cruel on either side of a syphilitic nose. The moon glinted on the sharp line of the jaw and the high cheekbones. His right hand, which had a gold ring on the thumb, rested on the hilt of a short curved dagger in a leather scabbard tipped with filigree silver.

The gipsy finished talking. Kerim said a few words, forceful and apparently complimentary, about Bond, at the same time stretching his hand out in Bond's direction as if he was a compère in a night-club commending a new turn. The gipsy stepped up to Bond and scrutinized him. He bowed abruptly. Bond followed suit. The gipsy said a few words through a sardonic smile. Kerim laughed and turned to Bond. 'He says if you are ever out of work you should come to him. He will give you a job — taming his women and killing for him. That is a great compliment to a *gajo* — a foreigner. You should say something in reply.'

'Tell him that I can't imagine he needs any help in these matters.'

Kerim translated. The gipsy politely bared his teeth. He said something and walked back to the table, clapping his hands sharply. Two women got up and came towards him. He spoke to them curtly and they went back to the table and picked up a large earthen-ware dish and disappeared among the trees.

Kerim took Bond's arm and led him to one side.

'We have come on a bad night,' he said. 'The restaurant is closed. There are family troubles here which have to be solved — drastically, and in private. But I am an old friend and we are invited to share their supper. It will be disgusting but I have sent for raki. Then we may watch — but on condition that we do not interfere. I hope you understand, my friend.' Kerim gave Bond's arm an additional pressure. 'Whatever you see, you must not move or comment. A court has just been held and justice is to be done — their kind of justice. It is an affair of love and jealousy. Two girls of the tribe are in love with one of his sons. There is a lot of death in the air. They both threaten to kill the other to get him. If he chooses one, the unsuccessful one has sworn to kill him and the girl. It is an *impasse*. There is much argument in the tribe. So the son has been sent up into the hills and the two girls are to fight it out here tonight — to the death. The son has agreed to take the winner. The women are locked up in separate caravans. It will not be for the squeamish, but it will be a remarkable affair. It is a great privilege that we may be present. You understand? We are *gajos*. You will forget your sense of the proprieties? You will not interfere? They would kill you, and possibly me, if you did.'

'Darko,' said Bond. 'I have a French friend. A man called Mathis who is head of the Deuxième. He once said to me: "*J'aime les sensations fortes*." I am like him. I shall not disgrace you. Men fighting women is one thing. Women fighting women is another. But what about the bomb? The bomb that blew up your office. What did he say about that?'

'It was the leader of the Faceless Ones. He put it there himself. They came down the Golden Horn in a boat and he climbed up a ladder and fixed it to the wall. It was bad luck he didn't get me. The operation was well thought out. The man is a gangster. A Bulgarian "refugee" called Krilencu. I shall have to have a reckoning with him. God knows why they suddenly want to kill me, but I cannot allow such annoyances. I may decide to take action later tonight. I know where he lives. In case Vavra knew the answer, I told my chauffeur to come back with the necessary equipment.'

A fiercely attractive young girl in a thick old-fashioned black frock, with strings of gold coins round her neck and about ten thin gold bracelets on each wrist, came over from the table and swept a low jingling curtsey in front of Kerim. She said something and Kerim replied.

'We are bidden to the table,' said Kerim. 'I hope you are good at eating with your fingers. I see they are all wearing their smartest clothes tonight. That girl would be worth marrying. She has a lot of gold on her. It is her dowry.'

They walked over to the table. Two places had been cleared on either side of the head gipsy. Kerim gave what sounded like a polite greeting to the table. There was a curt nod of acknowledgment. They sat down. In front of each of them was a large plate of some sort of ragout smelling strongly of garlic, a bottle of raki, a pitcher of water and a cheap tumbler. More bottles of raki, untouched, were on the table. When Kerim reached for his and poured himself half a tumblerful, everyone followed suit. Kerim added some water and raised his glass. Bond did the same. Kerim made a short and vehement speech and all raised their glasses and drank. The atmosphere became easier. An old woman next to Bond passed him a long loaf of bread and said something. Bond smiled and said 'thank you'. He broke off a piece and handed the loaf to Kerim who was picking among his ragout with thumb and forefinger. Kerim took the loaf with one hand and at the same time, with the other, he put a large piece of meat in his mouth and began to eat.

Bond was about to do the same when Kerim said sharply and quietly, 'With the right hand, James. The left hand is used for only one purpose among these people.'

Bond halted his left hand in mid-air and moved it on to grasp the nearest raki bottle. He poured himself another half tumblerful and started to eat with his right hand. The ragout was delicious but steaming hot. Bond winced each time he dipped his fingers into it. Everyone watched them eat and from time to time the old woman dipped her fingers into Bond's stew and chose a piece for him.

When they had scoured their plates, a silver bowl of water, in which rose leaves floated, and a clean linen cloth, were put between Bond and Kerim. Bond washed his fingers and his greasy chin and turned to his host and dutifully made a short speech of thanks which

Kerim translated. The table murmured its appreciation. The head gipsy bowed towards Bond and said, according to Kerim, that he hated all *gajos* except Bond, whom he was proud to call his friend. Then he clapped his hands sharply and everybody got up from the table and began pulling the benches away and arranging them round the dance floor.

Kerim came round the table to Bond. They walked off together. 'How do you feel? They've gone to get the two girls.'

Bond nodded. He was enjoying the evening. The scene was beautiful and thrilling — the white moon blazing down on the ring of figures now settling on the benches, the glint of gold or jewellery as somebody shifted his position, the glaring pool of terrazza and, all around, the quiet, sentinel trees standing guard in their black skirts of shadow.

Kerim led Bond to a bench where the chief gipsy sat alone. They took their places on his right.

A black cat with green eyes walked slowly across the terrazza and joined a group of children who were sitting quietly as if someone was about to come on to the dance floor and teach them a lesson. It sat down and began licking its chest.

Beyond the high wall, a horse neighed. Two of the gipsies looked over their shoulders towards the sound as if they were reading the cry of the horse. From the road came the silvery spray of a bicycle bell as someone sped down the hill.

The crouching silence was broken by the clang of a bolt being drawn. The door in the wall crashed back and two girls, spitting and fighting like angry cats, hurtled through and across the grass and into the ring.

CHAPTER 18

Strong Sensations

T HE head gipsy's voice cracked out. The girls separated reluctantly and stood facing him. The gipsy began to speak in a tone of harsh denunciation.

Kerim put his hand up to his mouth and whispered behind it. 'Vavra is telling them that this is a great tribe of gipsies and they have brought dissension among it. He says there is no room for hatred among themselves, only against those outside. The hatred they have created must be purged so that the tribe can live peacefully again. They are to fight. If the loser is not killed she will be banished for ever. That will be the same as death. These people wither and die outside the tribe. They cannot live in our world. It is like wild beasts forced to live in a cage.'

While Kerim spoke, Bond examined the two beautiful, taut, sullen animals in the centre of the ring.

They were both gipsy-dark, with coarse black hair to their shoulders, and they were both dressed in the collection of rags you associate with shanty-town negroes — tattered brown shifts that were mostly darns and patches. One was bigger-boned than the other, and obviously stronger, but she looked sullen and slow-eyed and might not be quick on her feet. She was handsome in a rather leonine way, and there was a slow red glare in her heavy lidded eyes as she stood and listened impatiently to the head of the tribe. She ought to win, thought Bond. She is half an inch taller, and she is stronger.

Where this girl was a lioness, the other was a panther — lithe and quick and with cunning sharp eyes that were not on the speaker but sliding sideways, measuring inches, and the hands at her sides were curled into claws. The muscles of her fine legs looked hard as a man's. The breasts were small, and, unlike the big breasts of the other girl, hardly swelled the rags of her shift. She looks a dangerous little bitch of a girl, thought Bond. She will certainly get in the first blow. She will be too quick for the other.

At once he was proved wrong. As Vavra spoke his last word, the big girl, who, Kerim whispered, was called Zora, kicked hard sideways, without taking aim, and caught the other girl square in the stomach and, as the smaller girl staggered, followed up with a swinging blow of the fist to the side of the head that knocked her sprawling on to the stone floor.

'Oi, Vida,' lamented a woman in the crowd. She needn't have worried. Even Bond could see that Vida was shamming as she lay on the ground, apparently winded. He could see her eyes glinting under her bent arm as Zora's foot came flashing at her ribs.

Vida's hands flickered out together. They grasped the ankle and her head struck into the instep like a snake's. Zora gave a scream of pain and wrenched furiously at her trapped foot. It was too late. The other girl was up on one knee, and then standing erect, the foot still in her hands. She heaved upwards and Zora's other foot left the ground and she crashed full length.

The thud of the big girl's fall shook the ground. For a moment she lay still. With an animal snarl, Vida dived on top of her, clawing and tearing.

My God, what a hell-cat, thought Bond. Beside him, Kerim's breath hissed tensely through his teeth.

But the big girl protected herself with her elbows and knees and at last she managed to kick Vida off. She staggered to her feet and backed away, her lips bared from her teeth and the shift hanging in tatters from her splendid body. At once she went in to the attack again, her arms groping forward for a hold and, as the smaller girl leapt aside, Zora's hand caught the neck of her shift and split it down to the hem. But immediately Vida twisted in close under the reaching arms and her fists and knees thudded into the attacker's body.

This in-fighting was a mistake. The strong arms clamped shut round the smaller girl, trapping Vida's hands low down so that they could not reach up for Zora's eyes. And, slowly, Zora began to squeeze, while Vida's legs and knees thrashed ineffectually below.

Bond thought that now the big girl must win. All Zora had to do was to fall on the other girl. Vida's head would crack down on the stone and then Zora could do as she liked. But all of a sudden it was the big girl who began to scream. Bond saw that Vida's head was buried deep in the other's breasts. Her teeth were at work. Zora's arms let go as she reached for Vida's hair to pull the head back and away from her. But now Vida's hands were free and they were scrabbling at the big girl's body.

The girls tore apart and backed away like cats, their shining bodies glinting through the last rags of their shifts and blood showing on the exposed breasts of the big girl.

They circled warily, both glad to have escaped, and as they circled they tore off the the last of their rags and threw them into the audience.

Bond held his breath at the sight of the two glistening, naked bodies, and he could feel Kerim's body tense beside him. The ring of gipsies seemed to have come closer to the two fighters. The moon shone on glittering eyes and there was the whisper of hot, panting breath.

Still the two girls circled slowly, their teeth bared and their breath coming harshly. The light glinted off their heaving breasts and stomachs and off their hard, boyish flanks. Their feet left dark sweat marks on the white stones.

Again it was the big girl, Zora, who made the first move with a sudden forward leap and arms held out like a wrestler's. But Vida stood her ground. Her right foot lashed out in a furious *coup de savate* that made a slap like a pistol shot. The big girl gave a wounded cry and clutched at herself. At once Vida's other foot kicked up to the stomach and she threw herself in after it.

There was a low growl from the crowd as Zora went down on her knees. Her hands went up to protect her face, but it was too late. The smaller girl was astride her, and her hands grasped Zora's wrists as she bore down on her with all her weight and bent her to the ground, her bared white teeth reaching towards the offered neck.

'BOOM!'

The explosion cracked the tension like a nut. A flash of flame lit the darkness behind the dance floor and a chunk of masonry sang past Bond's ear. Suddenly the orchard was full of running men and the head gipsy was slinking forward across the stone with his curved dagger held out in front of him. Kerim was going after him, a gun in his hand. As the gipsy passed the two girls, now standing wild-eyed and trembling, he shouted a word at them and they took to their heels and disappeared among the trees where the last of the women and children were already vanishing among the shadows.

Bond, the Beretta held uncertainly in his hand, followed slowly in the wake of Kerim towards the wide breach that had been blown out of the garden wall, and wondered what the hell was going on.

The stretch of grass between the hole in the wall and the dance floor was a turmoil of fighting, running figures. It was only as Bond came up with the fight that he distinguished the squat, conventionally dressed Bulgars from the swirling finery of the gipsies. There seemed to be more of the Faceless Ones than of the gipsies, almost two to one. As Bond peered into the struggling mass, a gipsy youth was ejected from it, clutching his stomach. He groped towards Bond, coughing terribly. Two small dark men came after him, their knives held low.

Instinctively Bond stepped to one side so that the crowd was not behind the two men. He aimed at their legs above the knees and the gun in his hand cracked twice. The two men fell, soundlessly, face downwards in the grass.

Two bullets gone. Only six left. Bond edged closer to the fight.

A knife hissed past his head and clanged on to the dance floor.

It had been aimed at Kerim, who came running out of the shadows with two men on his heels. The second man stopped and raised his knife to throw and Bond shot from the hip, blindly, and saw him fall. The other man turned and fled among the trees and Kerim dropped to one knee beside Bond, wrestling with his gun.

'Cover me,' he shouted. 'Jammed on the first shot. It's those bloody Bulgars. God knows what they think they're doing.'

A hand caught Bond round the mouth and yanked him backwards. On his way to the ground he smelled carbolic soap and nicotine. He felt a boot thud into the back of his neck. As he whirled over sideways in the grass he expected to feel the searing flame of a knife. But the men, and there were three of them, were after Kerim, and as Bond scrambled to one knee he saw the squat black figures pile down on the crouching man, who gave one lash upwards with his useless gun and then went down under them.

At the same moment as Bond leaped forward and brought his gun butt down on a round shaven head, something flashed past his eyes and the curved dagger of the head gipsy was growing out of a heaving back. Then Kerim was on his feet and the third man was running and a man was standing in the breach in the wall shouting one word, again and again, and one by one the attackers broke off their fights and doubled over to the man and past him and out on to the road.

'Shoot, James, shoot!' roared Kerim. 'That's Krilencu.' He started to run forward. Bond's gun spat once. But the man had dodged round the wall, and thirty yards is too far for night shooting with an automatic. As Bond lowered his hot gun, there came the staccato firing of a squadron of Lambrettas, and Bond stood and listened to the swarm of wasps flying down the hill.

There was silence except for the groans of the wounded. Bond listlessly watched Kerim and Vavra come back through the breach in the wall and walk among the bodies, occasionally turning one over with a foot. The other gipsies seeped back from the road and the older women came hurrying out of the shadows to tend their men.

Bond shook himself. What the hell had it all been about? Ten or a dozen men had been killed. What for? Whom had they been trying to get? Not him, Bond. When he was down and ready for the killing they had passed him by and made for Kerim. This was the second attempt on Kerim's life. Was it anything to do with the Romanova business? How could it possibly tie in?

Bond tensed. His gun spoke twice from the hip. The knife clattered harmlessly off Kerim's back. The figure that had risen from the dead twirled slowly round like a ballet dancer and toppled forward on his face. Bond ran forward. He had been just in time. The moon had caught the blade and he had had a clear field of fire. Kerim looked down at the twitching body. He turned to meet Bond.

Bond stopped in his tracks. 'You bloody fool,' he said angrily. 'Why the hell can't you take more care! You ought to have a nurse.' Most of Bond's anger came from knowing that it was he who had brought a cloud of death around Kerim.

Darko Kerim grinned shamefacedly. 'Now it is not good, James. You have saved my life too often. We might have been friends. Now the distance between us is too great. Forgive me, for I can never pay you back.' He held out his hand.

Bond brushed it aside. 'Don't be a damn fool, Darko,' he said roughly. 'My gun worked, that's all. Yours didn't. You'd better get one that does. For Christ's sake tell me what the hell this is all about. There's been too much blood splashing about tonight. I'm sick of it. I want a drink. Come and finish that raki.' He took the big man's arm.

As they reached the table, littered with the remains of the supper, a piercing, terrible scream came out of the depths of the orchard. Bond put his hand on his gun. Kerim shook his head. 'We shall soon know what the Faceless Ones were after,' he said gloomily. 'My friends are finding out. I can guess what they will discover. I think they will never forgive me for having been here tonight. Five of their men are dead.'

'There might have been a dead woman too,' said Bond unsympathetically. 'At least you've saved her life. Don't be stupid, Darko. These gipsies knew the risks when they started spying for you against the Bulgars. It was gang warfare.' He added a dash of water to two tumblers of raki.

They both emptied the glasses at one swallow. The head gipsy came up, wiping the tip of his curved dagger on a handful of grass. He sat down and accepted a glass of raki from Bond. He seemed quite cheerful. Bond had the impression that the fight had been too short for him. The gipsy said something, slyly.

Kerim chuckled. 'He said that his judgment was right. You killed well. Now he wants you to take on those two women.'

'Tell him even one of them would be too much for me. But tell him I think they are fine women. I would be glad if he would do me a favour and call the fight a draw. Enough of his people have been killed tonight. He will need these two girls to bear children for the tribe.'

Kerim translated. The gipsy looked sourly at Bond and said a few bitter words.

'He says that you should not have asked him such a difficult favour. He says that your heart is too soft for a good fighter. But he says he will do what you ask.'

The gipsy ignored Bond's smile of thanks. He started talking fast to Kerim, who listened attentively, occasionally interrupting the flow with a question. Krilencu's name was often mentioned. Kerim talked back. There was deep contrition in his voice and he refused to allow himself to be stopped by protests from the other. There came a last reference to Krilencu. Kerim turned to Bond.

'My friend,' he said drily. 'It is a curious affair. It seems the Bulgars were ordered to kill Vavra and as many of his men as possible. That is a simple matter. They knew the gipsy had been working for me. Perhaps, rather drastic. But in killing, the Russians have not much finesse. They like mass death. Vavra was a main target. I was another. The declaration of war against me personally I can also understand. But it seems that you were not to be harmed. You were exactly described so that there should be no mistake. That is odd. Perhaps it was desired that there should be no diplomatic repercussions. Who can tell? The attack was well planned. They came to the top of the hill by a roundabout route and free-wheeled down so that we should hear nothing. This is a lonely place and there is not a policeman for miles. I blame myself for having treated these people too lightly.' Kerim looked puzzled and unhappy. He seemed to make up his mind. He said, 'But now it is midnight. The Rolls will be here. There remains a small piece of work to be done before we go home to bed. And it is time we left these people. They have much to do before it is light. There are many bodies to go into the Bosphorus and there is the wall to be repaired. By daylight there must be no trace of these troubles. Our friend wishes you very well. He says you must return, and that Zora and Vida are yours until their breasts fall. He refuses to blame me for what has happened. He says that I am to continue sending him Bulgars. Ten were killed tonight. He would like some more. And now we will shake him by the hand and go. That is all he asks of us. We are good friends, but we are also *gajos*. And I expect he does not want us to see his women weeping over their dead.'

Kerim stretched out his huge hand. Vavra took it and held it and looked into Kerim's eyes. For a moment his own fierce eyes seemed to go opaque. Then the gipsy let the hand drop and turned to Bond. The hand was dry and rough and padded like the paw of a big animal. Again the eyes went opaque. He let go of Bond's hand. He spoke rapidly and urgently to Kerim and turned his back on them and walked away towards the trees.

Nobody looked up from his work as Kerim and Bond climbed through the breach in the wall. The Rolls stood, glittering in the moonlight, a few yards down the road opposite the café entrance.

A young man was sitting beside the chauffeur. Kerim gestured with his hand. 'That is my tenth son. He is called Boris. I thought I might need him. I shall.'

The youth turned and said, 'Good evening, sir.' Bond recognized him as one of the clerks in the warehouse. He was as dark and lean as the head clerk, and his eyes also were blue.

The car moved down the hill. Kerim spoke to the chauffeur in English. 'It is a small street off the Hippodrome Square. When we get there we will proceed softly. I will tell you when to stop. Have you got the uniforms and the equipment?'

'Yes, Kerim Bey.'

'All right. Make good speed. It is time we were all in bed.'

Kerim sank back in his seat. He took out a cigarette. They sat and smoked. Bond gazed out at the drab streets and reflected that sparse street-lighting is the sure sign of a poor town.

It was some time before Kerim spoke. Then he said, 'The gipsy said we both have the wings of death over us. He said that I am to beware of a son of the snows and you must beware of a man who is owned by the moon.' He laughed harshly. 'That is the sort of rigmarole they talk. But he says that Krilencu isn't either of these men. That is good.'

'Why?'

'Because I cannot sleep until I have killed that man. I do not know if what happened tonight has any connection with you and your assignment. I do not care. For some reason, war has been declared on me. If I do not kill Krilencu, at the third attempt he will certainly kill me. So we are now on our way to keep an appointment with him in Samarra.'

CHAPTER 19

The Mouth of Marilyn Monroe

THE car sped through the deserted streets, past shadowy mosques from which dazzling minarets lanced up towards the three-quarter moon, under the ruined Aqueduct and across the Ataturk Boulevard and north of the barred entrances to the Grand Bazaar. At the Column of Constantine the car turned right, through mean twisting streets that smelled of garbage, and finally debouched into a long ornamental square in which three stone columns fired themselves like a battery of space-rockets into the spangled sky.

'Slow,' said Kerim softly. They crept round the square under the shadow of the lime trees. Down a street on the east side, the lighthouse below the Seraglio Palace gave them a great yellow wink.

'Stop.'

The car pulled up in the darkness under the limes. Kerim reached for the door handle. 'We shan't be long, James. You sit up front in the driver's seat and if a policeman comes along just say "*Ben Bey Kerim'in ortagiyim*". Can you remember that? It means "I am Kerim Bey's partner". They'll leave you alone.'

Bond snorted. 'Thanks very much. But you'll be surprised to hear I'm coming with you. You're bound to get into trouble without me. Anyway I'm damned if I'm going to sit here trying to bluff policemen. The worst of learning one good phrase is that it sounds as if one knew the language. The policeman will come back with a barrage of Turkish and when I can't answer he'll smell a rat. Don't argue, Darko.'

'Well, don't blame me if you don't like this.' Kerim's voice was embarrassed. 'It's going to be a straight killing in cold blood. In my country you let sleeping dogs lie, but when they wake up and bite, you shoot them. You don't offer them a duel. All right?'

'Whatever you say,' said Bond. 'I've got one bullet left in case you miss.'

'Come on then,' said Kerim reluctantly. 'We've got quite a walk. The other two will be going another way.'

Kerim took a long walking-stick from the chauffeur, and a leather case. He slung them over his shoulder and they started off down the street into the yellow wink of the lighthouse. Their footsteps echoed hollowly back at them from the iron-shuttered shop frontages. There was not a soul in sight, not a cat, and Bond was glad he was not walking alone down this long street towards the distant baleful eye.

From the first, Istanbul had given him the impression of a town where, with the night, horror creeps out of the stones. It seemed to him a town the centuries had so drenched in blood and violence that, when daylight went out, the ghosts of its dead were its only population. His instinct told him, as it has told other travellers, that Istanbul was a town he would be glad to get out of alive.

They came to a narrow stinking alley that dived steeply down the hill to their right. Kerim turned into it and started gingerly down its cobbled surface. 'Watch your feet,' he said softly. 'Garbage is a polite word for what my charming people throw into their streets.'

The moon shone whitely down the moist river of cobbles. Bond kept his mouth shut and breathed through his nose. He put his feet down one after the other, flat-footedly, and with his knees bent, as if he was walking down a snow-slope. He thought of his bed in the hotel and of the comfortable cushions of the car under the sweetly smelling lime trees, and he wondered how many more kinds of dreadful stench he was going to run into during his present assignment.

They stopped at the bottom of the alley. Kerim turned to him with a broad white grin. He pointed upwards at a towering block of black shadow. 'Mosque of Sultan Ahmet. Famous Byzantine frescoes. Sorry I haven't got time to show you more of the beauties of my country.' Without waiting for Bond's reply, he cut off to the right and along a dusty boulevard, lined with cheap shops, that sloped down towards the distant glint that was the Sea of Marmara. For ten minutes they walked in silence. Then Kerim slowed and beckoned Bond into the shadows.

'This will be a simple operation,' he said softly. 'Krilencu lives down there, beside the railway line.' He gestured vaguely towards a cluster of red and green lights at the end of the boulevard. 'He hides out in a shack behind a bill-hoarding. There is a front door to the shack. Also a trapdoor to the street through the hoarding. He thinks no one knows of this. My two men will go in at the front door. He will slip out through the hoarding. Then I shoot him. All right?'

'If you say so.'

They walked on down the boulevard, keeping close to the wall. After ten minutes, they came in sight of the twenty-foot-high hoarding that formed a facing wall to the T intersection at the bottom of the street. The moon was behind the hoarding and its face was in shadow. Now Kerim walked even more carefully, putting each foot softly in front of him. About a hundred yards from the hoarding the shadows ended and the moon blazed whitely down on the intersection. Kerim stopped in the last dark doorway and stationed Bond in front of him, up against his chest. 'Now we must wait,' he whispered. Bond heard Kerim fiddling behind him. There came a soft plop as the lid of the leather case came off. A thin, heavy steel tube, about two feet long, with a bulge at each end, was pressed into Bond's hand. 'Sniperscope. German model,' whispered Kerim. 'Infra-red lens. Sees in the dark. Have a look at that big film advertisement over there. That face. Just below the nose. You'll see the outline of a trap-door. In direct line down from the signal box.'

Bond rested his forearm against the door jamb and raised the tube to his right eye. He focused it on the patch of black shadow opposite. Slowly the black dissolved into grey. The outline of a huge woman's face and some lettering appeared. Now Bond could read the lettering. It said: 'NIYAGARA. MARILYN MONROE VE JOSEPH COTTEN' and underneath, the cartoon feature, 'BONZO FUTBOLOU'. Bond inched the glass down the vast pile of Marilyn Monroe's hair, and the cliff of forehead, and down the two feet of nose to the cavernous nostrils. A faint square showed in the poster. It ran from below the nose into the great alluring curve of the lips. It was about three feet deep. From it, there would be a longish drop to the ground.

Behind Bond there sounded a series of soft clicks. Kerim held forward his walking-stick. As Bond had supposed, it was a gun, a rifle, with a skeleton butt which was also a twist breech. The squat bulge of a silencer had taken the place of the rubber tip.

'Barrel from the new 88 Winchester,' whispered Kerim proudly. 'Put together for me by a man in Ankara. Takes the .308 cartridge. The short one. Three of them. Give me the glass. I want to get that trap-door lined up before my men go in at the front. Mind if I use your shoulder as a rest?'

'All right.' Bond handed Kerim the Sniperscope. Kerim clipped it to the top of the barrel and slid the gun along Bond's shoulder.

'Got it,' whispered Kerim. 'Where Vavra said. He's a good man that.' He lowered his gun just as two policemen appeared at the right-hand corner of the intersection. Bond stiffened.

'It's all right,' whispered Kerim. 'That's my boy and the chauffeur.' He put two fingers in his mouth. A very quick, very low-pitched whistle sounded for a fraction of a second. One of the policemen lifted his hand to the back of his neck. The two policemen turned and walked away, their boots ringing loudly on the paving stones.

'Few minutes more,' whispered Kerim. 'They've got to get round the back of that hoarding.' Bond felt the heavy barrel of the gun slip into place along his right shoulder.

The moonstruck silence was broken by a loud iron clang from the signal box behind the hoarding. One of the signal arms dropped. A green pinpoint of light showed among the cluster of reds. There was a soft slow rumble in the distance, away to the left by Seraglio Point. It came closer and sorted itself into the heavy pant of an engine and the grinding clangour of a string of badly coupled goods trucks. A faint yellow glimmer shone along the embankment to the left. The engine came labouring into view above the hoarding.

The train slowly clanked by on its hundred-mile journey to the Greek frontier, a broken black silhouette against the silver sea, and the heavy cloud of smoke from its cheap fuel drifted towards them on the still air. As the red light on the brake van glimmered briefly and disappeared, there came the deeper rumble as the engine entered a cutting, and then two harsh, mournful whoops as it whistled its approach to the little station of Buyuk, a mile further down the line.

The rumble of the train died away. Bond felt the gun press deeper into his shoulder. He strained his eyes into the target of shadow. In the centre of it, a deeper square of blackness showed.

Bond cautiously lifted his left hand to shade his eyes from the moon. There came a hiss of breath from behind his right ear. 'He's coming.'

Out of the mouth of the huge, shadowed poster, between the great violet lips, half-open in ecstasy, the dark shape of a man emerged and hung down like a worm from the mouth of a corpse.

The man dropped. A ship going up towards the Bosphorus growled in the night like a sleepless animal in a zoo. Bond felt a trickle of sweat on his forehead. The barrel of the rifle depressed as the man stepped softly off the pavement towards them.

When he's at the edge of the shadow, he'll start to run, thought Bond. You damn fool, get the sights further down.

Now. The man bent for a quick sprint across the dazzling white street. He was coming out of the shadow. His right leg was bent forward and his shoulder was twisted to give him momentum.

At Bond's ear there was the clunk of an axe hitting into a tree trunk. The man dived forward, his arms outstretched. There was a sharp 'tok' as his chin or his forehead hit the ground.

An empty cartridge tinkled down at Bond's feet. He heard the click of the next round going into the chamber.

The man's fingers scrabbled briefly at the cobbles. His shoe knocked on the road. Then he lay absolutely still.

Kerim grunted. The rifle came down off Bond's shoulder, Bond listened to the noises of Kerim folding up the gun and putting away the Sniperscope in its leather case.

Bond looked away from the sprawling figure in the road, the figure of the man who had been, but was no more. He had a moment of resentment against the life that made him witness these things. The resentment was not against Kerim. Kerim had twice been this man's target. In a way it had been a long duel, in which the man had fired twice to Kerim's once. But Kerim was the cleverer, cooler man, and the luckier, and that had been that. But Bond had never killed in cold blood, and he hadn't liked watching, and helping, someone else do it.

Kerim silently took his arm. They walked slowly away from the scene and back the way they had come.

Kerim seemed to sense Bond's thoughts. 'Life is full of death, my friend,' he said philosophically. 'And sometimes one is made the instrument of death. I do not regret killing that man. Nor would I regret killing any of those Russians we saw in that office today. They are hard people. With them, what you don't get from strength, you won't get from mercy. They are all the same, the Russians. I wish your government would realize it and be strong with them. Just an occasional little lesson in manners like I have taught them tonight.'

'In power politics, one doesn't often have the chance of being as quick and neat as you were tonight, Darko. And don't forget it's only one of their satellites you've punished, one of the men they always find to do their dirty work. Mark you,' said Bond, 'I quite agree about the Russians. They simply don't understand the carrot. Only the stick has any effect. Basically they're masochists. They love the knout. That's why they were so happy under Stalin. He gave it them. I'm not sure how they're going to react to the scraps of carrot they're being fed by Khrushchev and Co. As for England, the trouble today is that carrots for all are the fashion. At home and abroad. We don't show teeth any more — only gums.'

Kerim laughed harshly, but made no comment. They were climbing back up the stinking alley and there was no breath for talk. They rested at the top and then walked slowly towards the trees of the Hippodrome Square.

'So you forgive me for today?' It was odd to hear the longing for reassurance in the big man's usually boisterous voice.

'Forgive you? Forgive what? Don't be ridiculous.' There was affection in Bond's voice. 'You've got a job to do and you're doing it. I've been very impressed. You've got a wonderful set-up here. I'm the one who ought to apologize. I seem to have brought a great deal of trouble down on your head. And you've dealt with it. I've just tagged along behind. And I've got absolutely nowhere with my main job. M. will be getting pretty impatient. Perhaps there'll be some sort of message at the hotel.'

But when Kerim took Bond back to the hotel and went with him to the desk there was nothing for Bond. Kerim clapped him on the back. 'Don't worry, my friend,' he said cheerfully. 'Hope makes a good breakfast. Eat plenty of it. I will send the car in the morning and if nothing has happened I will think of some more little adventures to pass the time. Clean your gun and sleep on it. You both deserve a rest.'

Bond climbed the few stairs and unlocked his door and locked and bolted it behind him. Moonlight filtered through the curtains. He walked across and turned on the pink-shaded lights on the dress-

ing-table. He stripped off his clothes and went into the bathroor
and stood for a few minutes under the shower. He thought how
much more eventful Saturday the fourteenth had been than Frida
the thirteenth. He cleaned his teeth and gargled with a shar
mouthwash to get rid of the taste of the day and turned off th
bathroom light and went back into the bedroom.

Bond drew aside one curtain and opened wide the tall window
and stood, holding the curtains open and looking out across th
great boomerang curve of water under the riding moon. The nigh
breeze felt wonderfully cool on his naked body. He looked at hi
watch. It said two o'clock.

Bond gave a shuddering yawn. He let the curtains drop bac
into place. He bent to switch off the lights on the dressing-tabl
Suddenly he stiffened and his heart missed a beat.

There had been a nervous giggle from the shadows at the bac
of the room. A girl's voice said, 'Poor Mister Bond. You must b
tired. Come to bed.'

CHAPTER 20

Black on Pink

BOND whirled round. He looked over to the bed, but his eyes were blind from gazing at the moon. He crossed the room and turned on the pink-shaded light by the bed. There was a long body under the single sheet. Brown hair was spread out on the pillow. The tips of fingers showed, holding the sheet up over the face. Lower down the breasts stood up like hills under snow.

Bond laughed shortly. He leaned forward and gave the hair a soft tug. There was a squeak of protest from under the sheet. Bond sat down on the edge of the bed. After a moment's silence a corner of the sheet was cautiously lowered and one large blue eye inspected him.

'You look very improper.' The voice was muffled by the sheet.

'What about you! And how did you get here?'

'I walked down two floors. I live here too.' The voice was deep and provocative. There was very little accent.

'Well, I'm going to get into bed.'

The sheet came quickly down to the chin and the girl pulled herself up on the pillows. She was blushing. 'Oh no. You mustn't.'

'But it's my bed. And anyway you told me to.' The face wa
incredibly beautiful. Bond examined it coolly. The blush deepened

'That was only a phrase. To introduce myself.'

'Well I'm very glad to meet you. My name's James Bond.'

'Mine's Tatiana Romanova.' She sounded the second A o
Tatiana and the first A of Romanova very long. 'My friends call m
Tania.'

There was a pause while they looked at each other, the girl wit
curiosity, and with what might have been relief. Bond with coo
surmise.

She was the first to break the silence. 'You look just like you
photographs,' she blushed again. 'But you must put something on
It upsets me.'

'You upset me just as much. That's called sex. If I got into be
with you it wouldn't matter. Anyway, what have *you* got on?'

She pulled the sheet a fraction lower to show a quarter-inc
black velvet ribbon round her neck. 'This.'

Bond looked down into the teasing blue eyes, now wide as i
asking if the ribbon was inadequate. He felt his body getting out o
control.

'Damn you, Tania. Where are the rest of your things? Or di
you come down in the lift like that?'

'Oh no. That would not have been *kulturny*. They are unde
the bed.'

'Well, if you think you are going to get out of this room withou
. . .'

Bond left the sentence unfinished. He got up from the bed an
went to put on one of the dark blue silk pyjama coats he wor
instead of pyjamas.

'What you are suggesting is not *kulturny*.'

'Oh isn't it,' said Bond sarcastically. He came back to the be
and pulled up a chair beside it. He smiled down at her. 'Well I'
tell you something *kulturny*. You're one of the most beautifu
women in the world.'

The girl blushed again. She looked at him seriously. 'Are yo speaking the truth? I think my mouth is too big. Am I as beautiful as Western girls? I was once told I look like Greta Garbo. Is that so?'

'More beautiful,' said Bond. 'There is more light in your face. And your mouth isn't too big. It's just the right size. For me, anyway.'

'What is that — "light in the face"? What do you mean?'

Bond meant that she didn't look to him like a Russian spy. She seemed to show none of the reserve of a spy. None of the coldness, none of the calculation. She gave the impression of warmth of heart and gaiety. These things shone out through the eyes. He searched for a non-committal phrase. 'There is a lot of gaiety and fun in your eyes,' he said lamely.

Tatiana looked serious. 'That is curious,' she said. 'There is not much fun and gaiety in Russia. No one speaks of these things. I have never been told that before.'

Gaiety? She thought, after the last two months? How could she be looking gay? And yet, yes, there was a lightness in her heart. Was she a loose woman by nature? Or was it something to do with this man she had never seen before? Relief about him after the agony of thinking about what she had to do? It was certainly much easier than she had expected. He made it easy — made it fun, with a spice of danger. He was terribly handsome. And he looked very clean. Would he forgive her when they got to London and she told him? Told him that she had been sent to seduce him? Even the night on which she must do it and the number of the room? Surely he wouldn't mind very much. It was doing him no harm. It was only a way for her to get to England and make those reports. 'Gaiety and fun in her eyes.' Well, why not? It was possible. There was a wonderful sense of freedom being alone with a man like this and knowing that she would not be punished for it. It was really terribly exciting.

'You are very handsome,' she said. She searched for a comparison that would give him pleasure. 'You are like an American film star.'

She was startled by his reaction. 'For God's sake! That's th
worst insult you can pay a man!'

She hurried to make good her mistake. How curious that th
compliment didn't please him. Didn't everyone in the West wan
to look like a film star? 'I was lying,' she said. 'I wanted to giv
you pleasure. In fact you are like my favourite hero. He's in
book by a Russian called Lermontov. I will tell you about hir
one day.'

One day? Bond thought it was time to get down to business.

'Now listen, Tania.' He tried not to look at the beautiful face o
the pillow. He fixed his eyes on the point of her chin. 'We've go
to stop fooling and be serious. What *is* all this about? Are yor
really going to come back to England with me?' He raised his eye
to hers. It was fatal. She had opened them wide again in tha
damnable guilelessness.

'But of course!'

'Oh!' Bond was taken aback by the directness of her answer
He looked at her suspiciously. 'You're sure?'

'Yes.' Her eyes were truthful now. She had stopped flirting.

'You're not afraid?'

He saw a shadow cross her eyes. But it was not what he though
She had remembered that she had a part to play. She was to b
frightened of what she was doing. Terrified. It had sounded s
easy, this acting, but now it was difficult. How odd! She decide
to compromise.

'Yes. I am afraid. But not so much now. You will protect me
I thought you would.'

'Well, yes, of course I will.' Bond thought of her relatives i
Russia. He quickly put the thought out of his mind. What was h
doing? Trying to dissuade her from coming? He closed his min
to the consequences he imagined for her. 'There's nothing t
worry about. I'll look after you.' And now for the question he ha
been shirking. He felt a ridiculous embarrassment. This girl wasn'
in the least what he had expected. It was spoiling everything to as
the question. It had to be done.

'What about the machine?'

Yes. It was as if he had cuffed her across the face. Pain showed n her eyes, and the edge of tears.

She pulled the sheet over her mouth and spoke from behind it. Her eyes above the sheet were cold.

'So that's what you want.'

'Now listen.' Bond put nonchalance in his voice. 'This machine's got nothing to do with you and me. But my people in London want it.' He remembered security. He added blandly. 'It's not all hat important. They know all about the machine and they think t's a wonderful Russian invention. They just want one to copy. Like your people copy foreign cameras and things.' God, how lame t sounded!

'Now you're lying,' a big tear rolled out of one wide blue eye and down the soft cheek and on to the pillow. She pulled the sheet up over her eyes.

Bond reached out and put his hand on her arm under the sheet. The arm flinched angrily away.

'Damn the bloody machine,' he said impatiently. 'But for God's sake, Tania, you must know that I've got a job to do. Just say one way or the other and we'll forget about it. There are lots more things to talk about. We've got to arrange our journey and so on. Of course my people want it or they wouldn't have sent me out to bring you home with it.'

Tatiana dabbed her eyes with the sheet. Brusquely she pulled the sheet down to her shoulders again. She knew that she had been forgetting her job. It had just been that ... Oh well. If only he had said that the machine didn't matter to him so long as she would come. But that was too much to hope for. He was right. He had a job to do. So had she.

She looked up at him calmly. 'I will bring it. Have no fear. But do not let us mention it again. And now listen.' She sat up straighter in the pillows. 'We must go tonight.' She remembered her lesson. It is the only chance. This evening I am on night duty from six o'clock. I shall be alone in the office and I will take the Spektor.'

Bond's eyes narrowed. His mind raced as he thought of the problems that would have to be faced. Where to hide her. How to get her out to the first plane after the loss had been discovered. It was going to be a risky business. They would stop at nothing to get her and the Spektor back. Roadblock on the way to the airport. Bomb in the plane. Anything.

'That's wonderful, Tania.' Bond's voice was casual. 'We'll keep you hidden and then we'll take the first plane tomorrow morning.'

'Don't be foolish.' Tatiana had been warned that here would be some difficult lines in her part. 'We will take the train. This Orient Express. It leaves at nine tonight. Do you think I haven't been thinking this thing out? I won't stay a minute longer in Istanbul than I have to. We will be over the frontier at dawn. You must get the tickets and a passport. I will travel with you as your wife.' She looked happily up at him. 'I shall like that. In one of those coupé I have read about. They must be very comfortable. Like a tiny house on wheels. During the day we will talk and read and at night you will stand in the corridor outside our house and guard it.'

'Like hell I will,' said Bond. 'But look here, Tania. That's crazy. They're bound to catch up with us somewhere. It's four days and five nights to London on that train. We've got to think of something else.'

'I won't,' said the girl flatly. 'That's the only way I'll go. If you are clever, how can they find out?'

Oh God, she thought. Why had they insisted on this train? But they had been definite. It was a good place for love, they had said. She would have four days to get him to love her. Then, when they got to London, life would be easy for her. He would protect her. Otherwise, if they flew to London, she would be put straight into prison. The four days were essential. And, they had warned her, we will have men on the train to see you don't get off. So be careful and obey your orders. Oh God. Oh God. Yet now she longed for those four days with him in the little house on wheels. How curious! It had been her duty to force him. Now it was her passionate desire.

She watched Bond's thoughtful face. She longed to stretch out a
hand to him and reassure him that it would be all right; that this
was a harmless *konspiratsia* to get her to England: that no harm
could come to either of them, because that was not the object of the
plot.

'Well, I still think it's crazy,' said Bond, wondering what M.'s
reaction would be. 'But I suppose it may work. I've got the passport. It will need a Yugoslav visa,' he looked at her sternly. 'Don't
think I'm going to take you on the part of the train that goes
through Bulgaria, or I shall think you want to kidnap me.'

'I do.' Tatiana giggled. 'That's exactly what I want to do.'

'Now shut up, Tania. We've got to work this out. I'll get the
tickets and I'll have one of our men come along. Just in case. He's
a good man. You'll like him. Your name's Caroline Somerset.
Don't forget it. How are you going to get to the train?'

'Karolin Siomerset,' the girl turned the name over in her mind.
'It is a pretty name. And you are Mister Siomerset.' She laughed
happily. 'That is fun. Do not worry about me. I will come to the
train just before it leaves. It is the Sirkeci Station. I know where it
is. So that is all. And we do not worry any more. Yes?'

'Suppose you lose your nerve? Suppose they catch you?' Suddenly Bond was worried at the girl's confidence. How could she be
so certain? A sharp tingle of suspicion ran down his spine.

'Before I saw you, I was frightened. Now I am not.' Tatiana
tried to tell herself that this was the truth. Somehow it nearly was.
'Now I shall not lose my nerve, as you call it. And they cannot
catch me. I shall leave my things in the hotel and take my usual
bag to the office. I cannot leave my fur coat behind. I love it too
dearly. But today is Sunday and that will be an excuse to come to
the office in it. Tonight at half-past eight I shall walk out and take a
taxi to the station. And now you must stop looking so worried.'
Impulsively, because she had to, she stretched out a hand towards
him. 'Say that you are pleased.'

Bond moved to the edge of the bed. He took her hand and
looked down into her eyes. God, he thought. I hope it's all right.

I hope this crazy plan will work. Is this wonderful girl a cheat? Is she true? Is she real? The eyes told him nothing except that the girl was happy, and that she wanted him to love her, and that she was surprised at what was happening to her. Tatiana's other hand came up and round his neck and pulled him fiercely down to her. At first the mouth trembled under his and then, as passion took her, the mouth yielded into a kiss without end.

Bond lifted his legs on to the bed. While his mouth went on kissing her, his hand went to her left breast and held it, feeling the peak hard with desire under his fingers. His hand strayed on down across her flat stomach. Her legs shifted languidly. She moaned softly and her mouth slid away from his. Below the closed eyes the long lashes quivered like humming birds' wings.

Bond reached up and took the edge of the sheet and pulled it right down and threw it off the end of the huge bed. She was wearing nothing but the black ribbon round her neck and black silk stockings rolled above her knees. Her arms groped up for him.

Above them, and unknown to both of them, behind the gold-framed false mirror on the wall over the bed, the two photographers from SMERSH sat close together in the cramped *cabinet de voyeur*, as, before them, so many friends of the proprietor had sat on a honeymoon night in the stateroom of the Kristal Palas.

And the view-finders gazed coldly down on the passionate arabesques the two bodies formed and broke and formed again, and the clockwork mechanism of the cine-cameras whirred softly on and on as the breath rasped out of the open mouths of the two men and the sweat of excitement trickled down their bulging faces into their cheap collars.

CHAPTER 21

Orient Express

THE great trains are going out all over Europe, one by one, but still, three times a week, the Orient Express thunders superbly over the 1400 miles of glittering steel track between Istanbul and Paris.

Under the arc-lights, the long-chassied German locomotive panted quietly with the laboured breath of a dragon dying of asthma. Each heavy breath seemed certain to be the last. Then came another. Wisps of steam rose from the couplings between the carriages and died quickly in the warm August air. The Orient Express was the only live train in the ugly, cheaply architectured burrow that is Istanbul's main station. The trains on the other lines were engineless and unattended — waiting for tomorrow. Only Track No. 3, and its platform, throbbed with the tragic poetry of departure.

The heavy bronze cipher on the side of the dark blue coach said, 'COMPAGNIE INTERNATIONALE DES WAGON-LITS ET DES GRANDS XPRESS EUROPÉENS'. Above the cipher, fitted into metal slots, was

a flat iron sign that announced, in black capitals on white, ORIENT
EXPRESS, and underneath, in three lines:

ISTANBUL   THESSALONIKI   BEOGRAD

VENEZIA   MILAN

LAUSANNE   PARIS

James Bond gazed vaguely at one of the most romantic signs in
the world. For the tenth time he looked at his watch. 8.51. His
eyes went back to the sign. All the towns were spelled in the language of the country except MILAN. Why not MILANO? Bond took
out his handkerchief and wiped his face. Where the hell was the
girl? Had she been caught? Had she had second thoughts? Had he
been too rough with her last night, or rather this morning, in the
great bed?

8.55. The quiet pant of the engine had stopped. There came an
echoing whoosh as the automatic safety-valve let off the excess
steam. A hundred yards away, through the milling crowd, Bond
watched the station-master raise a hand to the engine driver and
fireman and start walking slowly back down the train, banging the
doors of the third-class carriages up front. Passengers, mostly
peasants going back into Greece after a week-end with their relatives
in Turkey, hung out of the windows and jabbered at the grinning
crowd below.

Beyond, where the faded arc-lights stopped and the dark blue
night and the stars showed through the crescent mouth of the
station, Bond saw a red pinpoint turn to green.

The station-master came nearer. The brown uniformed wagon-
lit attendant tapped Bond on the arm. '*En voiture, s'il vous plaît.*
The two rich-looking Turks kissed their mistresses — they were
too pretty to be wives — and, with a barrage of laughing injunc-
tions, stepped on to the little iron pedestal and up the two tall steps
into the carriage. There were no other wagon-lit travellers on the
platform. The conductor, with an impatient glance at the tall
Englishman, picked up the iron pedestal and climbed with it into
the train.

The station-master strode purposefully by. Two more compartments, the first- and second-class carriages, and then, when he
reached the guard's van, he would lift the dirty green flag.

There was no hurrying figure coming up the platform from the
guichet. High up above the *guichet*, near the ceiling of the station,
the minute hand of the big illuminated clock jumped forward an
inch and said 'Nine'.

A window banged down above Bond's head. Bond looked up.
His immediate reaction was that the black veil was too wide-
meshed. The intention to disguise the luxurious mouth and the
excited blue eyes was amateurish.

'Quick.'

The train had begun to move. Bond reached for the passing
hand-rail and swung up on to the step. The attendant was still
holding open the door. Bond stepped unhurriedly through.

'Madam was late,' said the attendant. 'She came along the corridor. She must have entered by the last carriage.'

Bond went down the carpeted corridor to the centre coupé.
A black 7 stood above a black 8 on the white metal lozenge. The
door was ajar. Bond walked in and shut it behind him. The girl
had taken off her veil and her black straw hat. She was sitting in the
corner by the window. A long, sleek sable coat was thrown open to
show a natural coloured shantung dress with a pleated skirt, honey-
coloured nylons and a black crocodile belt and shoes. She looked
composed.

'You have no faith, James.'

Bond sat down beside her. 'Tania,' he said, 'if there was a bit
more room I'd put you across my knee and spank you. You nearly
gave me heart failure. What happened?'

'Nothing,' said Tatiana innocently. 'What could happen? I
said I would be here, and I am here. You have no faith. Since I
am sure you are more interested in my dowry than in me, it is up
here.'

Bond looked casually up. Two small cases were on the rack beside
his suitcase. He took her hand. He said, 'Thank God you're safe.'

Something in his eyes, perhaps the flash of guilt, as he admitted to himself that he had been more interested in the girl than the machine, reassured her. She kept his hand in hers and sank contentedly back in her corner.

The train screeched slowly round Seraglio Point. The lighthouse lit up the roofs of the dreary shacks along the railway line. With his free hand Bond took out a cigarette and lit it. He reflected that they would soon be passing the back of the great bill-board where Krilencu had lived — until less than twenty-four hours ago. Bond saw again the scene in every detail. The white cross roads, the two men in the shadows, the doomed man slipping out through the purple lips.

The girl watched his face with tenderness. What was this man thinking? What was going on behind those cold level grey-blue eyes that sometimes turned soft and sometimes, as they had done last night before his passion had burned out in her arms, blazed like diamonds. Now they were veiled in thought. Was he worrying about them both? Worrying about their safety? If only she could tell him that there was nothing to fear, that he was only her passport to England — him and the heavy case the Resident Director had given her that evening in the office. The Director had said the same thing. 'Here is your passport to England, Corporal,' he had said cheerfully. 'Look.' He had unzipped the bag: 'A brand new Spektor. Be certain not to open the bag again or let it out of your compartment until you get to the other end. Or this Englishman will take it away from you and throw you on the dust-heap. It is this machine they want. Do not let them take it from you, or you will have failed in your duty. Understood?'

A signal box loomed up in the blue dusk outside the window. Tatiana watched Bond get up and pull down the window and crane out into the darkness. His body was close to her. She moved her knee so that it touched him. How extraordinary, this passionate tenderness that had filled her ever since she had seen him last night standing naked at the window, his arms up to hold the curtain back, his profile, under the tousled black hair, intent and pale in the moonlight. And then the extraordinary fusing of their eyes and their bodies. The flame that had suddenly lit between them — between the two secret agents, thrown together from enemy camps a whole world apart, each involved in his own plot against the country of the other, antagonists by profession, yet turned, and by the orders of their governments, into lovers.

Tatiana stretched out a hand and caught hold of the edge of the coat and tugged at it. Bond pulled up the window and turned. He smiled down at her. He read her eyes. He bent and put his hands on the fur over her breasts and kissed her hard on the lips. Tatiana leant back, dragging him with her.

There came a soft double knock on the door. Bond stood up. He pulled out his handkerchief and brusquely scrubbed the rouge off his lips. 'That'll be my friend Kerim,' he said. 'I must talk to him. I will tell the conductor to make up the beds. Stay here while he does it. I won't be long. I shall be outside the door.' He leant forward and touched her hand and looked at her wide eyes and at her rueful, half-open lips. 'We shall have all the night to ourselves. First I must see that you are safe.' He unlocked the door and slipped out.

Darko Kerim's huge bulk was blocking the corridor. He was leaning on the brass guard-rail, smoking and gazing moodily out towards the Sea of Marmara that receded as the long train snaked away from the coast and turned inland and northwards. Bond leaned on the rail beside him. Kerim looked into the reflection of Bond's face in the dark window. He said softly, 'The news is not good. There are three of them on the train.'

'Ah!' An electric tingle ran up Bond's spine.

'It's the three strangers we saw in that room. Obviously they're on to you and the girl.' Kerim glanced sharply sideways. 'That makes her a double. Or doesn't it?'

Bond's mind was cool. So the girl had been bait. And yet, and yet. No, damn it. She couldn't be acting. It wasn't possible. The cipher machine? Perhaps after all it wasn't in that bag. Wait a minute,' he said. He turned and knocked softly on the door.

He heard her unlock it and slip the chain. He went in and shut the door. She looked surprised. She had thought it was the conductor come to make up the beds.

She smiled radiantly. 'You have finished?'

'Sit down, Tatiana. I've got to talk to you.'

Now she saw the coldness in his face and her smile went out. She sat down obediently with her hands in her lap.

Bond stood over her. Was there guilt in her face, or fear? No, only surprise and a coolness to match his own expression.

'Now listen, Tatiana,' Bond's voice was deadly. 'Something's come up. I must look into that bag and see if the machine is there.'

She said indifferently. 'Take it down and look.' She examined the hands in her lap. So now it was going to come. What the Director had said. They were going to take the machine and throw her aside, perhaps have her put off the train. Oh God! This man was going to do that to her.

Bond reached up and hauled down the heavy case and put it on the seat. He tore the zip sideways and looked in. Yes, a grey japanned metal case with three rows of squat keys, rather like a typewriter. He held the bag open towards her. 'Is that a Spektor?'

She glanced casually into the gaping bag. 'Yes.'

Bond zipped the bag shut and put it back on the rack. He sat down beside the girl. 'There are three M.G.B. men on the train. We know they are the ones who arrived at your centre on Monday. What are they doing here, Tatiana?' Bond's voice was soft. He watched her, searched her with all his senses.

She looked up. There were tears in her eyes. Were they the tears of a child found out? But there was no trace of guilt in her face. She only looked terrified of something.

She reached out a hand and then drew it back. 'You aren't going to throw me off the train now you've got the machine?'

'Of course not,' Bond said impatiently. 'Don't be idiotic. But we must know what these men are doing. What's it all about? Did you know they were going to be on the train?' He tried to read some clue in her expression. He could only see a great relief.

And what else? A look of calculation? Of reserve? Yes, she was hiding something. But what?

Tatiana seemed to make up her mind. Brusquely she wiped the back of her hand across her eyes. She reached forward and put the hand on his knee. The streak of tears showed on the back of the hand. She looked into Bond's eyes, forcing him to believe her.

'James,' she said. 'I did not know these men were on the train. I was told they were leaving today. For Germany. I assumed they would fly. That is all I can tell you. Until we arrive in England, out of reach of my people, you must not ask me more. I have done what I said I would. I am here with the machine. Have faith in me. Do not be afraid for us. I am certain these men do not mean us harm. Absolutely certain. Have faith.' (Was she so certain, wondered Tatiana? Had the Klebb woman told her all the truth? But she also must have faith — faith in the orders she had been given. These men must be the guards to see that she didn't get off the train. They could mean no harm. Later, when they got to London, this man would hide her away out of reach of SMERSH and she would tell him everything he wanted to know. She had already decided this in the back of her mind. But God knew what would happen if she betrayed *Them* now. *They* would somehow get her, and him. She knew it. There were no secrets from these people. And *They* would have no mercy. So long as she played out her role, all would be well.) Tatiana watched Bond's face for a sign that he believed her.

Bond shrugged his shoulders. He stood up. 'I don't know what to think, Tatiana,' he said. 'You are keeping something from me, but I think it's something you don't know is important. And I believe you think we are safe. We may be. It may be a coincidence that these men are on the train. I must talk to Kerim and decide what to do. Don't worry. We will look after you. But now we must be very careful.'

Bond looked round the compartment. He tried the communicating door with the next coupé. It was locked. He decided to wedge it when the conductor had gone. He would do the same for the

door into the passage. And he would have to stay awake. So
much for the honeymoon on wheels! Bond smiled grimly to himself and rang for the conductor. Tatiana was looking anxiously
up at him. 'Don't worry, Tania,' he said again. 'Don't worry about
anything. Go to bed when the man has gone. Don't open the door
unless you know it's me. I will sit up tonight and watch. Perhaps
tomorrow it will be easier. I will make a plan with Kerim. He is a
good man.'

The conductor knocked. Bond let him in and went out into
the corridor. Kerim was still there gazing out. The train had
picked up speed and was hurtling through the night, its harsh
melancholy whistle echoing back at them from the walls of a deep
cutting against the sides of which the lighted carriage windows
flickered and danced. Kerim didn't move, but his eyes in the mirror
of the window were watchful.

Bond told him of the conversation. It was not easy to explain to
Kerim why he trusted the girl as he did. He watched the mouth in
the window curl ironically as he tried to describe what he had read
in her eyes and what his intuition told him.

Kerim sighed resignedly. 'James,' he said, 'you are now in
charge. This is your part of the operation. We have already argued
most of this out today — the danger of the train, the possibility of
getting the machine home in the diplomatic bag, the integrity, or
otherwise, of this girl. It certainly appears that she has surrendered
unconditionally to you. At the same time you admit that you have
surrendered to her. Perhaps only partially. But you have decided
to trust her. In this morning's telephone talk with M. he said
that he would back your decision. He left it to you. So be it. But he
didn't know we were to have an escort of three M.G.B. men. Nor
did we. And I think that would have changed all our views. Yes?'

'Yes.'

'Then the only thing to do is eliminate these three men. Get them
off the train. God knows what they're here for. I don't believe in
coincidences any more than you. But one thing is certain. We are
not going to share the train with these men. Right?'

'Of course.'

'Then leave it to me. At least for tonight. This is still my country and I have certain powers in it. And plenty of money. I cannot afford to kill them. The train would be delayed. You and the girl might get involved. But I shall arrange something. Two of them have sleeping berths. The senior man with the moustache and the little pipe is next door to you — here, in No. 6.' He gestured backwards with his head. 'He is travelling on a German passport under the name of "Melchior Benz, salesman". The dark one, the Armenian, is in No. 12. He, too, has a German passport — "Kurt Goldfarb, construction engineer". They have through tickets to Paris. I have seen their documents. I have a police card. The conductor made no trouble. He has all the tickets and passports in his cabin. The third man, the man with a boil on the back of his neck, turns out also to have boils on his face. A stupid, ugly looking brute. I have not seen his passport. He is travelling sitting up in the first-class, in the next compartment to me. He does not have to surrender his passport until the frontier. But he has surrendered his ticket.' Like a conjuror, Kerim flicked a yellow first-class ticket out of his coat pocket. He slipped it back. He grinned proudly at Bond.

'How the hell?'

Kerim chuckled. 'Before he settled down for the night, this dumb ox went to the lavatory. I was standing in the corridor and I suddenly remembered how we used to steal rides on the train when I was a boy. I gave him a minute. Then I walked up and rattled the lavatory door. I hung on to the handle very tight. "Ticket collector," I said in a loud voice. "Tickets please." I said it in French and again in German. There was a mumble from inside. I felt him try to open the door. I hung on tight so that he would think the door had stuck. "Do not derange yourself, *Monsieur*," I said politely. "Push the ticket under the door." There was more fiddling with the door handle and I could hear heavy breathing. Then there was a pause and a rustle under the door. There was the ticket. I said, "*Merci, Monsieur*" very politely. I picked up the ticket and stepped across the coupling into the next carriage.' Kerim airily waved a hand. 'The stupid oaf will be sleeping peacefully by now. He will think that his ticket will be given back to him at the frontier. He is mistaken. The ticket will be in ashes and the ashes will be on the four winds,' Kerim gestured towards the darkness outside. 'I will see that the man is put off the train, however much money he has got. He will be told that the circumstances must be investigated, his statements corroborated with the ticket agency. He will be allowed to proceed on a later train.'

Bond smiled at the picture of Kerim playing his private school trick. 'You're a card, Darko. What about the other two?'

Darko Kerim shrugged his massive shoulders. 'Something will occur to me,' he said confidently. 'The way to catch Russians is to make them look foolish. Embarrass them. Laugh at them. They can't stand it. We will somehow make these men sweat. Then we will leave it to the M.G.B. to punish them for failing in their duty. Doubtless they will be shot by their own people.'

While they were talking, the conductor had come out of No. 7. Kerim turned to Bond and put a hand on his shoulder. 'Have no fear, James,' he said cheerfully. 'We will defeat these people. Go to your girl. We will meet again in the morning. We shall not sleep much tonight, but that cannot be helped. Every day is different. Perhaps we shall sleep tomorrow.'

Bond watched the big man move off easily down the swaying corridor. He noticed that, despite the movement of the train, Kerim's shoulders never touched the walls of the corridor. Bond felt a wave of affection for the tough, cheerful professional spy.

Kerim disappeared into the conductor's cabin. Bond turned and knocked softly on the door of No. 7.

CHAPTER 22

Out of Turkey

THE train howled on through the night. Bond sat and watched the hurrying moonlit landscape and concentrated on keeping awake.

Everything conspired to make him sleep — the hasty metal gallop of the wheels, the hypnotic swoop of the silver telegraph wires, the occasional melancholy, reassuring moan of the steam whistle clearing their way, the drowsy metallic chatter of the couplings at each end of the corridor, the lullaby creak of the woodwork in the little room. Even the deep violet glimmer of the night-light above the door seemed to say, 'I will watch for you. Nothing can happen while I am burning. Close your eyes and sleep, sleep.'

The girl's head was warm and heavy on his lap. There was so obviously just room for him to slip under the single sheet and fit close up against her, the front of his thighs against the backs of hers, his head in the spread curtain of her hair on the pillow.

Bond screwed up his eyes and opened them again. He cautiously lifted his wrist. Four o'clock. Only one more hour to the Turkish frontier. Perhaps he would be able to sleep during the day. He would give her the gun and wedge the doors again and she could watch.

He looked down at the beautiful sleeping profile. How innocent she looked, this girl from the Russian Secret Service — the lashes fringing the soft swell of the cheek, the lips parted and unaware, the long strand of hair that had strayed untidily across her forehead and that he wanted to brush back neatly to join the rest, the steady slow throb of the pulse in the offered neck. He felt a surge of tenderness and the impulse to gather her up in his arms and strain her tight against him. He wanted her to wake, from a dream perhaps, so that he could kiss her and tell her that everything was all right, and see her settle happily back to sleep.

The girl had insisted on sleeping like this. 'I won't go to sleep unless you hold me,' she had said. 'I must know you're there all the time. It would be terrible to wake up and not be touching you. Please James. Please *duschka*.'

Bond had taken off his coat and tie and had arranged himself in the corner with his feet up on his suitcase and the Beretta under the pillow within reach of his hand. She had made no comment about the gun. She had taken off all her clothes, except the black ribbon round her throat, and had pretended not to be provocative as she scrambled impudically into bed and wriggled herself into a comfortable position. She had held up her arms to him. Bond had pulled her head back by her hair and had kissed her once, long and cruelly. Then he had told her to go to sleep and had leant back and waited icily for his body to leave him alone. Grumbling sleepily, she had settled herself, with one arm flung across his thighs. At first she had held him tightly, but her arm had gradually relaxed and then she was asleep.

Brusquely Bond closed his mind to the thought of her and focused on the journey ahead.

Soon they would be out of Turkey. But would Greece be any easier? No love lost between Greece and England. And Yugoslavia? Whose side was Tito on? Probably both. Whatever the orders of the three M.G.B. men, either they already knew Bond and

Tatiana were on the train or they would soon find out. He and the girl couldn't sit for four days in this coupé with the blinds drawn. Their presence would be reported back to Istanbul, telephoned from some station, and by the morning the loss of the Spektor would have been discovered. Then what? A hasty démarche through the Russian embassy in Athens or Belgrade? Have the girl taken off the train as a thief? Or was that all too simple? And if it was more complicated — if all this was part of some mysterious plot, some tortuous Russian conspiracy — should he dodge it? Should he and the girl leave the train at a wayside station, on the wrong side of the track, and hire a car and somehow get a plane to London?

Outside, the luminous dawn had begun to edge the racing trees and rocks with blue. Bond looked at his watch. Five o'clock. They would soon be at Uzunkopru. What was going on down the train behind him? What had Kerim achieved?

Bond sat back, relaxed. After all there was a simple, common-sense answer to his problem. If, between them, they could quickly get rid of the three M.G.B. agents, they would stick to the train and to their original plan. If not, Bond would get the girl and the machine off the train, somewhere in Greece, and take another route home. But, if the odds improved, Bond was for going on. He and Kerim were resourceful men. Kerim had an agent in Belgrade who was going to meet the train. There was always the Embassy

Bond's mind raced on, adding up the pros, dismissing the cons. Behind his reasoning, Bond calmly admitted to himself that he had an insane desire to play the game out and see what it was all about. He wanted to take these people on and solve the mystery and, if it was some sort of a plot, defeat it. M. had left him in charge. He had the girl and the machine under his hand. Why panic? What was there to panic about? It would be mad to run away and perhaps only escape one trap in order to fall into another one.

The train gave a long whistle and began to slacken speed.

Now for the first round. If Kerim failed. If the three men stayed on the train. . . .

Some goods-trucks, led by a straining engine, filed by. The silhouette of sheds showed briefly. With a jolt and a screech of couplings, the Orient Express took the points and swerved away from the through line. Four sets of rails with grass growing between them showed outside the window, and the empty length of the down platform. A cock crowed. The express slowed to walking speed and finally, with a sigh of vacuum brakes and a noisy whoosh of let-off steam, ground to a stop. The girl stirred in her sleep. Bond softly shifted her head on to the pillow and got up and slipped out of the door.

It was a typical Balkan wayside station — a façade of dour buildings in over-pointed stone, a dusty expanse of platform, not raised, but level with the ground so that there was a long step down from the train, some chickens pecking about and a few drab officials standing idly, unshaven, not even trying to look important. Up towards the cheap half of the train, a chattering horde of peasants with bundles and wicker baskets waited for the customs and passport control so that they could clamber aboard and join the swarm inside.

Across the platform from Bond was a closed door with a sign over it which said POLIS. Through the dirty window beside the door Bond thought he caught a glimpse of the head and shoulders of Kerim.

'*Passeports. Douanes!*'

A plain-clothes man and two policemen in dark green uniform with pistol holsters at their black belts entered the corridor. The wagon-lit conductor preceded them, knocking on the doors.

At the door of No. 12 the conductor made an indignant speech in Turkish, holding out the stack of tickets and passports and fanning through them as if they were a pack of cards. When he had finished, the plain-clothes man, beckoning forward the two policemen, knocked smartly on the door and, when it was opened, stepped inside. The two policemen stood guard behind him.

Bond edged down the corridor. He could hear a jumble of bad German. One voice was cold, the other was frightened and hot.

The passport and ticket of Herr Kurt Goldfarb were missing. Had Herr Goldfarb removed them from the conductor's cabin? Certainly not. Had Herr Goldfarb in truth ever surrendered his papers to the conductor? Naturally. Then the matter was unfortunate. An inquiry would have to be held. No doubt the German Legation in Istanbul would put the matter right (Bond smiled at this suggestion). Meanwhile, it was regretted that Herr Goldfarb could not continue his journey. No doubt he would be able to proceed tomorrow. Herr Goldfarb would get dressed. His luggage would be transported to the waiting-room.

The M.G.B. man who erupted into the corridor was the dark Caucasian type man, the junior of the 'visitors'. His sallow face was grey with fear. His hair was awry and he was dressed only in the bottom half of his pyjamas. But there was nothing comical about his desperate flurry down the corridor. He brushed past Bond. At the door of No. 6 he paused and pulled himself together. He knocked with tense control. The door opened on the chain and Bond glimpsed a thick nose and part of a moustache. The chain was slipped and Goldfarb went in. There was silence, during which the plain-clothes man dealt with the papers of two elderly French women in 9 and 10, and then with Bond's.

The officer barely glanced at Bond's passport. He snapped it shut and handed it to the conductor. 'You are travelling with Kerim Bey?' he asked in French. His eyes were remote.

'Yes.'

'*Merci, Monsieur. Bon voyage.*' The man saluted. He turned and rapped sharply on the door of No. 6. The door opened and he went in.

Five minutes later the door was flung back. The plain-clothes man, now erect with authority, beckoned forward the policemen. He spoke to them harshly in Turkish. He turned back to the coupé. 'Consider yourself under arrest, Mein Herr. Attempted bribery of officials is a grave crime in Turkey.' There was an angry clamour in Goldfarb's bad German. It was cut short by one hard sentence in Russian. A different Goldfarb, a Goldfarb with madman's eyes, emerged and walked blindly down the corridor and went into No. 12. A policeman stood outside the door and waited.

'And *your* papers, Mein Herr. Please step forward. I must verify this photograph.' The plain-clothes man held the green-backed German passport up to the light. 'Forward please.'

Reluctantly, his heavy face pale with anger, the M.G.B. man who called himself Benz stepped out into the corridor in a brilliant blue silk dressing-gown. The hard brown eyes looked straight into Bond's, ignoring him.

The plain-clothes man slapped the passport shut and handed it to the conductor. 'Your papers are in order, Mein Herr. And now, if you please, the baggage.' He went in, followed by the second policeman. The M.G.B. man turned his blue back on Bond and watched the search.

Bond noticed the bulge under the left arm of the dressing-gown, and the ridge of a belt round the waist. He wondered if he should tip off the plain-clothes man. He decided it would be better to keep quiet. He might be hauled in as a witness.

The search was over. The plain-clothes man saluted coldly and moved on down the corridor. The M.G.B. man went back into No. 6 and slammed the door behind him.

Pity, thought Bond. One had got away.

Bond turned back to the window. A bulky man, wearing a grey Homburg, and with an angry boil on the back of his neck, was being escorted through the door marked POLIS. Down the corridor a door slammed. Goldfarb, escorted by the policeman, stepped down off the train. With bent head, he walked across the dusty platform and disappeared through the same door.

The engine whistled, a new kind of whistle, the brave shrill blast of a Greek engine-driver. The door of the wagon-lit carriage clanged shut. The plain-clothes man and the second policeman appeared walking over to the station. The guard at the back of the train looked at his watch and held out his flag. There was a jerk and a diminishing crescendo of explosive puffs from the engine and the front section of the Orient Express began to move. The section that would be taking the northern route through the Iron Curtain — through Dragoman on the Bulgarian frontier, only fifty miles away — was left beside the dusty platform, waiting.

Bond pulled down the window and took a last look back at the Turkish frontier, where two men would be sitting in a bare room under what amounted to sentence of death. Two birds down, he thought. Two out of three. The odds looked more respectable.

He watched the dead, dusty platform, with its chickens and the small black figure of the guard, until the long train took the points and jerked harshly on to the single main line. He looked away across the ugly, parched countryside towards the golden guinea sun climbing out of the Turkish plain. It was going to be a beautiful day.

Bond drew his head in out of the cool, sweet morning air. He pulled up the window with a bang.

He had made up his mind. He would stay on the train and see the thing through.

———————

CHAPTER 23

Out of Greece

H OT coffee from the meagre little buffet at Pithion (there would be no restaurant car until midday), a painless visit from the Greek customs and passport control, and then the berths were folded away as the train hurried south towards the Gulf of Enez at the head of the Aegean. Outside, there was extra light and colour. The air was drier. The men at the little stations and in the fields were handsome. Sunflowers, maize, vines and racks of tobacco were ripening in the sun. It was, as Darko had said, another day.

Bond washed and shaved under the amused eyes of Tatiana. She approved of the fact that he put no oil on his hair. 'It is a dirty habit,' she said. 'I was told that many Europeans have it. We would not think of doing it in Russia. It dirties the pillows. But it is odd that you in the West do not use perfume. All our men do.'

'We wash,' said Bond dryly.

In the heat of her protests, there came a knock on the door. It was Kerim. Bond let him in. Kerim bowed towards the girl.

What a charming domestic scene,' he commented cheerfully, lowering his bulk into the corner near the door. 'I have rarely seen a handsomer pair of spies.'

Tatiana glowered at him. 'I am not accustomed to Western jokes,' she said coldly.

Kerim's laugh was disarming. 'You'll learn, my dear. In England, they are great people for jokes. There it is considered proper to make a joke of everything. I also have learned to make jokes. They grease the wheels. I have been laughing a lot this morning. Those poor fellows at Uzunkopru. I wish I could be there when the police telephone the German Consulate in Istanbul. That is the worst of forged passports. They are not difficult to make, but it is almost impossible to forge also their birth certificate — the files of the country which is supposed to have issued them. I fear the careers of your two comrades have come to a sad end, Mrs. Somerset.'

'How did you do it?' Bond knotted his tie.

'Money and influence. Five hundred dollars to the conductor. Some big talk to the police. It was lucky our friend tried a bribe. A pity that crafty Benz next door,' he gestured at the wall, 'didn't get involved. I couldn't do the passport trick twice. We will have to get him some other way. The man with the boils was easy. He knew no German and travelling without a ticket is a serious matter. Ah well, the day has started favourably. We have won the first round, but our friend next door will now be very careful. He knows what he has to reckon with. Perhaps that is for the best. It would have been a nuisance having to keep you both under cover all day. Now we can move about — even have lunch together, as long as you bring the family jewels with you. We must watch to see if he makes a telephone call at one of the stations. But I doubt if he could tackle the Greek telephone exchange. He will probably wait until we are in Yugoslavia. But there I have my machine. We can get reinforcements if we need them. It should be a most interesting journey. There is always excitement on the Orient Express,' Kerim got to his feet. He opened the door, 'and romance.'

He smiled across the compartment. 'I will call for you at lunch-time! Greek food is worse than Turkish, but even my stomach is in the service of the Queen.'

Bond got up and locked the door. Tatiana snapped, 'Your friend is not *kulturny*! It is disloyal to refer to your Queen in that manner.'

Bond sat down beside her. 'Tania,' he said patiently, 'that is a wonderful man. He is also a good friend. As far as I am concerned he can say anything he likes. He is jealous of me. He would like to have a girl like you. So he teases you. It is a form of flirting. You should take it as a compliment.'

'You think so?' she turned her large blue eyes on his. 'But what he said about his stomach and the head of your State. That was being rude to your Queen. It would be considered very bad manners to say such a thing in Russia.'

They were still arguing when the train ground to a halt in the sunbaked, fly-swarming station of Alexandropolis. Bond opened the door into the corridor and the sun poured in across a pale mirrored sea that married, almost without horizon, into a sky the colour of the Greek flag.

They had lunch, with the heavy bag under the table between Bond's feet. Kerim quickly made friends with the girl. The M.G.B. man called Benz avoided the restaurant car. They saw him on the platform buying sandwiches and beer from a buffet on wheels. Kerim suggested they ask him to make a four at bridge. Bond suddenly felt very tired and his tiredness made him feel that they were turning this dangerous journey into a picnic. Tatiana noticed his silence. She got up and said that she must rest. As they went out of the wagon-restaurant they heard Kerim calling gaily for brandy and cigars.

Back in the compartment, Tatiana said firmly, 'Now it is you who will sleep.' She drew down the blind and shut out the hard afternoon light and the endless baked fields of maize and tobacco and wilting sunflowers. The compartment became a dark green underground cavern. Bond wedged the doors and gave her his gun

and stretched out with his head in her lap and was immediately
asleep.

The long train snaked along the north of Greece below the foothills of the Rhodope Mountains. Xanthi came, and Drama, and
Serrai, and then they were in the Macedonian highlands and the
line swerved due south towards Salonica.

It was dusk when Bond awoke in the soft cradle of her lap. At
once, as if she had been waiting for the moment, Tatiana took his
face between her hands and looked down into his eyes and said
urgently, '*Dushka*, how long shall we have this for?'

'For long.' Bond's thoughts were still luxurious with sleep.

'But for how long?'

Bond gazed up into the beautiful, worried eyes. He cleared the
sleep out of his mind. It was impossible to see beyond the next three
days on the train, beyond their arrival in London. One had to face
the fact that this girl was an enemy agent. His feelings would be of
no interest to the interrogators from his Service and from the Ministries. Other intelligence services would also want to know what
this girl had to tell them about the machine she had worked for.
Probably at Dover she would be taken away to 'The Cage',
that well-sentried private house near Guildford, where she would
be put in a comfortable, but oh so well-wired room. And the
efficient men in plain clothes would come one by one and sit and
talk with her, and the recorder would spin in the room below and
the records would be transcribed and sifted for their grains of new
fact — and, of course, for the contradictions they would trap
her into. Perhaps they would introduce a stool-pigeon — a nice
Russian girl who would commiserate with Tatiana over her
treatment and suggest ways of escape, of turning double, of getting
'harmless' information back to her parents. This might go on for
weeks or months. Meanwhile Bond would be tactfully kept away
from her, unless the interrogators thought he could extract further
secrets by using their feelings for each other. Then what? The
changed name, the offer of a new life in Canada, the thousand
pounds a year she would be given from the secret funds? And

where would he be when she came out of it all? Perhaps the other side of the world. Or, if he was still in London, how much of her feeling for him would have survived the grinding of the interrogation machine? How much would she hate or despise the English after going through all this? And, for the matter of that, how much would have survived of his own hot flame?

'*Dushka*,' repeated Tatiana impatiently. 'How long?'

'As long as possible. It will depend on us. Many people will interfere. We shall be separated. It will not always be like this in a little room. In a few days we shall have to step out into the world. It will not be easy. It would be foolish to tell you anything else.'

Tatiana's face cleared. She smiled down at him. 'You are right. I will not ask any more foolish questions. But we must waste no more of these days.' She shifted his head and got up and lay down beside him.

An hour later, when Bond was standing in the corridor, Darko Kerim was suddenly beside him. He examined Bond's face. He said slyly, 'You should not sleep so long. You have been missing the historic landscape of northern Greece. And it is time for the *premier service*.'

'All you think about is food,' said Bond. He gestured back with his head. 'What about our friend?'

'He has not stirred. The conductor has been watching for me. That man will end up the richest conductor in the wagon-lit company. Five hundred dollars for Goldfarb's papers, and now a hundred dollars a day retainer until the end of the journey.' Kerim chuckled. 'I have told him he may even get a medal for his service to Turkey. He believes we are after a smuggling gang. They're always using this train for running Turkish opium to Paris. He is not surprised, only pleased that he is being paid so well. And now have you found out anything more from this Russian princess you have in there? I still feel disquiet. Everything is too peaceful. Those two men we left behind may have been quite innocently bound for Berlin as the girl says. This Benz may be keeping to his oom because he is frightened of us. All is going well with our ourney. And yet, and yet . . .' Kerim shook his head. 'These Russians are great chess players. When they wish to execute a plot, they execute it brilliantly. The game is planned minutely, the gambits of the enemy are provided for. They are foreseen and countered. At the back of my mind,' Kerim's face in the window was gloomy, 'I have a feeling that you and I and this girl are pawns on a very big board — that we are being allowed our moves because they do not interfere with the Russian game.'

'But what is the object of the plot?' Bond looked out into the darkness. He spoke to his reflection in the window. What can they want to achieve? We always get back to that. Of course we have all smelt a conspiracy of some sort. And the girl may not even know that she's involved in it. I know she's hiding something, but I think it's only some small secret she thinks is unimportant. She says she'll tell me everything when we get to London. Everything? What does she mean? She only says that I must have faith — that there is no danger. You must admit, Darko,' Bond looked up for confirmation into the slow crafty eyes, 'that she's lived up to her story.'

There was no enthusiasm in Kerim's eyes. He said nothing.

Bond shrugged. 'I admit I've fallen for her. But I'm not a fool, Darko. I've been watching for any clue, anything that would help. You know one can tell a lot when certain barriers are down. Well they are down, and I know she's telling the truth. At any rate ninety per cent of it. And I know she thinks the rest doesn't matter. If she's cheating, she's also being cheated herself. On our chess analogy, that is possible. But you still get back to the question of what it's all in aid of.' Bond's voice hardened. 'And, if you want to know, all I ask is to go on with the game until we find out.'

Kerim smiled at the obstinate look on Bond's face. He laughed abruptly. 'If it was me, my friend, I would slip off the train at Salonica — with the machine, and, if you like, with the girl also,

though that is not so important. I would take a hired car to Athens
and get on the next plane for London. But I was not brought up
"to be a sport".' Kerim put irony into the words. 'This is not a
game to me. It is a business. For you it is different. You are a
gambler. M. also is a gambler. He obviously is, or he would not
have given you a free hand. He also wants to know the answer
to this riddle. So be it. But I like to play safe, to make certain, to
leave as little as possible to chance. You think the odds look right,
that they are in your favour?' Darko Kerim turned and faced
Bond. His voice became insistent. 'Listen, my friend,' he put a
huge hand on Bond's shoulder. 'This is a billiard table. An easy,
flat, green billiard table. And you have hit your white ball and it is
travelling easily and quietly towards the red. The pocket is
alongside. Fatally, inevitably, you are going to hit the red and
the red is going into that pocket. It is the law of the billiard table,
the law of the billiard room. But, outside the orbit of these things, a
jet pilot has fainted and his plane is diving straight at that billiard
room, or a gas main is about to explode, or lightning is about to
strike. And the building collapses on top of you and on top of the
billiard table. Then what has happened to that white ball that
could not miss the red ball, and to the red ball that could not miss
the pocket? The white ball could not miss according to the laws of
the billiard table. But the laws of the billiard table are not the only
laws, and the laws governing the progress of this train, and of you
to your destination, are also not the only laws in this particular
game.'

Kerim paused. He dismissed his harangue with a shrug of
the shoulders. 'You already know these things, my friend,' he
said apologetically. 'And I have made myself thirsty talking
platitudes. Hurry the girl up and we will go and eat. But watch for
surprises, I beg of you.' He made a cross with his finger over the
centre of his coat. 'I do not cross my heart. That is being too
serious. But I cross my stomach, which is an important oath for
me. There are surprises on the way for both of us. The gipsy said
to watch out. Now I say the same. We can play the game of

the billiard table, but we must both be on guard against the world outside the billiard room. My nose,' he tapped it, 'tells me so.'

Kerim's stomach made an indignant noise like a forgotten telephone receiver with an angry caller on the other end. 'There,' he said solicitously. 'What did I say? We must go and eat.'

They finished their dinner as the train pulled into the hideous modern junction of Thessaloniki. With Bond carrying the heavy little bag, they went back down the train and parted for the night. 'We shall soon be disturbed again,' warned Kerim. 'There is the frontier at one o'clock. The Greeks will be no trouble, but those Yugoslavs like waking up anyone who is travelling soft. If they annoy you, send for me. Even in their country there are some names I can mention. I am in the second compartment in the next carriage. I have it to myself. Tomorrow I will move into our friend Goldfarb's bed in No. 12. For the time being, the first-class is an adequate stable.'

Bond dozed wakefully as the train laboured up the moonlit valley of the Vardar towards the instep of Yugoslavia. Tatiana again slept with her head in his lap. He thought of what Darko had said. He wondered if he should not send the big man back to Istanbul when they had got safely through Belgrade. It was not fair to drag him across Europe on an adventure that was outside his territory and with which he had little sympathy. Darko obviously suspected that Bond had become infatuated with the girl and wasn't seeing the operation straight any more. Well, there was a grain of truth in that. It would certainly be safer to get off the train and take another route home. But, Bond admitted to himself, he couldn't bear the idea of running away from this plot, if it was a plot. If it wasn't, he equally couldn't bear the idea of sacrificing the three more days with Tatiana. And M. had left the decision to him. As Darko had said, M. also was curious to see the game through. Perversely, M. too wanted to see what this whole rigmarole was about. Bond dismissed the problem. The journey was going well. Once again, why panic?

Ten minutes after they had arrived at the Greek frontier station of Idomeni there was a hasty knocking on the door. It woke the girl. Bond slipped from under her head. He put his ear to the door. 'Yes?'

'*Le conducteur, Monsieur.* There has been an accident. Your friend Kerim Bey.'

'Wait,' said Bond fiercely. He fitted the Beretta into its holster and put on his coat. He tore open the door.

'What is it?'

The conductor's face was yellow under the corridor light. 'Come.' He ran down the corridor towards the first-class.

Officials were clustered round the open door of the second compartment. They were standing, staring.

The conductor made a path for Bond. Bond reached the door and looked in.

The hair stirred softly on his head. Along the right-hand seat were two bodies. They were frozen in a ghastly death-struggle that might have been posed for a film.

Underneath was Kerim, his knees up in a last effort to rise. The taped hilt of a dagger protruded from his neck near the jugular vein. His head was thrust back and the empty bloodshot eyes stared up at the light. The mouth was contorted into a snarl. A thin trickle of blood ran down the chin.

Half on top of him sprawled the heavy body of the M.G.B. man called Benz, locked there by Kerim's left arm round his neck. Bond could see a corner of the Stalin moustache and the side of a blackened face. Kerim's right arm lay across the man's back, almost casually. The hand ended in a closed fist and the knob of a knife-hilt, and there was a wide stain on the coat under the hand.

Bond listened to his imagination. It was like watching a film. The sleeping Darko, the man slipping quietly through the door, the two steps forward and the swift stroke at the jugular. Then the last violent spasm of the dying man as he flung up an arm and clutched his murderer to him and plunged the knife down towards the fifth rib.

This wonderful man who had carried the sun with him. Now he was extinguished, totally dead.

Bond turned brusquely and walked out of sight of the man who had died for him.

He began, carefully, non-committally, to answer questions.

CHAPTER 24

Out of Danger?

THE Orient Express steamed slowly into Belgrade at three o'clock in the afternoon, half an hour late. There would be an eight hours' delay while the other section of the train came in through the Iron Curtain from Bulgaria.

Bond looked out at the crowds and waited for the knock on the door that would be Kerim's man. Tatiana sat huddled in her sable coat beside the door, watching Bond, wondering if he would come back to her.

She had seen it all from the window — the long wicker baskets being brought out to the train, the flash of the police photographer's bulbs, the gesticulating *chef de train* trying to hurry up the formalities, and the tall figure of James Bond, straight and hard and cold as a butcher's knife, coming and going.

Bond had come back and had sat looking at her. He had asked sharp, brutal questions. She had fought desperately back, sticking coldly to her story, knowing that now, if she told him everything, told him for instance that SMERSH was involved, she would certainly lose him for ever.

Now she sat and was afraid, afraid of the web in which she was caught, afraid of what might have been behind the lies she had been told in Moscow — above all afraid that she might lose this man who had suddenly become the light in her life.

There was a knock on the door. Bond got up and opened it. A tough cheerful india-rubbery man, with Kerim's blue eyes and a mop of tangled fair hair above a brown face, exploded into the compartment.

'Stefan Trempo at your service,' the big smile embraced them both. 'They call me "Tempo". Where is the Chef?'

'Sit down,' said Bond. He thought to himself, I know it. This is another of Darko's sons.

The man looked sharply at them both. He sat down carefully between them. His face was extinguished. Now the bright eyes stared at Bond with a terrible intensity in which there was fear and suspicion. His right hand slipped casually into the pocket of his coat.

When Bond had finished, the man stood up. He didn't ask any questions. He said, 'Thank you, sir. Will you come, please. We will go to my apartment. There is much to be done.' He walked into the corridor and stood with his back to them, looking out across the rails. When the girl came out he walked down the corridor without looking back. Bond followed the girl, carrying the heavy bag and his little attaché case.

They walked down the platform and into the station square. It had started to drizzle. The scene, with its sprinkling of battered taxis and vista of dull modern buildings, was depressing. The man opened the rear door of a shabby Morris Oxford saloon. He got in front and took the wheel. They bumped their way over the cobbles and on to a slippery tarmac boulevard and drove for a quarter of an hour through wide, empty streets. They saw few pedestrians and not more than a handful of other cars.

They stopped half way down a cobbled side-street. Tempo led them through a wide apartment-house door and up two flights of stairs that had the smell of the Balkans — the smell of very old

sweat and cigarette smoke and cabbage. He unlocked a door and
showed them into a two-roomed flat with nondescript furniture and heavy red plush curtains drawn back to show the blank
windows on the other side of the street. On a sideboard stood
a tray with several unopened bottles, glasses and plates of fruit
and biscuits — the welcome to Darko and to Darko's friends.

Tempo waved vaguely towards the drinks. 'Please, sir, make
yourself and Madam at home. There is a bathroom. No doubt you
would both like to have a bath. If you will excuse me, I must
telephone!' The hard façade of the face was about to crumble. The
man went quickly into the bedroom and shut the door behind him.

There followed two empty hours during which Bond sat and
looked out of the window at the wall opposite. From time to time
he got up and paced to and fro and then sat down again. For the
first hour, Tatiana sat and pretended to look through a pile of
magazines. Then she abruptly went into the bathroom and Bond
vaguely heard water gushing into the bath.

At about 6 o'clock, Tempo came out of the bedroom. He told
Bond that he was going out. 'There is food in the kitchen. I will
return at nine and take you to the train. Please treat my flat as
your own.' Without waiting for Bond's reply, he walked out and
softly shut the door. Bond heard his foot on the stairs and the
click of the front door and the self-starter of the Morris.

Bond went into the bedroom and sat on the bed and picked up
the telephone and talked in German to the long-distance exchange.

Half an hour later there was the quiet voice of M.

Bond spoke as a travelling salesman would speak to the managing
director of Universal Export. He said that his partner had gone
very sick. Were there any fresh instructions?

'Very sick?'

'Yes, sir, very.'

'How about the other firm?'

'There were three with us, sir. One of them caught the same
thing. The other two didn't feel well on the way out of Turkey.
They left us at Uzunkopru — that's the frontier.'

'So the other firm's packed up?'

Bond could see M.'s face as he sifted the information. He wondered if the fan was slowly revolving in the ceiling, if M. had a pipe in his hand, if the Chief of Staff was listening on the other wire.

'What are your ideas? Would you and your wife like to take another way home?'

'I'd rather you decided, sir. My wife's all right. The sample's in good condition. I don't see why it should deteriorate. I'm still keen to finish the trip. Otherwise it'll remain virgin territory. We shan't know what the possibilities are.'

'Would you like one of our other salesmen to give you a hand?'

'It shouldn't be necessary, sir. Just as you feel.'

'I'll think about it. So you really want to see this sales campaign through?'

Bond could see M.'s eyes glittering with the same perverse curiosity, the same rage to know, as he himself felt. 'Yes, sir. Now that I'm half way, it seems a pity not to cover the whole route.'

'All right then. I'll think about giving you another salesman to lend a hand.' There was a pause on the end of the line. 'Nothing else on your mind?'

'No, sir.'

'Goodbye, then.'

'Goodbye, sir.'

Bond put down the receiver. He sat and looked at it. He suddenly wished he had agreed with M.'s suggestion to give him reinforcements, just in case. He got up from the bed. At least they would soon be out of these damn Balkans and down into Italy. Then Switzerland, France — among friendly people, away from the furtive lands.

And the girl, what about her? Could he blame her for the death of Kerim? Bond went into the next room and stood again by the window, looking out, wondering, going back over everything, every expression and every gesture she had made since he had first heard her voice on that night in the Kristal Palas. No, he knew he couldn't put the blame on her. If she was an agent, she was an unconscious agent. There wasn't a girl of her age in the world who could have played this role, if it was a role she was playing, without betraying herself. And he liked her. And he had faith in his instincts. Besides, with the death of Kerim, had not the plot, whatever it was, played itself out? One day he would find out what the plot had been. For the moment he was certain. Tatiana was not a conscious part of it.

His mind made up, Bond walked over to the bathroom door and knocked.

She came out and he took her in his arms and held her to him and kissed her. She clung to him. They stood and felt the animal warmth come back between them, feeling it push back the cold memory of Kerim's death.

Tatiana broke away. She looked up at Bond's face. She reached up and brushed the black comma of hair away from his forehead.

Her face was alive. 'I am glad you have come back, James,' she said. And then, matter-of-factly, 'And now we must eat and drink and start our lives again.'

Later, after Slivovic and smoked ham and peaches, Tempo came and took them to the station and to the waiting express under the hard lights of the arcs. He said goodbye, quickly and coldly and vanished down the platform and back into his dark existence.

Punctually at nine the new engine gave its new kind of noise and took the long train out on its all-night run down the valley of the Sava. Bond went along to the conductor's cabin to give him money and look through the passports of the new passengers.

Bond knew most of the signs to look for in forged passports, the blurred writing, the too exact imprints of the rubber stamps, the trace of old gum round the edges of the photograph, the slight transparencies on the pages where the fibres of the paper had been tampered with to alter a letter or a number, but the five new passports — three American and two Swiss — seemed innocent. The Swiss papers, favourites with the Russian forgers, belonged to a husband and wife, both over seventy, and Bond finally passed them and went back to the compartment and prepared for another night with Tatiana's head on his lap.

Vincovci came and Brod and then, against a flaming dawn, the ugly sprawl of Zagreb. The train came to a stop between lines of rusting locomotives captured from the Germans and still standing forlornly amongst the grass and weeds on the sidings. Bond read the plate on one of them — BERLINER MASCHINENBAU GMBH — as they slid out through the iron cemetery. Its long black barrel had been raked with machine gun bullets. Bond heard the scream of the dive-bomber and saw the upflung arms of the driver. For a moment he thought nostalgically and unreasonably of the excitement and turmoil of the hot war, compared with his own underground skirmishings since the war had turned cold.

They hammered into the mountains of Slovenia where the apple trees and the chalets were almost Austrian. The train laboured its way through Ljubliana. The girl awoke. They had breakfast of fried eggs and hard brown bread and coffee that was mostly chicory. The restaurant car was full of cheerful English and American tourists from the Adriatic coast, and Bond thought with a lift of the heart that by the afternoon they would be over the frontier into western Europe and that a third dangerous night was gone.

He slept until Sezana. The hard-faced Yugoslav plain-clothes men came on board. Then Yugoslavia was gone and Poggioreale came and the first smell of the soft life with the happy jabbering of Italian officials and the carefree upturned faces of the station crowd. The new diesel-electric engine gave a slap-happy whistle, the meadow of brown hands fluttered, and they were loping easily down into Venezia, towards the distant sparkle of Trieste and the gay blue of the Adriatic.

We've made it, thought Bond. I really think we've made it. He thrust the memory of the last three days away from him. Tatiana saw the tense lines in his face relax. She reached over and took his hand. He moved and sat close beside her. They looked out at the gay villas on the Corniche and at the sailing-boats and the people water-skiing.

The train clanged across some points and slid quietly into the gleaming station of Trieste. Bond got up and pulled down the window and they stood side by side, looking out. Suddenly Bond felt happy. He put an arm around the girl's waist and held her hard against him.

They gazed down at the holiday crowd. The sun shone through the tall clean windows of the station in golden shafts. The sparkling scene emphasized the dark and dirt of the countries the train had come from, and Bond watched with an almost sensuous pleasure the gaily dressed people pass through the patches of sunshine towards the entrance, and the sunburned people, the ones who had had their holidays, hasten up the platform to get their seats on the train.

A shaft of sun lit up the head of one man who seemed typical of this happy, playtime world. The light flashed briefly on golden hair under a cap, and on a young golden moustache. There was plenty of time to catch the train. The man walked unhurriedly. It crossed Bond's mind that he was an Englishman. Perhaps it was the familiar shape of the dark green Kangol cap, or the beige, rather well-used macintosh, that badge of the English tourist, or it may have been the grey-flannelled legs, or the scuffed brown shoes. But Bond's eyes were drawn to him, as if it was someone he knew, as the man approached up the platform.

The man was carrying a battered Revelation suitcase and, under the other arm, a thick book and some newspapers. He looks like an athlete, thought Bond. He has the wide shoulders and the healthy, good-looking bronzed face of a professional tennis player going home after a round of foreign tournaments.

The man came nearer. Now he was looking straight at Bond. With recognition? Bond searched his mind. Did he know this man? No. He would have remembered those eyes that stared out so coldly under the pale lashes. They were opaque, almost dead. The eyes of a drowned man. But they had some message for him. What was it? Recognition? Warning? Or just the defensive reaction to Bond's own stare?

The man came up with the wagon-lit. His eyes were now gazing levelly up the train. He walked past, the crêpe-soled shoes making no sound. Bond watched him reach for the rail and swing himself easily up the steps into the first-class carriage.

Suddenly Bond knew what the glance had meant, who the man was. Of course! This man was from the Service. After all M. had decided to send along an extra hand. That was the message of those queer eyes. Bond would bet anything that the man would soon be along to make contact.

How like M. to make absolutely sure!

CHAPTER 25

A Tie with a Windsor Knot

To make the contact easy, Bond went out and stood in the corridor. He ran over the details of the code of the day, the few harmless phrases, changed on the first of each month, that served as a simple recognition signal between English agents.

The train gave a jerk and moved slowly out into the sunshine. At the end of the corridor the communicating door slammed. There was no sound of steps, but suddenly the red and gold face was mirrored in the window.

'Excuse me. Could I borrow a match?'

'I use a lighter.' Bond produced his battered Ronson and handed it over.

'Better still.'

'Until they go wrong.'

Bond looked up into the man's face, expecting a smile at the completion of the childish 'Who goes there? Pass, Friend' ritual.

The thick lips writhed briefly. There was no light in the very pale blue eyes.

The man had taken off his macintosh. He was wearing an old

reddish-brown tweed coat with his flannel trousers, a pale yellow
Viyella summer shirt, and the dark blue and maroon zig-zagged tie
of the Royal Artillery. It was tied with a Windsor knot. Bond mis-
trusted anyone who tied his tie with a Windsor knot. It showed too
much vanity. It was often the mark of a cad. Bond decided to
forget his prejudice. A gold signet ring, with an indecipherable
crest, glinted on the little finger of the right hand that gripped the
guard rail. The corner of a red bandana handkerchief flopped out
of the breast pocket of the man's coat. On his left wrist there was
a battered silver wrist watch with an old leather strap.

Bond knew the type — a minor public school and then caught
up by the war. Field Security perhaps. No idea what to do afterwards so he stayed with the occupation troops. At first he would
have been with the military police, then, as the senior men drifted
home, there came promotion into one of the security services.
Moved to Trieste where he did well enough. Wanted to stay on
and avoid the rigours of England. Probably had a girl friend, or had
married an Italian. The Secret Service had needed a man for the
small post that Trieste had become after the withdrawal. This
man was available. They took him on. He would be doing routine
jobs — have some low-grade sources in the Italian and Yugoslav
police, and in their intelligence networks. A thousand a year. A
good life, without much being expected from him. Then, out of the
blue, this had come along. Must have been a shock getting one of
those Most Immediate signals. He'd probably be a bit shy of Bond.
Odd face. The eyes looked rather mad. But so they did in most of
these men doing secret work abroad. One had to be a bit mad to
take it on. Powerful chap, probably on the stupid side, but useful
for this kind of guard work. M. had just taken the nearest man and
told him to join the train.

All this went through Bond's mind as he photographed an
impression of the man's clothes and general appearance. Now he
said, 'Glad to see you. How did it happen?'

'Got a signal. Late last night. Personal from M. Shook me I can
tell you, old man.'

Curious accent. What was it? A hint of brogue — cheap brogue. And something else Bond couldn't define. Probably came from living too long abroad and talking foreign languages all the time. And that dreadful 'old man' at the end. Shyness.

'Must have,' said Bond sympathetically. 'What did it say?'

'Just told me to get on the Orient this morning and contact a man and a girl in the through carriage. More or less described what you look like. Then I was to stick by you and see you both through to Gay Paree. That's all, old man.'

Was there defensiveness in the voice? Bond glanced sideways. The pale eyes swivelled to meet his. There was a quick red glare in them. It was as if the safety door of a furnace had swung open. The blaze died. The door to the inside of the man was banged shut. Now the eyes were opaque again — the eyes of an introvert, of a man who rarely looks out into the world but is for ever surveying the scene inside him.

There's madness there all right, thought Bond, startled by the sight of it. Shell-shock perhaps, or schizophrenia. Poor chap, with that magnificent body. One day he would certainly crack. The madness would take control. Bond had better have a word to Personnel. Check up on his medical. By the way, what was his name?

'Well I'm very glad to have you along. Probably not much for you to do. We started off with three Redland men on our tail. They've been got rid of, but there may be others on the train. Or some more may get on. And I've got to get this girl to London without trouble. If you'd just hang about. Tonight we'd better stay together and share watches. It's the last night and I don't want to take any chances. By the way, my name's James Bond. Travelling as David Somerset. And that's Caroline Somerset in there.'

The man fished in his inside pocket and produced a battered note case which seemed to contain plenty of money. He extracted a visiting card and handed it to Bond. It said 'Captain Norman Nash', and, in the left-hand bottom corner, 'Royal Automobile Club'.

As Bond put the card in his pocket he slipped his finger across it. It was engraved. 'Thanks,' he said. 'Well, Nash, come and meet Mrs. Somerset. No reason why we shouldn't travel more or less together.' He smiled encouragingly.

Again the red glare quickly extinguished. The lips writhed under the young golden moustache. 'Delighted, old man.'

Bond turned to the door and knocked softly and spoke his name.

The door opened. Bond beckoned Nash in and shut the door behind him.

The girl looked surprised.

'This is Captain Nash, Norman Nash. He's been told to keep an eye on us.'

'How do you do.' The hand came out hesitantly. The man touched it briefly. His stare was fixed. He said nothing. The girl gave an embarrassed little laugh, 'Won't you sit down?'

'Er, thank you.' Nash sat stiffly on the edge of the banquette. He seemed to remember something, something one did when one had nothing to say. He groped in the side pocket of his coat and produced a packet of Players. 'Will you have a, er, cigarette?' He prized open the top with a fairly clean thumbnail, stripped down the silver paper and pushed out the cigarettes. The girl took one. Nash's other hand flashed forward a lighter with the obsequious speed of a motor salesman.

Nash looked up. Bond was standing leaning against the door and wondering how to help this clumsy, embarrassed man. Nash held out the cigarettes and the lighter as if he was offering glass beads to a native chief. 'What about you, old man?'

'Thanks,' said Bond. He hated Virginia tobacco, but he was prepared to do anything to help put the man at ease. He took a cigarette and lit it. They certainly had to make do with some queer fish in the Service nowadays. How the devil did this man manage to get along in the semi-diplomatic society he would have to frequent in Trieste?

Bond said lamely. 'You look very fit, Nash. Tennis?'

'Swimming.'

'Been long in Trieste?'

There came the brief red glare. 'About three years.'

'Interesting work?'

'Sometimes. You know how it is, old man.'

Bond wondered how he could stop Nash calling him 'old man'. He couldn't think of a way. Silence fell.

Nash obviously felt it was his turn again. He fished in his pocket and produced a newspaper cutting. It was the front page of the *Corriere de la Sera*. He handed it to Bond. 'Seen this, old man?' The eyes blazed and died.

It was the front page lead. The thick black lettering on the cheap newsprint was still wet. The headlines said:

TERRIBILE ESPLOSIONE IN ISTANBUL

UFFICIO SOVIETICO DISTRUTTO

TUTTI I PRESENTI UCCISI

Bond couldn't understand the rest. He folded the cutting and handed it back. How much did this man know? Better treat him as a strong-man arm and nothing else. 'Bad show,' he said. 'Gas main I suppose.' Bond saw again the obscene belly of the bomb hanging down from the roof of the alcove in the tunnel, the wires that started off down the damp wall on their way back to the plunger in the drawer of Kerim's desk. Who had pressed the plunger yesterday afternoon when Tempo had got through? The 'Head Clerk'? Or had they drawn lots and then stood round and watched as the hand went down and the deep roar had gone up in the Street of Books on the hill above. They would all have been there, in the cool room. With eyes that glittered with hate. The tears would be reserved for the night. Revenge would have come first. And the rats? How many thousand had been blasted down the tunnel? What time would it have been? About four o'clock. Had the daily meeting been on? Three dead in the room. How many more in the rest of the building? Friends of Tatiana, perhaps. He would have to keep the story from her. Had Darko been watching?

From a window in Valhalla? Bond could hear the great laugh of triumph echoing round its walls. At any rate Kerim had taken plenty with him.

Nash was looking at him. 'Yes, I daresay it was a gas main,' he said without interest.

A hand-bell tinkled down the corridor, coming nearer. '*Deux-ième Service. Deuxième Service. Prenez vos places, s'il vous plaît.*'

Bond looked across at Tatiana. Her face was pale. In her eyes there was an appeal to be saved from any more of this clumsy, non-*kulturny* man. Bond said, 'What about lunch?' She got up at once. 'What about you, Nash?'

Captain Nash was already on his feet. 'Had it, thanks old man. And I'd like to have a look up and down the train. Is the conductor — you know . . . ?' he made a gesture of fingering money.

'Oh yes, he'll co-operate all right,' said Bond. He reached up and pulled down the heavy little bag. He opened the door for Nash. 'See you later.'

Captain Nash stepped into the corridor. He said, 'Yes, I expect so, old man.' He turned left and strode off down the corridor, moving easily with the swaying of the train, his hands in his trouser pockets and the light blazing on the tight golden curls at the back of his head.

Bond followed Tatiana up the train. The carriages were crowded with holiday-makers going home. In the third-class corridors people sat on their bags chattering and munching at oranges and at hard-looking rolls with bits of Salami sticking out of them. The men carefully examined Tatiana as she squeezed by. The women looked appraisingly at Bond, wondering whether he made love to her well.

In the restaurant car, Bond ordered Americanos and a bottle of Chianti Broglio. The wonderful European hors d'œuvres came. Tatiana began to look more cheerful.

'Funny sort of man,' Bond watched her pick about among the little dishes. 'But I'm glad he's come along. I'll have a chance to get some sleep. I'm going to sleep for a week when we get home.'

'I do not like him,' the girl said indifferently. 'He is not *kulturny*. I do not trust his eyes.'

Bond laughed. 'Nobody's *kulturny* enough for you.'

'Did you know him before?'

'No. But he belongs to my firm.'

'What did you say his name is?'

'Nash. Norman Nash.'

She spelled it out. 'N.A.S.H.? Like that?'

'Yes.'

The girl's eyes were puzzled. 'I suppose you know what that means in Russian. *Nash* means "ours". In our Services, a man is *nash* when he is one of "our" men. He is *svoi* when he is one of "theirs" — when he belong to the enemy. And this man calls himself Nash. That is not pleasant.'

Bond laughed. 'Really, Tania. You do think of extraordinary reasons for not liking people. Nash is quite a common English name. He's perfectly harmless. At any rate he's tough enough for what we want him for.'

Tatiana made a face. She went on with her lunch.

Some *tagliatelli verdi* came, and the wine, and then a delicious escalope. 'Oh it is so good,' she said. 'Since I came out of Russia I am all stomach.' Her eyes widened. 'You won't let me get too fat, James. You won't let me get so fat that I am no use for making love? You will have to be careful, or I shall just eat all day long and sleep. You will beat me if I eat too much?'

'Certainly I will beat you.'

Tatiana wrinkled her nose. He felt the soft caress of her ankles. The wide eyes looked at him hard. The lashes came down demurely. 'Please pay,' she said. 'I feel sleepy.'

The train was pulling into Maestre. There was the beginning of the canals. A cargo gondola full of vegetables was moving slowly along a straight sheet of water into the town.

'But we shall be coming into Venice in a minute,' protested Bond. 'Don't you want to see it?'

'It will be just another station. And I can see Venice another day.

Now I want you to love me. Please, James.' Tatiana leaned forward. She put a hand over his. 'Give me what I want. There is so little time.'

Then it was the little room again and the smell of the sea coming through the half-open window and the drawn blind fluttering with the wind of the train. Again there were the two piles of clothes on the floor, and the two whispering bodies on the banquette, and the slow searching hands. And the love-knot formed, and, as the train jolted over the points into the echoing station of Venice, there came the final lost despairing cry.

Outside the vacuum of the tiny room there sounded a confusion of echoing calls and metallic clanging and shuffling footsteps that slowly faded into sleep.

Padua came, and Vicenza, and a fabulous sunset over Verona flickered gold and red through the cracks of the blind. Again the little bell came tinkling down the corridor. They woke. Bond dressed and went into the corridor and leant against the guard rail. He looked out at the fading pink light over the Lombardy Plain and thought of Tatiana and of the future.

Nash's face slid up alongside his in the dark glass. Nash came very close so that his elbow touched Bond's. 'I think I've spotted one of the oppo, old man,' he said softly.

Bond was not surprised. He had assumed that, if it came, it would come tonight. Almost indifferently he said, 'Who is he?'

'Don't know what his real name is, but he's been through Trieste once or twice. Something to do with Albania. May be the Resident Director there. Now he's on an American passport. "Wilbur Frank." Calls himself a banker. In No. 9, right next to you. I don't think I could be wrong about him, old man.'

Bond glanced at the eyes in the big brown face. Again the furnace door was ajar. The red glare shone out and was extinguished.

'Good thing you spotted him. This may be a tough night. You'd better stick by us from now on. We mustn't leave the girl alone.'

'That's what I thought, old man.'

They had dinner. It was a silent meal. Nash sat beside the girl and kept his eyes on his plate. He held his knife like a fountain pen and frequently wiped it on his fork. He was clumsy in his movements. Half way through the meal, he reached for the salt and knocked over Tatiana's glass of Chianti. He apologized profusely. He made a great show of calling for another glass and filling it.

Coffee came. Now it was Tatiana who was clumsy. She knocked over her cup. She had gone very pale and her breath was coming quickly.

'Tatiana!' Bond half rose to his feet. But it was Captain Nash who jumped up and took charge.

'Lady's come over queer,' he said shortly. 'Allow me.' He reached down and put an arm round the girl and lifted her to her feet. 'I'll take her back to the compartment. You'd better look after the bag. And there's the bill. I can take care of her till you come.'

'Is all right,' protested Tatiana with the slack lips of deepening unconsciousness. 'Don' worry, James, I lie down.' Her head lolled against Nash's shoulder. Nash put one thick arm round her waist and manœuvred her quickly and efficiently down the crowded aisle and out of the restaurant car.

Bond impatiently snapped his fingers for the waiter. Poor darling. She must be dead beat. Why hadn't he thought of the strain she was going through? He cursed himself for his selfishness. Thank heavens for Nash. Efficient sort of chap, for all his uncouthness.

Bond paid the bill. He took up the heavy little bag and walked as quickly as he could down the crowded train.

He tapped softly on the door of No. 7. Nash opened the door. He came out with his finger on his lips. He closed the door behind him. 'Threw a bit of a faint,' he said. 'She's all right now. The beds were made up. She's gone to sleep in the top one. Been a bit much for the girl I expect, old man.'

Bond nodded briefly. He went into the compartment. A hand hung palely down from under the sable coat. Bond stood on the bottom bunk and gently tucked the hand under the corner of the coat. The hand felt very cold. The girl made no sound.

Bond stepped softly down. Better let her sleep. He went into the corridor.

Nash looked at him with empty eyes. 'Well, I suppose we'd better settle in for the night. I've got my book.' He held it up. '*War and Peace*. Been trying to plough through it for years. You take the first sleep, old man. You look pretty flaked out yourself. I'll wake you up when I can't keep my eyes open any longer.' He gestured with his head at the door of No. 9. 'Hasn't shown yet. Don't suppose he will if he's up to any monkey tricks.' He paused. 'By the way, you got a gun, old man?'

'Yes. Why, haven't you?'

Nash looked apologetic. "Fraid not. Got a Luger at home, but it's too bulky for this sort of job.'

'Oh, well,' said Bond reluctantly. 'You'd better take mine. Come on in.'

They went in and Bond shut the door. He took out the Beretta and handed it over. 'Eight shots,' he said softly. 'Semi-automatic. It's on safe.'

Nash took the gun and weighed it professionally in his hand. He clicked the safe on and off.

Bond hated someone else touching his gun. He felt naked without it. He said gruffly, 'Bit on the light side, but it'll kill if you put the bullets in the right places.'

Nash nodded. He sat down near the window at the end of the bottom bunk. 'I'll take this end,' he whispered. 'Good field of fire.' He put his book down on his lap and settled himself.

Bond took off his coat and tie and laid them on the bunk beside him. He leant back against the pillows and propped his feet on the bag with the Spektor that stood on the floor beside his attaché case. He picked up his Ambler and found his place and tried to read. After a few pages he found that his concentration was going. He was too tired. He laid the book down on his lap and closed his eyes. Could he afford to sleep? Was there any other precaution they could take?

The wedges! Bond felt for them in the pocket of his coat. He slipped off the bunk and knelt and forced them hard under the two doors. Then he settled himself again and switched off the reading light behind his head.

The violet eye of the nightlight shone softly down.

'Thanks, old man,' said Captain Nash softly.

The train gave a moan and crashed into a tunnel.

CHAPTER 26

The Killing Bottle

THE light nudge at his ankle woke Bond. He didn't move. His senses came to life like an animal's.

Nothing had changed. There were the noises of the train — the soft iron stride, pounding out the kilometres, the quiet creak of the woodwork, a tinkle from the cupboard over the washbasin where a toothglass was loose in its holder.

What had woken him? The spectral eye of the nightlight cast its deep velvet sheen over the little room. No sound came from the upper bunk. By the window, Captain Nash sat in his place, his book open on his lap, a flicker of moonlight from the edge of the blind showing white on the double page.

He was looking fixedly at Bond. Bond registered the intentness of the violet eyes. The black lips parted. There was a glint of teeth.

'Sorry to disturb you, old man. I feel in the mood for a talk!'

What was there new in the voice? Bond put his feet softly down to the floor. He sat up straighter. Danger, like a third man, was standing in the room.

'Fine,' said Bond easily. What had there been in those few

words that had set his spine tingling? Was it the note of authority
in Nash's voice? The idea came to Bond that Nash might have gone
mad. Perhaps it was madness in the room, and not danger, that
Bond could smell. His instincts about this man had been right. It
would be a question of somehow getting rid of him at the next
station. Where had they got to? When would the frontier come?

Bond lifted his wrist to look at the time. The violet light defeated the phosphorus numerals. Bond tilted the face towards the
strip of moonlight from the window.

From the direction of Nash there came a sharp click. Bond felt a
violent blow on his wrist. Splinters of glass hit him in the face. His
arm was flung back against the door. He wondered if his wrist had
been broken. He let his arm hang and flexed his fingers. They all
moved.

The book was still open on Nash's lap, but now a thin wisp of
smoke was coming out of the hole at the top of its spine and there
was a faint smell of fireworks in the room.

The saliva dried in Bond's mouth as if he had swallowed alum.

So there had been a trap all along. And the trap had closed.
Captain Nash had been sent to him by Moscow. Not by M. And
the M.G.B. agent in No. 9, the man with an American passport, was
a myth. And Bond had given Nash his gun. He had even put
wedges under the doors so that Nash would feel more secure.

Bond shivered. Not with fear. With disgust.

Nash spoke. His voice was no longer a whisper, no longer oily.
It was loud and confident.

'That will save us a great deal of argument, old man. Just a
little demonstration. They think I'm pretty good with this little
bag of tricks. There are ten bullets in it — .25 dum-dum, fired by
an electric battery. You must admit the Russians are wonderful
chaps for dreaming these things up. Too bad that book of yours is
only for reading, old man.'

'For God's sake stop calling me "old man".' When there was
so much to know, so much to think about, this was Bond's first
reaction to utter catastrophe. It was the reaction of someone in a

burning house who picks up the most trivial object to save from the flames.

'Sorry, old man. It's got to be a habit. Part of trying to be a bloody gentleman. Like these clothes. All from the wardrobe department. They said I'd get by like this. And I did, didn't I, old man? But let's get down to business. I expect you'd like to know what this is all about. Be glad to tell you. We've got about half an hour before you're due to go. It'll give me an extra kick telling the famous Mister Bond of the Secret Service what a bloody fool he is. You see, old man, you're not so good as you think. You're just a stuffed dummy and I've been given the job of letting the sawdust out of you.' The voice was even and flat, the sentences trailing away on a dead note. It was as if Nash was bored by the act of speaking.

'Yes,' said Bond. 'I'd like to know what it's all about. I can spare you half an hour.' Desperately he wondered: was there any way of putting this man off his stride? Upsetting his balance?

'Don't kid yourself, old man,' the voice was uninterested in Bond, or in the threat of Bond. Bond didn't exist except as a target. 'You're going to die in half an hour. No mistake about it. I've never made a mistake or I wouldn't have my job.'

'What is your job?'

'Chief Executioner of SMERSH.' There was a hint of life in the voice, a hint of pride. The voice went flat again. 'You know the name I believe, old man.'

SMERSH. So that was the answer — the worst answer of all. And this was their chief killer. Bond remembered the red glare that flickered in the opaque eyes. A killer. A psychopath — manic depressive, probably. A man who really enjoyed it. What a useful man for SMERSH to have found! Bond suddenly remembered what Vavra had said. He tried a long shot. 'Does the moon have any effect on you, Nash?'

The black lips writhed. 'Clever aren't you, Mister Secret Service. Think I'm barmy. Don't worry. I wouldn't be where I am if I was barmy.'

The angry sneer in the man's voice told Bond that he had touched a nerve. But what could he achieve by getting the man out of control? Better humour him and gain some time. Perhaps Tatiana. . . .

'Where does the girl come into all this?'

'Part of the bait,' the voice was bored again. 'Don't worry. She won't butt in on our talk. Fed her a pinch of chloral hydrate when I poured her that glass of wine. She'll be out for the night. And then for every other night. She's to go with you.'

'Oh really.' Bond slowly lifted his aching hand on to his lap, flexing the fingers to get the blood moving. 'Well, let's hear the story.'

'Careful, old man. No tricks. No Bulldog Drummond stuff'll get you out of this one. If I don't like even the smell of a move, it'll be just one bullet through the heart. Nothing more. That's what you'll be getting in the end. One through the centre of the heart. If you move it'll come a bit quicker. And don't forget who I am. Remember your wrist watch? I don't miss. Not ever.'

'Good show,' said Bond carelessly. 'But don't be frightened. You've got my gun. Remember? Get on with your story.'

'All right, old man, only don't scratch your ear while I'm talking. Or I'll shoot it off. See? Well, SMERSH decided to kill you — at least I gather it was decided even higher up, right at the top. Seems they want to take one good hard poke at the Secret Service — bring them down a peg or two. Follow me?'

'Why choose *me*?'

'Don't ask me, old man. But they say you've got quite a reputation in your outfit. The way you're going to be killed is going to bust up the whole show. It's been three months cooking, this plan, and it's a beaut. Got to be. SMERSH has made one or two mistakes lately. That Khoklov business for one. Remember the explosive cigarette case and all that? Gave the job to the wrong man. Should have given it to me. I wouldn't have gone over to the Yanks. However, to get back. You see, old man, we've got quite a planner in SMERSH. Man called Kronsteen. Great chess player. He said vanity would get you and greed and a bit of craziness in the plot. He said you'd all fall for the craziness in London. And you did, didn't you, old man?'

Had they? Bond remembered just how much the eccentric angles of the story had aroused their curiosity. And vanity? Yes, he had to admit that the idea of this Russian girl being in love with him had helped. And there had been the Spektor. That had decided the whole thing — plain greed for it. He said non-committally: 'We were interested.'

'Then came the operation. Our Head of Operations is quite a character. I'd say she's killed more people than anyone in the world — or arranged for them to be killed. Yes, it's a woman. Name of Klebb — Rosa Klebb. Real swine of a woman. But she certainly knows all the tricks.'

Rosa Klebb. So at the top of SMERSH there was a woman! If he could somehow survive this and get after her! The fingers of Bond's right hand curled softly.

The flat voice in the corner went on: 'Well, she found this Romanova girl. Trained her for the job. By the way, how was she in bed? Pretty good?'

No! Bond didn't believe it. That first night must have been staged. But afterwards? No. Afterwards had been real. He took the opportunity to shrug his shoulders. It was an exaggerated shrug. To get the man accustomed to movement.

'Oh, well. Not interested in that sort of thing myself. But they got some nice pictures of you two.' Nash tapped his coat pocket. 'Whole reel of 16 millimetre. That's going into her handbag. It'll look fine in the papers.' Nash laughed — a harsh, metallic laugh. 'They'll have to cut some of the juiciest bits, of course.'

The change of rooms at the hotel. The honeymoon suite. The big mirror behind the bed. How well it all fitted! Bond felt his hands wet with perspiration. He wiped them down his trousers.

'Steady, old man. You nearly got it then. I told you not to move, remember?'

Bond put his hands back on the book in his lap. How much could he develop these small movements? How far could he go? 'Get on with the story,' he said. 'Did the girl know these pictures were being taken? Did she know SMERSH was involved in all this?'

Nash snorted. 'Of course she didn't know about the pictures. Rosa didn't trust her a yard. Too emotional. But I don't know much about that side. We all worked in compartments. I'd never seen her until today. I only know what I picked up. Yes, of course the girl knew she was working for SMERSH. She was told she had to get to London and do a bit of spying there.'

The silly idiot, thought Bond. Why the hell hadn't she told him that SMERSH was involved? She must have been frightened even to speak the name. Thought he would have her locked up or something. She had always said she would tell him everything when she got to England. That he must have faith and not be afraid. Faith! When she hadn't the foggiest idea herself what was going on. Oh, well. Poor child. She had been as fooled as he had been. But any hint would have been enough — would have saved the life of Kerim, for instance. And what about hers and his own?

'Then this Turk of yours had to be got rid of. I gather that took a bit of doing. Tough nut. I suppose it was his gang that blew up our Centre in Istanbul yesterday afternoon. That's going to create a bit of a panic.'

'Too bad.'

'Doesn't worry me, old man. My end of the job's going to be easy.' Nash took a quick glance at his wrist watch. 'In about twenty minutes we go into the Simplon tunnel. That's where they want it done. More drama for the papers. One bullet for you. As we go into the tunnel. Just one in the heart. The noise of the tunnel will help in case you're a noisy dier — rattle and so forth. Then one in the back of the neck for her — with your gun — and out of the window she goes. Then one more for you with *your* gun. With your fingers wrapped round it, of course. Plenty of powder on your shirt. Suicide. That's what it'll look like at first. But there'll be two bullets in your heart. That'll come out later. More mystery! Search the Simplon again. Who was the man with the fair hair?

They'll find the film in her bag, and in your pocket there'll be a long love letter from her to you — a bit threatening. It's a good one. SMERSH wrote it. It says that she'll give the film to the newspapers unless you marry her. That you promised to marry her if she stole the Spektor . . .' Nash paused and added in parenthesis, 'As a matter of fact, old man, the Spektor's booby-trapped. When your cipher experts start fiddling with it, it's going to blow them all to glory. Not a bad dividend on the side.' Nash chuckled dully. 'And then the letter says that all she's got to offer you is the machine and her body — and all about her body and what you did with it. Hot stuff, that part! Right? So what's the story in the papers — the Left Wing ones that will be tipped off to meet the train? Old man, the story's got everything. Orient Express. Beautiful Russian spy murdered in Simplon tunnel. Filthy pictures. Secret cipher machine. Handsome British spy with career ruined murders her and commits suicide. Sex, spies, luxury train, Mr. and Mrs. Somerset . . . ! Old man, it'll run for months! Talk of the Khoklov case! This'll knock spots off it. And what a poke in the eye for the famous Intelligence Service! Their best man, the famous James Bond. What a shambles. Then bang goes the cipher machine! What's your chief going to think of you? What's the public going to think? And the Government. And the Americans? Talk about security! No more atom secrets from the Yanks.' Nash paused to let it all sink in. With a touch of pride he said, 'Old man, this is going to be the story of the century!'

Yes, thought Bond. Yes. He was certainly right about that. The French papers would give it such a send-off there'd be no stopping it. They wouldn't mind how far they went with the pictures or anything else. There wasn't a press in the world that wouldn't pick it up. And the Spektor! Would M.'s people or the Deuxième have the sense to guess it was booby-trapped? How many of the best cryptographers in the West would go up with it? God, he must get out of this jam! But how?

The top of Nash's *War and Peace* yawned at him. Let's see. There would be the roar as the train went into the tunnel. Then at once the muffled click and the bullet. Bond's eyes stared into the violet gloom, measuring the depth of the shadow in his corner under the roof of the top bunk, remembering exactly where his attaché case stood on the floor, guessing what Nash would do after he had fired.

Bond said: 'You took a bit of a gamble on my letting you team up at Trieste. And how did you know the code of the month?'

Nash said patiently, 'You don't seem to get the picture, old man. SMERSH is good — really good. There's nothing better. We know your code of the month for every year. If anyone in your show noticed these things, noticed the pattern of them, like my show does, you'd realize that every January you lose one of your small chaps somewhere — maybe Tokyo, maybe Timbuctoo. SMERSH just picks one and takes him. Then they screw the code for the year out of him. Anything else he knows, of course. But it's the code they're after. Then it's passed round to the Centres. Simple as falling off a log, old man.'

Bond dug his nails into the palms of his hands.

'As for picking you up at Trieste, old man, I didn't. Rode down with you — in the front of the train. Got out as we stopped and walked back up the platform. You see, old man, we were waiting for you in Belgrade. Knew you'd call your Chief — or the Embassy or someone. Been listening in on that Yugoslav's telephone for weeks. Pity we didn't understand the codeword he shot through to Istanbul. Might have stopped the firework display, or anyway saved our chaps. But the main target was you, old man, and we certainly had you sewn up all right. You were in the killing bottle from the minute you got off that plane in Turkey. It was only a question of when to stuff the cork in.' Nash took another quick glance at his watch. He looked up. His grinning teeth glistened violet. 'Pretty soon now, old man. It's just cork-hour minus fifteen.'

Bond thought: we knew SMERSH was good, but we never knew they were as good as this. The knowledge was vital. Somehow he must get it back. He MUST. Bond's mind raced round the details of his pitifully thin, pitifully desperate plan.

He said: 'SMERSH seems to have thought things out pretty well. Must have taken a lot of trouble. There's only one thing . . .' Bond let his voice hang in the air.

'What's that, old man?' Nash, thinking of his report, was alert.

The train began to slow down. Domodossola. The Italian frontier. What about customs? But Bond remembered. There were no formalities for the through carriages until they got to France, to the frontier, Vallorbes. Even then not for the sleeping cars. These expresses cut straight across Switzerland. It was only people who got out at Brigue or Lausanne who had to go through customs in the stations.

'Well, come on, old man.' Nash sounded hooked.

'Not without a cigarette.'

'Okay. Go ahead. But if there's a move I don't like, you'll be dead.'

Bond slipped his right hand into his hip-pocket. He drew out his broad gunmental cigarette case. Opened it. Took out a cigarette. Took his lighter out of his trouser pocket. Lit the cigarette and put the lighter back. He left the cigarette case on his lap beside the book. He put his left hand casually over the book and the cigarette case as if to prevent them slipping off his lap. He puffed away at his cigarette. If only it had been a trick one — magnesium flare, or anything he could throw in the man's face! If only his Service went in for those explosive toys! But at least he had achieved his objective and hadn't been shot in the process. That was a start.

'You see.' Bond described an airy circle with his cigarette to distract Nash's attention. His left hand slipped the flat cigarette case between the pages of his book. 'You see, it looks all right, but what about you? What are you going to do after we come out of the Simplon? The conductor knows you're mixed up with us. They'll be after you in a flash.'

'Oh that,' Nash's voice was bored again. 'You don't seem to have hoisted in that the Russians think these things out. I get off at Dijon and take a car to Paris. I get lost there. A bit of "Third Man" stuff won't do the story any harm. Anyway it'll come out later when they dig the second bullet out of you and can't find the second gun. They won't catch up with me. Matter of fact, I've got a date at noon tomorrow — Room 204 at the Ritz Hotel, making my report to Rosa. She wants to get the kudos for this job. Then turn into her chauffeur and we drive to Berlin. Come to think of it old man,' the flat voice showed emotion, became greedy, 'I think she may have the Order of Lenin for me in her bag. Lovely grub as they say.'

The train began to move. Bond tensed. In a few minutes it would come. What a way to die, if he was going to die. Through his own stupidity — blind, lethal stupidity. And lethal for Tatiana. Christ! At any moment he could have done something to dodge this shambles. There had been no lack of opportunity. But conceit and curiosity and four days of love had sucked him along on the easy stream down which it had been planned that he should drift. That was the damnable part of the whole business — the triumph for SMERSH, the one enemy he had always sworn to defeat wherever he met it. We will do this, and he will do that. 'Comrades, it is easy with a vain fool like this Bond. Watch him take the bait. You will see. I tell you he's a fool. All Englishmen are fools.' And Tatiana the lure — the darling lure. Bond thought of their first night. The black stockings and the velvet ribbon. And all the time SMERSH had been watching, watching him go through his conceited paces as it had been planned that he would, so that the smear could be built up — the smear on him, the smear on M. who had sent him to Istanbul, the smear on the Service that lived on the myth of its name. God, what a mess! If only ... if only his tiny grain of plan might work!

Ahead, the rumble of the train became a deep boom.

A few more seconds. A few more yards.

The oval mouth between the white pages seemed to gape wider. In a second the dark tunnel would switch out the moonlight on the pages and the blue tongue would lick out for him.

'Sweet dreams, you English bastard.'

The rumble became a great swift clanging roar.

The spine of the book bloomed flame.

The bullet, homing on Bond's heart, flashed over its two quiet ards.

Bond pitched forward on to the floor and lay sprawled under the uneral violet light.

CHAPTER 27

Ten Pints of Blood

IT had all depended on the man's accuracy. Nash had said that Bond would get one bullet through the heart. Bond had taken the gamble that Nash's aim was as good as he said it was. And it had been.

Bond lay like a dead man lies. Before the bullet, he had recalled the corpses he had seen — how their bodies had looked in death. Now he lay totally collapsed, like a broken doll, his arms and legs carefully outflung.

He explored his sensations. Where the bullet had crashed into the book, his ribs were on fire. The bullet must have gone through the cigarette case and then through the other half of the book. He could feel the hot lead over his heart. It felt as if it was burning inside his ribs. It was only a sharp pain in his head where it had hit the woodwork, and the violet sheen on the scuffed toecaps against his nose, that said he wasn't dead.

Like an archaeologist, Bond explored the carefully planned ruin of his body. The position of the sprawled feet. The angle of the half-bent knee that would give purchase when it was needed. The right hand that seemed to be clawing at his pierced heart, was within inches, when he could release the book, of the little attaché case — within inches of the lateral stitching that held the flat-bladed throw-ing-knives, two edged and sharp as razors, that he had mocked when Q Branch had demonstrated the catch that held them. And his left hand, outflung in the surrender of death, rested on the floor and would provide upward leverage when the moment came.

Above him there sounded a long, cavernous yawn. The brown toecaps shifted. Bond watched the shoe-leather strain as Nash stood up. In a minute, with Bond's gun in his right hand, Nash would climb on to the bottom bunk and reach up and feel through the curtain of hair for the base of the girl's neck. Then the snout of the Beretta would nuzzle in after the probing fingers, Nash would press the trigger. The roar of the train would cover the muffled boom.

It would be a near thing. Bond desperately tried to remember simple anatomy. Where were the mortal places in the lower body of a man? Where did the main artery run? The Femoral. Down the inside of the thigh. And the External Iliac, or whatever it was called, that became the Femoral? Across the centre of the groin. If he missed both, it would be bad. Bond had no illusions about being able to beat this terrific man in unarmed combat. The first violent stab of his knife had to be decisive.

The brown toecaps moved. They pointed towards the bunk. What was the man doing? There was no sound except the hollow iron clang as the great train tore through the Simplon — through the heart of the Wasenhorn and Monte Leone. The toothglass tinkled. The woodwork creaked comfortably. For a hundred yards on both sides of the little death cell rows of people were sleep-ing, or lying awake, thinking of their lives and loves, making little plans, wondering who would meet them at the Gare de Lyon. And, all the while, just along the corridor, death was riding with them down the same dark hole, behind the same great Diesel, on the same hot rails.

One brown shoe left the floor. It would have stepped half across Bond. The vulnerable arch would be open above Bond's head.

Bond's muscles coiled like a snake's. His right hand flickered a few centimetres to the hard stitching on the edge of the case. Pressed sideways. Felt the narrow shaft of the knife. Drew it softly half way out without moving his arm.

The brown heel lifted off the ground. The toe bent and took the weight.

Now the second foot had gone.

Softly move the weight here, take the purchase there, grasp the knife hard so that it wouldn't turn on a bone, and then. . . .

In one violent corkscrew of motion, Bond's body twisted up from the floor. The knife flashed.

The fist with the long steel finger, and all Bond's arm and shoulder behind it, lunged upwards. Bond's knuckles felt flannel. He held the knife in, forcing it further.

A ghastly wailing cry came down to him. The Beretta clattered to the floor. Then the knife was wrenched from Bond's hand as the man gave a convulsive twist and crashed down.

Bond had planned for the fall, but, as he sidestepped towards the window, a flailing hand caught him and sent him thudding on to the lower bunk. Before he could recover himself, up from the floor rose the terrible face, its eyes shining violet, the violet teeth bared. Slowly, agonizingly, the two huge hands groped for him.

Bond, half on his back, kicked out blindly. His shoe connected but then his foot was held and twisted and he felt himself slipping downwards.

Bond's fingers scrabbled for a hold in the stuff of the bunk. Now the other hand had him by the thigh. Nails dug into him.

Bond's body was being twisted and pulled down. Soon the teeth would be at him. Bond hammered out with his free leg. It made no difference. He was going.

Suddenly Bond's scrabbling fingers felt something hard. The book! How did one work the thing? Which way up was it? Would it shoot him or Nash? Desperately Bond held it out towards the great sweating face. He pressed at the base of the cloth spine.

'Click!' Bond felt the recoil. 'Click-click-click-click.' Now
Bond felt the heat under his fingers. The hands on his legs were
going limp. The glistening face was drawing back. A noise came
from the throat, a terrible gurgling noise. Then, with a slither and
a crack, the body fell forward on to the floor and the head crashed
back against the woodwork.

Bond lay and panted through clenched teeth. He stared up at the
violet light above the door. He noticed that the loop of the filament
waxed and waned. It crossed his mind that the dynamo under the
carriage must be defective. He blinked his eyes to focus the light
more closely. The sweat ran into them and stung. He lay still, doing
nothing about it.

The galloping boom of the train began to change. It sounded
hollower. With a final echoing roar, the Orient Express sped out
into the moonlight and slackened speed.

Bond lazily reached up and pulled at the edge of the blind. He
saw warehouses and sidings. Lights shone brightly, cleanly on the
rails. Good, powerful lights. The lights of Switzerland.

The train slid quietly to a stop.

In the steady, singing silence, a small noise came from the floor.
Bond cursed himself for not having made certain. He quickly bent
down, listening. He held the book forward at the ready, just in
case. No movement. Bond reached and felt for the jugular vein.
No pulse. The man was quite dead. The corpse had been settling.

Bond sat back and waited impatiently for the train to move again.
There was a lot to be done. Even before he could see to Tatiana,
there would have to be the cleaning up.

With a jerk the long express started softly rolling. Soon the train
would be slaloming fast down through the foothills of the Alps into
the Canton Valais. Already there was a new sound in the wheels —
a hurrying lilt, as if they were glad the tunnel was past.

Bond got to his feet and stepped over the sprawling legs of the
dead man and turned on the top light.

What a shambles! The place looked like a butcher's shop. How much blood did a body contain? He remembered. Ten pints. Well, it would soon all be there. As long as it didn't spread into the passage! Bond stripped the bed-clothes off the bottom bunk and set to work.

At last the job was done — the walls swabbed down around the covered bulk on the floor, the suitcases piled ready for the get-away at Dijon.

Bond drank down a whole carafe of water. Then he stepped up and gently shook the shoulder of fur.

There was no response. Had the man lied? Had he killed her with the poison?

Bond thrust his hand in against her neck. It was warm. Bond felt for the lobe of an ear and pinched it hard. The girl stirred sluggishly and moaned. Again Bond pinched the ear, and again. At last a muffled voice said, 'Don't.'

Bond smiled. He shook her. He went on shaking until Tatiana slowly turned over on her side. Two doped blue eyes gazed into his and closed again. 'What is it?' The voice was sleepily angry.

Bond talked to her and bullied her and cursed her. He shook her more roughly. At last she sat up. She gazed vacantly at him. Bond pulled her legs out so that they hung down over the edge. Some-how he manhandled her down on to the bottom bunk.

Tatiana looked terrible — the slack mouth, the upturned, sleep-drunk eyes, the tangle of damp hair. Bond got to work with a wet towel and her comb.

Lausanne came and, an hour later, the French frontier at Val-lorbes. Bond left Tatiana and went out and stood in the corridor just in case. But the customs and passport men brushed past him to the conductor's cabin, and, after five inscrutable minutes, went on down the train.

Bond stepped back into the compartment. Tatiana was asleep again. Bond looked at Nash's watch, which was now on his own wrist. 4.30. Another hour to Dijon. Bond set to work.

At last Tatiana's eyes opened wide. Her pupils were more or less centred. She said, 'Stop it now, James.' She closed her eyes again. Bond wiped the sweat off his face. He took the bags, one by one, to the end of the corridor and piled them against the exit. Then he went along to the conductor and told him that Madame was not well and that they would be leaving the train at Dijon.

Bond gave the conductor a final tip. 'Do not derange yourself,' he said. 'I have taken the luggage out so as not to disturb Madame. My friend, the one with fair hair, is a doctor. He has been sitting up with us all night. I have put him to sleep in my bunk. The man was exhausted. It would be kind not to waken him until ten minutes before Paris.'

'*Certainement, Monsieur.*' The conductor had not been showered with money like this since the good days of travelling millionaires. He handed over Bond's passport and tickets. The train began to slacken speed. '*Voilà que nous y sommes.*'

Bond went back to the compartment. He dragged Tatiana to her feet and out into the corridor and shut the door on the white pile of death beside the bunk.

At last they were down the steps and on to the hard, wonderful, motionless platform. A blue-smocked porter took their luggage.

The sun was beginning to rise. At that hour of the morning there were very few passengers awake. Only a handful in the third class, who had ridden 'hard' through the night, saw a young man help a young girl away from the dusty carriage with the romantic names on its side towards the drab door that said 'SORTIE'.

CHAPTER 28

La Tricoteuse

THE taxi drew up at the Rue Cambon entrance to the Ritz Hotel.

Bond looked at Nash's watch. 11.45. He must be dead punctual. He knew that if a Russian spy was even a few minutes early or late for a rendezvous the rendezvous was automatically cancelled. He paid off the taxi and went through the door on the left that leads into the Ritz bar.

Bond ordered a double vodka martini. He drank it half down. He felt wonderful. Suddenly the last four days, and particularly last night, were washed off the calendar. Now he was on his own, having his private adventure. All his duties had been taken care of. The girl was sleeping in a bedroom at the Embassy. The Spektor, still pregnant with explosive, had been taken away by the bomb-disposal squad of the Deuxième Bureau. He had spoken to his old friend René Mathis, now head of the Deuxième, and the concierge at the Cambon entrance to the Ritz had been told to give him a pass-key and to ask no questions.

René had been delighted to find himself again involved with

Bond in *une affaire noire*. 'Have confidence, *cher* James,' he had said. 'I will execute your mysteries. You can tell me the story afterwards. Two laundry-men with a large laundry basket will come to Room 204 at 12.15. I shall accompany them dressed as the driver of their camion. We are to fill the laundry basket and take it to Orly and await an R.A.F. Canberra which will arrive at two o'clock. We hand over the basket. Some dirty washing which was in France will be in England. Yes?'

Head of Station F had spoken to M. on the scrambler. He had passed over a short written report from Bond. He had asked for the Canberra. No, he had no idea what it was for. Bond had only shown up to deliver the girl and the Spektor. He had eaten a huge breakfast and had left the Embassy saying he would be back after lunch.

Bond looked again at the time. He finished his martini. He paid for it and walked out of the bar and up the steps to the concierge's lodge.

The concierge looked sharply at him and handed over a key. Bond walked over to the lift and got in and went up to the third floor.

The lift door clanged behind him. Bond walked softly down the corridor, looking at the numbers.

204. Bond put his right hand inside his coat and on to the taped butt of the Beretta. It was tucked into the waistband of his trousers. He could feel the metal of the silencer warm across his stomach.

He knocked once with his left hand.

'Come in.'

It was a quavering voice. An old woman's voice.

Bond tried the handle of the door. It was unlocked. He slipped the pass-key into his coat-pocket. He pushed the door open with one swift motion and stepped in and shut it behind him.

It was a typical Ritz sitting-room, extremely elegant, with good Empire furniture. The walls were white and the curtains and chair covers were of a small patterned chintz of red roses on white. The carpet was wine-red and close-fitted.

In a pool of sunshine, in a low armed chair beside a Directoire writing desk, a little old woman sat knitting.

The tinkle of the steel needles continued. The eyes behind light-blue tinted bi-focals examined Bond with polite curiosity.

'*Oui, Monsieur?*' The voice was deep and hoarse. The thickly powdered, rather puffy face under the white hair showed nothing but well-bred interest.

Bond's hand on the gun under his coat was taut as a steel spring. His half-closed eyes flickered round the room and back to the little old woman in the chair.

Had he made a mistake? Was this the wrong room? Should he apologize and get out? Could this woman possibly belong to SMERSH? She looked so exactly like the sort of respectable rich widow one would expect to find sitting by herself in the Ritz, whiling the time away with her knitting. The sort of woman who would have her own table, and her favourite waiter, in a corner of the restaurant downstairs — not, of course, the grill room. The sort of woman who would doze after lunch and then be fetched by an elegant black limousine with white side-walled tyres and be driven to the tea-room in the rue de Berri to meet some other rich crone. The old-fashioned black dress with the touch of lace at the throat and wrists, the thin gold chain that hung down over the shapeless bosom and ended in a folding lorgnette, the neat little feet in the sensible black-buttoned boots that barely touched the floor. It couldn't be Klebb! Bond had got the number of the room wrong. He could feel the perspiration under his arms. But now he would have to play the scene through.

'My name is Bond, James Bond.'

'And I, Monsieur, am the Comtesse Metterstein. What can I do for you?' The French was rather thick. She might be German, Swiss. The needles tinkled busily.

'I am afraid Captain Nash has met with an accident. He won't be coming today. So I came instead.'

Did the eyes narrow a fraction behind the pale blue spectacles?

'I have not the pleasure of the Captain's acquaintance, Monsieur.

Nor of yours. Please sit down and state your business.' The woman inclined her head an inch towards the high-backed chair beside the writing desk.

One couldn't fault her. The graciousness of it all was devastating. Bond walked across the room and sat down. Now he was about six feet away from her. The desk held nothing but a tall old-fashioned telephone with a receiver on a hook, and, within reach of her hand, an ivory-buttoned bellpush. The black mouth of the telephone yawned at Bond politely.

Bond stared rudely into the woman's face, examining it. It was an ugly face, toadlike, under the powder and under the tight cottage-loaf of white hair. The eyes were so light brown as to be almost yellow. The pale lips were wet and blubbery below the fringe of nicotine-stained moustache. Nicotine? Where were her cigarettes? There was no ashtray — no smell of smoke in the room.

Bond's hand tightened again on his gun. He glanced down at the bag of knitting, at the shapeless length of small-denier beige wool the woman was working on. The steel needles. What was there odd about them? The ends were discoloured as if they had been held in fire. Did knitting needles ever look like that?

'*Eh bien, Monsieur?*' Was there an edge to the voice? Had she read something in his face?

Bond smiled. His muscles were tense, waiting for any movement, any trick. 'It's no use,' he said cheerfully, gambling. 'You are Rosa Klebb. And you are Head of Otdyel II of SMERSH. You are a torturer and a murderer. You wanted to kill me and the Romanov girl. I am very glad to meet you at last.'

The eyes had not changed. The harsh voice was patient and polite. The woman reached out her left hand towards the bellpush. 'Monsieur, I am afraid you are deranged. I must ring for the *valet de chambre* and have you shown to the door.'

Bond never knew what saved his life. Perhaps it was the flash of realization that no wires led from the bellpush to the wall or into the carpet. Perhaps it was the sudden memory of the English 'Come in' when the expected knock came on the door. But, as her finger reached the ivory knob, he hurled himself sideways out of the chair.

As Bond hit the ground there was a sharp noise of tearing calico. Splinters from the back of his chair sprayed around him. The chair crashed to the floor.

Bond twisted over, tugging at his gun. Out of the corner of his eye he noticed a curl of blue smoke coming from the mouth of the 'telephone'. Then the woman was on him, the knitting needles glinting in her clenched fists.

She stabbed downwards at his legs. Bond lashed out with his feet and hurled her sideways. She had aimed at his legs! As he got to one knee, Bond knew what the coloured tips of the needles meant. It was poison. Probably one of those German nerve poisons. All she had to do was scratch him, even through his clothes.

Bond was on his feet. She was coming at him again. He tugged furiously at his gun. The silencer had caught. There was a flash of light. Bond dodged. One of the needles rattled against the wall behind him and the dreadful chunk of woman, the white bun of wig askew on her head, the slimy lips drawn back from her teeth, was on top of him.

Bond, not daring to use his naked fists against the needles, vaulted sideways over the desk.

Panting and talking to herself in Russian, Rosa Klebb scuttled round the desk, the remaining needle held forward like a rapier. Bond backed away, working at the stuck gun. The back of his legs came against a small chair. He let go the gun and reached behind him and snatched it up. Holding it by the back, with its legs pointing like horns, he went round the desk to meet her. But she was beside the bogus telephone. She swept it up and aimed it. Her hand went to the button. Bond leapt forward. He crashed the chair down. Bullets sprayed into the ceiling and plaster pattered down on his head.

Bond lunged again. The legs of the chair clutched the woman round the waist and over her shoulders. God she was strong! She gave way, but only to the wall. There she held her ground, spitting at Bond over the top of the chair, while the knitting needle quested towards him like a long scorpion's sting.

Bond stood back a little, holding the chair at arms' length. He took aim and high-kicked at the probing wrist. The needle sailed away into the room and pinged down behind him.

Bond came in closer. He examined the position. Yes, the woman was held firmly against the wall by the four legs of the chair. There was no way she could get out of the cage except by brute force. Her arms and legs and head were free, but the body was pinned to the wall.

The woman hissed something in Russian. She spat at him over the chair. Bond bent his head and wiped his face against his sleeve. He looked up and into the mottled face.

'That's all, Rosa,' he said. 'The Deuxième will be here in a minute. In an hour or so you'll be in London. You won't be seen leaving the hotel. You won't be seen going into England. In fact very few people will see you again. From now on you're just a number on a secret file. By the time we've finished with you you'll be ready for the lunatic asylum.'

The face, a few feet away, was changing. Now the blood had drained out of it, and it was yellow. But not, thought Bond, with fear. The pale eyes looked levelly into his. They were not defeated.

The wet, shapeless mouth lengthened in a grin.

'And where will you be when I am in the asylum, Mister Bond?'

'Oh, getting on with my life.'

'I think not, *Angliski spion.*'

Bond hardly noticed the words. He had heard the click of the door opening. A burst of laughter came from the room behind him.

'*Eh bien,*' it was the voice of delight that Bond remembered so well. 'The 70th position! Now, at last, I have seen everything. And invented by an Englishman! James, this really is an insult to my countrymen.'

'I don't recommend it,' said Bond over his shoulder. 'It's too strenuous. Anyway, you can take over now. I'll introduce you.

Her name's Rosa. You'll like her. She's a big noise in SMERSH
— she looks after the murdering, as a matter of fact.'

Mathis came up. There were two laundry-men with him. The
three of them stood and looked respectfully into the dreadful face.

'Rosa,' said Mathis thoughtfully. 'But, this time, a Rosa Malheur.
Well, well! But I am sure she is uncomfortable in that position. You
two, bring along the *panier de fleurs* — she will be more comfortable lying down.

The two men walked to the door. Bond heard the creak of the
laundry basket.

The woman's eyes were still locked in Bond's. She moved a
little, shifting her weight. Out of Bond's sight, and not noticed
by Mathis, who was still examining her face, the toe of one shiny
buttoned boot pressed under the instep of the other. From the point
of its toe there slid forward half an inch of thin knife blade. Like
the knitting needles, the steel had a dirty bluish tinge.

The two men came up and put the big square basket down beside
Mathis.

'Take her,' said Mathis. He bowed slightly to the woman. 'It
has been an honour.'

'*Au revoir*, Rosa,' said Bond.

The yellow eyes blazed briefly.

'Farewell, Mister Bond.'

The boot, with its tiny steel tongue, flashed out.

Bond felt a sharp pain in his right calf. It was only the sort of
pain you would get from a kick. He flinched and stepped back.
The two men seized Rosa Klebb by the arms.

Mathis laughed. 'My poor James,' he said. 'Count on SMERSH
to have the last word.'

The tongue of dirty steel had withdrawn into the leather. Now
it was only a harmless bundle of old woman that was being lifted
into the basket.

Mathis watched the lid being secured. He turned to Bond.
'It is a good day's work you have done, my friend,' he said. 'But
you look tired. Go back to the Embassy and have a rest because

this evening we must have dinner together. The best dinner in Paris.
And I will find the loveliest girl to go with it.'

Numbness was creeping up Bond's body. He felt very cold.
He lifted his hand to brush back the comma of hair over his right
eyebrow. There was no feeling in his fingers. They seemed as big
as cucumbers. His hand fell heavily to his side.

Breathing became difficult. Bond sighed to the depth of his
lungs. He clenched his jaws and half closed his eyes, as people do
when they want to hide their drunkenness.

Through his eyelashes he watched the basket being carried to the
door. He prised his eyes open. Desperately he focused Mathis.

'I shan't need a girl, René,' he said thickly.

Now he had to gasp for breath. Again his hand moved up
towards his cold face. He had an impression of Mathis starting
towards him.

Bond felt his knees begin to buckle.

He said, or thought he said, 'I've already got the loveliest. . . .'

Bond pivoted slowly on his heel and crashed headlong to the
wine-red floor.

DOCTOR NO

I

HEAR YOU LOUD AND CLEAR

PUNCTUALLY at six o'clock the sun set with a last yellow flash behind the Blue Mountains, a wave of violet shadow poured down Richmond Road, and the crickets and tree frogs in the fine gardens began to zing and tinkle.

Apart from the background noise of the insects, the wide empty street was quiet. The wealthy owners of the big, withdrawn houses — the bank managers, company directors and top civil servants — had been home since five o'clock and they would be discussing the day with their wives or taking a shower and changing their clothes. In half an hour the street would come to life again with the cocktail traffic, but now this very superior half-mile of 'Rich Road', as it was known to the tradesmen of Kingston, held nothing but the suspense of an empty stage and the heavy perfume of night-scented jasmine.

Richmond Road is the 'best' road in all Jamaica. It is Jamaica's Park Avenue, its Kensington Palace Gardens, its Avenue D'Iéna. The 'best' people live in its big old-fashioned houses, each in an acre or two of beautiful lawn set, too trimly, with the finest trees and flowers from the Botanical Gardens at Hope. The long, straight road is cool and quiet and withdrawn from the hot, vulgar sprawl of Kingston where its residents earn their money, and, on the other side of the T-intersection at its top, lie the grounds of King's House, where the Governor and Commander-in-Chief of Jamaica lives with his family. In Jamaica, no road could have a finer ending.

On the eastern corner of the top intersection stands No. 1 Richmond Road, a substantial two-storey house with broad white-painted verandas running round both floors. From the road a gravel path leads up to the pillared entrance through wide lawns marked out with tennis courts on which this evening, as on all evenings, the sprinklers are at work. This mansion is the social Mecca of Kingston. It is Queen's Club, which, for fifty years, has boasted the power and frequency of its blackballs.

Such stubborn retreats will not long survive in modern Jamaica. One day Queen's Club will have its windows smashed and perhaps be burned to the ground, but for the time being it is a useful place to find in a sub-tropical island — well run, well staffed and with the finest cuisine and cellar in the Caribbean.

At that time of day, on most evenings of the year, you would find the same four motor cars standing in the road outside the club. They were the cars belonging to the high bridge game that assembled punctually at five and played until around midnight. You could almost set your watch by these cars. They belonged, reading from the order in which they now stood against the kerb, to the Brigadier in command of the Caribbean Defence Force, to Kingston's leading criminal lawyer, and to the Mathematics Professor from Kingston University. At the tail of the line stood the black Sunbeam Alpine of Commander John Strangways, R.N. (Ret.), Regional Control Officer for the Caribbean — or, less discreetly, the local representative of the British Secret Service.

Just before six-fifteen, the silence of Richmond Road was softly broken. Three blind beggars came round the corner of the intersection and moved slowly down the pavement towards the four cars. They were Chigroes — Chinese negroes — bulky men, but bowed as they shuffled along, tapping at the kerb with their white sticks. They walked in file. The first man, who wore blue glasses and could presumably see better than the others, walked in front holding a tin cup against the crook of the stick in his left hand. The right hand of the second man rested on his shoulder and the right hand of the third on the shoulder of the second. The eyes of the second and third men were shut. The three men were dressed in rags and wore dirty jippa-jappa baseball caps with long peaks. They said nothing and no noise came from them except the soft tapping of their sticks as they came slowly down the shadowed pavement towards the group of cars.

The three-blind men would not have been incongruous in Kingston, where there are many diseased people on the streets, but, in this quiet rich empty street, they made an unpleasant impression. And it was odd that they should all be Chinese negroes. This is not a common mixture of bloods.

In the cardroom, the sunburned hand reached out into the green pool of the centre table and gathered up the four cards. There was a quiet snap as the trick went to join the rest. 'Hundred honours,' said Strangways, 'and ninety below!' He looked at his watch and stood up. 'Back in twenty minutes. Your deal, Bill. Order some drinks. Usual for me. Don't bother to cook a hand for me while I'm gone. I always spot them.'

Bill Templar, the Brigadier, laughed shortly. He pinged the bell by his side and raked the cards in towards him. He said, 'Hurry up, blast you. You always let the cards go cold just as your partner's in the money.'

Strangways was already out of the door. The three men sat back resignedly in their chairs. The coloured steward came in and they ordered drinks for themselves and a whisky and water for Strangways.

There was this maddening interruption every evening at six-fifteen, about half way through their second rubber. At this time precisely, even if they were in the middle of a hand, Strangways had to go to his 'office' and 'make a call'. It was a damned nuisance. But Strangways was a vital part of their four and they put up with it. It was never explained what 'the call' was, and no one asked. Strangways's job was 'hush' and that was that. He was rarely away for more than twenty minutes and it was understood that he paid for his absence with a round of drinks.

The drinks came and the three men began to talk racing.

In fact, this was the most important moment in Strangways's day — the time of his duty radio contact with the powerful transmitter on the roof of the building in Regent's Park that is the headquarters of the Secret Service. Every day, at eighteen-thirty local time, unless he gave warning the day before that he would not be on the air — when he had business on one of the other islands in his territory, for instance, or was seriously ill — he would transmit his daily report and receive his orders. If he failed to come on the air precisely at six-thirty, there would be a second call, the 'Blue' call, at seven, and, finally, the 'Red' call at seven-thirty. After this, if his transmitter remained silent, it was 'Emergency', and Section III, his controlling authority in London, would urgently get on the job of finding out what had happened to him.

Even a 'Blue' call means a bad mark for an agent unless his 'Reasons in Writing' are unanswerable. London's radio schedules round the world are desperately tight and their minute disruption by even one extra call is a dangerous nuisance. Strangways had never suffered the ignominy of a 'Blue' call, let alone a 'Red', and was as certain as could be that he never would do so. Every evening, at precisely six-fifteen, he left Queen's Club, got into his car and drove for ten minutes up into the foothills of the Blue Mountains to his neat bungalow with the fabulous view over Kingston harbour. At six twenty-five he walked through the hall to the office at the back. He unlocked the door and locked it again behind him. Miss Trueblood, who passed as his secretary, but was in fact his No. 2 and a former Chief Officer W.R.N.S., would already be sitting in front of the dials inside the dummy filing cabinet. She would have the earphones on and would be making first contact, tapping out his call-sign, WXN, on 14 megacycles. There would be a shorthand pad on her elegant knees. Strangways would drop into the chair beside her and pick up the other pair of headphones and, at exactly six twenty-eight, he would take over from her and wait for the sudden hollowness in the ether that meant that WWW in London was coming in to acknowledge.

It was an iron routine. Strangways was a man of iron routine. Unfortunately, strict patterns of behaviour can be deadly if they are read by an enemy.

Strangways, a tall lean man with a black patch over the right eye and the sort of aquiline good looks you associate with the bridge of a destroyer, walked quickly across the mahogany panelled hallway of Queen's Club and pushed through the light mosquito-wired doors and ran down the three steps to the path.

There was nothing very much on his mind except the sensual pleasure of the clean fresh evening air and the memory of the finesse that had given him his three spades. There was this case, of course, the case he was working on, a curious and complicated affair that M had rather nonchalantly tossed over the air at him two weeks earlier. But it was going well. A chance lead into the Chinese community had paid off. Some odd angles had come to light — for the present the merest shadows of angles — but if they jelled, thought Strangways as he strode down the gravel path and into Richmond Road, he might find himself involved in something very odd indeed.

Strangways shrugged his shoulders. Of course it wouldn't turn out like that. The fantastic never materialized in his line of business. There would be some drab solution that had been embroidered by overheated imaginations and the usual hysteria of the Chinese.

Automatically, another part of Strangways's mind took in the three blind men. They were tapping slowly towards him down the sidewalk. They were about twenty yards away. He calculated that they would pass him a second or two before he reached his car. Out of shame for his own health and gratitude for it, Strangways felt for a coin. He ran his thumbnail down its edge to make sure it was a florin and not a penny. He took it out. He was parallel with the beggars. How odd, they were all Chigroes! How very odd! Strangways's hand went out. The coin clanged in the tin cup.

'Bless you, Master,' said the leading man. 'Bless you,' echoed the other two.

The car key was in Strangways's hand. Vaguely he registered the moment of silence as the tapping of the white sticks ceased. It was too late.

As Strangways had passed the last man, all three had swivelled. The back two had fanned out a step to have a clear field of fire. Three revolvers, ungainly with their sausage-shaped silencers, whipped out of holsters concealed among the rags. With disciplined precision the three men aimed at different points down Strangways's spine — one between the shoulders, one in the small of the back, one at the pelvis.

The three heavy coughs were almost one. Strangways's body was hurled forward as if it had been kicked. It lay absolutely still in the small puff of dust from the sidewalk.

It was six-seventeen. With a squeal of tyres, a dingy motor hearse with black plumes flying from the four corners of its roof took the T-intersection into Richmond Road and shot down towards the group on the pavement. The three men had just had time to pick up Strangways's body when the hearse slid to a stop abreast of them. The double doors at the back were open. So was the plain deal coffin inside. The three men manhandled the body through the doors and into the coffin. They climbed in. The lid was put on and the doors pulled shut. The three negroes sat down on three of the four little seats at the corners of the coffin and unhurriedly laid their white sticks beside them. Roomy black alpaca coats hung over the backs of the seats. They put the coats on over their rags. Then they took off their baseball caps and reached down to the floor and picked up black top hats and put them on their heads.

The driver, who also was a Chinese negro, looked nervously over his shoulder.

'Go, man. Go!' said the biggest of the killers. He glanced down at the luminous dial of his wrist watch. It said six-twenty. Just three minutes for the job. Dead on time.

The hearse made a decorous U-turn and moved at a sedate speed up to the intersection. There it turned right and at thirty miles an hour it cruised genteelly up the tarmac highway towards the hills, its black plumes streaming the doleful signal of its burden and the three mourners sitting bolt upright with their arms crossed respectfully over their hearts.

'WXN calling WWW.... WXN calling WWW.... WXN ... WXN ... WXN ...'

The centre finger of Mary Trueblood's right hand stabbed softly, elegantly, at the key. She lifted her left wrist. Six twenty-eight. He was a minute late. Mary Trueblood smiled at the thought of the little open Sunbeam tearing up the road towards her. Now, in a second, she would hear the quick step, then the key in the lock and he would be sitting beside her. There would be the apologetic smile as he reached for the earphones. 'Sorry Mary. Damned car wouldn't start.' Or, 'You'd think the blasted police knew my number by now. Stopped me at Halfway Tree.' Mary Trueblood took the second pair of earphones off their hook and put them on his chair to save him half a second.

'WXN calling WWW.... WXN calling WWW.' She tuned the dial a hair's breadth and tried again. Her watch said six twenty-nine. She began to worry. In a matter of seconds, London would be coming in. Suddenly she thought, God, what could she do if Strangways wasn't on time! It was useless for her to acknowledge London and pretend she was him — useless and dangerous. Radio Security would be monitoring the call, as they monitored every call from an agent. Those instruments which measured the minute peculiarities in an operator's 'fist' would at once detect it wasn't Strangways at the key. Mary Trueblood had been shown the forest of dials in the quiet room on the top floor at headquarters, had watched as the dancing hands registered the weight of each pulse, the speed of each cipher group, the stumble over a particular letter. The Controller had explained it all to her when she had joined the Caribbean station five years before — how a buzzer would sound and the contact be automatically broken if the wrong operator had come on the air. It was the basic protection against a Secret Service transmitter falling into enemy hands. And, if an agent had been captured and was being forced to contact London under torture, he had only to add a few hairbreadth peculiarities to his usual 'fist' and they would tell the story of his capture as clearly as if he had announced it *en clair*.

Now it had come! Now she was hearing the hollowness in the ether that meant London was coming in. Mary Trueblood glanced at her watch. Six-thirty. Panic! But now, at last, there were the footsteps in the hall. Thank God! In a second he would come in. She *must* protect him! Desperately she decided to take a chance and keep the circuit open.

'WWW calling WXN.... WWW calling WXN.... Can you hear me? ... can you hear me?' London was coming over strong, searching for the Jamaica station.

The footsteps were at the door.

Coolly, confidently, she tapped back: 'Hear you loud and clear.... Hear you loud and clear.... Hear you ...'

Behind her there was an explosion. Something hit her on the ankle. She looked down. It was the lock of the door.

Mary Trueblood swivelled sharply on her chair. A man stood in the doorway. It wasn't Strangways. It was a big negro with yellowish skin and slanting eyes. There was a gun in his hand. It ended in a thick black cylinder.

Mary Trueblood opened her mouth to scream.

The man smiled broadly. Slowly, lovingly, he lifted the gun and shot her three times in and around the left breast.

The girl slumped sideways off her chair. The earphones slipped off her golden hair on to the floor. For perhaps a second the tiny chirrup of London sounded out into the room. Then it stopped. The buzzer at the Controller's desk in Radio Security had signalled that something was wrong on WXN.

The killer walked out of the door. He came back carrying a box with a coloured label on it that said PRESTO FIRE, and a big sugar-sack marked TATE & LYLE. He put the box down on the floor and went to the body and roughly forced the sack over the head and down to the ankles. The feet stuck out. He bent them and crammed them in. He dragged the bulky sack out into the hall and came back. In the corner of the room the safe stood open, as he had been told it would, and the cipher books had been taken out and laid on the desk ready for work on the London signals. The man threw these and all the papers in the safe into the centre of the room. He tore down the curtains and added them to the pile. He topped it up with a couple of chairs. He opened the box of Presto firelighters and took out a handful and tucked them into the pile and lit them. Then he went out into the hall and lit similar bonfires in appropriate places. The tinder-dry furniture caught quickly and the flames began to lick up the panelling. The man went to the front door and opened it. Through the hibiscus hedge he could see the glint of the hearse. There was no noise except the zing of crickets and the soft tick-over of the car's engine. Up and down the road there was no other sign of life. The man went back into the smoke-filled hall and easily shouldered the sack and came out again, leaving the door open to make a draught. He walked swiftly down the path to the road. The back doors of the hearse were open. He handed in the sack and watched the two men force it into the coffin on top of Strangways's body. Then he climbed in and shut the doors and sat down and put on his top hat.

As the first flames showed in the upper windows of the bungalow, the hearse moved quietly from the sidewalk and went on its way up towards the Mona Reservoir. There the weighted coffin would slip down into its fifty-fathom grave and, in just forty-five minutes, the personnel and records of the Caribbean station of the Secret Service would have been utterly destroyed.

II

CHOICE OF WEAPONS

THREE weeks later, in London, March came in like a rattlesnake.

From first light on March 1st, hail and icy sleet, with a Force 8 gale behind them, lashed at the city and went on lashing as the people streamed miserably to work, their legs whipped by the wet hems of their macintoshes and their faces blotching with the cold.

It was a filthy day and everybody said so — even M, who rarely admitted the existence of weather even in its extreme forms. When the old black Silver Wraith Rolls with the nondescript number-plate stopped outside the tall building in Regent's Park and he climbed stiffly out on to the pavement, hail hit him in the face like a whiff of small-shot. Instead of hurrying inside the building, he walked deliberately round the car to the window beside the chauffeur.

'Won't be needing the car again today, Smith. Take it away and go home. I'll use the tube this evening. No weather for driving a car. Worse than one of those PQ convoys.'

Ex-Leading Stoker Smith grinned gratefully. 'Aye-aye, sir. And thanks.' He watched the elderly erect figure walk round the bonnet of the Rolls and across the pavement and into the building. Just like the old boy. He'd always see the men right first. Smith clicked the gear lever into first and moved off, peering forward through the streaming windscreen. They didn't come like that any more.

M went up in the lift to the eighth floor and along the thick-carpeted corridor to his office. He shut the door behind him, took off his overcoat and scarf and hung them behind the door. He took out a large blue silk bandanna handkerchief and brusquely wiped it over his face. It was odd, but he wouldn't have done this in front of the porters or the liftman. He went over to his desk and sat down and bent towards the intercom. He pressed a switch. 'I'm in, Miss Moneypenny. The signals please, and anything else you've got. Then get me Sir James Molony. He'll be doing his rounds at St Mary's about now. Tell the Chief of Staff I'll see 007 in half an hour. And let me have the Strangways file.' M waited for the metallic 'Yes, sir' and released the switch.

He sat back and reached for his pipe and began filling it thoughtfully. He didn't look up when his secretary came in with the stack of papers and he even ignored the half dozen pink Most Immediates on top of the signal file. If they had been vital he would have been called during the night.

A yellow light winked on the intercom. M picked up the black telephone from the row of four. 'That you, Sir James? Have you got five minutes?'

'Six, for you.' At the other end of the line the famous neurologist chuckled. 'Want me to certify one of Her Majesty's Ministers?'

'Not today.' M frowned irritably. The old Navy had respected governments. 'It's about that man of mine you've been handling. We won't bother about the name. This is an open line. I gather you let him out yesterday. Is he fit for duty?'

There was a pause on the other end. Now the voice was professional, judicious. 'Physically he's as fit as a fiddle. Leg's healed up. Shouldn't be any after-effects. Yes, he's all right.' There was another pause. 'Just one thing, M. There's a lot of tension there, you know. You work these men of yours pretty hard. Can you give him something easy to start with? From what you've told me he's been having a tough time for some years now.'

M said gruffly, 'That's what he's paid for. It'll soon show if he's not up to the work. Won't be the first one that's cracked. From what you say, he sounds in perfectly good shape. It isn't as if he'd really been damaged like some of the patients I've sent you — men who've been properly put through the mangle.'

'Of course, if you put it like that. But pain's an odd thing. We know very little about it. You can't measure it — the difference in suffering between a woman having a baby and a man having a renal colic. And, thank God, the body seems to forget fairly quickly. But this man of yours has been in *real* pain, M. Don't think that just because nothing's been broken ...'

'Quite, quite.' Bond had made a mistake and he had suffered for it. In any case M didn't like being lectured, even by one of the most famous doctors in the world, on how he should handle his agents. There had been a note of criticism in Sir James Molony's voice. M said abruptly, 'Ever hear of a man called Steincrohn — Dr Peter Steincrohn?'

'No, who's he?'

'American doctor. Written a book my Washington people sent over for our library. This man talks about how much punishment the human body can put up with. Gives a list of the bits of the body an average man can do without. Matter of fact, I copied it out for future reference. Care to hear the list?' M dug into his coat pocket and put some letters and scraps of paper on the desk in front of him. With his left hand he selected a piece of paper and unfolded it. He wasn't put out by the silence on the other end of the line. 'Hullo, Sir James! Well, here they are: "Gall bladder, spleen, tonsils, appendix, one of his two kidneys, one of his two lungs, two of his four or five quarts of blood, two-fifths of his liver, most of his stomach, four of his twenty-three feet of intestines and half of his brain."' M paused. When the silence continued at the other end, he said, 'Any comments, Sir James?'

There was a reluctant grunt at the other end of the telephone. 'I wonder he didn't add an arm and a leg, or all of them. I don't quite see what you're trying to prove.'

M gave a curt laugh. 'I'm not trying to prove anything, Sir James. It just struck me as an interesting list. All I'm trying to say is that my man seems to have got off pretty lightly compared with that sort of punishment. But,' M relented, 'don't let's argue about it.' He said in a milder voice, 'As a matter of fact I did have it in mind to let him have a bit of a breather. Something's come up in Jamaica.' M glanced at the streaming windows. 'It'll be more of a rest cure than anything. Two of my people, a man and a girl, have gone off together. Or that's what it looks like. Our friend can have a spell at being an inquiry agent – in the sunshine too. How's that?'

'Just the ticket. I wouldn't mind the job myself on a day like this.' But Sir James Molony was determined to get his message through. He persisted mildly, 'Don't think I wanted to interfere, M, but there are limits to a man's courage. I know you have to treat these men as if they were expendable, but presumably you don't want them to crack at the wrong moment. This one I've had here is tough. I'd say you'll get plenty more work out of him. But you know what Moran has to say about courage in that book of his.'

'Don't recall.'

'He says that courage is a capital sum reduced by

expenditure. I agree with him. All I'm trying to say is that this particular man seems to have been spending pretty hard since before the war. I wouldn't say he's overdrawn — not yet, but there are limits.'

'Just so.' M decided that was quite enough of that. Nowadays, softness was everywhere. 'That's why I'm sending him abroad. Holiday in Jamaica. Don't worry, Sir James. I'll take care of him. By the way, did you ever discover what the stuff was that Russian woman put into him?'

'Got the answer yesterday.' Sir James Molony also was glad the subject had been changed. The old man was as raw as the weather. Was there any chance that he had got his message across into what he described to himself as M's thick skull? 'Taken us three months. It was a bright chap at the School of Tropical Medicine who came up with it. The drug was *fugu* poison. The Japanese use it for committing suicide. It comes from the sex organs of the Japanese globe-fish. Trust the Russians to use something no one's ever heard of. They might just as well have used curare. It has much the same effect — paralysis of the central nervous system. *Fugu*'s scientific name is Tetrodotoxin. It's terrible stuff and very quick. One shot of it like your man got and in a matter of seconds the motor and respiratory muscles are paralysed. At first the chap sees double and then he can't keep his eyes open. Next he can't swallow. His head falls and he can't raise it. Dies of respiratory paralysis.'

'Lucky he got away with it.'

'Miracle. Thanks entirely to that Frenchman who was with him. Got your man on the floor and gave him artificial respiration as if he was drowning. Somehow kept his lungs going until the doctor came. Luckily the doctor had worked in South America. Diagnosed curare and treated him accordingly. But it was a chance in a million.

By the same token, what happened to the Russian woman?'

M said shortly, 'Oh, she died. Well, many thanks, Sir James. And don't worry about your patient. I'll see he has an easy time of it. Goodbye.'

M hung up. His face was cold and blank. He pulled over the signal file and went quickly through it. On some of the signals he scribbled a comment. Occasionally he made a brief telephone call to one of the Sections. When he had finished he tossed the pile into his *Out* basket and reached for his pipe and the tobacco jar made out of the base of a fourteen-pounder shell. Nothing remained in front of him except a buff folder marked with the Top Secret red star. Across the centre of the folder was written in block capitals: CARIBBEAN STATION, and underneath, in italics, *Strangways and Trueblood.*

A light winked on the Intercom. M pressed down the switch. 'Yes?'

'007's here, sir.'

'Send him in. And tell the Armourer to come up in five minutes.'

M sat back. He put his pipe in his mouth and set a match to it. Through the smoke he watched the door to his secretary's office. His eyes were very bright and watchful.

James Bond came through the door and shut it behind him. He walked over to the chair across the desk from M and sat down.

'Morning, 007.'

'Good morning, sir.'

There was silence in the room except for the rasping of M's pipe. It seemed to be taking a lot of matches to get it going. In the background the fingernails of the sleet slashed against the two broad windows.

It was all just as Bond had remembered it through the months of being shunted from hospital to hospital, the weeks of dreary convalescence, the hard work of getting his body back into shape. To him this represented stepping back into life. Sitting here in this room opposite M was the symbol of normality he had longed for. He looked across through the smoke clouds into the shrewd grey eyes. They were watching him. What was coming? A post-mortem on the shambles which had been his last case? A curt relegation to one of the home sections for a spell of desk work? Or some splendid new assignment M had been keeping on ice while waiting for Bond to get back to duty?

M threw the box of matches down on the red leather desk. He leant back and clasped his hands behind his head.

'How do you feel? Glad to be back?'

'Very glad, sir. And I feel fine.'

'Any final thoughts about your last case? Haven't bothered you with it till you got well. You heard I ordered an inquiry. I believe the Chief of Staff took some evidence from you. Anything to add?'

M's voice was businesslike, cold. Bond didn't like it. Something unpleasant was coming. He said, 'No, sir. It was a mess. I blame myself for letting that woman get me. Shouldn't have happened.'

M took his hands from behind his neck and slowly leant forward and placed them flat on the desk in front of him. His eyes were hard. 'Just so.' The voice was velvet, dangerous. 'Your gun got stuck, if I recall. This Beretta of yours with the silencer. Something wrong there, 007. Can't afford that sort of mistake if you're to carry an oo number. Would you prefer to drop it and go back to normal duties?'

Bond stiffened. His eyes looked resentfully into M's. The licence to kill for the Secret Service, the double-o prefix, was a great honour. It had been earned hardly. It brought Bond the only assignments he enjoyed, the dangerous ones. 'No, I wouldn't, sir.'

'Then we'll have to change your equipment. That was one of the findings of the Court of Inquiry. I agree with it. D'you understand?'

Bond said obstinately, 'I'm used to that gun, sir. I like working with it. What happened could have happened to anyone. With any kind of gun.'

'I don't agree. Nor did the Court of Inquiry. So that's final. The only question is what you're to use instead.' M bent forward to the intercom. 'Is the Armourer there? Send him in.'

M sat back. 'You may not know it, 007, but Major Boothroyd's the greatest small-arms expert in the world. He wouldn't be here if he wasn't. We'll hear what he has to say.'

The door opened. A short slim man with sandy hair came in and walked over to the desk and stood beside Bond's chair. Bond looked up into his face. He hadn't often seen the man before, but he remembered the very wide apart clear grey eyes that never seemed to flicker. With a non-committal glance down at Bond, the man stood relaxed, looking across at M. He said 'Good morning, sir,' in a flat, unemotional voice.

'Morning, Armourer. Now I want to ask you some questions.' M's voice was casual. 'First of all, what do you think of the Beretta, the ·25?'

'Ladies' gun, sir.'

M raised ironic eyebrows at Bond. Bond smiled thinly.

'Really! And why do you say that?'

'No stopping power, sir. But it's easy to operate. A bit fancy-looking too, if you know what I mean, sir. Appeals to the ladies.'

'How would it be with a silencer?'

'Still less stopping power, sir. And I don't like silencers. They're heavy and get stuck in your clothing when you're in a hurry. I wouldn't recommend anyone to try a combination like that, sir. Not if they were meaning business.'

M said pleasantly to Bond, 'Any comment, 007?'

Bond shrugged his shoulders. 'I don't agree. I've used the ·25 Beretta for fifteen years. Never had a stoppage and I haven't missed with it yet. Not a bad record for a gun. It just happens that I'm used to it and I can point it straight. I've used bigger guns when I've had to — the ·45 Colt with the long barrel, for instance. But for close-up work and concealment I like the Beretta.' Bond paused. He felt he should give way somewhere. 'I'd agree about the silencer, sir. They're a nuisance. But sometimes you have to use them.'

'We've seen what happens when you do,' said M drily. 'And as for changing your gun, it's only a question of practice. You'll soon get the feel of a new one.' M allowed a trace of sympathy to enter his voice. 'Sorry, 007. But I've decided. Just stand up a moment. I want the Armourer to get a look at your build.'

Bond stood up and faced the other man. There was no warmth in the two pairs of eyes. Bond's showed irritation. Major Boothroyd's were indifferent, clinical. He walked round Bond. He said 'Excuse me' and felt Bond's biceps and forearms. He came back in front of him and said, 'Might I see your gun?'

Bond's hand went slowly into his coat. He handed over the taped Beretta with the sawn barrel. Boothroyd examined the gun and weighed it in his hand. He put it down on the desk. 'And your holster?'

Bond took off his coat and slipped off the chamois leather holster and harness. He put his coat on again.

With a glance at the lips of the holster, perhaps to see if they showed traces of snagging, Boothroyd tossed the holster down beside the gun with a motion that sneered. He looked across at M. 'I think we can do better than this, sir.' It was the sort of voice Bond's first expensive tailor had used.

Bond sat down. He just stopped himself gazing rudely at the ceiling. Instead he looked impassively across at M.

'Well, Armourer, what do you recommend?'

Major Boothroyd put on the expert's voice. 'As a matter of fact, sir,' he said modestly, 'I've just been testing most of the small automatics. Five thousand rounds each at twenty-five yards. Of all of them, I'd choose the Walther PPK 7·65 mm. It only came fourth after the Japanese M-14, the Russian Tokarev and the Sauer M-38. But I like its light trigger pull and the extension spur of the magazine gives a grip that should suit 007. It's a real stopping gun. Of course it's about a ·32 calibre as compared with the Beretta's ·25, but I wouldn't recommend anything lighter. And you can get ammunition for the Walther anywhere in the world. That gives it an edge on the Japanese and the Russian guns.'

M turned to Bond. 'Any comments?'

'It's a good gun, sir,' Bond admitted. 'Bit more bulky than the Beretta. How does the Armourer suggest I carry it?'

'Berns Martin Triple-draw holster,' said Major Boothroyd succinctly. 'Best worn inside the trouser band to the left. But it's all right below the shoulder. Stiff saddle leather. Holds the gun in with a spring. Should make for a quicker draw than that,' he gestured towards the desk. 'Three-fifths of a second to hit a man at twenty feet would be about right.'

'That's settled then.' M's voice was final. 'And what about something bigger?'

'There's only one gun for that, sir,' said Major Boothroyd stolidly. 'Smith & Wesson Centennial Airweight. Revolver. ·38 calibre. Hammerless, so it won't catch in clothing. Overall length of six and a half inches and it only weighs thirteen ounces. To keep down the weight, the cylinder holds only five cartridges. But by the time they're gone,' Major Boothroyd allowed himself a wintry smile, 'somebody's been killed. Fires the ·38 S & W Special. Very accurate cartridge indeed. With standard loading it has a muzzle velocity of eight hundred and sixty feet per second and muzzle energy of two hundred and sixty foot-pounds. There are various barrel lengths, three-and-a-half-inch, five-inch...'

'All right, all right.' M's voice was testy. 'Take it as read. If you say it's the best I'll believe you. So it's the Walther and the Smith & Wesson. Send up one of each to 007. With the harness. And arrange for him to fire them in. Starting today. He's got to be expert in a week. All right? Then thank you very much, Armourer. I won't detain you.'

'Thank you, sir,' said Major Boothroyd. He turned and marched stiffly out of the room.

There was a moment's silence. The sleet tore at the windows. M swivelled his chair and watched the streaming panes. Bond took the opportunity to glance at his watch. Ten o'clock. His eyes slid to the gun and holster on the desk. He thought of his fifteen years' marriage to the ugly bit of metal. He remembered the times its single word had saved his life — and the times when its threat alone had been enough. He thought of the days when he had literally dressed to kill — when he had dismantled the gun and oiled it and packed the bullets carefully into the springloaded magazine and tried the action once or twice, pumping the cartridges out on to the bedspread in some hotel bedroom somewhere round the world. Then the last wipe of a dry rag and the gun into the little holster and a pause in front of the mirror to see that nothing showed. And then out of the door and on his way to the rendezvous that was to end with either darkness or light. How many times had it saved his life? How many death sentences had it signed? Bond felt unreasonably sad. How could one have such ties with an inanimate object, an ugly one at that, and, he had to admit it, with a weapon that was not in the same class as the ones chosen by the Armourer? But he had the ties and M was going to cut them.

M swivelled back to face him. 'Sorry, James,' he said, and there was no sympathy in his voice. 'I know how you like that bit of iron. But I'm afraid it's got to go. Never give a weapon a second chance — any more than a man. I can't afford to gamble with the double-o section. They've got to be properly equipped. You understand that? A gun's more important than a hand or a foot in your job.'

Bond smiled thinly. 'I know, sir. I shan't argue. I'm just sorry to see it go.'

'All right then. We'll say no more about it. Now I've got some more news for you. There's a job come up. In Jamaica. Personnel problem. Or that's what it looks like. Routine investigation and report. The sunshine'll do you good and you can practise your new guns on the turtles or whatever they have down there. You can do with a bit of holiday. Like to take it on?'

Bond thought: He's got it in for me over the last job. Feels I let him down. Won't trust me with anything tough. Wants to see. Oh well! He said: 'Sounds rather like the soft life, sir. I've had almost too much of that lately. But if it's got to be done ... If you say so, sir ...'

'Yes,' said M. 'I say so.'

III

HOLIDAY TASK

IT was getting dark. Outside the weather was thickening.
M reached over and switched on the green-shaded
desklight. The centre of the room became a warm
yellow pool in which the leather top of the desk glowed
blood-red.

M pulled the thick file towards him. Bond noticed it
for the first time. He read the reversed lettering without
difficulty. What had Strangways been up to? Who was
Trueblood?

M pressed a button on his desk. 'I'll get the Chief of
Staff in on this,' he said. 'I know the bones of the case,
but he can fill in the flesh. It's a drab little story, I'm
afraid.'

The Chief of Staff came in. He was a colonel in the
Sappers, a man of about Bond's age, but his hair was
prematurely grey at the temples from the endless grind of
work and responsibility. He was saved from a nervous
breakdown by physical toughness and a sense of humour.
He was Bond's best friend at headquarters. They smiled
at each other.

'Bring up a chair, Chief of Staff. I've given 007 the
Strangways case. Got to get the mess cleared up before
we make a new appointment there. 007 can be acting
Head of Station in the meantime. I want him to leave in a
week. Would you fix that with the Colonial Office and the

Governor? And now let's go over the case.' He turned to
Bond. 'I think you knew Strangways, 007. See you worked
with him on that treasure business about five years ago.
What did you think of him?'

'Good man, sir. Bit highly strung. I'd have thought he'd
have been relieved by now. Five years is a long time in
the tropics.'

M ignored the comment. 'And his number two, this
girl Trueblood, Mary Trueblood. Ever come across her?'

'No, sir.'

'I see she's got a good record. Chief Officer W.R.N.S.
and then came to us. Nothing against her on her Confidential Record. Good-looker to judge from her photographs. That probably explains it. Would you say
Strangways was a bit of a womanizer?'

'Could have been,' said Bond carefully, not wanting to
say anything against Strangways, but remembering the
dashing good looks. 'But what's happened to them, sir?'

'That's what we want to find out,' said M. 'They've
gone, vanished into thin air. Both went on the same evening about three weeks ago. Left Strangways's bungalow
burned to the ground — radio, codebooks, files. Nothing
left but a few charred scraps. The girl left all her things
intact. Must have taken only what she stood up in. Even
her passport was in her room. But it would have been
easy for Strangways to cook up two passports. He had
plenty of blanks. He was Passport Control Officer for the
island. Any number of planes they could have taken — to
Florida or South America or one of the other islands in
his area. Police are still checking the passenger lists.
Nothing's come up yet, but they could always have gone
to ground for a day or two and then done a bunk. Dyed
the girl's hair and so forth. Airport security doesn't
amount to much in that part of the world. Isn't that so,
Chief of Staff?'

'Yes, sir.' The Chief of Staff sounded dubious. 'But I still can't understand that last radio contact.' He turned to Bond. 'You see, they began to make their routine contact at eighteen-thirty Jamaican time. Someone, Radio Security thinks it was the girl, acknowledged our WWW and then went off the air. We tried to regain contact but there was obviously something fishy and we broke off. No answer to the Blue Call, or to the Red. So that was that. Next day Section III sent 258 down from Washington. By that time the police had taken over and the Governor had already made up his mind and was trying to get the case hushed up. It all seemed pretty obvious to him. Strangways has had occasional girl trouble down there. Can't blame the chap myself. It's a quiet station. Not much to occupy his time. The Governor jumped to the obvious conclusions. So, of course, did the local police. Sex and machete fights are about all they understand. 258 spent a week down there and couldn't turn up a scrap of contrary evidence. He reported accordingly and we sent him back to Washington. Since then the police have been scraping around rather ineffectually and getting nowhere.' The Chief of Staff paused. He looked apologetically at M. 'I know you're inclined to agree with the Governor, sir, but that radio contact sticks in my throat. I just can't see where it fits into the runaway-couple picture. And Strangways's friends at his club say he was perfectly normal. Left in the middle of a rubber of bridge — always did, when it was getting close to his deadline. Said he'd be back in twenty minutes. Ordered drinks all round — again just as he always did — and left the club dead on six-fifteen, exactly to schedule. Then he vanished into thin air. Even left his car in front of the club. Now, why should he set the rest of his bridge four looking for him if he wanted to skip with the girl? Why not leave in the morning, or better still, late at night, after they'd made their radio call and tidied up their lives? It just doesn't make sense to me.'

M grunted non-committally. 'People in — er — love do stupid things,' he said gruffly. 'Act like lunatics sometimes. And anyway, what other explanation is there? Absolutely no trace of foul play — no reason for it that anyone can see. It's a quiet station down there. Same routines every month — an occasional communist trying to get into the island from Cuba, crooks from England thinking they can hide away just because Jamaica's so far from London. I don't suppose Strangways has had a big case since 007 was there.' He turned to Bond. 'On what you've heard, what do you think, 007? There's not much else to tell you.'

Bond was definite. 'I just can't see Strangways flying off the handle like that, sir. I daresay he was having an affair with the girl, though I wouldn't have thought he was a man to mix business with pleasure. But the Service was his whole life. He'd never have let it down. I can see him handing in his papers, and the girl doing the same, and then going off with her after you'd sent out reliefs. But I don't believe it was in him to leave us in the air like this. And from what you say of the girl, I'd say it would be much the same with her. Chief Officers W.R.N.S. don't go out of their senses.'

'Thank you, 007.' M's voice was controlled. 'These considerations had also crossed my mind. No one's been jumping to conclusions without weighing all the possibilities. Perhaps you can suggest another solution.'

M sat back and waited. He reached for his pipe and began filling it. The case bored him. He didn't like personnel problems, least of all messy ones like this. There were plenty of other worries waiting to be coped with round the world. It was only to give Bond the pretence of a job, mixed with a good rest, that he had decided to send him out to Jamaica to close the case. He put the pipe in his mouth and reached for the matches. 'Well?'

Bond wasn't going to be put off his stride. He had liked Strangways and he was impressed by the points the Chief of Staff had made. He said: 'Well, sir. For instance, what was the last case Strangways was working on? Had he reported anything, or was there anything Section III had asked him to look into. Anything at all in the last few months?'

'Nothing whatsoever.' M was definite. He took the pipe out of his mouth and cocked it at the Chief of Staff. 'Right?'

'Right, sir,' said the Chief of Staff. 'Only that damned business about the birds.'

'Oh that,' said M contemptuously. 'Some rot from the Zoo or somebody. Got wished on us by the Colonial Office. About six weeks ago, wasn't it?'

'That's right, sir. But it wasn't the Zoo. It was some people in America called the Audubon Society. They protect rare birds from extinction or something like that. Got on to our Ambassador in Washington, and the F.O. passed the buck to the Colonial Office. They shoved it on to us. Seems these bird people are pretty powerful in America. They even got an atom bombing range shifted on the West Coast because it interfered with some birds' nests.'

M snorted. 'Damned thing called a Whooping Crane. Read about it in the papers.'

Bond persisted. 'Could you tell me about it, sir? What did the Audubon people want us to do?'

M waved his pipe impatiently. He picked up the Strangways file and tossed it down in front of the Chief of Staff. 'You tell him, Chief of Staff,' he said wearily. 'It's all in there.'

The Chief of Staff took the file and riffled through the

pages towards the back. He found what he wanted and
bent the file in half. There was silence in the room while
he ran his eye over three pages of typescript which Bond
could see were headed with the blue and white cipher of
the Colonial Office. Bond sat quietly, trying not to feel
M's coiled impatience radiating across the desk.

The Chief of Staff slapped the file shut. He said, 'Well,
this is the story as we passed it to Strangways on January
20th. He acknowledged receipt, but after that we heard
nothing from him.' The Chief of Staff sat back in his
chair. He looked at Bond. 'It seems there's a bird called
a Roseate Spoonbill. There's a coloured photograph of
it in here. Looks like a sort of pink stork with an ugly
flat bill which it uses for digging for food in the mud. Not
many years ago these birds were dying out. Just before
the war there were only a few hundred left in the world,
mostly in Florida and thereabouts. Then somebody reported a colony of them on an island called Crab Key
between Jamaica and Cuba. It's British territory — a
dependency of Jamaica. Used to be a guano island, but
the quality of the guano was too low for the cost of digging
it. When the birds were found there, it had been unin-
habited for about fifty years. The Audubon people went
there and ended up by leasing a corner as a sanctuary for
these spoonbills. Put two wardens in charge and persuaded
the airlines to stop flying over the island and disturbing
the birds. The birds flourished and at the last count there
were about five thousand of them on the island. Then
came the war. The price of guano went up and some
bright chap had the idea of buying the island and starting
to work it again. He negotiated with the Jamaican
Government and bought the place for ten thousand
pounds with the condition that he didn't disturb the lease
of the sanctuary. That was in 1943. Well, this man
imported plenty of cheap labour and soon had the place

working at a profit and it's gone on making a profit until recently. Then the price of guano took a dip and it's thought that he must be having a hard time making both ends meet.'

'Who is this man?'

'Chinaman, or rather half Chinese and half German. Got a daft name. Calls himself Doctor No — Doctor Julius No.'

'No? Spelt like Yes?'

'That's right.'

'Any facts about him?'

'Nothing except that he keeps very much to himself. Hasn't been seen since he made his deal with the Jamaican Government. And there's no traffic with the island. It's his and he keeps it private. Says he doesn't want people disturbing the guanay birds who turn out his guano. Seems reasonable. Well, nothing happened until just before Christmas when one of the Audubon wardens, a Barbadian, good solid chap apparently, arrived on the north shore of Jamaica in a canoe. He was very sick. He was terribly burned — died in a few days. Before he died he told some crazy story about their camp having been attacked by a dragon with flames coming out of its mouth. This dragon had killed his pal and burned up the camp and gone roaring off into the bird sanctuary belching fire among the birds and scaring them off God knows where. He had been badly burned but he'd escaped to the coast and stolen a canoe and sailed all one night to Jamaica. Poor chap was obviously off his rocker. And that was that, except that a routine report had to be sent off to the Audubon Society. And they weren't satisfied. Sent down two of their big brass in a Beechcraft from Miami to investigate. There's an airstrip on the island. This Chinaman's got a Grumman Amphibian for bringing in supplies ...'

M interjected sourly, 'All these people seem to have a hell of a lot of money to throw about on their damned birds.'

Bond and the Chief of Staff exchanged smiles. M had been trying for years to get the Treasury to give him an Auster for the Caribbean Station.

The Chief of Staff continued: 'And the Beechcraft crashed on landing and killed the two Audubon men. Well, that aroused these bird people to a fury. They got a corvette from the U.S. Training Squadron in the Caribbean to make a call on Doctor No. That's how powerful these people are. Seems they've got quite a lobby in Washington. The captain of the corvette reported that he was received very civilly by Doctor No but was kept well away from the guano workings. He was taken to the airstrip and examined the remains of the plane. Smashed to pieces, but nothing suspicious — came in to land too fast probably. The bodies of the two men and the pilot had been reverently embalmed and packed in handsome coffins which were handed over with quite a ceremony. The captain was very impressed by Doctor No's courtesy. He asked to see the wardens' camp and he was taken out there and shown the remains of it. Doctor No's theory was that the two men had gone mad because of the heat and the loneliness, or at any rate that one of them had gone mad and burned down the camp with the other inside it. This seemed possible to the captain when he'd seen what a godforsaken bit of marsh the men had been living in for ten years or more. There was nothing else to see and he was politely steered back to his ship and sailed away.' The Chief of Staff spread his hands. 'And that's the lot except that the captain reported that he saw only a handful of roseate spoonbills. When his report got back to the Audubon Society it was apparently the loss of their blasted birds that infuriated these people most of all, and ever since then they've been nagging at us to have an inquiry into the whole business. Of course nobody at the Colonial Office or in Jamaica's in the least interested. So in the end the whole fairy story was dumped in our lap.' The Chief of Staff shrugged his shoulders with finality. 'And that's how this pile of bumf,' he waved the file, 'or at any rate the guts of it, got landed on Strangways.'

M looked morosely at Bond. 'See what I mean, 007? Just the sort of mares' nest these old women's societies are always stirring up. People start preserving something — churches, old houses, decaying pictures, birds — and there's always a hullabaloo of some sort. The trouble is these sort of people get really worked up about their damned birds or whatever it is. They get the politicians involved. And somehow they all seem to have stacks of money. God knows where it comes from. Other old women, I suppose. And then there comes a point when someone has to do something to keep them quiet. Like this case. It gets shunted off on to me because the place is British territory. At the same time it's private land. Nobody wants to interfere officially. So I'm supposed to do what? Send a submarine to the island? For what? To find out what's happened to a covey of pink storks.' M snorted. 'Anyway, you asked about Strangways's last case and that's it.' M leant forward belligerently. 'Any questions? I've got a busy day ahead.'

Bond grinned. He couldn't help it. M's occasional outbursts of rage were so splendid. And nothing set him going so well as any attempt to waste the time and energies and slim funds of the Secret Service. Bond got to his feet. 'Perhaps if I could have the file, sir,' he said placatingly. 'It just strikes me that four people seem to have died more or less because of these birds. Perhaps two more did — Strangways and the Trueblood girl. I agree it sounds ridiculous, but we've got nothing else to go on.'

'Take it, take it,' said M impatiently. 'And hurry up and get your holiday over. You may not have noticed it, but the rest of the world happens to be in a bit of a mess.'

Bond reached across and picked up the file. He also made to pick up his Beretta and the holster. 'No,' said M sharply. 'Leave that. And mind you've got the hang of the other two guns by the time I see you again.'

Bond looked across into M's eyes. For the first time in his life he hated the man. He knew perfectly well why M was being tough and mean. It was deferred punishment for having nearly got killed on his last job. Plus getting away from this filthy weather into the sunshine. M couldn't bear his men to have an easy time. In a way Bond felt sure he was being sent on this cushy assignment to humiliate him. The old bastard.

With the anger balling up inside him like cat's fur, Bond said, 'I'll see to it, sir,' and turned and walked out of the room.

RECEPTION COMMITTEE

THE sixty-eight tons deadweight of the Super Constellation hurtled high above the green and brown chequerboard of Cuba and, with only another hundred miles to go, started its slow declining flight towards Jamaica.

Bond watched the big green turtle-backed island grow on the horizon and the water below him turn from the dark blue of the Cuba Deep to the azure and milk of the inshore shoals. Then they were over the North Shore, over its rash of millionaire hotels, and crossing the high mountains of the interior. The scattered dice of small-holdings showed on the slopes and in clearings in the jungle, and the setting sun flashed gold on the bright worms of tumbling rivers and streams. 'Xaymaca' the Arawak Indians had called it — 'The Land of Hills and Rivers'. Bond's heart lifted with the beauty of one of the most fertile islands in the world.

The other side of the mountains was in deep violet shadow. Lights were already twinkling in the foothills and spangling the streets of Kingston, but, beyond, the far arm of the harbour and the airport were still touched with the sun against which the Port Royal lighthouse blinked ineffectually. Now the Constellation was getting its nose down into a wide sweep beyond the harbour. There was a slight thump as the tricycle landing gear extended under the aircraft and locked into position, and a shrill hydraulic whine as the brake flaps slid out of the trailing edge of the wings. Slowly the great aircraft turned in again towards the land and for a moment the setting sun poured gold into the cabin. Then, the plane had dipped below the level of the Blue Mountains and was skimming down towards the single north–south runway. There was a glimpse of a road and telephone wires. Then the concrete, scarred with black skid-marks, was under the belly of the plane and there was the soft double thump of a perfect landing and the roar of reversing props as they taxied in towards the low white airport buildings.

The sticky fingers of the tropics brushed Bond's face as he left the aircraft and walked over to Health and Immigration. He knew that by the time he had got through Customs he would be sweating. He didn't mind. After the rasping cold of London, the stuffy, velvet heat was easily bearable.

Bond's passport described him as 'Import and Export Merchant'.

'What company, sir?'

'Universal Export.'

'Are you here on business or pleasure, sir?'

'Pleasure.'

'I hope you enjoy your stay, sir.' The negro immigration officer handed Bond his passport with indifference.

'Thank you.'

Bond walked out into the Customs hall. At once he saw the tall brown-skinned man against the barrier. He was wearing the same old faded blue shirt and probably the same khaki twill trousers he had been wearing when Bond first met him five years before.

'Quarrel!'

From behind the barrier the Cayman Islander gave a broad grin. He lifted his right forearm across his eyes in the old salute of the West Indians. 'How you, cap'n?' he called delightedly.

'I'm fine,' said Bond. 'Just wait till I get my bag through. Got the car?'

'Sure, cap'n.'

The Customs officer who, like most men from the waterfront, knew Quarrel, chalked Bond's bag without opening it and Bond picked it up and went out through the barrier. Quarrel took it from him and held out his right hand. Bond took the warm dry calloused paw and looked into the dark grey eyes that showed descent from a Cromwellian soldier or a pirate of Morgan's time. 'You haven't changed, Quarrel,' he said affectionately. 'How's the turtle fishing?'

'Not so bad, cap'n, an' not so good. Much de same as always.' He looked critically at Bond. 'Yo been sick, or somepun?'

Bond was surprised. 'As a matter of fact I have. But I've been fit for weeks. What made you say that?'

Quarrel was embarrassed. 'Sorry, cap'n,' he said, thinking he might have offended Bond. 'Dere some pain lines in yo face since de las' time.'

'Oh well,' said Bond. 'It was nothing much. But I could do with a spell of your training. I'm not as fit as I ought to be.'

'Sho ting, cap'n.'

They were moving towards the exit when there came the sharp crack and flash of a press camera. A pretty Chinese girl in Jamaican dress was lowering her Speed Graphic. She came up to them. She said with synthetic charm, 'Thank you, gentlemen. I am from the *Daily Gleaner*.' She glanced down at a list in her hand. 'Mister Bond, isn't it? And how long will you be with us, Mister Bond?'

Bond was offhand. This was a bad start. 'In transit,' he

said shortly. 'I think you'll find there were more interesting people on the plane.'

'Oh no, I'm sure not, Mister Bond. You look very important. And what hotel will you be staying at?'

Damn, thought Bond. He said 'Myrtle Bank' and moved on.

'Thank you, Mister Bond,' said the tinkling voice. 'I hope you'll enjoy ...'

They were outside. As they walked towards the parking place Bond said, 'Ever seen that girl at the airport before?'

Quarrel reflected. 'Reck'n not, cap'n. But de *Gleaner* have plenty camera gals.'

Bond was vaguely worried. There was no earthly reason why his picture should be wanted by the Press. It was five years since his last adventures on the island, and anyway his name had been kept out of the papers.

They got to the car. It was a black Sunbeam Alpine. Bond looked sharply at it and then at the number plate. Strangways's car. What the hell? 'Where did you get this, Quarrel?'

'A.D.C. tell me fe to take him, cap'n. Him say hit de only spare car dey have. Why, cap'n? Him no good?'

'Oh, it's all right, Quarrel,' said Bond resignedly. 'Come on, let's get going.'

Bond got into the passenger seat. It was entirely his fault. He might have guessed at the chance of getting this car. But it would certainly put the finger on him and on what he was doing in Jamaica if anyone happened to be interested.

They moved off down the long cactus-fringed road towards the distant lights of Kingston. Normally, Bond would have sat and enjoyed the beauty of it all — the steady zing of the crickets, the rush of warm, scented air, the ceiling of stars, the necklace of yellow lights shimmering across the harbour — but now he was cursing his carelessness and knowing what he shouldn't have done.

What he *had* done was to send one signal through the Colonial Office to the Governor. In it he had first asked that the A.D.C. should get Quarrel over from the Cayman Islands for an indefinite period on a salary of ten pounds a week. Quarrel had been with Bond on his last adventure in Jamaica. He was an invaluable handyman with all the fine seaman's qualities of the Cayman Islander, and he was a passport into the lower strata of coloured life which would otherwise be closed to Bond. Everybody loved him and he was a splendid companion. Bond knew that Quarrel was vital if he was to get anywhere on the Strangways case — whether it was a case or just a scandal. Then Bond had asked for a single room and shower at the Blue Hills Hotel, for the loan of a car and for Quarrel to meet him with the car at the airport. Most of this had been wrong. In particular Bond should have taken a taxi to his hotel and made contact with Quarrel later. Then he would have seen the car and had a chance to change it.

As it was, reflected Bond, he might just as well have advertised his visit and its purpose in the *Gleaner*. He sighed. It was the mistakes one made at the beginning of a case that were the worst. They were the irretrievable ones, the ones that got you off on the wrong foot, that gave the enemy the first game. But was there an enemy? Wasn't he being over-cautious? On an impulse Bond turned in his seat. A hundred yards behind were two dim sidelights. Most Jamaicans drive with their headlights full on. Bond turned back. He said, 'Quarrel. At the end of the Palisadoes, where the left fork goes to Kingston and the right to Morant, I want you to turn quickly down the Morant road and stop at once and turn your lights off. Right? And now go like hell.'

'Okay, cap'n.' Quarrel's voice sounded pleased. He put his foot down to the floorboards. The little car gave a deep growl and tore off down the white road.

Now they were at the end of the straight. The car skidded round the curve where the corner of the harbour bit into the land. Another five hundred yards and they would be at the intersection. Bond looked back. There was no sign of the other car. Here was the signpost. Quarrel did a racing change and hurled the car round on a tight lock. He pulled in to the side and dowsed his lights. Bond turned and waited. At once he heard the roar of a big car at speed. Lights blazed on, looking for them. Then the car was past and tearing on towards Kingston. Bond had time to notice that it was a big American type taxicab and that there was no one in it but the driver. Then it was gone.

The dust settled slowly. They sat for ten minutes saying nothing. Then Bond told Quarrel to turn the car and take the Kingston road. He said, 'I think that car was interested in us, Quarrel. You don't drive an empty taxi back from the airport. It's an expensive run. Keep a watch out. He may find we've fooled him and be waiting for us.'

'Sho ting, cap'n,' said Quarrel happily. This was just the sort of life he had hoped for when he got Bond's message.

They came into the stream of Kingston traffic — buses, cars, horsedrawn carts, pannier-laden donkeys down from the hills, and the hand-drawn barrows selling violent coloured drinks. In the crush it was impossible to say if they were being followed. They turned off to the right and up towards the hills. There were many cars behind them. Any one of them could have been the American taxi. They drove for a quarter of an hour up to Halfway Tree and then on to the Junction Road, the main road across the island. Soon there was a neon sign of a green palm tree and underneath 'Blue Hills. THE hotel'. They drove in and up the drive lined with neatly rounded bushes of bougainvillaea.

A hundred yards higher up the road the black taxi waved the following drivers on and pulled in to the left. It made a U-turn in a break in the traffic and swept back down the hill towards Kingston.

The Blue Hills was a comfortable old-fashioned hotel with modern trimmings. Bond was welcomed with deference because his reservation had been made by King's House. He was shown to a fine corner room with a balcony looking out over the distant sweep of Kingston harbour. Thankfully he took off his London clothes, now moist with perspiration, and went into the glass-fronted shower and turned the cold water full on and stood under it for five minutes during which he washed his hair to remove the last dirt of big-city life. Then he pulled on a pair of Sea Island cotton shorts and, with sensual pleasure at the warm soft air on his nakedness, unpacked his things and rang for the waiter.

Bond ordered a double gin and tonic and one whole green lime. When the drink came he cut the lime in half, dropped the two squeezed halves into the long glass, almost filled the glass with ice cubes and then poured in the tonic. He took the drink out on to the balcony, and sat and looked out across the spectacular view. He thought how wonderful it was to be away from headquarters, and from London, and from hospitals, and to be here, at this moment, doing what he was doing and knowing, as all his senses told him, that he was on a good tough case again.

He sat for a while, luxuriously, letting the gin relax him. He ordered another and drank it down. It was seven-fifteen. He had arranged for Quarrel to pick him up at seven-thirty. They were going to have dinner together. Bond had asked Quarrel to suggest a place. After a moment of embarrassment, Quarrel had said that whenever he wanted to enjoy himself in Kingston he went to a waterfront nightspot called The Joy Boat. 'Hit no great shakes, cap'n,' he had said apologetically, 'but da food an' drinks an' music is good and I got a good fren' dere. Him owns de joint. Dey calls him "Pus-Feller" seein' how him once fought wit' a big hoctopus.'

Bond smiled to himself at the way Quarrel, like most West Indians, added an 'h' when it wasn't needed and took it off when it was. He went into his room and dressed in his old dark blue tropical worsted suit, a sleeveless white cotton shirt and a black knitted tie, looked in the glass to see that the Walther didn't show under his armpit and went down and out to where the car was waiting.

They swooped quietly down through the soft singing dusk into Kingston and turned to the left along the harbour side. They passed one or two smart restaurants and night clubs from which came the throb and twang of calypso music. There was a stretch of private houses that dwindled into a poor-class shopping centre and then into shacks. Then, where the road curved away from the sea, there was a blaze of golden neon in the shape of a Spanish galleon above green lettering that said 'The Joy Boat'. They pulled into a parking place and Bond followed Quarrel through the gate into a small garden of palm trees growing out of lawn. At the end was the beach and the sea. Tables were dotted about under the palms, and in the centre was a small deserted cement dance floor to one side of which a calypso trio in sequined scarlet shirts was softly improvising on 'Take her to Jamaica where the rum comes from'.

Only half the tables were filled, mostly by coloured people. There was a sprinkling of British and American sailors with their girls. An immensely fat negro in a smart white dinner jacket left one of the tables and came to meet them.

'Hi, Mister Q. Long time no see. Nice table for two?'

'That's right, Pus-Feller. Closer to da kitchen dan da music.'

The big man chuckled. He led them down towards the sea and placed them at a quiet table under a palm tree that grew out of the base of the restaurant building. 'Drinks gemmun?'

Bond ordered his gin and tonic with a lime, and Quarrel a Red Stripe beer. They scanned the menu and both decided on broiled lobster followed by a rare steak with native vegetables.

The drinks came. The glasses were dripping with condensation. The small fact reminded Bond of other times in hot climates. A few yards away the sea lisped on the flat sand. The three-piece began playing 'Kitch'. Above them the palm fronds clashed softly in the night breeze. A gecko chuckled somewhere in the garden. Bond thought of the London he had left the day before. He said, 'I like this place, Quarrel.'

Quarrel was pleased. 'Him a good fren of mine, da Pus-Feller. Him knows mostly what goes hon hin Kingston case you got hany questions, cap'n. Him come from da Caymans. Him an' me once share a boat. Then him go hoff one day catching boobies' heggs hat Crab Key. Went vimmin' to a rock for more heggs an' dis big hoctopus get him. Dey mosly small fellers roun' here but dey come bigger at da Crab seein' how its alongside de Cuba Deep, da deepest waters roun' dese parts. Pus-Feller have hisself a bad time wit dis hanimal. Bust one lung cuttin' hisself free. Dat scare him an him sell me his half of da boat an' come to Kingston. Dat were 'fore da war. Now him rich man whiles I go hon fishin'.' Quarrel chuckled at the quirk of fate.

'Crab Key,' said Bond. 'What sort of a place is that?'

Quarrel looked at him sharply. 'Dat a bad luck place now, cap'n,' he said shortly. 'Chinee gemmun buy hit

durin' da war and bring in men and dig bird-dirt. Don'
let nobody land dere and don' let no one get hoff. We
gives it a wide bert'.'

'Why's that?'

'Him have plenty watchmen. An' guns — machine guns.
An' a radar. An' a spottin' plane. Frens o' mine have
landed dere and him never been seen again. Dat Chinee
keep him island plenty private. Tell da trut', cap'n,'
Quarrel was apologetic, 'dat Crab Key scare me plenty.'

Bond said thoughtfully, 'Well, well.'

The food came. They ordered another round of drinks
and ate. While they ate, Bond gave Quarrel an outline of
the Strangways case. Quarrel listened carefully, occasionally asking questions. He was particularly interested in the
birds on Crab Key, and what the watchmen had said, and
how the plane was supposed to have crashed. Finally he
pushed his plate away. He wiped the back of his hand
across his mouth. He took out a cigarette and lit it. He
leant forward. 'Cap'n,' he said softly, 'I no mind if hit was
birds or butterflies or bees. If dey was on Crab Key and da
Commander was stickin' his nose into da business, yo
kin bet yo bottom dollar him been mashed. Him and him
girl. Da Chinee mash dem for sho.'

Bond looked carefully into the urgent grey eyes. 'What
makes you so certain?'

Quarrel spread his hands. To him the answer was simple.
'Dat Chinee love him privacy. Him want be left alone. I
know him kill ma frens order keep folk away from da
Crab. Him a mos' powerful man. Him kill hanyone what
hinterfere with him.'

'Why?'

'Don' rightly know, cap'n', said Quarrel indifferently.
'People dem want different tings in dis world. An what
dem want sufficient dem gits.'

A glint of light caught the corner of Bond's eye. He

turned quickly. The Chinese girl from the airport was standing in the near-by shadows. Now she was dressed in a tight-fitting sheath of black satin slashed up one side almost to her hip. She had a Leica with a flash attachment in one hand. The other hand was in a leather case at her side. The hand came out holding a flashbulb. The girl slipped the base into her mouth to wet it and improve the contact and made to screw it into the reflector.

'Get that girl,' said Bond quickly.

In two strides Quarrel was up with her. He held out his hand. 'Evenin', missy,' he said softly.

The girl smiled. She let the Leica hang on the thin strap round her neck. She took Quarrel's hand. Quarrel swung her round like a ballet dancer. Now he had her hand behind her back and she was in the crook of his arm.

She looked up at him angrily. 'Don't. You're hurting.'

Quarrel smiled down into the flashing dark eyes in the pale, almond-shaped face. 'Cap'n like you take a drink wit' we,' he said soothingly. He came back to the table, moving the girl along with him. He hooked a chair out with his foot and sat her down beside him, keeping the grip on her wrist behind her back. They sat bolt upright, like quarrelling lovers.

Bond looked into the pretty, angry little face. 'Good evening. What are you doing here? Why do you want another picture of me?'

'I'm doing the nightspots,' the Cupid's bow of a mouth parted persuasively. 'The first picture of you didn't come out. Tell this man to leave me alone.'

'So you work for the *Gleaner*? What's your name?'

'I won't tell you.'

Bond cocked an eyebrow at Quarrel.

Quarrel's eyes narrowed. His hand behind the girl's back turned slowly. The girl struggled like an eel, her teeth clenched on her lower lip. Quarrel went on twisting.

Suddenly she said 'Ow!' sharply and gasped, 'I'll tell!' Quarrel eased his grip. The girl looked furiously at Bond: 'Annabel Chung.'

Bond said to Quarrel, 'Call the Pus-Feller.'

Quarrel picked up a fork with his free hand and clanged it against a glass. The big negro hurried up.

Bond looked up at him. 'Ever seen this girl before?'

'Yes, boss. She come here sometimes. She bein' a nuisance? Want for me to send her away?'

'No. We like her,' said Bond amiably, 'but she wants to take a studio portrait of me and I don't know if she's worth the money. Would you call up the *Gleaner* and ask if they've got a photographer called Annabel Chung? If she really is one of their people she ought to be good enough.'

'Sure, boss.' The man hurried away.

Bond smiled at the girl. 'Why didn't you ask that man to rescue you?'

The girl glowered at him.

'I'm sorry to have to exert pressure,' said Bond, 'but my export manager in London said that Kingston was full of shady characters. I'm sure you're not one of them, but I really can't understand why you're so anxious to get my picture. Tell me why.'

'What I told you,' said the girl sulkily. 'It's my job.'

Bond tried other questions. She didn't answer them.

The Pus-Feller came up. 'That's right, boss. Annabel Chung. One of their freelance girls. They say she takes fine pictures. You'll be okay with her.' He looked bland. Studio portrait! Studio bed, more like.

'Thanks,' said Bond. The negro went away. Bond turned back to the girl. 'Freelance,' he said softly. 'That still doesn't explain who wanted my picture.' His face went cold. 'Now give!'

'No,' said the girl sullenly.

'All right, Quarrel. Go ahead.' Bond sat back. His instincts told him that this was the sixty-four thousand dollar question. If he could get the answer out of the girl he might be saved weeks of legwork.

Quarrel's right shoulder started to dip downwards. The girl squirmed towards him to ease the pressure, but he held her body away with his free hand. The girl's face strained towards Quarrel's. Suddenly she spat full in his eyes. Quarrel grinned and increased the twist. The girl's feet kicked wildly under the table. She hissed out words in Chinese. Sweat beaded on her forehead.

'Tell,' said Bond softly. 'Tell and it will stop and we'll be friends and have a drink.' He was getting worried. The girl's arm must be on the verge of breaking.

'—— you.' Suddenly the girl's left hand flew up and into Quarrel's face. Bond was too slow to stop her. Something glinted and there was a sharp explosion. Bond snatched at her arm and dragged it back. Blood was streaming down Quarrel's cheek. Glass and metal tinkled on to the table. She had smashed the flashbulb on Quarrel's face. If she had been able to reach an eye it would have been blinded.

Quarrel's free hand went up and felt his cheek. He put it in front of his eyes and looked at the blood. 'Aha!' There was nothing but admiration and a feline pleasure in his voice. He said equably to Bond, 'We get nuthen out of dis gal, cap'n. She plenty tough. You want fe me to break she's arm?'

'Good God, no.' Bond let go the arm he was holding. 'Let her go.' He felt angry with himself for having hurt the girl and still failed. But he had learned something. Whoever was behind her held his people by a steel chain.

Quarrel brought the girl's right arm from behind her back. He still held on to the wrist. Now he opened the girl's hand. He looked into her eyes. His own were cruel. 'You mark me, Missy. Now I mark you.' He brought up his other hand and took the Mount of Venus, the soft lozenge of flesh in the palm below her thumb, between his thumb and forefinger. He began to squeeze it. Bond could see his knuckles go white with the pressure. The girl gave a yelp. She hammered at Quarrel's hand and then at his face. Quarrel grinned and squeezed harder. Suddenly he let go. The girl shot to her feet and backed way from the table, her bruised hand at her mouth. She took her hand down and hissed furiously, 'He'll get you, you bastards!' Then, her Leica dangling, she ran off through the trees.

Quarrel laughed shortly. He took a napkin and wiped it down his cheek and threw it on the ground and took up another. He said to Bond, 'She's Love Moun' be sore long after ma face done get healed. Dat a fine piece of a woman, de Love Moun'. When him fat like wit' dat girl you kin tell her'll be good in bed. You know dat, cap'n?'

'No,' said Bond. 'That's new to me.'

'Sho ting. Dat piece of da han' most hindicative. Don' you worry 'bout she,' he added, noticing the dubious expression on Bond's face. 'Hers got nuttin but a big bruise on she's Love Moun'. But boy, was dat a fat Love Moun'! I come back after dat gal sometime, see if ma teory is da troof.'

Appropriately the band started playing 'Don' touch me tomato'. Bond said, 'Quarrel, it's time you married and settled down. And you leave that girl alone or you'll get a knife between your ribs. Now come on. We'll get the check and go. It's three o'clock in the morning in London where I was yesterday. I need a night's sleep. You've got to start getting me into training. I think I'm going to need it. And it's about time you put some plaster on that cheek of yours. She's written her name and address on it.'

Quarrel grunted reminiscently. He said with quiet pleasure, 'Dat were some tough baby.' He picked up a fork and clanged it against his glass.

FACTS AND FIGURES

'HE'LL get you.... He'll get you.... He'll get you, you bastards.'

The words were still ringing in Bond's brain the next day as he sat on his balcony and ate a delicious breakfast and gazed out across the riot of tropical gardens to Kingston, five miles below him.

Now he was sure that Strangways and the girl had been killed. Someone had needed to stop them looking any further into his business, so he had killed them and destroyed the records of what they were investigating. The same person knew or suspected that the Secret Service would follow up Strangways's disappearance. Somehow he had known that Bond had been given the job. He had wanted a picture of Bond and he had wanted to know where Bond was staying. He would be keeping an eye on Bond to see if Bond picked up any of the leads that had led to Strangways's death. If Bond did so, Bond also would have to be eliminated. There would be a car smash or a street fight or some other innocent death. And how, Bond wondered, would this person react to their treatment of the Chung girl? If he was as ruthless as Bond supposed, that would be enough. It showed that Bond was on to something. Perhaps Strangways had made a preliminary report to London before he was killed. Perhaps someone had leaked. The enemy would be foolish to take chances.

If he had any sense, after the Chung incident, he would deal with Bond and perhaps also with Quarrel without delay.

Bond lit his first cigarette of the day — the first Royal Blend he had smoked for five years — and let the smoke come out between his teeth in a luxurious hiss. That was his 'Enemy Appreciation'. Now, who was this enemy?

Well, there was only one candidate, and a pretty insubstantial one at that, Doctor No, Doctor Julius No, the German Chinese who owned Crab Key and made his money out of guano. There had been nothing on this man in Records and a signal to the F.B.I. had been negative. The affair of the roseate spoonbills and the trouble with the Audubon Society meant precisely nothing except, as M had said, that a lot of old women had got excited about some pink storks. All the same, four people had died because of these storks and, most significant of all to Bond, Quarrel was scared of Doctor No and his island. That was very odd indeed. Cayman Islanders, least of all Quarrel, did not scare easily. And why had Doctor No got this mania for privacy? Why did he go to such expense and trouble to keep people away from his guano island? Guano — bird dung. Who wanted the stuff? How valuable was it? Bond was due to call on the Governor at ten o'clock. After he had made his number he would get hold of the Colonial Secretary and try and find out all about the damned stuff and about Crab Key and, if possible, about Doctor No.

There was a double knock on the door. Bond got up and unlocked it. It was Quarrel, his left cheek decorated with a piratical cross of sticking-plaster. 'Mornin', cap'n. Yo said eight-tirty.'

'Yes, come on in, Quarrel. We've got a busy day. Had some breakfast?'

'Yes, tank you, cap'n. Salt fish an' ackee an' a tot of rum.'

'Good God,' said Bond. 'That's tough stuff to start the day on.'

'Mos' refreshin',' said Quarrel stolidly.

They sat down outside on the balcony. Bond offered Quarrel a cigarette and lit one himself. 'Now then,' he said. 'I'll be spending most of the day at King's House and perhaps at the Jamaica Institute. I shan't need you till tomorrow morning, but there are some things for you to do downtown. All right?'

'Okay, cap'n. Jes' yo say.'

'First of all, that car of ours is hot. We've got to get rid of it. Go down to Motta's or one of the other hire people and pick up the newest and best little self-drive car you can find, the one with the least mileage. Saloon. Take it for a month. Right? Then hunt around the waterfront and find two men who look as near as possible like us. One must be able to drive a car. Buy them both clothes, at least for their top halves, that look like ours. And the sort of hats we might wear. Say we want a car taken over to Montego tomorrow morning — by the Spanish Town, Ocho Rios road. To be left at Levy's garage there. Ring up Levy and tell him to expect it and to keep it for us. Right?'

Quarrel grinned. 'Yo want fox someone?'

'That's right. They'll get ten pounds each. Say I'm a rich American and I want my car to arrive in Montego Bay driven by a respectable couple of men. Make me out a bit mad. They must be here at six o'clock tomorrow morning. You'll be here with the other car. See they look the part and send them off in the Sunbeam with the roof down. Right?'

'Okay, cap'n.'

'What's happened to that house we had on the North Shore last time — Beau Desert at Morgan's Harbour? Do you know if it's let?'

'Couldn't say, cap'n. Hit's well away from de tourist places and dey askin' a big rent for it.'

'Well, go to Graham Associates and see if you can rent it for a month, or another bungalow near by. I don't mind what you pay. Say it's for a rich American, Mr James. Get the keys and pay the rent and say I'll write and confirm. I can telephone them if they want more details.' Bond reached into his hip pocket and brought out a thick wad of notes. He handed half of it to Quarrel. 'Here's two hundred pounds. That should cover all this. Get in touch if you want some more. You know where I'll be.'

'Tanks, cap'n,' said Quarrel, awestruck by the big sum. He stowed it away inside his blue shirt and buttoned the shirt up to his neck. 'Anyting helse?'

'No, but take a lot of trouble about not being followed. Leave the car somewhere downtown and walk to these places. And watch out particularly for any Chinese near you.' Bond got up and they went to the door. 'See you tomorrow morning at six-fifteen and we'll get over to the North Coast. As far as I can see that's going to be our base for a while.'

Quarrel nodded. His face was enigmatic. He said 'Okay, cap'n' and went off down the corridor.

Half an hour later Bond went downstairs and took a taxi to King's House. He didn't sign the Governor's book in the cool hall. He was put in a waiting room for the quarter of an hour necessary to show him that he was unimportant. Then the A.D.C. came for him and took him up to the Governor's study on the first floor.

It was a large cool room smelling of cigar smoke. The Acting Governor, in a cream tussore suit and an inappropriate wing collar and spotted bow tie, was sitting at a broad mahogany desk on which there was nothing but the *Daily Gleaner*, the *Times Weekly* and a bowl of hibiscus blossoms. His hands lay flat on the desk in front of him. He was sixtyish with a red, rather petulant face and bright, bitter blue eyes. He didn't smile or get up. He said, 'Good morning, Mr — er — Bond. Please sit down.'

Bond took the chair across the desk from the Governor and sat down. He said, 'Good morning, sir,' and waited. A friend at the Colonial Office had told him his reception would be frigid. 'He's nearly at retiring age. Only an interim appointment. We had to find an Acting Governor to take over at short notice when Sir Hugh Foot was promoted. Foot was a great success. This man's not even trying to compete. He knows he's only got the job for a few months while we find someone to replace Foot. This man's been passed over for the Governor Generalship of Rhodesia. Now all he wants is to retire and get some directorships in the City. Last thing he wants is any trouble in Jamaica. He keeps on trying to close this Strangways case of yours. Won't like you ferreting about.'

The Governor cleared his throat. He recognized that Bond wasn't one of the servile ones. 'You wanted to see me?'

'Just to make my number, sir,' said Bond equably. 'I'm here on the Strangways case. I think you had a signal from the Secretary of State.' This was a reminder that the people behind Bond were powerful people. Bond didn't like attempts to squash him or his Service.

'I recall the signal. And what can I do for you? So far as we're concerned here the case is closed.'

'In what way "closed", sir?'

The Governor said roughly, 'Strangways obviously did a bunk with the girl. Unbalanced sort of fellow at the best of times. Some of your — er — colleagues, don't seem to be able to leave women alone.' The Governor clearly included Bond. 'Had to bail the chap out of various scandals before now. Doesn't do the Colony any good Mr — er — Bond. Hope your people will be sending us a rather better type of man to take his place. That is,' he added coldly, 'if a Regional Control man is really needed here. Personally I have every confidence in our police.'

Bond smiled sympathetically. 'I'll report your views, sir. I expect my Chief will like to discuss them with the Minister of Defence and the Secretary of State. Naturally, if you would like to take over these extra duties it will be a saving in manpower so far as my Service is concerned. I'm sure the Jamaican Constabulary is most efficient.'

The Governor looked at Bond suspiciously. Perhaps he had better handle this man a bit more carefully. 'This is an informal discussion, Mr Bond. When I have decided on my views I will communicate them myself to the Secretary of State. In the meantime, is there anyone you wish to see on my staff?'

'I'd like to have a word with the Colonial Secretary, sir.'

'Really? And why, pray?'

'There's been some trouble on Crab Key. Something about a bird sanctuary. The case was passed to us by the Colonial Office. My Chief asked me to look into it while I'm here.'

The Governor looked relieved. 'Certainly, certainly. I'll see that Mr Pleydell-Smith receives you straight away. So you feel we can leave the Strangways case to sort itself out? They'll turn up before long, never fear.' He reached over and rang a bell. The A.D.C. came in. 'This gentleman would like to see the Colonial Secretary, A.D.C. Take him along, would you? I'll call Mr Pleydell-Smith myself and ask him to make himself available.' He got up and came round the desk. He held out his hand. 'Goodbye then, Mr Bond. And I'm so glad we see eye to eye. Crab Key, eh? Never been there myself, but I'm sure it would repay a visit.'

Bond shook hands. 'That was what I was thinking. Goodbye, sir.'

'Goodbye, goodbye.' The Governor watched Bond's back retreating out of the door and himself returned well satisfied to his desk. 'Young whippersnapper,' he said to the empty room. He sat down and said a few peremptory words down the telephone to the Colonial Secretary. Then he picked up the *Times Weekly* and turned to the Stock Exchange prices.

The Colonial Secretary was a youngish shaggy-haired man with bright, boyish eyes. He was one of those nervous pipe smokers who are constantly patting their pockets for matches, shaking the box to see how many are left in it, or knocking the dottle out of their pipes. After he had gone through this routine two or three times in his first ten minutes with Bond, Bond wondered if he ever got any smoke into his lungs at all.

After pumping energetically at Bond's hand and waving vaguely at a chair, Pleydell-Smith walked up and down the room scratching his temple with the stem of his pipe. 'Bond. Bond. Bond! Rings a bell. Now let me see. Yes, by jove! You were the chap who was mixed up in that treasure business here. By jove, yes! Four, five years ago. Found the file lying around only the other day. Splendid show. What a lark! I say, wish you'd start another bonfire like that here. Stir the place up a bit. All they think of nowadays is Federation and their bloody self-importance. Self-determination indeed! They can't even run a bus service. And the colour problem! My dear chap, there's far more colour problem between the straight-haired and the crinkly-haired Jamaicans than there is between me and my black cook. However,' Pleydell-Smith came to rest beside his desk. He sat down opposite Bond and draped one leg over the arm of his chair. Reaching for a tobacco jar with the arms of King's College, Cambridge, on it, he dug into it and started filling his pipe. 'I mean to say I don't want to bore you with all that. You go ahead and bore me. What's your problem? Glad to help. I bet it's more interesting than this muck,' he waved at the pile of papers in his *In* tray.

Bond grinned at him. This was more like it. He had found an ally, and an intelligent one at that. 'Well,' he said seriously. 'I'm here on the Strangways case. But first of all I want to ask you a question that may sound odd. Exactly how did you come to be looking at that other case of mine? You say you found the file lying about. How was that? Had someone asked for it? I don't want to be indiscreet, so don't answer if you don't want to. I'm just inquisitive.'

Pleydell-Smith cocked an eye at him. 'I suppose that's your job.' He reflected, gazing at the ceiling. 'Well, now I come to think of it I saw it on my secretary's desk. She's a new girl. Said she was trying to get up to date with the files. Mark you,' the Colonial Secretary hastened to exonerate his girl, 'there were plenty of other files on her desk. It was just this one that caught my eye.'

'Oh, I see,' said Bond. 'It was like that.' He smiled apologetically. 'Sorry, but various people seem to be rather interested in me being here. What I really wanted to talk to you about was Crab Key. Anything you know about the place. And about this Chinaman, Doctor No, who bought it. And anything you can tell me about his guano business. Rather a tall order, I'm afraid, but any scraps will help.'

Pleydell-Smith laughed shortly through the stem of his pipe. He jerked the pipe out of his mouth and talked while he tamped down the burning tobacco with his matchbox. 'Bitten off a bit more than you can chew on guano. Talk to you for hours about it. Started in the Consular before I transferred to the Colonial Office. First job was in Peru.

Had a lot to do with their people who administer the whole trade — *Compañía Administradora del Guano*. Nice people.' The pipe was going now and Pleydell-Smith threw his matchbox down on the table. 'As for the rest, it's just a question of getting the file.' He rang a bell. In a minute the door opened behind Bond. 'Miss Taro, the file on Crab Key, please. The one on the sale of the place and the other one on that warden fellow who turned up before Christmas. Miss Longfellow will know where to find them.'

A soft voice said, 'Yes, sir.' Bond heard the door close.

'Now then, guano.' Pleydell-Smith tilted his chair back. Bond prepared to be bored. 'As you know, it's bird dung. Comes from the rear end of two birds, the masked booby and the guanay. So far as Crab Key is concerned, it's only the guanay, otherwise known as the green cormorant, same bird as you find in England. The guanay is a machine for converting fish into guano. They mostly eat anchovies. Just to show you how much fish they eat, they've found up to seventy anchovies inside one bird!' Pleydell-Smith took out his pipe and pointed it impressively at Bond. 'The whole population of Peru eats four thousands tons of fish a year. The sea birds of the country eat five hundred thousand tons!'

Bond pursed his lips to show he was impressed. 'Really.'

'Well, now,' continued the Colonial Secretary, 'every day each one of these hundreds of thousands of guanays eat a pound or so of fish and deposit an ounce of guano on the guanera — that's the guano island.'

Bond interrupted, 'Why don't they do it in the sea?'

'Don't know.' Pleydell-Smith took the question and turned it over in his mind. 'Never occurred to me. Anyway they don't. They do it on the land and they've been doing it since before Genesis. That makes the hell of a lot of bird dung — millions of tons of it on the Pescadores and the other guanera. Then, around 1850 someone discovered it was the greatest natural fertilizer in the world — stuffed with nitrates and phosphates and what have you. And the ships and the men came to the guaneras and simply ravaged them for twenty years or more. It's a time known as the "Saturnalia" in Peru. It was like the Klondyke. People fought over the muck, hi-jacked each other's ships, shot the workers, sold phoney maps of secret guano islands — anything you like. And people made fortunes out of the stuff.'

'Where does Crab Key come in?' Bond wanted to get down to cases.

'That was the only worthwhile guanera so far north. It was worked too, God knows who by. But the stuff had a low nitrate content. Water's not as rich round here as it is down along the Humboldt Current. So the fish aren't so rich in chemicals. So the guano isn't so rich either. Crab Key got worked on and off when the price was high enough, but the whole industry went bust, with Crab Key and the other poor-quality deposits in the van, when the Germans invented artificial chemical manure. By this time Peru had realized that she had squandered a fantastic capital asset and she set about organizing the remains of the industry and protecting the guanera. She nationalized the industry and protected the birds, and slowly, very slowly, the supplies built up again. Then people found that there were snags about the German stuff, it impoverishes the soil, which guano doesn't do, and gradually the price of guano improved and the industry staggered back to its feet. Now it's going fine, except that Peru keeps most of the guano to herself, for her own agriculture. And that was where Crab Key came in again.'

'Ah.'

'Yes,' said Pleydell-Smith, patting his pockets for the matches, finding them on the desk, shaking them against his ear, and starting his pipe-filling routine, 'at the beginning of the war, this Chinaman, who must be a wily devil, by the way, got the idea that he could make a good thing out of the old guanera on Crab Key. The price was about fifty dollars a ton on this side of the Atlantic and he bought the island from us, for about ten thousand pounds as I recall it, brought in labour and got to work. Been working it ever since. Must have made a fortune. He ships direct to Europe, to Antwerp. They send him a ship once a month. He's installed the latest crushers and separators. Sweats his labour, I daresay. To make a decent profit, he'd have to. Particularly now. Last year I heard he was only getting about thirty-eight to forty dollars a ton c.i.f. Antwerp. God knows what he must pay his labour to make a profit at that price. I've never been able to find out. He runs that place like a fortress — sort of forced labour camp. No one ever gets off it. I've heard some funny rumours, but no one's ever complained. It's his island, of course, and he can do what he likes on it.'

Bond hunted for clues. 'Would it really be so valuable to him, this place? What do you suppose it's worth?'

Pleydell-Smith said, 'The guanay is the most valuable bird in the world. Each pair produces about two dollars' worth of guano in a year without any expense to the owner. Each female lays an average of three eggs and raises two young. Two broods a year. Say they're worth fifteen dollars a pair, and say there are one hundred thousand birds on Crab Key, which is a reasonable guess on the old figures we have. That makes his birds worth a million and a half dollars. Pretty valuable property. Add the value of the installations, say another million, and you've got a small fortune on that hideous little place. Which reminds me,' Pleydell-Smith pressed the bell, 'what the hell has happened to those files? You'll find all the dope you want in them.'

The door opened behind Bond.

Pleydell-Smith said irritably, 'Really, Miss Taro. **What** about those files?'

'Very sorry, sir,' said the soft voice. 'But we can't find them anywhere.'

'What do you mean "can't find them"? Who had them last?'

'Commander Strangways, sir.'

'Well, I remember distinctly him bringing them back to this room. What happened to them then?'

'Can't say, sir,' the voice was unemotional. 'The covers are there but there's nothing inside them.'

Bond turned in his chair. He glanced at the girl and turned back. He smiled grimly to himself. He knew where the files had gone. He also knew why the old file on himself had been out on the Secretary's desk. He also guessed how the particular significance of 'James Bond, Import and Export Merchant,' seemed to have leaked out of King's House, the only place where the significance was known.

Like Doctor No, like Miss Annabel Chung, the demure, efficient-looking little secretary in the hornrimmed glasses was a Chinese.

VI

THE FINGER ON THE TRIGGER

THE Colonial Secretary gave Bond lunch at Queen's Club. They sat in a corner of the elegant mahogany-panelled dining room with its four big ceiling fans and gossiped about Jamaica. By the time coffee came, Pleydell-Smith was delving well below the surface of the prosperous, peaceful island the world knows.

'It's like this.' He began his antics with the pipe. 'The Jamaican is a kindly lazy man with the virtues and vices of a child. He lives on a very rich island but he doesn't get rich from it. He doesn't know how to and he's too lazy. The British come and go and take the easy pickings, but for about two hundred years no Englishman has made a fortune out here. He doesn't stay long enough. He takes a fat cut and leaves. It's the Portuguese Jews who make the most. They came here with the British and they've stayed. But they're snobs and they spend too much of their fortunes on building fine houses and giving dances. They're the names that fill the social column in the *Gleaner* when the tourists have gone. They're in rum and tobacco and they represent the big British firms over here — motor cars, insurance and so forth. Then come the Syrians, very rich too, but not such good businessmen. They have most of the stores and some of the best hotels. They're not a very good risk. Get overstocked and have to have an occasional fire to get liquid again. Then there are the Indians with

their usual flashy trade in soft goods and the like. They're
not much of a lot. Finally there are the Chinese, solid,
compact, discreet — the most powerful clique in Jamaica.
They've got the bakeries and the laundries and the best
food stores. They keep to themselves and keep their strain
pure.' Pleydell-Smith laughed, 'Not that they don't take
the black girls when they want them. You can see the
result all over Kingston — Chigroes — Chinese negroes
and negresses. The Chigroes are a tough, forgotten race.
They look down on the negroes and the Chinese look
down on them. One day they may become a nuisance.
They've got some of the intelligence of the Chinese and
most of the vices of the black man. The police have a lot
of trouble with them.'

Bond said, 'That secretary of yours. Would she be one
of them?'

'That's right. Bright girl and very efficient. Had her for
about six months. She was far the best of the ones that
answered our advertisement.'

'She looks bright,' said Bond non-committally. 'Are they
organized, these people? Is there some head of the Chinese
negro community?'

'Not yet. But someone'll get hold of them one of these
days. They'd be a useful little pressure group.' Pleydell-
Smith glanced at his watch. 'That reminds me. Must be
getting along. Got to go and read the riot act about those
files. Can't think what happened to them. I distinctly
remember ...' He broke off. 'However, main point is that
I haven't been able to give you much dope about Crab
Key and this doctor fellow. But I can tell you there wasn't
much you'd have found out from the files. He seems to
have been a pleasant spoken chap. Very businesslike. Then
there was that argument with the Audubon Society. I
gather you know all about that. As for the place itself,
there was nothing on the files but one or two pre-war

reports and a copy of the last ordnance survey. God-forsaken bloody place it sounds. Nothing but miles of mangrove swamps and a huge mountain of bird dung at one end. But you said you were going down to the Institute. Why don't I take you there and introduce you to the fellow who runs the map section?'

An hour later Bond was ensconced in a corner of a sombre room with the ordnance survey map of Crab Key, dated 1910, spread out on a table in front of him. He had a sheet of the Institute's writing-paper and had made a rough sketch-map and was jotting down the salient points.

The overall area of the island was about fifty square miles. Three-quarters of this, to the east, was swamp and shallow lake. From the lake a flat river meandered down to the sea and came out halfway along the south coast into a small sandy bay. Bond guessed that somewhere at the headwaters of the river would be a likely spot for the Audubon wardens to have chosen for their camp. To the west, the island rose steeply to a hill stated to be five hundred feet high and ended abruptly with what appeared to be a sheer drop to the sea. A dotted line led from this hill to a box in the corner of the map which contained the words 'Guano deposits. Last workings 1880'.

There was no sign of a road, or even of a track on the island, and no sign of a house. The relief map showed that the island looked rather like a swimming water rat — a flat spine rising sharply to the head — heading west. It appeared to be about thirty miles due north of Galina Point on the north shore of Jamaica and about sixty miles south of Cuba.

Little else could be gleaned from the map. Crab Key was surrounded by shoal water except below the western cliff where the nearest marking was five hundred fathoms. After that came the plunge into the Cuba Deep.

Bond folded the map and handed it in to the librarian.

Suddenly he felt exhausted. It was only four o'clock, but it was roasting in Kingston and his shirt was sticking to him. Bond walked out of the Institute and found a taxi and went back up into the cool hills to his hotel. He was well satisfied with his day, but nothing else could be done on this side of the island. He would spend a quiet evening at his hotel and be ready to get up early next morning and be away.

Bond went to the reception desk to see if there was a message from Quarrel. 'No messages, sir,' said the girl. 'But a basket of fruit came from King's House. Just after lunch. The messenger took it up to your room.'

'What sort of a messenger?'

'Coloured man, sir. Said he was from the A.D.C.'s office.'

'Thank you.' Bond took his key and went up the stairs to the first floor. It was ridiculously improbable. His hand on the gun under his coat, Bond softly approached his door. He turned the key and kicked the door open. The empty room yawned at him. Bond shut and locked the door. On his dressing table was a large, ornate basket of fruit — tangerines, grapefruit, pink bananas, soursop, star-apples and even a couple of hot-house nectarines. Attached to a broad ribbon on the handle was a white envelope. Bond removed it and held it up to the light. He opened it. On a plain sheet of expensive white writing paper was typed 'With the Compliments of His Excellency the Governor'.

Bond snorted. He stood looking at the fruit. He bent his ear to it and listened. He then took the basket by the handle and tipped its contents out on to the floor. The fruit bounced and rolled over the coconut matting. There was nothing but fruit in the basket. Bond grinned at his precautions. There was a last possibility. He picked up one of the nectarines, the most likely for a greedy man to choose first, and took it into the bathroom. He dropped it in the washbasin and went back to the bedroom and, after inspecting the lock, unlocked the wardrobe. Gingerly he lifted out his suitcase and stood it in the middle of the room. He knelt down and looked for the traces of talcum powder he had dusted round the two locks. They were smeared and there were minute scratches round the keyholes. Bond sourly examined the marks. These people were not as careful as some others he had had to deal with. He unlocked the case and stood it up on end. There were four innocent copper studs in the welting at the front right-hand corner of the lid. Bond prised at the top one of these studs with his nail and it eased out. He took hold of it and pulled out three feet of thick steel wire and put it on the floor beside him. This wire threaded through small wire loops inside the lid and sewed the case shut. Bond lifted the lid and verified that nothing had been disturbed. From his 'tool case' he took out a jeweller's glass and went back into the bathroom and switched on the light over the shaving mirror. He screwed the glass into his eye and gingerly picked the nectarine out of the washbasin and revolved it slowly between finger and thumb.

Bond stopped turning the nectarine. He had come to a minute pinhole, its edges faintly discoloured brown. It was in the crevice of the fruit, invisible except under a magnifying glass. Bond put the nectarine carefully down in the washbasin. He stood for a moment and looked thoughtfully into his eyes in the mirror.

So it *was* war! Well, well. How very interesting. Bond felt the slight tautening of the skin at the base of his stomach. He smiled thinly at his reflection in the mirror. So his instincts and his reasoning had been correct. Strangways and the girl had been murdered and their records destroyed because they had got too hot on the

trail. Then Bond had come on the scene and, thanks to
Miss Taro, they had been waiting for him. Miss Chung,
and perhaps the taxi driver, had picked up the scent. He
had been traced to the Blue Hills hotel. The first shot had
been fired. There would be others. And whose finger was
on the trigger? Who had got him so accurately in his
sights? Bond's mind was made up. The evidence was nil.
But he was certain of it. This was long range fire, from
Crab Key. The man behind the gun was Doctor No.

Bond walked back into the bedroom. One by one he
picked up the fruit and took each piece back to the
bathroom and examined it through his glass. The pin-
prick was always there, concealed in the stalk-hole or a
crevice. Bond rang down and asked for a cardboard box
and paper and string. He packed the fruit carefully in the
box and picked up the telephone and called King's House.
He asked for the Colonial Secretary. 'That you, Pleydell-
Smith? James Bond speaking. Sorry to bother you. Got a
bit of a problem. Is there a public analyst in Kingston?
I see. Well, I've got something I want analysed. If I sent
the box down to you, would you be very kind and pass
it on to this chap? I don't want my name to come into
this. All right? I'll explain later. When you get his report
would you send me a short telegram telling me the answer?
I'll be at Beau Desert, over at Morgan's Harbour, for the
next week or so. Be glad if you'd keep that to yourself too. Sorry to be so damned mysterious. I'll explain
everything when I see you next. I expect you'll get a
clue when you see what the analyst has to say. And by
the way, tell him to handle the specimens carefully,
would you. Warn him there's more in them than meets
the eye. Very many thanks. Lucky I met you this
morning. Goodbye.'

Bond addressed the parcel and went down and paid a
taxi to deliver it at once to King's House. It was six

o'clock. He went back to his room and had a shower and changed and ordered his first drink. He was about to take it out on the balcony when the telephone rang. It was Quarrel.

'Everyting fixed, cap'n.'

'Everything? That's wonderful. That house all right?'

'Everyting okay.' Quarrel repeated, his voice careful. 'See yo as yo done said, cap'n.'

'Fine,' said Bond. He was impressed with Quarrel's efficiency and a sense of security. He put down the telephone and went out on to the balcony.

The sun was just setting. The wave of violet shadow was creeping down towards the town and the harbour. When it hits the town, thought Bond, the lights will go on. It happened as he had expected. Above him there was the noise of a plane. It came into sight, a Super Constellation, the same flight that Bond had been on the night before. Bond watched it sweep out over the sea and then turn and come in to land at the Palisadoes airport. What a long way he had come since that moment, only twenty-four hours before, when the door of the plane had clanged open and the loudspeaker had said, 'This is Kingston, Jamaica. Will passengers please remain seated until the aircraft has been cleared by the Health Authorities.'

Should he tell M how the picture had changed? Should he make a report to the Governor? Bond thought of the Governor and dismissed that idea. But what about M? Bond had his own cipher. He could easily send M a signal through the Colonial Office. What would he say to M? That Doctor No had sent him some poisoned fruit? But he didn't even know that it was poisoned, or, for the matter of that, that it had come from Doctor No. Bond could see M's face as he read the signal. He saw him press down the lever on the intercom: 'Chief of Staff, 007's gone round the bend. Says someone's been trying to feed him a poisoned banana. Fellow's lost his nerve. Been in hospital too long. Better call him home.'

Bond smiled to himself. He got up and rang down for another drink. It wouldn't be quite like that, of course. But still ... No, he'd wait until he had something more to show. Of course if something went badly wrong, and he hadn't sent a warning, he'd be in trouble. It was up to him to see that nothing did go wrong.

Bond drank his second drink and thought over the details of his plan. Then he went down and had dinner in the half-deserted dining-room and read the *Handbook of the West Indies*. By nine o'clock he was half asleep. He went back to his room and packed his bag ready for the morning. He telephoned down and arranged to be called at five-thirty. Then he bolted the door on the inside, and also shut and bolted the slatted jalousies across the windows. It would mean a hot, stuffy night. That couldn't be helped. Bond climbed naked under the single cotton sheet and turned over on his left side and slipped his right hand on to the butt of the Walther PPK under the pillow. In five minutes he was asleep.

The next thing Bond knew was that it was three o'clock in the morning. He knew it was three o'clock because the luminous dial of his watch was close to his face. He lay absolutely still. There was not a sound in the room. He strained his ears. Outside, too, it was deathly quiet. Far in the distance a dog started to bark. Other dogs joined in and there was a brief hysterical chorus which stopped as suddenly as it had begun. Then it was quite quiet again. The moon coming through the slats in the jalousies threw black and white bars across the corner of the room next to his bed. It was as if he was lying in a cage. What had woken him up? Bond moved softly, preparing to slip out of bed.

Bond stopped moving. He stopped as dead as a live man can.

Something had stirred on his right ankle. Now it was moving up the inside of his shin. Bond could feel the hairs on his leg being parted. It was an insect of some sort. A very big one. It was long, five or six inches — as long as his hand. He could feel dozens of tiny feet lightly touching his skin. What was it?

Then Bond heard something he had never heard before — the sound of the hair on his head rasping up on the pillow. Bond analysed the noise. It couldn't be! It simply couldn't! Yes, his hair was standing on end. Bond could even feel the cool air reaching his scalp between the hairs. How extraordinary! How very extraordinary! He had always thought it was a figure of speech. But why? Why was it happening to him?

The thing on his leg moved. Suddenly Bond realized that he was afraid, terrified. His instincts, even before they had communicated with his brain, had told his body that he had a centipede on him.

Bond lay frozen. He had once seen a tropical centipede in a bottle of spirit on the shelf in a museum. It had been pale brown and very flat and five or six inches long — about the length of this one. On either side of the blunt head there had been curved poison claws. The label on the bottle had said that its poison was mortal if it hit an artery. Bond had looked curiously at the corkscrew of dead cuticle and had moved on.

The centipede had reached his knee. It was starting up his thigh. Whatever happened he mustn't move, mustn't even tremble. Bond's whole consciousness had drained down to the two rows of softly creeping feet. Now they had reached his flank. God, it was turning down towards his groin! Bond set his teeth. Supposing it liked the warmth there! Supposing it tried to crawl into the crevices! Could he stand it? Supposing it chose that place to bite? Bond could feel it questing amongst the first hairs. It tickled.

The skin on Bond's belly fluttered. There was nothing he could do to control it. But now the thing was turning up and along his stomach. Its feet were gripping tighter to prevent it falling. Now it was at his heart. If it bit there, surely it would kill him. The centipede trampled steadily on through the thin hairs on Bond's right breast up to his collar bone. It stopped. What was it doing? Bond could feel the blunt head questing blindly to and fro. What was it looking for? Was there room between his skin and the sheet for it to get through? Dare he lift the sheet an inch to help it. No. Never! The animal was at the base of his jugular. Perhaps it was intrigued by the heavy pulse there. Christ, if only he could control the pumping of his blood. Damn you! Bond tried to communicate with the centipede. It's nothing. It's not dangerous, that pulse. It means you no harm. Get on out into the fresh air!

As if the beast had heard, it moved on up the column of the neck and into the stubble on Bond's chin. Now it was at the corner of his mouth, tickling madly. On it went, up along the nose. Now he could feel its whole weight and length. Softly Bond closed his eyes. Two by two the pairs of feet, moving alternately, trampled across his right eyelid. When it got off his eye, should he take a chance and shake it off — rely on its feet slipping in his sweat? No, for God's sake! The grip of the feet was endless. He might shake one lot off, but not the rest.

With incredible deliberation the huge insect ambled across Bond's forehead. It stopped below the hair. What the hell was it doing now? Bond could feel it nuzzling at his skin. It was drinking! Drinking the beads of salt sweat. Bond was sure of it. For minutes it hardly moved. Bond felt weak with the tension. He could feel the sweat pouring off the rest of his body on to the sheet. In a second his limbs would start to tremble. He could feel it coming on.

He would start to shake with an ague of fear. Could he control it, could he? Bond lay and waited, the breath coming softly through his open, snarling mouth.

The centipede started to move again. It walked into the forest of hair. Bond could feel the roots being pushed aside as it forced its way along. Would it like it there? Would it settle down? How did centipedes sleep? Curled up or at full length? The tiny millipedes he had known as a child, the ones that always seemed to find their way up the plughole into the empty bath, curled up when you touched them. Now it had come to where his head lay against the sheet. Would it walk out on to the pillow or would it stay on in the warm forest? The centipede stopped. Out! OUT! Bond's nerves screamed at it.

The centipede stirred. Slowly it walked out of his hair on to the pillow.

Bond waited a second. Now he could hear the rows of feet picking softly at the cotton. It was a tiny scraping noise, like soft fingernails.

With a crash that shook the room Bond's body jack-knifed out of bed and on to the floor.

At once Bond was on his feet and at the door. He turned on the light. He found he was shaking uncontroll-ably. He staggered to the bed. There it was, crawling out of sight over the edge of the pillow. Bond's first instinct was to twitch the pillow on to the floor. He controlled himself, waiting for his nerves to quieten. Then softly, deliberately, he picked up the pillow by one corner and walked into the middle of the room and dropped it. The centipede came out from under the pillow. It started to make swiftly away across the matting. Now Bond was uninterested. He looked round for something to kill it with. Slowly he went and picked up a shoe and came back. The danger was past. His mind was now wondering how the centipede had got into his bed. He lifted the shoe and slowly, almost carelessly, smashed it down. He heard the crack of the hard carapace.

Bond lifted the shoe.

The centipede was whipping from side to side in its agony — five inches of grey-brown, shiny death. Bond hit it again. It burst open, yellowly.

Bond dropped the shoe and ran for the bathroom and was violently sick.

VII

NIGHT PASSAGE

'Bʏ the way, Quarrel —' Bond dared a bus with 'Brown Bomber' painted above its windshield. The bus pulled over and roared on down the hill towards Kingston sounding a furious chord on its triple windhorn to restore the driver's ego, — 'what do you know about centipedes?'

'Centipedes, cap'n?' Quarrel squinted sideways for a clue to the question. Bond's expression was casual. 'Well, we got some bad ones here in Jamaica. Tree, fo, five inches long. Dey kills folks. Dey mos'ly lives in de old houses in Kingston. Dey loves de rotten wood an' de mouldy places. Dey hoperates mos'ly at night. Why, cap'n? Yo seen one?'

Bond dodged the question. He had also not told Quarrel about the fruit. Quarrel was a tough man, but there was no reason to sow the seeds of fear. 'Would you expect to find one in a modern house, for instance? In your shoe, or in a drawer, or in your bed?'

'Nossir.' Quarrel's voice was definite. 'Not hunless dem put dere a purpose. Dese hinsecks love de holes and de crannies. Dey not love de clean places. Dey dirty-livin' hinsecks. Mebbe yo find dem in de bush, under logs an' stones. But never in de bright places.'

'I see.' Bond changed the subject. 'By the way, did those two men get off all right in the Sunbeam?'

'Sho ting, cap'n. Dey plenty happy wid de job. An' dey look plenty like yo an' me, cap'n.' Quarrel chuckled. He glanced at Bond and said hesitantly, 'I fears dey weren't very good citizens, cap'n. Had to find de two men wheres I could. Me, I'm a beggarman, cap'n. An' fo you, cap'n, I get a misrable no-good whiteman from Betsy's.'

'Who's Betsy?'

'She done run de lousiest brothel in town, cap'n,' Quarrel spat emphatically out of the window. 'Dis white-man, he does de book-keepin'.'

Bond laughed. 'So long as he can drive a car. I only hope they get to Montego all right.'

'Don' yo worry,' Quarrel misunderstood Bond's concern. 'I say I tell de police dey stole de car if dey don'.'

They were at the saddleback at Stony Hill where the Junction Road dives down through fifty S-bends towards the North Coast. Bond put the little Austin A.30 into second gear and let it coast. The sun was coming up over the Blue Mountain peak and dusty shafts of gold lanced into the plunging valley. There were few people on the road — an occasional man going off to his precipitous smallholding on the flank of a hill, his three-foot steel cutlass dangling from his right hand, chewing at his breakfast, a foot of raw sugar cane held in his left, or a woman sauntering up the road with a covered basket of fruit or vegetables for Stony Hill market, her shoes on her head, to be donned when she got near the village. It was a savage, peaceful scene that had hardly changed, except for the surface of the road, for two hundred years or more. Bond almost smelled the dung of the mule train in which he would have been riding over from Port Royal to visit the garrison at Morgan's Harbour in 1750.

Quarrel interrupted his thoughts. 'Cap'n,' he said apologetically, 'beggin' yo pardon, but kin yo tell me what yo have in mind for we? I'se bin puzzlin' an' Ah caint seem to figger hout yo game.'

'I've hardly figured it out myself, Quarrel.' Bond changed up into top and dawdled through the cool, beautiful glades of Castleton Gardens. 'I told you I'm here because Commander Strangways and his secretary have disappeared. Most people think they've gone off together. I think they've been murdered.'

'Dat so?' said Quarrel unemotionally. 'Who yo tink done hit?'

'I've come to agree with you. I think Doctor No, that Chinaman on Crab Key, had it done. Strangways was poking his nose into this man's affairs — something to do with the bird sanctuary. Doctor No has this mania for privacy. You were telling me so yourself. Seems he'll do anything to stop people climbing over his wall. Mark you, it's not more than a guess about Doctor No. But some funny things happened in the last twenty-four hours. That's why I sent the Sunbeam over to Montego, to lay a false scent. And that's why we're going to hide out at Beau Desert for a few days.'

'Den what, cap'n?'

'First of all I want you to get me absolutely fit — the way you trained me the last time I was here. Remember?'

'Sho, cap'n. Ah kin do dat ting.'

'And then I was thinking you and me might go and take a look at Crab Key.'

Quarrel whistled. The whistle ended on a downward note.

'Just sniff around. We needn't get too close to Doctor No's end. I want to take a look at this bird sanctuary. See for myself what happened to the wardens' camp. If we find anything wrong, we'll get away again and come back by the front door — with some soldiers to help. Have a full-dress inquiry. Can't do that until we've got something to go on. What do you think?'

Quarrel dug into his hip pocket for a cigarette. He made a fuss about lighting it. He blew a cloud of smoke through his nostrils and watched it whip out of the window. He said, 'Cap'n, Ah tink yo'se plumb crazy to trespass hon dat island.' Quarrel had wound himself up. He paused. There was no comment. He looked sideways at the quiet profile. He said more quietly, in an embarrassed voice, 'Jess one ting, cap'n. Ah have some folks back in da Caymans. Would yo consider takin' hout a life hinsurance hon me afore we sail?'

Bond glanced affectionately at the strong brown face. It had a deep cleft of worry between the eyes. 'Of course, Quarrel. I'll fix it at Port Maria tomorrow. We'll make it big, say five thousand pounds. Now then, how shall we go? Canoe?'

'Dat's right, cap'n.' Quarrel's voice was reluctant. 'We need a calm sea an' a light wind. Come hin on de Nor-easterly Trades. Mus' be a dark night. Dey startin' right now. By end of da week we git da secon' moon quarter. Where yo reckon to land, cap'n?'

'South shore near the mouth of the river. Then we'll go up the river to the lake. I'm sure that's where the wardens' camp was. So as to have fresh water and be able to get down to the sea to fish.'

Quarrel grunted without enthusiasm. 'How long we stayin', cap'n? Caint take a whole lot of food wit us. Bread, cheese, salt pork. No tobacco — caint risk da smoke an' light. Dat's mighty rough country, cap'n. Marsh an' mangrove.'

Bond said: 'Better plan for three days. Weather may break and stop us getting off for a night or two. Couple of good hunting knives. I'll take a gun. You never can tell.'

'No, sir,' said Quarrel emphatically. He relapsed into a brooding silence which lasted until they got to Port Maria.

They went through the little town and on round the

headland to Morgan's Harbour. It was just as Bond remembered — the sugar-loaf of the Isle of Surprise rising out of the calm bay, the canoes drawn up beside the mounds of empty conch shells, the distant boom of the surf on the reef which had so nearly been his grave. Bond, his mind full of memories, took the car down the little side road and through the cane fields in the middle of which the gaunt ruin of the old Great House of Beau Desert Plantation stood up like a stranded galleon.

They came to the gate leading to the bungalow. Quarrel got out and opened the gate, and Bond drove through and pulled up in the yard behind the white single-storeyed house. It was very quiet. Bond walked round the house and across the lawn to the edge of the sea. Yes, there it was, the stretch of deep, silent water — the submarine path he had taken to the Isle of Surprise. It sometimes came back to him in nightmares. Bond stood looking at it and thinking of Solitaire, the girl he had brought back, torn and bleeding, from that sea. He had carried her across the lawn to the house. What had happened to her? Where was she? Brusquely Bond turned and walked back into the house, driving the phantoms away from him.

It was eight-thirty. Bond unpacked his few things and changed into sandals and shorts. Soon there was the delicious smell of coffee and frying bacon. They ate their breakfast while Bond fixed his training routine — up at seven, swim a quarter of a mile, breakfast, an hour's sunbathing, run a mile, swim again, lunch, sleep, sunbathe, swim a mile, hot bath and massage, dinner and asleep by nine.

After breakfast the routine began.

Nothing interrupted the grinding week except a brief story in the *Daily Gleaner* and a telegram from Pleydell-Smith. The *Gleaner* said that a Sunbeam Talbot, H. 2473, had been involved in a fatal accident on the Devil's

Racecourse, a stretch of winding road between Spanish Town and Ocho Rios — on the Kingston–Montego route. A runaway lorry, whose driver was being traced, had crashed into the Sunbeam as it came round a bend. Both vehicles had left the road and hurtled into the ravine below. The two occupants of the Sunbeam, Ben Gibbons of Harbour Street, and Josiah Smith, no address, had been killed. A Mr Bond, an English visitor, who had been lent the car, was asked to contact the nearest police station.

Bond burned that copy of the *Gleaner*. He didn't want to upset Quarrel.

With only one day to go, the telegram came from Pleydell-Smith. It said:

EACH OBJECT CONTAINED ENOUGH CYANIDE TO KILL A HORSE STOP SUGGEST YOU CHANGE YOUR GROCER STOP GOOD LUCK SMITH

Bond also burned the telegram.

Quarrel hired a canoe and they spent three days sailing it. It was a clumsy shell cut out of a single giant cotton tree. It had two thin thwarts, two heavy paddles and a small sail of dirty canvas. It was a blunt instrument Quarrel was pleased with it.

'Seven, eight hours, cap'n,' he said. 'Den we bring down de sail an' use de paddles. Less target for de radar to see.'

The weather held. The forecast from Kingston radio was good. The nights were black as sin. The two men got in their stores. Bond fitted himself out with cheap black canvas jeans and a dark blue shirt and rope-soled shoes.

The last evening came. Bond was glad he was on his way. He had only once been out of the training camp — to get the stores and arrange Quarrel's insurance — and he was chafing to get out of the stable and on to the track He admitted to himself that this adventure excited him

It had the right ingredients — physical exertion, mystery, and a ruthless enemy. He had a good companion. His cause was just. There might also be the satisfaction of throwing the 'holiday in the sun' back in M's teeth. That had rankled. Bond didn't like being coddled.

The sun blazed beautifully into its grave.

Bond went into his bedroom and took out his two guns and looked at them. Neither was a part of him as the Beretta had been — an extension of his right hand — but he already knew them as better weapons. Which should he take? Bond picked up each in turn, hefting them in his hand. It had to be the heavier Smith & Wesson. There would be no close shooting, if there was any shooting, on Crab Key. Heavy, long-range stuff — if anything. The brutal, stumpy revolver had an extra twenty-five yards over the Walther. Bond fitted the holster into the waistband of his jeans and clipped in the gun. He put twenty spare rounds in his pocket. Was it over-insurance to take all this metal on what might only be tropical picnic?

Bond went to the icebox and took a pint of Canadian Club Blended Rye and some ice and soda-water and went and sat in the garden and watched the last light flame and die.

The shadows crept from behind the house and marched across the lawn and enveloped him. The Undertaker's Wind that blows at night from the centre of the island, clattered softly in the tops of the palm trees. The frogs began to tinkle among the shrubs. The fireflies, the 'blink-a-blinks', as Quarrel called them, came out and began flashing their sexual morse. For a moment the melancholy of the tropical dusk caught at Bond's heart. He picked up the bottle and looked at it. He had drunk a quarter of it. He poured another big slug into his glass and added some ice. What was he drinking for? Because of the thirty miles of black sea he had to cross tonight?

Because he was going into the unknown? Because of Doctor No?

Quarrel came up from the beach. 'Time, cap'n.'

Bond swallowed his drink and followed the Cayman Islander down to the canoe. It was rocking quietly in the water, its bows on the sand. Quarrel went aft and Bond climbed into the space between the forrard thwart and the bows. The sail, wrapped round the short mast, was at his back. Bond took up his paddle and pushed off, and they turned slowly and headed out for the break in the softly creaming waves that was the passage through the reef. They paddled easily, in unison, the paddles turning in their hands so that they did not leave the water on the forward stroke. The small waves slapped softly against the bows. Otherwise they made no noise. It was dark. Nobody saw them go. They just left the land and went off across the sea.

Bond's only duty was to keep paddling. Quarrel did the steering. At the opening through the reef there was a swirl and suck of conflicting currents and they were in amongst the jagged niggerheads and coral trees, bared like fangs by the swell. Bond could feel the strength of Quarrel's great sweeps with the paddle as the heavy craft wallowed and plunged. Again and again Bond's own paddle thudded against rock, and once he had to hold on as the canoe hit a buried mass of brain coral and slid off again. Then they were through, and far below the boat there were indigo patches of sand and around them the solid oily feel of deep water.

'Okay, cap'n,' said Quarrel softly. Bond shipped his paddle and got down off one knee and sat with his back to the thwart. He heard the scratching of Quarrel's nail against canvas as he unwrapped the sail and then the sharp flap as it caught the breeze. The canoe straightened and began to move. It tilted slowly. There was a so hiss under the bows. A handful of spray tossed up into Bond's face. The wind of their movement was cool and would soon get cold. Bond hunched up his knees and put his arms round them. The wood was already beginning to bite into his buttocks and his back. It crossed his mind that it was going to be the hell of a long and uncomfortable night.

In the darkness ahead Bond could just make out the rim of the world. Then came a layer of black haze above which the stars began, first sparsely and then merging into a dense bright carpet. The Milky Way soared overhead. How many stars? Bond tried counting a finger's length and was soon past the hundred. The stars lit the sea into a faint grey road and then arched away over the tip of the mast towards the black silhouette of Jamaica. Bond looked back. Behind the hunched figure of Quarrel there was a faraway cluster of lights which would be Port Maria. Already they were a couple of miles out. Soon they would be a tenth of the way, then a quarter, then half. That would be around midnight when Bond would take over. Bond sighed and put his head down to his knees and closed his eyes.

He must have slept because he was awakened by the clonk of a paddle against the boat. He lifted his arm to show that he had heard and glanced at the luminous blaze of his watch. Twelve-fifteen. Stiffly he unbent his legs and turned and scrambled over the thwart.

'Sorry, Quarrel,' he said, and it was odd to hear his voice. 'You ought to have shaken me up before.'

'Hit don signify, cap'n,' said Quarrel with a grey glint of teeth. 'Do yo good to sleep.'

Gingerly they slipped past each other and Bond settled in the stern and picked up the paddle. The sail was secured to a bent nail beside him. It was flapping. Bond brought the bows into the wind and edged them round so that the North Star was directly over Quarrel's bent head in the bows. For a time this would be fun. There was something to do.

There was no change in the night except that it seemed darker and emptier. The pulse of the sleeping sea seemed slower. The heavy swell was longer and the troughs deeper. They were running through a patch of phosphorus that winked at the bows and dripped jewels when Bond lifted the paddle out of the water. How safe it was, slipping through the night in this ridiculously vulnerable little boat. How kind and soft the sea could be. A covey of flying fish broke the surface in front of the bows and scattered like shrapnel. Some kept going for a time beside the canoe, flying as much as twenty yards before they dived into the wall of the swell. Was some bigger fish after them or did they think the canoe was a fish, or were they just playing? Bond thought of what was going on in the hundreds of fathoms below the boat, the big fish, the shark and barracuda and tarpon and sailfish quietly cruising, the shoals of kingfish and mackerel and bonito and, far below in the grey twilight of the great depths, the phosphorous jellied boneless things that were never seen, the fifty-foot squids, with eyes a foot wide, that streamed along like zeppelins, the last real monsters of the sea, whose size was only known from the fragments found inside whales. What would happen if a wave caught the canoe broadside and capsized them? How long would they last? Bond took an ounce more pains with his steering and put the thought aside.

One o'clock, two o'clock, three, four. Quarrel awoke and stretched. He called softly to Bond, 'Ah smells land, cap'n.' Soon there was a thickening of the darkness ahead. The low shadow slowly took on the shape of a huge swimming rat. A pale moon rose slowly behind them. Now the island showed distinctly, a couple of miles away, and there was the distant grumble of surf.

They changed places. Quarrel brought down the sail and they took up the paddles. For at least another mile, thought Bond, they would be invisible in the troughs of the waves. Not even radar would distinguish them from the crests. It was the last mile they would have to hurry over with the dawn not far off.

Now he too could smell the land. It had no particular scent. It was just something new in the nose after hours of clean sea. He could make out the white fringe of surf. The swell subsided and the waves became choppier. 'Now, cap'n,' called Quarrel, and Bond, the sweat already dropping off his chin, dug deeper and more often. God, it was hard work! The hulking log of wood which had sped along so well under the sail now seemed hardly to move. The wave at the bows was only a ripple. Bond's shoulders were aching like fire. The one knee he was resting on was beginning to bruise. His hands were cramped on the clumsy shaft of a paddle made of lead.

It was incredible, but they were coming up with the reef. Patches of sand showed deep under the boat. Now the surf was a roar. They followed along the edge of the reef, looking for an opening. A hundred yards inside the reef, breaking the sandline, was the shimmer of water running inland. The river! So the landfall had been all right. The wall of surf broke up. There was a patch of black oily current swelling over hidden coral heads. The nose of the canoe turned towards it and into it. There was a turmoil of water and a series of grating thuds, and then a sudden rush forward into peace and the canoe was moving slowly across a smooth mirror towards the shore.

Quarrel steered the boat towards the lee of a rocky promontory where the beach ended. Bond wondered why the beach didn't shine white under the thin moon. When they grounded and Bond climbed stiffly out he understood why. The beach was black. The sand was soft and wonderful to the feet but it must have been formed out of volcanic rock, pounded over the centuries, and Bond's naked feet on it looked like white crabs.

They made haste. Quarrel took three short lengths of thick bamboo out of the boat and laid them up the flat beach. They heaved the nose of the canoe on to the first and pushed the boat up the rollers. After each yard of progress, Bond picked up the back roller and brought it to the front. Slowly the canoe moved up the sand until at last it was over the back tideline and among the rocks and turtle grass and low sea-grape bushes. They pushed it another twenty yards inland into the beginning of the mangrove. There they covered it with dried seaweed and bits of driftwood from the tideline. Then Quarrel cut lengths of screwpalm and went back over their tracks, sweeping and tidying.

It was still dark, but the breath of grey in the east would soon be turning to pearl. It was five o'clock. They were dead tired. They exchanged a few words and Quarrel went off among the rocks on the promontory. Bond scooped out a depression in the fine dry sand under a thick bush of sea-grape. There were a few hermit crabs beside his bed. He picked up as many as he could find and hurled them into the mangrove. Then, not caring what other animals or insects might come to his smell and his warmth, he lay down full length in the sand and rested his head on his arm.

He was at once asleep.

VIII

THE ELEGANT VENUS

BOND awoke lazily. The feel of the sand reminded him where he was. He glanced at his watch. Ten o'clock. The sun through the round thick leaves of the sea-grape was already hot. A larger shadow moved across the dappled sand in front of his face. Quarrel? Bond shifted his head and peered through the fringe of leaves and grass that concealed him from the beach. He stiffened. His heart missed a beat and then began pounding so that he had to breathe deeply to quieten it. His eyes, as he stared through the blades of grass, were fierce slits.

It was a naked girl, with her back to him. She was not quite naked. She wore a broad leather belt round her waist with a hunting knife in a leather sheath at her right hip. The belt made her nakedness extraordinarily erotic. She stood not more than five yards away on the tideline looking down at something in her hand. She stood in the classical relaxed pose of the nude, all the weight on the right leg and the left knee bent and turning slightly inwards, the head to one side as she examined the things in her hand.

It was a beautiful back. The skin was a very light uniform *café au lait* with the sheen of dull satin. The gentle curve of the backbone was deeply indented, suggesting more powerful muscles than is usual in a woman, and the behind was almost as firm and rounded as a boy's. The legs were straight and beautiful and no pinkness showed under the slightly lifted left heel. She was not a coloured girl.

Her hair was ash blonde. It was cut to the shoulders and hung there and along the side of her bent cheek in thick wet strands. A green diving mask was pushed back above her forehead, and the green rubber thong bound her hair at the back.

The whole scene, the empty beach, the green and blue sea, the naked girl with the strands of fair hair, reminded Bond of something. He searched his mind. Yes, she was Botticelli's Venus, seen from behind.

How had she got there? What was she doing? Bond looked up and down the beach. It was not black, he now saw, but a deep chocolate brown. To the right he could see as far as the river mouth, perhaps five hundred yards away. The beach was empty and featureless except for a scattering of small pinkish objects. There were a lot of them, shells of some sort Bond supposed, and they looked decorative against the dark brown background. He looked to the left, to where, twenty yards away, the rocks of the small headland began. Yes, there was a yard or two of groove in the sand where a canoe had been drawn up into the shelter of the rocks. It must have been a light one or she couldn't have drawn it up alone. Perhaps the girl wasn't alone. But there was only one set of footprints leading down from the rocks to the sea and another set coming out of the sea and up the beach to where she now stood on the tideline. Did she live here, or had she too sailed over from Jamaica that night? Hell of a thing for a girl to do. Anyway, what in God's name *was* she doing here?

As if to answer him, the girl made a throwaway gesture of the right hand and scattered a dozen shells on the

sand beside her. They were violet pink and seemed to
Bond to be the same as he had noticed on the beach. The
girl looked down into her left hand and began to whistle
softly to herself. There was a happy note of triumph in the
whistle. She was whistling 'Marion', a plaintive little
calypso that has now been cleaned up and made famous
outside Jamaica. It had always been one of Bond's
favourites. It went:

> All day, all night, Marion,
> Sittin' by the seaside siftin' sand ...

The girl broke off to stretch her arms out in a deep
yawn. Bond smiled to himself. He wet his lips and took
up the refrain:

> 'The water from her eyes could sail a boat,
> The hair on her head could tie a goat ...'

The hands flew down and across her chest. The muscles
of her behind bunched with tension. She was listening,
her head, still hidden by the curtain of hair, cocked to
one side.

Hesitantly she began again. The whistle trembled and
died. At the first note of Bond's echo, the girl whirled
round. She didn't cover her body with the two classical
gestures. One hand flew downwards, but the other,
instead of hiding her breasts, went up to her face, covering
it below the eyes, now wide with fear. 'Who's that?' The
words came out in a terrified whisper.

Bond got to his feet and stepped out through the sea-
grape. He stopped on the edge of the grass. He held his
hands open at his sides to show they were empty. He
smiled cheerfully at her. 'It's only me. I'm another
trespasser. Don't be frightened.'

The girl dropped her hand down from her face. It went
to the knife at her belt. Bond watched the fingers curl

round the hilt. He looked up at her face. Now he realized why her hand had instinctively gone to it. It was a beautiful face, with wide-apart deep blue eyes under lashes paled by the sun. The mouth was wide and when she stopped pursing the lips with tension they would be full. It was a serious face and the jawline was determined — the face of a girl who fends for herself. And once, reflected Bond, she had failed to fend. For the nose was badly broken, smashed crooked like a boxer's. Bond stiffened with revolt at what had happened to this supremely beautiful girl. No wonder this was her shame and not the beautiful firm breasts that now jutted towards him without concealment.

The eyes examined him fiercely. 'Who are you? What are you doing here?' There was the slight lilt of a Jamaican accent. The voice was sharp and accustomed to being obeyed.

'I'm an Englishman. I'm interested in birds.'

'Oh,' the voice was doubtful. The hand still rested on the knife. 'How long have you been watching me? How did you get here?'

'Ten minutes, but no more answers until you tell me who *you* are.'

'I'm no one in particular. I come from Jamaica. I collect shells.'

'I came in a canoe. Did you?'

'Yes. Where is your canoe?'

'I've got a friend with me. We've hidden it in the mangroves.'

'There are no marks of a canoe landing.'

'We're careful. We covered them up. Not like you.' Bond gestured towards the rocks. 'You ought to take more trouble. Did you use a sail? Right up to the reef?'

'Of course. Why not? I always do.'

'Then they'll know you're here. They've got radar.'

'They've never caught me yet.' The girl took her hand away from her knife. She reached up and stripped off the diving mask and stood swinging it. She seemed to think she had the measure of Bond. She said, with some of the sharpness gone from her voice, 'What's your name?'

'Bond. James Bond. What's yours?'

She reflected. 'Rider.'

'What Rider?'

'Honeychile.'

Bond smiled.

'What's so funny about it?'

'Nothing. Honeychile Rider. It's a pretty name.'

She unbent. 'People call me "Honey".'

'Well, I'm glad to meet you.'

The prosaic phrase seemed to remind her of her nakedness. She blushed. She said uncertainly, 'I must get dressed.' She looked down at the scattered shells around her feet. She obviously wanted to pick them up. Perhaps she realized that the movement might be still more revealing than her present pose. She said sharply, 'You're not to touch those while I'm gone.'

Bond smiled at the childish challenge. 'Don't worry, I'll look after them.'

The girl looked at him doubtfully and then turned and walked stiff-legged over to the rocks and disappeared behind them.

Bond walked the few steps down the beach and bent and picked up one of the shells. It was alive and the two halves were shut tight. It appeared to be some kind of a cockle, rather deeply ribbed and coloured a mauve-pink. Along both edges of the hinge, thin horns stood out, about half a dozen to each side. It didn't seem to Bond a very distinguished shell. He replaced it carefully with the others.

He stood looking down at the shells and wondering. Was she really collecting them? It certainly looked like it. But what a risk to take to get them — the voyage over alone in the canoe and then back again. And she seemed to realize that this was a dangerous place. 'They've never caught me yet.' What an extraordinary girl. Bond's heart warmed and his senses stirred as he thought of her. Already, as he had found so often when people had deformities, he had almost forgotten her broken nose. It had somehow slipped away behind his memory of her eyes and her mouth and her amazingly beautiful body. Her imperious attitude and her quality of attack were exciting. The way she had reached for her knife to defend herself! She was like an animal whose cubs are threatened. Where did she live? Who were her parents? There was something uncared for about her — a dog that nobody wants to pet. Who was she?

Bond heard her footsteps riffling the sand. He turned to look at her. She was dressed almost in rags — a faded brown shirt with torn sleeves and a knee-length patched brown cotton skirt held in place by the leather belt with the knife. She had a canvas knapsack slung over one shoulder. She looked like a principal girl dressed as Man Friday.

She came up with him and at once went down on one knee and began picking up the live shells and stowing them in the knapsack.

Bond said, 'Are those rare?'

She sat back on her haunches and looked up at him. She surveyed his face. Apparently she was satisfied. 'You promise you won't tell anybody? Swear?'

'I promise,' said Bond.

'Well then, yes, they are rare. Very. You can get five dollars for a perfect specimen. In Miami. That's where I deal with. They're called *Venus elegans* — The Elegant Venus.' Her eyes sparkled up at him with excitement. 'This morning I found what I wanted. The bed where they live,' she waved towards the sea. 'You wouldn't find it though,' she added with sudden carefulness. 'It's very deep and hidden away. I doubt if you could dive that deep. And anyway,' she looked happy, 'I'm going to clear the whole bed today. You'd only get the imperfect ones if you came back here.'

Bond laughed. 'I promise I won't steal any. I really don't know anything about shells. Cross my heart.'

She stood up, her work completed. 'What about these birds of yours? What sort are they? Are they valuable too? I won't tell either if you tell me. I only collect shells.'

'They're called roseate spoonbills,' said Bond. 'Sort of pink stork with a flat beak. Ever seen any?'

'Oh, *those*,' she said scornfully. 'There used to be thousands of them here. But you won't find many now. They scared them all away.' She sat down on the sand and put her arms round her knees, proud of her superior knowledge and now certain that she had nothing to fear from this man.

Bond sat down a yard away. He stretched out and turned towards her, resting on his elbow. He wanted to preserve the picnic atmosphere and try to find out more about this queer, beautiful girl. He said, easily, 'Oh, really. What happened? Who did it?'

She shrugged impatiently. 'The people here did it. I don't know who they are. There's a Chinaman. He doesn't like birds or something. He's got a dragon. He sent the dragon after the birds and scared them away. The dragon burned up their nesting places. There used to be two men who lived with the birds and looked after them. They got scared away too, or killed or something.'

It all seemed quite natural to her. She gave the facts indifferently, staring out to sea.

Bond said, 'This dragon. What kind is he? Have you ever seen him?'

'Yes, I've seen him.' She screwed up her eyes and made a wry face as if she was swallowing bitter medicine. She looked earnestly at Bond to make him share her feelings. 'I've been coming here for about a year, looking for shells and exploring. I only found these,' she waved at the beach, 'about a month ago. On my last trip. But I've found plenty of other good ones. Just before Christmas I thought I'd explore the river. I went up it to the top, where the birdmen had their camp. It was all broken up. It was getting late and I decided to spend the night there. In the middle of the night I woke up. The dragon was coming by only a few chains away from me. It had two great glaring eyes and a long snout. It had sort of short wings and a pointed tail. It was all black and gold.' She frowned at the expression on Bond's face. 'There was a full moon. I could see it quite clearly. It went by me. It was making a sort of roaring noise. It went over the marsh and came to some thick mangrove and it simply climbed over the bushes and went on. A whole flock of birds got up in front of it and suddenly a lot of fire came out of its mouth and it burned a lot of them up and all the trees they'd been roosting in. It was horrible. The most horrible thing I've ever seen.'

The girl leant sideways and peered at Bond's face. She sat up straight again and stared obstinately out to sea. 'I can see you don't believe me,' she said in a furious, tense voice. 'You're one of these city people. You don't believe anything. Ugh,' she shuddered with dislike of him.

Bond said reasonably, 'Honey, there just aren't such things as dragons in the world. You saw something that looked very like a dragon. I'm just wondering what it was.'

'How do you know there aren't such things as dragons?' Now he had made her really angry. 'Nobody lives on this end of the island. One could easily have survived here. Anyway, what do you think you know about animals and things? I've lived with snakes and things since I was a child. Alone. Have you ever seen a praying mantis eat her husband after they've made love? Have you ever seen the mongoose dance? Or an octopus dance? How long is a humming bird's tongue? Have you ever had a pet snake that wore a bell round its neck and rang it to wake you? Have you seen a scorpion get sunstroke and kill itself with its own sting? Have you seen the carpet of flowers under the sea at night? Do you know that a John Crow can smell a dead lizard a mile away ... ?' The girl had fired these questions like scornful jabs with a rapier. Now she stopped, out of breath. She said hopelessly, 'Oh, you're just city folk like all the rest.'

Bond said, 'Honey, now look here. You know these things. I can't help it that I live in towns. I'd like to know about your things too. I just haven't had that sort of life. I know other things instead. Like ...' Bond searched his mind. He couldn't think of anything as interesting as hers. He finished lamely, 'Like for instance that this Chinaman is going to be more interested in your visit this time. This time he's going to try and stop you getting away.' He paused and added, 'And me for the matter of that.'

She turned and looked at him with interest. 'Oh. Why? But then it doesn't really matter. One just hides during the day and gets away at night. He's sent dogs after me and even a plane. He hasn't got me yet.' She examined Bond with a new interest. 'Is it you he's after?'

'Well, yes,' admitted Bond. 'I'm afraid it is. You see we dropped the sail about two miles out so that their radar wouldn't pick us up. I think the Chinaman may have been expecting a visit from me. Your sail will have been reported and I'd bet anything he'll think your canoe was mine. I'd better go and wake my friend up and we'll talk it over. You'll like him. He's a Cayman Islander, name of Quarrel.'

The girl said, 'Well, I'm sorry if ... ' the sentence trailed away. Apologies wouldn't come easy to someone so much on the defensive. 'But after all I couldn't know, could I?' She searched his face.

Bond smiled into the questing blue eyes. He said reassuringly, 'Of course you couldn't. It's just bad luck — bad luck for you too. I don't suppose he minds too much about a solitary girl who collects shells. You can be sure they've had a good look at your footprints and found clues like that' — he waved at the scattered shells on the beach. 'But I'm afraid he'd take a different view of me. Now he'll try and hunt me down with everything he's got. I'm only afraid he may get you into the net in the process. Anyway,' Bond grinned reassuringly, 'we'll see what Quarrel has to say. You stay here.'

Bond got to his feet. He walked along the promontory and cast about him. Quarrel had hidden himself well. It took Bond five minutes to find him. He was lying in a grassy depression between two big rocks, half covered by a board of grey driftwood. He was still fast asleep, the brown head, stern in sleep, cradled on his forearm. Bond whistled softly and smiled as the eyes sprang wide open like an animal's. Quarrel saw Bond and scrambled to his feet, almost guiltily. He rubbed his big hands over his face as if he was washing it.

'Mornin', cap'n,' he said. 'Guess Ah been down deep. Dat China girl come to me.'

Bond smiled. 'I got something different,' he said. They sat down and Bond told him about Honeychile Rider and her shells and the fix they were in. 'And now it's eleven o'clock,' Bond added. 'And we've got to make a new plan.'

Quarrel scratched his head. He looked sideways at Bond. 'Yo don' plan we jess ditch dis girl?' he asked hopefully. 'Ain't nuttin to do wit we ...' Suddenly he stopped. His head swivelled round and pointed like a dog's. He held up a hand for silence, listening intently.

Bond held his breath. In the distance, to the eastwards, there was a faint droning.

Quarrel jumped to his feet. 'Quick, cap'n,' he said urgently. 'Dey's a comin'.'

IX

CLOSE SHAVES

TEN minutes later the bay was empty and immaculate. Small waves curled lazily in across the mirrored water inside the reef and flopped exhausted on the dark sand where the mauve shells glittered like shed toenails. The heap of discarded shells had gone and there was no longer any trace of footprints. Quarrel had cut branches of mangrove and had walked backwards sweeping carefully as he went. Where he had swept, the sand was of a different texture from the rest of the beach, but not too different as to be noticed from outside the reef. The girl's canoe had been pulled deeper among the rocks and covered with seaweed and driftwood.

Quarrel had gone back to the headland. Bond and the girl lay a few feet apart under the bush of sea-grape where Bond had slept, and gazed silently out across the water to the corner of the headland round which the boat would come.

The boat was perhaps a quarter of a mile away. From the slow pulse of the twin diesels Bond guessed that every cranny of the coastline was being searched for signs of them. It sounded a powerful boat. A big cabin cruiser, perhaps. What crew would it have? Who would be in command of the search? Doctor No? Unlikely. He would not trouble himself with this kind of police work.

From the west a wedge of cormorants appeared, flying

low over the sea beyond the reef. Bond watched them. They were the first evidence he had seen of the guanay colony at the other end of the island. These, according to Pleydell-Smith's description, would be scouts looking for the silver flash of the anchovy near the surface. Sure enough, as he watched, they began to back-pedal in the air and then go into shallow dives, hitting the water like shrapnel. Almost at once a fresh file appeared from the west, then another and another that merged into a long stream and then into a solid black river of birds. For minutes they darkened the skyline and then they were down on the water, covering several acres of it, screeching and fighting and plunging their heads below the surface, cropping at the solid field of anchovy like piranha fish feasting on a drowned horse.

Bond felt a gentle nudge from the girl. She gestured with her head. 'The Chinaman's hens getting their corn.'

Bond examined the happy, beautiful face. She had seemed quite unconcerned by the arrival of the search party. To her it was only the game of hide-and-seek she had played before. Bond hoped she wasn't going to get a shock.

The iron thud of the diesels was getting louder. The boat must be just behind the headland. Bond took a last look round the peaceful bay and then fixed his eyes, through the leaves and grass, on the point of the headland inside the reef.

The knife of white bows appeared. It was followed by ten yards of empty polished deck, glass windshields, a low raked cabin with a siren and a blunt radio mast, the glimpse of a man inside at the wheel, then the long flat well of the stern and a drooping red ensign. Converted M.T.B., British Government surplus?

Bond's eyes went to the two men standing in the stern.

They were pale-skinned negroes. They wore neat khaki ducks and shirts, broad belts, and deep visored baseball caps of yellow straw. They were standing side by side, bracing themselves against the slow swell. One of them was holding a long black loud-hailer with a wire attached. The other was manning a machine gun on a tripod. It looked to Bond like a Spandau.

The man with the loud-hailer let it fall so that it swung on a strap round his neck. He picked up a pair of binoculars and began inching them along the beach. The low murmur of his comments just reached Bond above the glutinous flutter of the diesels.

Bond watched the eyes of the binoculars begin with the headland and then sweep the sand. The twin eyes paused among the rocks and moved on. They came back. The murmur of comment rose to a jabber. The man handed the glasses to the machine gunner who took a quick glance through them and gave them back. The scanner shouted something to the helmsman. The cabin cruiser stopped and backed up. Now she lay outside the reef exactly opposite Bond and the girl. The scanner again levelled the binoculars at the rocks where the girl's canoe lay hidden. Again the excited jabber came across the water. Again the glasses were passed to the machine gunner who glanced through. This time he nodded decisively.

Bond thought: now we've had it. These men know their job.

Bond watched the machine gunner pull the bolt back to load. The double click came to him over the bubbling of the diesels.

The scanner lifted his loud-hailer and switched it on. The twanging echo of the amplifier moaned and screeched across the water. The man brought it up to his lips. The voice roared across the bay.

'Okay, folks! Come on out and you won't get hurt.'

It was an educated voice. There was a trace of American accent.

'Now then, folks,' the voice thundered, 'make it quick! We've seen where you came ashore. We've spotted the boat under the driftwood. We ain't fools an' we ain't fooling. Take it easy. Just walk out with your hands up. You'll be okay.'

Silence fell. The waves lapped softly on the beach. Bond could hear the girl breathing. The thin screeching of the cormorants came to them muted across the mile of sea. The diesels bubbled unevenly as the swell covered the exhaust pipe and then opened it again.

Softly Bond reached over to the girl and tugged at her sleeve. 'Come close,' he whispered. 'Smaller target.' He felt her warmth nearer to him. Her cheek brushed against his forearm. He whispered, 'Burrow into the sand. Wriggle. Every inch'll help.' He began to worm his body carefully deeper into the depression they had scooped out for themselves. He felt her do the same. He peered out. Now his eyes were only just above the skyline of the top of the beach.

The man was lifting his loud-hailer. The voice roared. 'Okay, folks! Just so as you'll know this thing isn't for show.' He lifted his thumb. The machine gunner trained his gun into the tops of the mangroves behind the beach. There came the swift rattling roar Bond had last heard coming from the German lines in the Ardennes. The bullets made the same old sound of frightened pigeons whistling overhead. Then there was silence.

In the distance Bond watched the black cloud of cormorants take to the air and begin circling. His eyes went back to the boat. The machine gunner was feeling the barrel of his gun to see if it had warmed. The two men exchanged some words. The scanner picked up his loud-hailer.

''Kay, folks,' he said harshly. 'You've been warned. This is it.'

Bond watched the snout of the Spandau swing and depress. The man was going to start with the canoe among the rocks. Bond whispered to the girl, 'All right, Honey. Stick it. Keep right down. It won't last long.' He felt her hand squeeze his arm. He thought: poor little bitch, she's in this because of me. He leant to the right to cover her head and pushed his face deep into the sand.

This time the crash of noise was terrific. The bullets howled into the corner of the headland. Fragments of splintered rock whined over the beach like hornets. Ricochets twanged and buzzed off into the hinterland. Behind it all there was the steady road-drill hammer of the gun.

There was a pause. New magazine, thought Bond. Now it's us. He could feel the girl clutching at him. Her body was trembling along his flank. Bond reached out an arm and pressed her to him.

The roar of the gun began again. The bullets came zipping along the tideline towards them. There was a succession of quick close thuds. The bush above them was being torn to shreds. 'Zwip. Zwip. Zwip.' It was as if the thong of a steel whip was cutting the bush to pieces. Bits scattered around them, slowly covering them. Bond could smell the cooler air that meant they were now lying in the open. Were they hidden by the leaves and debris? The bullets marched away along the shoreline. In less than a minute the racket stopped.

The silence sang. The girl whimpered softly. Bond hushed her and held her tighter.

The loud-hailer boomed. 'Okay, folks. If you still got ears, we'll be along soon to pick up the bits. And we'll be bringing the dogs. 'Bye for now.'

The slow thud of the diesel quickened. The engine accelerated into a hasty roar and through the fallen leaves Bond watched the stern of the launch settle lower in the water as it made off to the west. Within minutes it was out of earshot.

Bond cautiously raised his head. The bay was serene, the beach unmarked. All was as before except for the stench of cordite and the sour smell of blasted rock. Bond pulled the girl to her feet. There were tear streaks down her face. She looked at him aghast. She said solemnly, 'That was horrible. What did they do it for? We might have been killed.'

Bond thought, this girl has always had to fend for herself, but only against nature. She knows the world of animals and insects and fishes and she's got the better of it. But it's been a small world, bounded by the sun and the moon and the seasons. She doesn't know the big world of the smoke-filled room, of the bullion broker's parlour, of the corridors and waiting rooms of government offices, of careful meetings on park seats — she doesn't know about the struggle for big power and big money by the big men. She doesn't know that she's been swept out of her rock pool into the dirty waters.

He said, 'It's all right, Honey. They're just a lot of bad men who are frightened of us. We can manage them.' Bond put his arm round her shoulders, 'And you were wonderful. As brave as anything. Come on now, we'll look for Quarrel and make some plans. Anyway, it's time we had something to eat. What do you eat on these expeditions?'

They turned and walked up the beach to the headland. After a minute she said in a controlled voice, 'Oh, there's stacks of food about. Sea urchins mostly. And there are wild bananas and things. I eat and sleep for two days before I come out here. I don't need anything.'

Bond held her more closely. He dropped his arm as Quarrel appeared on the skyline. Quarrel scrambled down among the rocks. He stopped, looking down. They came up with him. The girl's canoe was sawn almost in half by the bullets. The girl gave a cry. She looked desperately at Bond, 'My boat! How am I to get back?'

'Don' you worry, missy,' Quarrel appreciated the loss of a canoe better than Bond. He guessed it might be most of the girl's capital. 'Cap'n fix you up wit' anudder. An' yo come back wit' we. Us got a fine boat in de mangrove. Hit not get broke. Ah's bin to see him.' Quarrel looked at Bond. Now his face was worried. 'But cap'n, yo sees what I means about dese folk. Dey mighty tough men an' dey means business. Dese dogs dey speak of. Dose is police-houns — Pinschers dey's called. Big bastards. Mah frens tell me as der's a pack of twenty or moh. We better make plans quick — an' good.'

'All right, Quarrel. But first we must have something to eat. And I'm damned if I'm going to be scared off the island before I've had a good look. We'll take Honey with us.' He turned to the girl. 'Is that all right with you, Honey? You'll be all right with us. Then we'll sail home together.'

The girl looked doubtfully at him. 'I guess there's no alternative. I mean, I'd love to go with you if I won't be in the way. I really don't want anything to eat. But will you take me home as soon as you can? I don't want to see any more of those people. How long are you going to be looking at these birds?'

Bond said evasively, 'Not long. I've got to find out what happened to them and why. Then we'll be off.' He looked at his watch. 'It's twelve now. You wait here. Have a bathe or something. Don't walk about leaving footprints. Come on, Quarrel, we'd better get that boat hidden.'

It was one o'clock before they were ready. Bond and Quarrel filled the canoe with stones and sand until it sank in a pool among the mangroves. They smeared over their footprints. The bullets had left so much litter behind the shoreline that they could do most of their walking on broken leaves and twigs. They ate some of their rations — avidly, the girl reluctantly — and climbed across the rocks and into the shallow water off-shore. Then they trudged along the shallows towards the river mouth three hundred yards away down the beach.

It was very hot. A harsh, baking wind had sprung up from the north-east. Quarrel said this wind blew daily the year round. It was vital to the guanera. It dried the guano. The glare from the sea and from the shiny green leaves of the mangroves was dazzling. Bond was glad he had taken trouble to get his skin hardened to the sun.

There was a sandy bar at the river mouth and a long deep stagnant pool. They could either get wet or strip. Bond said to the girl, 'Honey, we can't be shy on this trip. We'll keep our shirts on because of the sun. Wear what's sensible and walk behind us.' Without waiting for her reply the two men took off their trousers. Quarrel rolled them and packed them in the knapsack with the provisions and Bond's gun. They waded into the pool, Quarrel in front, then Bond, then the girl. The water came up to Bond's waist. A big silver fish leaped out of the pool and fell back with a splash. There were arrows on the surface where others fled out of their way. 'Tarpon,' commented Quarrel.

The pool converged into a narrow neck over which the mangroves touched. For a time they waded through a cool tunnel, and then the river broadened into a deep sluggish channel that meandered ahead among the giant spider-legs of the mangroves. The bottom was muddy and at each step their feet sank inches into slime. Small fish or shrimps wriggled and fled from under their feet, and every now and then they had to stoop to brush away leeches before they got hold. But otherwise it was easy going and quiet and cool among the bushes and, at least to Bond, it was a blessing to be out of the sun.

Soon, as they got away from the sea, it began to smell bad with the bad egg, sulphuretted hydrogen smell of marsh gas. The mosquitoes and sandflies began to find them. They liked Bond's fresh body. Quarrel told him to dip himself in the river water. 'Dem like dere meat wid salt on him,' he explained cheerfully. Bond took off his shirt and did as he was told. Then it was better and after a while Bond's nostrils even got used to the marsh gas, except when Quarrel's feet disturbed some aged pocket in the mud and a vintage bubble wobbled up from the bottom and burst stinking under his nose.

The mangroves became fewer and sparser and the river slowly opened out. The water grew shallower and the bottom firmer. Soon they came round a bend and into the open. Honey said, 'Better watch out now. We'll be easier to see. It goes on like this for about a mile. Then the river gets narrower until the lake. Then there's the sandspit the birdmen lived on.'

They stopped in the shadow of the mangrove tunnel and looked out. The river meandered sluggishly away from them towards the centre of the island. Its banks, fringed with low bamboo and sea-grape, would give only half shelter. From its western bank the ground rose slowly and then sharply up to the sugar-loaf about two miles away which was the guanera. Round the base of the mountain there was a scattering of Quonset huts. A zigzag of silver ran down the hillside to the huts — a Decauderville Track, Bond guessed, to bring the guano from the diggings down to the crusher and separator. The summit of the sugar-loaf was white, as if with snow. From the peak flew a smoky flag of guano dust. Bond could see the black dots of cormorants against the white background. They were landing and taking off like bees at a hive.

Bond stood and gazed at the distant glittering mountain of bird dung. So this was the kingdom of Doctor No!

Bond thought he had never seen a more godforsaken landscape in his life.

He examined the ground between the river and the mountain. It seemed to be the usual grey dead coral broken, where there was a pocket of earth, by low scrub and screwpalm. No doubt a road or a track led down the mountainside to the central lake and the marshes. It looked bad stuff to cross unless there was. Bond noticed that all the vegetation was bent to the westwards. He imagined living the year round with that hot wind constantly scouring the island, the smell of the marsh gas and the guano. No penal colony could have a worse site than this.

Bond looked to the east. There the mangroves in the marshland seemed more hospitable. They marched away in a solid green carpet until they lost their outline in the dancing heat haze on the horizon. Over them a thick froth of birds tossed and settled and tossed again. Their steady scream carried over on the harsh wind.

Quarrel's voice broke in on Bond's thoughts. 'Dey's a comin', cap'n.'

Bond followed Quarrel's eyes. A big lorry was racing down from the huts, dust streaming from its wheels. Bond followed it for ten minutes until it disappeared amongst the mangroves at the head of the river. He listened. The baying of dogs came down on the wind.

Quarrel said, 'Dey'll come down de ribber, cap'n. Dem'll know we caint move 'cept up de ribber, assumin' we ain't dead. Dey'll surely come down de ribber to de beach and look for de pieces. Den mos' likely de boat come wit' a dinghy an' take de men and dogs off. Leastways, dat's what Ah'd do in dere place.'

Honey said, 'That's what they do when they look for me. It's quite all right. You cut a piece of bamboo and when they get near you go under the water and breathe through the bamboo till they've gone by.'

Bond smiled at Quarrel. He said, 'Supposing you get the bamboo while I find a good mangrove clump.'

Quarrel nodded dubiously. He started off upstream towards the bamboo thickets. Bond turned back into the mangrove tunnel.

Bond had avoided looking at the girl. She said impatiently, 'You needn't be so careful of looking at me. It's no good minding those things at a time like this. You said so yourself.'

Bond turned and looked at her. Her tattered shirt came down to the waterline. There was a glimpse of pale wavering limbs below. The beautiful face smiled at him. In the mangroves the broken nose seemed appropriate in its animalness.

Bond looked at her slowly. She understood. He turned and went on downstream and she followed him.

Bond found what he wanted, a crack in the wall of mangrove that seemed to go deeper. He said, 'Don't break a branch.' He bent his head and waded in. The channel went in ten yards. The mud under their feet became deeper and softer. Then there was a solid wall of roots and they could go no farther. The brown water flowed slowly through a wide, quiet pool. Bond stopped. The girl came close to him. 'This is real hide and seek,' she said tremulously.

'Yes, isn't it.' Bond was thinking of his gun. He was wondering how well it would shoot after a bath in the river — how many dogs and men he could get if they were found. He felt a wave of disquiet. It had been a bad break coming across this girl. In combat, like it or not, a girl is your extra heart. The enemy has two targets against your one.

Bond remembered his thirst. He scooped up some water. It was brackish and tasted of earth. It was all right. He drank some more. The girl put out her hand and stopped him. 'Don't drink too much. Wash your mouth out and spit. You could get fever.'

Bond looked at her quietly. He did as she told him.

Quarrel whistled from somewhere in the main stream. Bond answered and waded out towards him. They came back along the channel. Quarrel splashed the mangrove roots with water where their bodies might have brushed against them. 'Kill da smell of us,' he explained briefly. He produced his handful of bamboo lengths and began whittling and cutting them. Bond looked to his gun and the spare ammunition. They stood still in the pool so as not to stir up more mud.

The sunlight dappled down through the thick roof of leaves. The shrimps nibbled softly at their feet. Tension built up in the hot, crouching silence.

It was almost a relief to hear the baying of the dogs.

X

DRAGON SPOOR

THE search party was coming fast down the river. The two men in bathing trunks and tall waders were having to run to keep up with the dogs. They were big Chinese negroes wearing shoulder holsters across their naked sweating chests. Occasionally they exchanged shouts that were mostly swear-words. Ahead of them the pack of big Dobermann Pinschers swam and floundered through the water, baying excitedly. They had a scent and they quested frenziedly, the diamond-shaped ears erect on the smooth, serpentine heads.

'May be a —ing crocodile,' yelled the leading man through the hubbub. He was carrying a short whip which he occasionally cracked like a whipper-in on the hunting field.

The other man converged towards him. He shouted excitedly, 'For my money it's the —ing limey! Bet ya he's lying up in the mangrove. Mind he doesn't give us a —ing ambush.' The man took the gun out of its holster and put it under his armpit and kept his hand on the butt.

They were coming out of the open river into the mangrove tunnel. The first man had a whistle. It stuck out of his broad face like a cigar butt. He blew a shrill blast. When the dogs swept on he laid about him with the whip. The dogs checked, whimpering as the slow current forced them to disobey orders. The two men took their guns and waded slowly downstream through the straggly legs of the mangroves.

The leading man came to the narrow break that Bond had found. He grasped a dog by the collar and swung it into the channel. The dog snorted eagerly and paddled forward. The man's eyes squinted at the mangrove roots on either side of the channel to see if they were scratched.

The dog and the man came into the small enclosed pool at the end of the channel. The man looked round disgustedly. He caught the dog by the collar and pulled him back. The dog was reluctant to leave the place. The man lashed down into the water with his whip.

The second man had been waiting at the entrance to the little channel. The first man came out. He shook his head and they went on downstream, the dogs, now less excited, streaming ahead.

Slowly the noise of the hunt grew less and vanished.

For another five minutes nothing moved in the mangrove pool, then, in one corner among the roots, a thin periscope of bamboo rose slowly out of the water. Bond's face emerged, the forehead streaked with wet hair, like the face of a surfacing corpse. In his right hand under the water the gun was ready. He listened intently. There was dead silence, not a sound. Or was there? What was that soft swish out in the main stream? Was someone wading very quietly along in the wake of the hunt? Bond reached out on either side of him and softly touched the other two bodies that lay among the roots on the edge of the pool. As the two faces surfaced he put his finger to his lips. It was too late. Quarrel had coughed and spat. Bond made a grimace and nodded urgently towards the main stream. They all listened. There was dead silence. Then the soft swishing began again. Whoever it was was coming into the side-channel. The tubes of bamboo went back into the three mouths and the heads softly submerged again.

Underwater, Bond rested his head in the mud, pinched his nostrils with his left hand and pursed his lips round the tube. He knew the pool had been examined once already. He had felt the disturbance of the swimming dog. That time they had not been found. Would they get away with it again? This time there would have been less chance for the stirred mud to seep away out of the pool. If this searcher saw the darker brown stain, would he shoot into it or stab into it? What weapons would he have? Bond decided that he wouldn't take chances. At the first movement in the water near him he would get to his feet and shoot and hope for the best.

Bond lay and focused all his senses. What hell this controlled breathing was and how maddening the soft nibbling of the shrimps! It was lucky none of them had a sore on their bodies or the damned things would have eaten into it. But it had been a bright idea of the girl's. Without it the dogs would have got to them wherever they had hidden.

Suddenly Bond cringed. A rubber boot had stepped on his shin and slid off. Would the man think it was a branch? Bond couldn't chance it. With one surge of motion he hurled himself upwards, spitting out the length of bamboo.

Bond caught a quick impression of a huge body standing almost on top of him and of a swirling rifle butt. He lifted his left arm to protect his head and felt the jarring blow on his forearm. At the same time his right hand lunged forward and as the muzzle of his gun touched the glistening right breast below the hairless aureole he pulled the trigger.

The kick of the explosion, pent up against the man's body, almost broke Bond's wrist, but the man crashed back like a chopped tree into the water. Bond caught a glimpse of a huge rent in his side as he went under. The rubber waders thrashed once and the head, a Chinese negroid head, broke the surface, its eyes turned up and water pouring from its silently yelling mouth. Then the head went under again and there was nothing but muddy froth and a slowly widening red stain that began to seep away downstream.

Bond shook himself. He turned. Quarrel and the girl were standing behind him, water streaming from their bodies. Quarrel was grinning from ear to ear, but the girl's knuckles were at her mouth and her eyes were staring horror-struck at the reddened water.

Bond said curtly, 'I'm sorry, Honey. It had to be done. He was right on top of us. Come on, let's get going.' He took her roughly by the arm and thrust her away from the place and out into the main stream, only stopping when they had reached the open river at the beginning of the mangrove tunnel.

The landscape was empty again. Bond glanced at his watch. It had stopped at three o'clock. He looked at the westering sun. It might be four o'clock now. How much farther had they to go? Bond suddenly felt tired. Now he'd torn it. Even if the shot hadn't been heard — and it would have been well muffled by the man's body and by the mangroves — the man would be missed when the others rendezvoused, if Quarrel's guess was right, at the river mouth to be taken off to the launch. Would they come back up the river to look for the missing man? Probably not. It would be getting dark before they knew for certain that he was missing. They'd send out a search party in the morning. The dogs would soon get to the body. Then what?

The girl tugged at his sleeve. She said angrily, 'It's time you told me what all this is about! Why's everybody trying to kill each other? And who are you? I don't believe all this story about birds. You don't take a revolver after birds.'

Bond looked down into the angry, wide-apart eyes. 'I'm sorry, Honey. I'm afraid I've got you into a bit of a mess. I'll tell you all about it this evening when we get to the camp. It's just bad luck you being mixed up with me like this. I've got a bit of a war on with these people. They seem to want to kill me. Now I'm only interested in seeing us all off the island without anyone else getting hurt. I've got enough to go on now so that next time I can come back by the front door.'

'What do you mean? Are you some sort of a policeman? Are you trying to send this Chinaman to prison?'

'That's about it,' Bond smiled down at her. 'At least you're on the side of the angels. And now you tell me something. How much farther to the camp?'

'Oh, about an hour.'

'Is it a good place to hide? Could they find us there easily?'

'They'd have to come across the lake or up the river. It'll be all right so long as they don't send their dragon after us. He can go through the water. I've seen him do it.'

'Oh well,' said Bond diplomatically, 'let's hope he's got a sore tail or something.'

The girl snorted. 'All right, Mr Know-all,' she said angrily. 'Just you wait.'

Quarrel splashed out of the mangroves. He was carrying a rifle. He said apologetically. 'No harm 'n havin' anudder gun, cap'n. Looks like us may need hit.'

Bond took it. It was a U.S. Army Remington Carbine .300. These people certainly had the right equipment. He handed it back.

Quarrel echoed his thoughts. 'Dese is sly folks, cap'n. Dat man mus' of come sneakin' down soffly behind de udders to ketch us comin' out after de dawgs had passed. He sho is a sly mongoose, dat Doctor feller.'

Bond said thoughtfully, 'He must be quite a man.

He shrugged away his thoughts. 'Now let's get going. Honey says there's another hour to the camp. Better keep to the left bank so as to get what cover we can from the hill. For all we know they've got glasses trained on the river.' Bond handed his gun to Quarrel who stowed it in the sodden knapsack. They moved off again with Quarrel in the lead and Bond and the girl walking together.

They got some shade from the bamboo and bushes along the western bank, but now they had to face the full force of the scorching wind. They splashed water over their arms and faces to cool the burn. Bond's eyes were bloodshot with the glare and his arm ached intolerably where the gun butt had struck. And he was not looking forward to his dinner of soaking bread and cheese and salt pork. How long would they be able to sleep? He hadn't had much last night. It looked like the same ration again. And what about the girl? She had had none. He and Quarrel would have to keep watch and watch. And then tomorrow. Off into the mangrove again and work their way slowly back to the canoe across the eastern end of the island. It looked like that. And sail the following night. Bond thought of hacking a way for five miles through solid mangroves. What a prospect! Bond trudged on, thinking of M's 'holiday in the sunshine'. He'd certainly give something for M to be sharing it with him now.

The river grew narrower until it was only a stream between the bamboo clumps. Then it widened out into a flat marshy estuary beyond which the five square miles of shallow lake swept away to the other side of the island in a ruffled blue-grey mirror. Beyond, there was the shimmer of the airstrip and the glint of the sun on a single hangar. The girl told them to keep to the east and they worked their way slowly along inside the fringe of bushes.

Suddenly Quarrel stopped, his face pointing like a gun-dog's at the marshy ground in front of him. Two deep parallel grooves were cut into the mud, with a fainter groove in the centre. They were the tracks of something that had come down from the hill and gone across the marsh towards the lake.

The girl said indifferently, 'That's where the dragon's been.'

Quarrel turned the whites of his eyes towards her.

Bond walked slowly along the tracks. The outside ones were quite smooth with an indented curve. They could have been made by wheels, but they were vast — at least two feet across. The centre track was of the same shape but only three inches across, about the width of a motor tyre. The tracks were without a trace of tread, and they were fairly fresh. They marched along in a dead straight line and the bushes they crossed were squashed flat as if a tank had gone over them.

Bond couldn't imagine what kind of vehicle, if it was a vehicle, had made them. When the girl nudged him and whispered fiercely 'I told you so,' he could only say thoughtfully, 'Well, Honey, if it isn't a dragon, it's something else I've never seen before.'

Farther on, she tugged urgently at his sleeve. 'Look,' she whispered. She pointed forward to a big clump of bushes beside which the tracks ran. They were leafless and blackened. In the centre there showed the charred remains of birds' nests. 'He breathed on them,' she said excitedly.

Bond walked up to the bushes and examined them. 'He certainly did,' he admitted. Why had this particular clump been burned? It was all very odd.

The tracks swerved out towards the lake and disappeared into the water. Bond would have liked to follow them but there was no question of leaving cover. They trudged on, wrapped in their different thoughts.

Slowly the day began to die behind the sugar-loaf, and at last the girl pointed ahead through the bushes and Bond could see a long spit of sand running out into the lake. There were thick bushes of sea-grape along its spine and, halfway, perhaps a hundred yards from the shore, the remains of a thatched hut. It looked a reasonably attractive place to spend the night and it was well protected by the water on both sides. The wind had died and the water was soft and inviting. How heavenly it was going to be to take off their filthy shirts and wash in the lake, and, after the hours of squelching through the mud and stench of the river and the marsh, be able to lie down on the hard dry sand!

The sun blazed yellowly and sank behind the mountain. The day was still alive at the eastern tip of the island, but the black shadow of the sugar-loaf was slowly marching across the lake and would soon reach out and kill that too. The frogs started up, louder than in Jamaica, until the thick dusk was shrill with them. Across the lake a giant bull frog began to drum. The eerie sound was something between a tom-tom and an ape's roar. It sent out short messages that were suddenly throttled. Soon it fell silent. It had found what it had sent for.

They reached the neck of the sandspit and filed out along a narrow track. They came to the clearing with the smashed remains of the wattle hut. The big mysterious tracks led out of the water on both sides and through the clearing and over the near-by bushes as if the thing, whatever it was, had stampeded the place. Many of the bushes were burned or charred. There were the remains of a fireplace made of lumps of coral and a few scattered cooking pots and empty tins. They searched in the debris and Quarrel unearthed a couple of unopened tins of Heinz pork and beans. The girl found a crumpled sleeping-bag. Bond found a small leather purse containing five one-dollar notes, three Jamaica pounds and some silver. The two men had certainly left in a hurry.

They left the place and moved farther along to a small sandy clearing. Through the bushes they could see lights winking across the water from the mountain, perhaps two miles away. To the eastwards there was nothing but the soft black sheen of water under the darkening sky.

Bond said, 'As long as we don't show a light we should be fine here. The first thing is to have a good wash. Honey, you take the rest of the sandspit and we'll have the landward end. See you for dinner in about half an hour.'

The girl laughed. 'Will you be dressing?'

'Certainly,' said Bond. 'Trousers.'

Quarrel said, 'Cap'n, while dere's henough light I'll get dese tins open and get tings fixed for de night.' He rummaged in the knapsack. 'Here's yo trousers and yo gun. De bread don't feel so good but hit only wet. Hit eat okay an' mebbe hit dry hout come de mornin'. Guess we'd better eat de tins tonight an' keep de cheese an' pork. Dose tins is heavy an' we got plenty footin' tomorrow.'

Bond said, 'All right, Quarrel. I'll leave the menu to you.' He took the gun and the damp trousers and walked down into the shallow water and back the way they had come. He found a hard dry stretch of sand and took off his shirt and stepped back into the water and lay down. The water was soft but disgustingly warm. He dug up handfuls of sand and scrubbed himself with it, using it as soap. Then he lay and luxuriated in the silence and the loneliness.

The stars began to shine palely, the stars that had brought them to the island last night, a year ago, the stars that would take them away again tomorrow night, a year away. What a trip! But at least it had already paid off. Now he had enough evidence, and witnesses, to go back to the Governor and get a full-dress inquiry going into the activities of Doctor No. One didn't use machine guns on people, even on trespassers. And, by the same token, what was this thing of Doctor No's that had trespassed on the leasehold of the Audubon Society, the thing that had smashed their property and had possibly killed one of their wardens? That would have to be investigated too And what would he find when he came back to the island through the front door, in a destroyer, perhaps, and with a detachment of marines? What would be the answer to the riddle of Doctor No? What was he hiding? What did he fear? Why was privacy so important to him that he would murder, again and again, for it? Who *was* Doctor No?

Bond heard splashing away to his right. He thought of the girl. And who, for the matter of that, was Honeychile Rider? That, he decided, as he climbed out on to dry land, was at least something that he ought to be able to find out before the night was over.

Bond pulled on his clammy trousers and sat down on the sand and dismantled his gun. He did it by touch, using his shirt to dry each part and each cartridge. Then he reassembled the gun and clicked the trigger round the empty cylinder. The sound was healthy. It would be days before it rusted. He loaded it and tucked it into the holster inside the waistband of his trousers and got up and walked back to the clearing.

The shadow of Honey reached up and pulled him down beside her. 'Come on,' she said, 'we're starving. I got one of the cooking pots and cleaned it out and we poured the beans into it. There's about two full handfuls each and a cricket ball of bread. And I'm not feeling guilty about eating your food because you made me work far harder than I would if I'd been alone. Here, hold out your hand.'

Bond smiled at the authority in her voice. He could just make out her silhouette in the dusk. Her head looked sleeker. He wondered what her hair looked like when it was combed and dry. What would she be like when she was wearing clean clothes over that beautiful golden body? He could see her coming into a room or across the lawn at Beau Desert. She would be a beautiful, ravishing, Ugly Duckling. Why had she never had the broken nose mended? It was an easy operation. Then she would be the most beautiful girl in Jamaica.

Her shoulder brushed against him. Bond reached out and put his hand down in her lap, open. She picked up his hand and Bond felt the cold mess of beans being poured into it.

Suddenly he smelled her warm animal smell. It was so sensually thrilling that his body swayed against her and for a moment his eyes closed.

She gave a short laugh in which there was shyness and satisfaction and tenderness. She said 'There,' maternally, and carried his laden hand away from her and back to him.

XI

AMIDST THE ALIEN CANE

I T would be around eight o'clock, Bond thought.
Apart from the background tinkle of the frogs it was
very quiet. In the far corner of the clearing he could
see the dark outline of Quarrel. There was the soft clink
of metal as he dismantled and dried the Remington.

Through the bushes the distant yellow lights from the
guanera made festive pathways across the dark surface of
the lake. The ugly wind had gone and the hideous scenery
lay drowned in darkness. It was cool. Bond's clothes had
dried on him. The three big handfuls of food had warmed
his stomach. He felt comfortable and drowsy and at peace.
Tomorrow was a long way off and presented no problems
except a great deal of physical exercise. Life suddenly felt
easy and good.

The girl lay beside him in the sleeping-bag. She was
lying on her back with her head cradled in her hands,
looking up at the roof of stars. He could just make out the
pale pool of her face. She said, 'James. You promised to
tell me what this is all about. Come on. I shan't go to
sleep until you do.'

Bond laughed. 'I'll tell if you'll tell. I want to know what
you're all about.'

'I don't mind. I've got no secrets. But you first.'

'All right then.' Bond pulled his knees up to his chin and
put his arms round them. 'It's like this. I'm a sort of

policeman. They send me out from London when there's something odd going on somewhere in the world that isn't anybody else's business. Well, not long ago one of the Governor's staff in Kingston, a man called Strangways, friend of mine, disappeared. His secretary, who was a pretty girl, did too. Most people thought they'd run away together. I didn't. I ...'

Bond told the story in simple terms, with good men and bad men, like an adventure story out of a book. He ended, 'So you see, Honey, it's just a question of getting back to Jamaica tomorrow night, all three of us in the canoe, and then the Governor will listen to us and send over a lot of soldiers to get this Chinaman to own up. I expect that'll mean he'll go to prison. He'll know that too and that's why he's trying to stop us. That's all. Now it's your turn.'

The girl said, 'You seem to live a very exciting life. Your wife can't like you being away so much. Doesn't she worry about you getting hurt?'

'I'm not married. The only people who worry about me getting hurt are my insurance company.'

She probed, 'But I suppose you have girls.'

'Not permanent ones.'

'Oh.'

There was a pause. Quarrel came over to them. 'Cap'n, Ah'll take de fust watch if dat suits. Be out on de point of de sandspit. Ah'll come call yo around midnight. Den mebbe yo take on till five and den we all git goin'. Need to get well away from dis place afore it's light.'

'Suits me,' said Bond. 'Wake me if you see anything. Gun all right?'

'Him's jess fine,' said Quarrel happily. He said, 'Sleep well, missy,' with a hint of meaning, and melted noiselessly away into the shadows.

'I like Quarrel,' said the girl. She paused, then, 'Do

you really want to know about me? It's not as exciting as your story.'

'Of course I do. And don't leave anything out.'

'There's nothing to leave out. You could get my whole life on to the back of a postcard. To begin with I've never been out of Jamaica. I've lived all my life at a place called Beau Desert on the North Coast near Morgan's Harbour.'

Bond laughed. 'That's odd. So do I. At least for the moment. I didn't notice you about. Do you live up a tree?'

'Oh, I suppose you've taken the beach house. I never go near the place. I live in the Great House.'

'But there's nothing left of it. It's a ruin in the middle of the cane fields.'

'I live in the cellars. I've lived there since I was five. It was burned down then and my parents were killed. I can't remember anything about them so you needn't say you're sorry. At first I lived there with my black nanny. She died when I was fifteen. For the last five years I've lived there alone.'

'Good heavens.' Bond was appalled. 'But wasn't there anyone else to look after you? Didn't your parents leave any money?'

'Not a penny.' There was no bitterness in the girl's voice — pride if anything. 'You see the Riders were one of the old Jamaican families. The first one had been given the Beau Desert lands by Cromwell for having been one of the people who signed King Charles's death warrant. He built the Great House and my family lived in it on and off ever since. But then sugar collapsed and I suppose the place was badly run, and by the time my father inherited it there was nothing but debts — mortgages and things like that. So when my father and mother died the property was sold up. I didn't mind. I was too young. Nanny must have been wonderful. They wanted people to adopt me, the clergyman and the legal people did, but Nanny collected the sticks of furniture that hadn't been burned and we settled down in the ruins and after a bit no one came and interfered with us. She did a bit of sewing and laundry in the village and grew a few plantains and bananas and things and there was a big breadfruit tree up against the old house. We ate what the Jamaicans eat. And there was the sugar cane all round us and she made a fishpot which we used to go and take up every day. It was all right. We had enough to eat. Somehow she taught me to read and write. There was a pile of old books left from the fire. There was an encyclopedia. I started with A when I was about eight. I've got as far as the middle of T.' She said defensively, 'I bet I know more than you do about a lot of things.'

'I bet you do.' Bond was lost in the picture of the little flaxen-haired girl pattering about the ruins with the obstinate old negress watching over her and calling her in to do the lessons that must have been just as much a riddle to the old woman. 'Your nanny must have been a wonderful person.'

'She was a darling.' It was a flat statement. 'I thought I'd die when she did. It wasn't such fun after that. Before, I'd led a child's life; then I suddenly had to grow up and do everything for myself. And men tried to catch me and hurt me. They said they wanted to make love to me.' She paused. 'I used to be pretty then.'

Bond said seriously, 'You're one of the most beautiful girls I've ever seen.'

'With this nose? Don't be silly.'

'You don't understand.' Bond tried to find words that she would believe. 'Of course anyone can see your nose is broken. But since this morning I've hardly noticed it. When you look at a person you look into their eyes or at their mouth. That's where the expressions are. A broken nose isn't any more significant than a crooked ear. Noses and ears are bits of face-furniture. Some are prettier than others, but they're not nearly as important as the rest. They're part of the background of the face. If you had a beautiful nose as well as the rest of you you'd be the most beautiful girl in Jamaica.'

'Do you mean that?' her voice was urgent. 'Do you think I could be beautiful? I know some of me's all right, but when I look in the glass I hardly see anything except my broken nose. I'm sure its like that with other people who are, who are — well — sort of deformed.'

Bond said impatiently, 'You're not deformed! Don't talk such nonsense. And anyway you can have it put right by a simple operation. You've only got to get over to America and it would be done in a week.'

She said angrily, 'How do you expect me to do that? I've got about fifteen pounds under a stone in my cellar. I've got three skirts and three shirts and a knife and a fish-pot. I know all about these operations. The doctor at Port Maria found out for me. He's a nice man. He wrote to America. Do you know, to have it properly done it would cost me about five hundred pounds, what with the fare to New York and the hospital and everything?' Her voice became hopeless. 'How do you expect me to find that amount of money?'

Bond had already made up his mind what would have to be done about that. Now he merely said tenderly, 'Well, I expect there are ways. But anyway, go on with your story. It's very exciting — far more interesting than mine. You'd got to where your nanny died. What happened then?'

The girl began again reluctantly.

'Well, it's your fault for interrupting. And you mustn't talk about things you don't understand. I suppose people tell you you're good-looking. I expect you get all the girls you want. Well you wouldn't if you had a squint or a hare-lip or something. As a matter of fact,' he could hear the smile in her voice, 'I think I shall go to the obeahman when we get back and get him to put a spell on you and give you something like that.' She added lamely, 'Then we should be more alike.'

Bond reached out. His hand brushed against her. 'I've got other plans,' he said. 'But come on. I want to hear the rest of the story.'

'Oh well,' the girl sighed, 'I'll have to go back a bit. You see all the property is in cane and the old house stands in the middle of it. Well, about twice a year they cut the cane and send it off to the mill. And when they do that all the animals and insects and so on that live in the cane fields go into a panic and most of them have their houses destroyed and get killed. At cutting time some of them took to coming to the ruins of the house and hiding. My nanny was terrified of them to begin with, the mongooses and the snakes and the scorpions and so on, but I made a couple of the cellar rooms into sort of homes for them. I wasn't frightened of them and they never hurt me. They seemed to understand that I was looking after them. They must have told their friends or something because after a bit it was quite natural for them all to come trooping into their rooms and settling down there until the young cane had started to grow again. Then they all filed out and went back to living in the fields. I gave them what food we could spare when they were staying with us and they behaved very well except for making a bit of a smell and sometimes fighting amongst each other. But they all got quite tame with me, and their children did, too, and I could do anything with them. Of course the cane-cutters found out about this and saw me walking about with snakes round my neck and so forth, and they got frightened of me and thought I was obeah. So they left us absolutely alone.' She paused. 'That's where I found out so much about animals and insects. I used to spend a lot of time in the sea finding out about those people too. It was the same with birds. If you find out what all these people like to eat and what they're afraid of, and if you spend all your time with them you can make friends.' She looked up at him. 'You miss a lot not knowing about these things.'

'I'm afraid I do,' said Bond truthfully. 'I expect they're much nicer and more interesting than humans.'

'I don't know about that,' said the girl thoughtfully. 'I don't know many human people. Most of the ones I have met have been hateful. But I suppose they can be interesting too.' She paused. 'I hadn't ever really thought of liking them like I like the animals. Except for Nanny, of course. Until ...' She broke off with a shy laugh. 'Well, anyway we all lived happily together until I was fifteen and Nanny died and then things got difficult. There was a man called Mander. A horrible man. He was the white overseer for the people who own the property. He kept coming to see me. He wanted me to move up to his house near Port Maria. I hated him and I used to hide when I heard his horse coming through the cane. One night he came on foot and I didn't hear him. He was drunk. He came into the cellar and fought with me because I wouldn't do what he wanted me to do. You know, the things people in love do.'

'Yes, I know.'

'I tried to kill him with my knife, but he was very strong and he hit me as hard as he could in the face and broke my nose. He knocked me unconscious and then I think he did things to me. I mean I know he did. Next day I wanted to kill myself when I saw my face and when I found what he had done. I thought I would have a baby. I would certainly have killed myself if I'd had a baby by that man. Anyway I didn't, so that was that. I went to the doctor and he did what he could for my nose and didn't charge me anything. I didn't tell him about the rest. I was too ashamed. The man didn't come back. I waited and did nothing until the next cane-cutting. I'd got my plan. I was waiting for the Black Widow spiders to come in for shelter. One day they came. I caught the biggest of the females and shut her in a box with nothing to eat. They're the bad ones, the females. Then I waited for a dark night without any moon. I took the box with the spider in it and walked and walked until I came to the man's house. It was very dark and I was frightened of the duppies I might meet on the road but I didn't see any. I waited in his garden in the bushes and watched him go up to bed. Then I climbed a tree and got on to his balcony. I waited there until I heard him snoring and then I crept through the window. He was lying naked on the bed under the mosquito net. I lifted the edge and opened the box and shook the spider out on to his stomach. Then I went away and came home.'

'God Almighty!' said Bond reverently. 'What happened to him?'

She said happily, 'He took a week to die. It must have hurt terribly. They do, you know. The obeahmen say there's nothing like it.' She paused. When Bond made no comment, she said anxiously, 'You don't think I did wrong, do you?'

'It's not a thing to make a habit of,' said Bond mildly. 'But I can't say I blame you the way it was. So what happened then?'

'Well then I just settled down again,' her voice was matter-of-fact. 'I had to concentrate on getting enough food, and of course all I wanted to do was save up money to get my nose made good again.' She said persuasively, 'It really was quite a pretty nose before. Do you think the doctors can put it back to how it was?'

'They can make it any shape you like,' said Bond definitely. 'What did you make money at?'

'It was the encyclopedia. It told me that people collect seashells. That one could sell the rare ones. I talked to the local schoolmaster, without telling him my secret of course, and he found out that there's an American magazine called *Nautilus* for shell collectors. I had just enough money to subscribe to it and I began looking for the shells that people said they wanted in the advertisements. I wrote to a dealer in Miami and he started buying from me. It was thrilling. Of course I made some awful mistakes to begin with. I thought people would like the prettiest shells, but they don't. Very often they want the ugliest. And then when I found rare ones I cleaned them and polished them to make them look better. That's wrong too. They want shells just as they come out of the sea, with the animal in and all. So I got some formalin from the doctor and put it into the live shells to stop them smelling and sent them off to this man in Miami. I only got it right about a year ago and I've already made fifteen pounds. I'd worked out that now I knew how they wanted them, and if I was lucky, I ought to make at least fifty pounds a year. Then in ten years I would be able to go to America and have the operation. And then,' she giggled delightedly, 'I had a terrific stroke of luck. I went over to Crab Key. I'd been there before, but this was just before Christmas, and I found these purple shells. They didn't look very exciting, but I sent one or two to Miami and the man wrote back at once and said he could take as many as I could get at five dollars each for the whole ones. He said that I must keep the place where they live a dead secret as otherwise we'd what he called "spoil the market" and the price would get cheaper. It's just like having one's private gold mine. Now I may be able to save up the money in five years. That's why I was so suspicious of you when I found you on my beach. I thought you'd come to steal my shells.'

'You gave me a bit of a shock. I thought you must be Doctor No's girl friend.'

'Thanks very much.'

'But when you've had the operation, what are you going to do then? You can't go on living alone in a cellar all your life.'

'I thought I'd be a call girl.' She said it as she might have said 'nurse' or 'secretary'.

'Oh, what do you mean by that?' Perhaps she had picked up the expression without understanding it.

'One of those girls who has a beautiful flat and lovely clothes. You know what I mean,' she said impatiently. 'People ring them up and come and make love to them and pay them for it. They get a hundred dollars for each time in New York. That's where I thought I'd start. Of course,' she admitted, 'I might have to do it for less to begin with. Until I learned to do it really well. How much do you pay the untrained ones?'

Bond laughed. 'I really can't remember. It's quite a long time since I had one.'

She sighed. 'Yes, I suppose you can have as many women as you want for nothing. I suppose it's only the ugly men that pay. But that can't be helped. Any kind of job in the big towns must be dreadful. At least you can earn much more being a call girl. Then I can come back to Jamaica and buy Beau Desert. I'd be rich enough to find a nice husband and have some children. Now that I've found these Venus shells I've worked out that I might be back in Jamaica by the time I'm thirty. Won't that be lovely?'

'I like the last part of the plan. But I'm not so sure of the first. Anyway, where did you find out about these call girls? Were they under C in the encyclopedia?'

'Of course not. Don't be silly. There was a big case about them in New York about two years ago. There was a rich playboy called Jelke. He had a whole string of girls. There was a lot about the case in the *Gleaner*. They gave all the prices and everything. And anyway, there are thousands of those sort of girls in Kingston, only of course not such good ones. They only get about five shillings and they have nowhere to go and do it except the bush. My nanny told me about them. She said I mustn't grow up like them or I'd be very unhappy. I can see that for only five shillings. But for a hundred dollars ...!'

Bond said, 'You wouldn't be able to keep all of that. You'd have to have a sort of manager to get the men, and then you'd have to bribe the police to leave you alone. And you could easily go to prison if something went wrong. I really don't think you'd like the work. I'll tell you what, with all you know about animals and insects and so on you could get a wonderful job looking after them in one of the American zoos. Or what about the Jamaica Institute? I'm sure you'd like that better. You'd be just as likely to meet a nice husband. Anyway you mustn't think of being a call girl any more. You've got a beautiful body. You must keep it for the men you love.'

'That's what people say in books,' she said doubtfully. 'The trouble is there aren't any men to love at Beau Desert.' She said shyly, 'You're the first Englishman I've ever talked to. I liked you from the beginning. I don't mind telling you these things at all. I suppose there are plenty of other people I should like if I could get away.'

'Of course there are. Hundreds. And you're a wonderful girl. I thought so directly I saw you.'

'Saw my behind, you mean.' The voice was getting drowsy, but it was full of pleasure.

Bond laughed. 'Well, it was a wonderful behind. And the other side was wonderful too.' Bond's body began to stir with the memory of how she had been. He said gruffly, 'Now come on, Honey. It's time to go to sleep. There'll be plenty of time to talk when we get back to Jamaica.'

'Will there?' she said sleepily. 'Promise?'

'Promise.'

He heard her stir in the sleeping-bag. He looked down. He could just make out the pale profile turned towards him. She gave the deep sigh of a child before it falls asleep.

There was silence in the clearing. It was getting cold. Bond put his head down on his hunched knees. He knew it was no good trying to get to sleep. His mind was full of the day and of this extraordinary Girl Tarzan who had come into his life. It was as if some beautiful animal had attached itself to him. There would be no dropping the leash until he had solved her problems for her. He knew it. Of course there would be no difficulty about most of them. He could fix the operation — even, with the help of friends, find a proper job and a home for her. He had the money. He would buy her dresses, have her hair done, get her started in the big world. It would be fun. But what about the other side? What about the physical desire he felt for her? One could not make love to a child. But was she a child? There was nothing childish about her body or her personality. She was fully grown and highly intelligent in her fashion, and far more capable of taking care of herself than any girl of twenty Bond had ever met.

Bond's thoughts were interrupted by a tug at his sleeve. The small voice said, 'Why don't you go to sleep? Are you cold?'

'No, I'm fine.'

'It's nice and warm in the sleeping-bag. Would you like to come in? There's plenty of room.'

'No thank you, Honey. I'll be all right.'

There was a pause, then, almost in a whisper, 'If you're

thinking ... I mean — you don't have to make love to me ... We could go to sleep back to front, you know, like spoons.'

'Honey, darling, you go to sleep. It'd be lovely to be like that, but not tonight. Anyway I'll have to take over from Quarrel soon.'

'Yes, I see.' The voice was grudging. 'Perhaps when we get back to Jamaica.'

'Perhaps.'

'Promise. I won't go to sleep until you promise.'

Bond said desperately, 'Of course I promise. Now go to sleep, Honeychile.'

The voice whispered triumphantly, 'Now you owe me slave-time. You've promised. Good night, darling James.'

'Good night, darling Honey.'

XII

THE THING

THE grip on Bond's shoulder was urgent. He was instantly on his feet.

Quarrel whispered fiercely, 'Somepn comin' across de water, cap'n! It de dragon fo sho!'

The girl woke up. She said anxiously, 'What's happened?'

Bond said, 'Stay there, Honey! Don't move. I'll be back.' He broke through the bushes on the side away from the mountain and ran along the sand with Quarrel at his elbow.

They came to the tip of the sandspit, twenty yards from the clearing. They stopped under cover of the final bushes. Bond parted them and looked through.

What was it? Half a mile away, coming across the lake, was a shapeless thing with two glaring orange eyes with black pupils. From between these, where the mouth might be, fluttered a yard of blue flame. The grey luminescence of the stars showed some kind of a domed head above two short batlike wings. The thing was making a low moaning roar that overlaid another noise, a deep rhythmic thud. It was coming towards them at about ten miles an hour, throwing up a creamy wake.

Quarrel whispered, 'Gawd, cap'n! What's dat fearful ting?'

Bond stood up. He said shortly, 'Don't know exactly.

Some sort of a tractor affair dressed up to frighten. It's running on a diesel engine, so you can forget about dragons. Now let's see,' Bond spoke half to himself. 'No good running away. The thing's too fast for us and we know it can go over mangroves and swamp. Have to fight it here. What'll its weak spots be? The drivers. Of course they'll have protection. We don't know how much. Quarrel, you start firing at that dome on top when it gets to two hundred yards. Aim carefully and keep on firing. I'll go for its headlights when it gets to fifty yards. It's not running on tracks. Must have some kind of giant tyres, aeroplane tyres probably. I'll go for them too. Stay here. I'll go ten yards along. They may start firing back and we've got to keep the bullets away from the girl. Okay?' Bond reached out and squeezed the big shoulder. 'And don't worry too much. Forget about dragons. It's just some gadget of Doctor No's. We'll kill the drivers and capture the damn thing and ride it down to the coast. Save us shoe-leather. Right?'

Quarrel laughed shortly. 'Okay, cap'n. Since yo says so. But Ah sho hopes de Almighty knows he's no dragon too!'

Bond ran down the sand. He broke through the bushes until he had a clear field of fire. He called softly, 'Honey!'

'Yes, James.' There was relief in the near-by voice.

'Make a hole in the sand like we did on the beach. Behind the thickest roots. Get into it and lie down. There may be some shooting. Don't worry about dragons. This is just a painted up motor car with some of Doctor No's men in it. Don't be frightened. I'm quite close.'

'All right, James. Be careful.' The voice was high with fright.

Bond knelt on one knee in the leaves and sand and peered out.

Now the thing was only about three hundred yards

away and its yellow headlights were lighting up the sandspit. Blue flames were still fluttering from the mouth. They were coming from a long snout mocked-up with gaping jaws and gold paint to look like a dragon's mouth. Flame-thrower! That would explain the burned bushes and the warden's story. The blue flames would be coming from some kind of an after-burner. The apparatus was now in neutral. What would its range be when the compression was unleashed?

Bond had to admit that the thing was an awesome sight as it moaned forward through the shallow lake. It was obviously designed to terrify. It would have frightened him but for the earthy thud of the diesel. Against native intruders it would be devastating. But how vulnerable would it be to people with guns who didn't panic?

He was answered at once. There came the crack of Quarrel's Remington. A spark flew off the domed cabin and there was a dull clang. Quarrel fired another single shot and then a burst. The bullets hammered ineffectually against the cabin. There was not even a check in speed. The thing rolled on, swerving slightly to make for the source of the gunfire. Bond cradled the Smith & Wesson on his forearm and took careful aim. The deep cough of his gun sounded above the rattle of the Remington. One of the headlamps shattered and went out. He fired four shots at the other and got it with the fifth and last round in the cylinder. The thing didn't care. It rolled straight on towards Quarrel's hiding place. Bond reloaded and began firing at the huge bulge of the tyres under the bogus black and gold wings. The range was now only thirty yards and he could have sworn that he hit the nearest wheel again and again. No effect. Solid rubber? The first breath of fear stirred Bond's skin.

He reloaded. Was the damn thing vulnerable from the rear? Should he dash out into the lake and try and board it? He took a step forward through the bushes. Then he froze, incapable of movement.

Suddenly, from the dribbling snout, a yellow-tipped bolt of blue flame had howled out towards Quarrel's hiding place. There was a single puff of orange and red flame from the bushes to Bond's right and one unearthly scream, immediately choked. Satisfied, the searing tongue of fire licked back into the snout. The thing turned on its axis and stopped dead. Now the blue hole of its mouth aimed straight at Bond.

Bond stood and waited for his unspeakable end. He looked into the blue jaws of death and saw the glowing red filament of the firer deep inside the big tube. He thought of Quarrel's body — there was no time to think of Quarrel — and imagined the blackened, smoking figure lying in the melted sand. Soon he, too, would flame like a torch. The single scream would be wrung from him and his limbs would jerk into the dancing pose of burned bodies. Then it would be Honey's turn. Christ, what had he led them into! Why had he been so insane as to take on this man with his devastating armoury. Why hadn't he been warned by the long finger that had pointed at him in Jamaica? Bond set his teeth. Hurry up, you bastards. Get it over.

There came the twang of a loud-hailer. A voice howled metallically, 'Come on out, Limey. And the doll. Quick, or you'll fry in hell like your pal.' To rub in the command, the bolt of flame spat briefly towards him. Bond stepped back from the searing heat. He felt the girl's body against his back. She said hysterically, 'I had to come. I had to come.'

Bond said, 'It's all right, Honey. Keep behind me.'

He had made up his mind. There was no alternative. Even if death was to come later it couldn't be worse than this kind of death. Bond reached for the girl's hand and drew her after him out on to the sand.

The voice howled. 'Stop there. Good boy. And drop the pea-shooter. No tricks or the crabs'll be getting a cooked breakfast.'

Bond dropped his gun. So much for the Smith & Wesson. The Beretta would have been just as good against this thing. The girl whimpered. Bond squeezed her hand. 'Stick it, Honey,' he said. 'We'll get out of this somehow.' Bond sneered at himself for the lie.

There was the clang of an iron door being opened. From the back of the dome a man dropped into the water and walked towards them. There was a gun in his hand. He kept out of the line of fire of the flame-thrower. The fluttering blue flame lit up his sweating face. He was a Chinese negro, a big man, clad only in trousers. Something dangled from his left hand. When he came closer, Bond saw it was handcuffs.

The man stopped a few yards away. He said, 'Hold out your hands. Wrists together. Then walk towards me. You first, Limey. Slowly or you get an extra navel.'

Bond did as he was told. When he was within sweat-smell of the man, the man put his gun between his teeth and reached out and snapped the handcuffs on Bond's wrists. Bond looked into the face, gunmetal-coloured from the blue flames. It was a brutal, squinting face. It sneered at him. 'Dumb bastard,' said the man.

Bond turned his back on the man and started walking away. He was going to see Quarrel's body. He had to say goodbye to it. There was the roar of a gun. A bullet kicked up sand close to his feet. Bond stopped and turned slowly round. 'Don't be nervous,' he said. 'I'm going to take a look at the man you've just murdered. I'll be back.'

The man lowered his gun. He laughed harshly. 'Okay. Enjoy yourself. Sorry we ain't got a wreath. Come back quick or we give the doll a toastin'. Two minutes.'

Bond walked on towards the smoking clump of bushes.

He got there and looked down. His eyes and mouth winced. Yes, it had been just as he had visualized. Worse. He said softly, 'I'm sorry Quarrel.' He kicked into the ground and scooped up a handful of cool sand between his manacled hands and poured it over the remains of the eyes. Then he walked slowly back and stood beside the girl.

The man waved them forward with his gun. They walked round the back of the machine. There was a small square door. A voice from inside said, 'Get in and sit on the floor. Don't touch anything or you get your fingers broke.'

They scrambled into the iron box. It stank of sweat and oil. There was just room for them to sit with their knees hunched up. The man with the gun followed them in and banged the door. He switched on a light and sat down on an iron tractor seat beside the driver. He said, 'Okay, Sam. Let's get goin'. You can put out the fire. It's light enough to steer by.'

There was a row of dials and switches on the instrument panel. The driver reached forward and pulled down a couple of the switches. He put the machine into gear and peered out through a narrow slit in the iron wall in front of him. Bond felt the machine turn. There came a faster beat from the engine and they moved off.

The girl's shoulder pressed against his. 'Where are they taking us?' The whisper trembled.

Bond turned his head and looked at her. It was the first time he had been able to see her hair when it was dry. Now it was disarrayed by sleep, but it was no longer a bunch of rats' tails. It hung heavily straight down to her shoulders, where it curled softly inwards. It was of the palest ash blonde and shone almost silver under the electric light. She looked up at him. The skin round her eyes and at the corners of her mouth was white with fear.

Bond shrugged with an indifference he didn't feel. He whispered, 'Oh, I expect we're going to see Doctor No. Don't worry too much, Honey. These men are just little gangsters. It'll be different with him. When we get to him don't you say anything, I'll talk for both of us.' He pressed her shoulder. 'I like the way you do your hair. I'm glad you don't cut it too short.'

Some of the tension went out of her face. 'How can you think of things like that?' She half smiled at him. 'But I'm glad you like it. I wash it in coconut oil once a week.' At the memory of her other life her eyes grew bright with tears. She bent her head down to her manacled hands to hide her tears. She whispered almost to herself, 'I'll try to be brave. It'll be all right as long as you're there.'

Bond shifted so that he was right up against her. He brought his handcuffed hands close up to his eyes and examined them. They were the American police model. He contracted his left hand, the thinner of the two, and tried to pull it through the squat ring of steel. Even the sweat on his skin was no help. It was hopeless.

The two men sat on their iron seats with their backs to them, indifferent. They knew they had total command. There wasn't room for Bond to give any trouble. Bond couldn't stand up or get enough momentum into his hands to do any damage to the backs of their heads with his handcuffs. If Bond somehow managed to open the hatch and drop into the water, where would that get him? They would at once feel the fresh air on their backs and stop the machine, and either burn him in the water or pick him up. It annoyed Bond that they didn't worry about him, that they knew he was utterly in their power. He also didn't like the idea that these men were intelligent enough to know that he presented no threat. Stupider men would have sat over him with a gun out, would have trussed him and the girl with inexpert thoroughness, might even have knocked them unconscious. These two knew their business. They were professionals, or had been trained to be professionals.

The two men didn't talk to each other. There was no nervous chatter about how clever they had been, about their destination, about how tired they were. They just drove the machine quietly, efficiently along, finishing their competent job.

Bond still had no idea what this contraption was. Under the black and gold paint and the rest of the fancy dress it was some sort of a tractor, but of a kind he had never seen or heard of. The wheels, with their vast smooth rubber tyres, were nearly twice as tall as himself. He had seen no trade name on the tyres, it had been too dark, but they were certainly either solid or filled with porous rubber. At the rear there had been a small trailing wheel for stability. An iron fin, painted black and gold, had been added to help the dragon effect. The high mud-guards had been extended into short backswept wings. A long metal dragon's head had been added to the front of the radiator and the headlamps had been given black centres to make 'eyes'. That was all there was to it, except that the cabin had been covered with an armoured dome and the flame-thrower added. It was, as Bond had thought, a tractor dressed up to frighten and burn — though why it had a flame-thrower instead of a machine gun he couldn't imagine. It was clearly the only sort of vehicle that could travel the island. Its huge wide wheels would ride over mangrove and swamp and across the shallow lake. It would negotiate the rough coral uplands and, since its threat would be at night, the heat in the iron cabin would remain at least tolerable.

Bond was impressed. He was always impressed by professionalism. Doctor No was obviously a man who took immense pains. Soon Bond would be meeting him. Soon he would be up against the secret of Doctor No. And then what? Bond smiled grimly to himself. He wouldn't be allowed to get away with his knowledge. He would certainly be killed unless he could escape or talk his way out. And what about the girl? Could Bond prove her innocence and have her spared? Conceivably, but she would never be let off the island. She would have to stay there for the rest of her life, as the mistress or wife of one of the men, or Doctor No himself if she appealed to him.

Bond's thoughts were interrupted by rougher going under the wheels. They had crossed the lake and were on the track that led up the mountain to the huts. The cabin tilted and the machine began to climb. In five minutes they would be there.

The co-driver glanced over his shoulder at Bond and the girl. Bond smiled cheerfully up at him. He said, 'You'll get a medal for this.'

The brown and yellow eyes looked impassively into his. The purple, blubbery lips parted in a sneer in which there was slow hate: 'Shut your —ing mouth.' The man turned back.

The girl nudged him and whispered, 'Why are they so rude? Why do they hate us so much?'

Bond grinned down at her, 'I expect it's because we made them afraid. Perhaps they're still afraid. That's because we don't seem to be frightened of them. We must keep them that way.'

The girl pressed against him. 'I'll try.'

Now the climb was getting steeper. Grey light showed through the slots in the armour. Dawn was coming up. Outside, another day of brazen heat and ugly wind and the smell of marsh gas would be beginning. Bond thought of Quarrel, the brave giant who would not be seeing it, with whom they should now be setting off for the long trek through the mangrove swamps. He remembered the life insurance. Quarrel had smelled his death. Yet he had followed Bond unquestioningly. His faith in Bond had been stronger than his fear. And Bond had let him down. Would Bond also be the death of the girl?

The driver reached forward to the dashboard. From the front of the machine there sounded the brief howl of a police siren. It meandered into a dying moan. After a minute the machine stopped, idling in neutral. The man pressed a switch and took a microphone off a hook beside him. He spoke into it and Bond could hear the echoing voice of the loud-hailer outside. 'Okay. Got the Limey and the girl. Other man's dead. That's the lot. Open up.'

Bond heard a door being pulled sideways on iron rollers. The driver put in the clutch and they rolled slowly forward a few yards and stopped. The man switched off the engine. There was a clang as the iron hatch was opened from the outside. A gush of fresh air and a flood of brighter light came into the cabin. Hands took hold of Bond and dragged him roughly out backwards on to a cement floor. Bond stood up. He felt the prod of a gun in his side. A voice said, 'Stay where you are. No tricks.' Bond looked at the man. He was another Chinese negro, from the same stable as the others. The yellow eyes examined him curiously. Bond turned away indifferently. Another man was prodding the girl with his gun. Bond said sharply, 'Leave the girl alone.' He walked over and stood beside her. The two men seemed surprised. They stood, pointing their guns indecisively.

Bond looked around him. They were in one of the Quonset huts he had seen from the river. It was a garage and workshop. The 'dragon' had been halted over an examination pit in the concrete. A dismantled outboard motor lay on one of the benches. Strips of white sodium lighting ran along the ceiling. There was a smell of oil and exhaust smoke. The driver and his mate were examining the machine. Now they sauntered up.

One of the guards said, 'Passed the message along. The word is to send them through. Everything go okay?'

The co-driver, who seemed to be the senior man present, said, 'Sure. Bit of gunfire. Lights gone. May be some holes in the tyres. Get the boys crackin' – full overhaul. I'll put these two through and go get myself some shuteye.' He turned to Bond. 'Okay, git moving,' he gestured down the long hut.

Bond said, 'Get moving yourself. Mind your manners. And tell those apes to take their guns off us. They might let one off by mistake. They look dumb enough.'

The man came closer. The other three closed up behind him. Hate shone redly in their eyes. The leading man lifted a clenched fist as big as a small ham and held it under Bond's nose. He was controlling himself with an effort. He said tensely, 'Listen, mister. Sometimes us boys is allowed to join in the fun at the end. I'm just praying this'll be one of those times. Once we made it last a whole week. An, Jees, if I get you ...' He broke off. His eyes were alight with cruelty. He looked past Bond at the girl. The eyes became mouths that licked their lips. He wiped his hands down the sides of his trousers. The tip of his tongue showed pinkly between the purple lips. He turned to the other three. 'What say, fellers?'

The three men were also looking at the girl. They nodded dumbly, like children in front of a Christmas tree.

Bond longed to run berserk among them, laying into their faces with his manacled wrists, accepting their bloody revenge. But for the girl he would have done it. Now all he had achieved with his brave words was to get her frightened. He said, 'All right, all right. You're four and we're two and we've got our hands tied. Come on.

We won't hurt you. Just don't push us around too much. Doctor No might not be pleased.'

At the name, the men's faces changed. Three pairs of eyes looked whitely from Bond to the leader. For a minute the leader stared suspiciously at Bond, wondering, trying to fathom whether perhaps Bond had got some edge on their boss. His mouth opened to say something. He thought better of it. He said lamely, 'Okay, okay. We was just kiddin'.' He turned to the men for confirmation. 'Right?'

'Sure! Sure thing.' It was a ragged mumble. The men looked away.

The leader said gruffly, 'This way, mister.' He walked off down the long hut.

Bond took the girl's wrist and followed. He was impressed with the weight of Doctor No's name. That was something to remember if they had any more dealings with the staff.

The man came to a rough wooden door at the end of the hut. There was a bellpush beside it. He rang twice and waited. There came a click and the door opened to reveal ten yards of carpeted rock passage with another door, smarter and cream-painted, at the end.

The man stood aside. 'Straight ahead, mister. Knock on the door. The receptionist'll take over.' There was no irony in his voice and his eyes were impassive.

Bond led the girl into the passage. He heard the door shut behind them. He stopped and looked down at her. He said, 'Now what?'

She smiled tremulously. 'It's nice to feel carpet under one's feet.'

Bond squeezed her wrist. He walked forward to the cream-painted door and knocked.

The door opened. Bond went through with the girl at his heels. When he stopped dead in his tracks, he didn't feel the girl bump into him. He just stood and stared.

XIII

MINK-LINED PRISON

I T was the sort of reception room the largest American corporations have on the President's floor in their New York skyscrapers. It was of pleasant proportions, about twenty feet square. The floor was close-carpeted in the thickest wine-red Wilton and the walls and ceiling were painted a soft dove grey. Colour lithograph reproductions of Degas ballet sketches were well hung in groups on the walls and the lighting was by tall modern standard lamps with dark green silk shades in a fashionable barrel design.

To Bond's right was a broad mahogany desk with a green leather top, handsome matching desk furniture and the most expensive type of intercom. Two tall antique chairs waited for visitors. On the other side of the room was a refectory-type table with shiny magazines and two more chairs. On both the desk and the table were tall vases of freshly cut hibiscus. The air was fresh and cool and held a slight, expensive fragrance.

There were two women in the room. Behind the desk, with pen poised over a printed form, sat an efficient-looking Chinese girl with hornrimmed spectacles below a bang of black hair cut short. Her eyes and mouth wore the standard receptionist's smile of welcome — bright, helpful, inquisitive.

Holding the door through which they had come, and

waiting for them to move farther into the room so that she could close it, stood an older, rather matronly woman of about forty-five. She also had Chinese blood. Her appearance, wholesome, bosomy, eager, was almost excessively gracious. Her square cut pince-nez gleamed with the hostess's desire to make them feel at home.

Both women were dressed in spotless white, with white stockings and white suede brogues, like assistants in the most expensive American beauty-parlours. There was something soft and colourless about their skins as if they rarely went out of doors.

While Bond took in the scene, the woman at the door twittered conventional phrases of welcome as if they had been caught in a storm and had arrived late at a party.

'You poor dears. We simply didn't know when to expect you. We kept on being told you were on your way. First it was teatime yesterday, then dinner, and it was only half an hour ago we heard you would only be here in time for breakfast. You must be famished. Come along now and help Sister Rose fill in your forms and then I'll pack you both straight off to bed. You must be tired out.'

Clucking softly, she closed the door and ushered them forward to the desk. She got them seated in the chairs and rattled on, 'Now I'm Sister Lily and this is Sister Rose. She just wants to ask you a few questions. Now, let me see, a cigarette?' She picked up a tooled leather box. She opened it and put it on the desk in front of them. It had three compartments. She pointed with a little finger, 'Those are American, and those are Players, and those are Turkish.' She picked up an expensive desk-lighter and waited.

Bond reached out his manacled hands to take a Turkish cigarette.

Sister Lily gave a squeak of dismay. 'Oh, but really.' She sounded genuinely embarrassed. 'Sister Rose, the key, quickly. I've said again and again that patients are never to be brought in like that.' There was impatience and distaste in her voice. 'Really, that outside staff! It's time they had a talking to.'

Sister Rose was just as much put out. Hastily she scrabbled in a drawer and handed a key across to Sister Lily who, with much cooing and tut-tutting, unlocked the two pairs of handcuffs and walked behind the desk and dropped them as if they were dirty bandages into the wastepaper basket.

'Thank you.' Bond was unable to think of any way to handle the situation except to fall in with what was happening on the stage. He reached out and took a cigarette and lit it. He glanced at Honeychile Rider who sat looking dazed and nervously clutching the arms of her chair. Bond gave her a reassuring smile.

'Now, if you please.' Sister Rose bent over a long printed form on expensive paper. 'I promise to be as quick as I can. Your name please Mister—er ...'

'Bryce, John Bryce.'

She wrote busily. 'Permanent address?'

'Care of the Royal Zoological Society, Regent's Park, London, England.'

'Profession.'

'Ornithologist.'

'Oh dear,' she dimpled at him, 'could you please spell that?'

Bond did so.

'Thank you so much. Now, let me see, Purpose of Visit?'

'Birds,' said Bond. 'I am also a representative of the Audubon Society of New York. They have a lease of part of this island.'

'Oh, really.' Bond watched the pen writing down exactly what he had said. After the last word she put a neat query in brackets.

'And', Sister Rose smiled politely in the direction of Honeychile, 'your wife? Is she also interested in birds?'

'Yes, indeed.'

'And her first name?'

'Honeychile.'

Sister Rose was delighted, 'What a pretty name.' She wrote busily. 'And now just your next of kin and then we're finished.'

Bond gave M's real name as next of kin for both of them. He described him as 'uncle' and gave his address as 'Managing Director, Universal Export, Regent's Park, London'.

Sister Rose finished writing and said, 'There, that's done. Thank you so much, Mr Bryce, and I do hope you both enjoy your stay.'

'Thank you very much. I'm sure we will.' Bond got up. Honeychile Rider did the same, her face still expressionless.

Sister Lily said, 'Now come along with me, you poor dears.' She walked to a door in the far wall. She stopped with her hand on the cut-glass doorknob. 'Oh deary me, now I've gone and forgotten the number of their rooms! It's the Cream Suite, isn't it, Sister?'

'Yes, that's right. Fourteen and fifteen.'

'Thank you, my dear. And now,' she opened the door, 'if you'll just follow me. I'm afraid it's a terribly long walk.' She shut the door behind them and led the way. 'The Doctor's often talked of putting in one of those moving stairway things, but you know how it is with a busy man,' she laughed gaily. 'So many other things to think of.'

'Yes, I expect so,' said Bond politely.

Bond took the girl's hand and they followed the motherly bustling figure down a hundred yards of lofty corridor in the same style as the reception room but lit at frequent intervals by discreetly expensive wall-brackets.

Bond answered with polite monosyllables the occasional twittering comments Sister Lily threw over her shoulder. His whole mind was focused on the extraordinary circumstances of their reception. He was quite certain the two women had been genuine. Not a look or a word had been dropped that was out of place. It was obviously a front of some kind, but a solid one, meticulously supported by the decor and the cast. The lack of resonance in the room, and now in the corridor, suggested that they had stepped from the Quonset hut into the side of the mountain and that they were now walking through its base. At a guess they would be walking towards the west — towards the cliff-face with which the island ended. There was no moisture on the walls and the air was cool and pure with a strongish breeze coming towards them. A lot of money and good engineering had gone into the job. The pallor of the two women suggested that they spent all their time inside the mountain. From what Sister Lily had said it sounded as if they were part of an inside staff that had nothing to do with the strong-arm squad outside and perhaps didn't even understand what sort of men they were.

It was grotesque, concluded Bond as they came nearer to a door at the end of the corridor, dangerously grotesque, but it was no good wondering about it. He could only follow the lines of the gracious script. At least this was better than the backstage of the island outside.

At the door, Sister Lily rang. They had been expected. The door opened at once. An enchanting Chinese girl in a mauve and white flowered kimono stood smiling and bowing as Chinese girls are supposed to do. Again there was nothing but warmth and welcome in the pale, flowerlike face. Sister Lily cried, 'Here they are at last, May! Mr and

Mrs John Bryce. And I know they must be exhausted so we must take them straight to their rooms for some break-fast and a sleep.' She turned to Bond. 'This is May. Such a dear girl. She will be looking after you both. Anything you want, just ring for May. She's a favourite with all our patients.'

Patients, thought Bond. That's the second time she's used the word. He smiled politely at the girl. 'How do you do. Yes, we'd certainly both of us like to get to our rooms.'

May embraced them both with a warm smile. She said in a low, attractive voice, 'I do hope you'll both be com-fortable, Mr Bryce. I took the liberty of ordering break-fast as soon as I heard you had come in. Shall we ... ?' Corridors branched off to left and right of double lift-doors set in the wall opposite. The girl led the way to the right. Bond and Honeychile followed with Sister Lily taking up the rear.

Numbered doors led off the corridor on either side. Now the decor was in the lightest pink with a dove grey carpet. The numbers on the doors were in the tens. The corridor came to an abrupt end with two doors side by side, 14 and 15. May opened the door of 14 and they followed her in.

It was a charming double bedroom in modern Miami style with dark green walls, dark polished mahogany floor with occasional thick white rugs, and well-designed bamboo furniture with a chintz of large red roses on a white back-ground. There was a communicating door into a more masculine dressing-room and another that led into an extremely luxurious modern bathroom with a step-down bath and a bidet.

It was like being shown into the very latest Florida hotel suite — except for two details which Bond noticed. There were no windows and no inside handles to the doors.

May looked hopefully from one to the other.

Bond turned to Honeychile. He smiled at her. 'It looks very comfortable, don't you think, darling?'

The girl played with the edge of her skirt. She nodded, not looking at him.

There was a timid knock on the door and another girl, as pretty as May, tripped in with a loaded tray balanced on her upturned hand. She put it down on the centre table and pulled up two chairs. She whisked off the speckless linen cloth that covered the dishes and pattered out of the room. There was a delicious smell of bacon and coffee.

May and Sister Lily backed to the door. The older woman stopped on the threshold. 'And now we'll leave you two dear people in peace. If you want anything, just ring. The bells are by the bed. Oh, and by the way, you'll find plenty of fresh clothes in the cupboards. Chinese style, I'm afraid,' she twinkled apologetically, 'but I hope they're the right sizes. The wardrobe room only got the measurements yesterday evening. The Doctor has given strict orders that you're not be to disturbed. He'd be delighted if you'd join him for dinner this evening. He wants you to have the whole of the rest of the day to yourselves — to get settled down, you know.' She paused and looked from one to the other in smiling inquiry. 'Shall I say you ... ?'

'Yes, please,' said Bond. 'Tell the Doctor we shall be delighted to join him for dinner.'

'Oh, I know he'll be so pleased.' With a last twitter the two women softly withdrew and closed the door behind them.

Bond turned towards Honeychile. She looked embarrassed. She still avoided his eyes. It occurred to Bond that she could never have met such soft treatment or seen such luxury in her life. To her, all this must be far more strange and terrifying than what they had gone through outside.

She stood and fiddled at the hem of her Man Friday skirt. There were streaks of dried sweat and salt and dust on her face. Her bare legs were filthy and Bond noticed that her toes were moving softly as they gripped nervously into the wonderful thick pile carpet.

Bond laughed. He laughed with real pleasure that her fear had been drowned in the basic predicament of clothes and how to behave, and he laughed at the picture they made — she in her rags and he in his dirty blue shirt and black jeans and muddy canvas shoes.

He went to her and took her hands. They were cold. He said, 'Honey, we're a couple of scarecrows. There's only one problem. Shall we have breakfast first while it's hot, or shall we get out of these rags and have a bath and eat the breakfast when it's cold? Don't worry about anything else. We're here in this wonderful little house and that's all that matters. Now then, what shall we do?'

She smiled uncertainly. The blue eyes searched his face for reassurance. 'You're not worried about what's going to happen to us?' She nodded at the room. 'Don't you think this is all a trap?'

'If it's a trap we're in it. There's nothing we can do now but eat the cheese. The only question is whether we eat it hot or cold.' He pressed her hands. 'Really, Honey. Leave the worrying to me. Just think where we were an hour ago. Isn't this better? Now come on and decide the really important things. Bath or breakfast?'

She said reluctantly, 'Well, if you think ... I mean — I'd rather get clean first.' She added quickly, 'But you've got to help me.' She jerked her head towards the bathroom door. 'I don't know how to work one of those places. What do you do?'

Bond said seriously, 'It's quite easy. I'll fix it all ready for you. While you're having your bath, I'll have my breakfast. I'll keep yours warm.' Bond went to one of the built-in clothes cupboards and ran the door back. There were half a dozen kimonos, some silk and some linen. He took out a linen one at random. 'You take off your clothes and get into this and I'll get the bath ready. Later on you can choose the things you want to wear for bed and dinner.'

She said gratefully, 'Oh yes, James. If you'll just show me ...' She started to unbutton her shirt.

Bond wanted to take her in his arms and kiss her. Instead he said abruptly, 'That's fine, Honey,' and went into the bathroom and turned on the taps.

There was everything in the bathroom — Floris Lime bath essence for men and Guerlain bathcubes for women. He crushed a cube into the water and at once the room smelled like an orchid house. The soap was Guerlain's Sapoceti, *Fleurs des Alpes*. In a medicine cupboard behind the mirror over the washbasin were toothbrushes and toothpaste, Steradent toothpicks, Rose mouthwash, dental floss, Aspirin and Milk of Magnesia. There was also an electric razor, Lentheric after-shave lotion, and two nylon hairbrushes and combs. Everything was brand new and untouched.

Bond looked at his filthy unshaven face in the mirror and smiled grimly into the grey, sunburned castaway's eyes. The coating on the pill was certainly of the very finest sugar. It would be wise to expect that the medicine inside would be of the bitterest.

He turned back to the bath and felt the water. It would be too hot for someone who presumably had never had a hot bath before. He let in some cold. As he bent over, two arms were thrown round his neck. He stood up. The golden body blazed in the white tiled bathroom. She kissed him hard and clumsily on the lips. He put his arms round her and crushed her to him, his heart pounding. She said breathlessly at his ear, 'The Chinese dress felt strange. Anyway, you told that woman we were married.'

Bond's hand was on her left breast. Its peak was hard with passion. Her stomach pressed against his. Why not? Why not? Don't be a fool! This is a crazy time for it. You're both in deadly danger. You must stay cold as ice to have any chance of getting out of this mess. Later! Later! Don't be weak.

Bond took his hand away from her breast and put it round her neck. He rubbed his face against hers and then brought his mouth round to hers and gave her one long kiss.

He stood away and held her at arm's length. For a moment they looked at each other, their eyes bright with desire. She was breathing fast, her lips parted so that he could see the glint of teeth. He said unsteadily, 'Honey, get into that bath before I spank you.'

She smiled. Without saying anything she stepped down into the bath and lay at full length. She looked up. The fair hair on her body glittered up through the water like golden sovereigns. She said provocatively, 'You've got to wash me. I don't know what to do. You've got to show me.'

Bond said desperately, 'Shut up, Honey. And stop flirting. Just take the soap and the sponge and start scrubbing. Damn you! This isn't the time for making love. I'm going to have breakfast.' He reached for the door handle and opened the door. She said softly, 'James!' He looked back. She was sticking her tongue out at him. He grinned savagely back at her and slammed the door.

Bond went into the dressing-room and stood in the middle of the floor and waited for his heart to stop pounding. He rubbed his hands over his face and shook his head to get rid of the thought of her.

To clear his mind he went carefully over both rooms looking for exits, possible weapons, microphones — anything that would add to his knowledge. There were none of these things. There was an electric clock on the wall which said eight-thirty and a row of bells beside the double bed. They said, Room Service, Coiffeur, Manicurist, Maid. There was no telephone. High up in a corner of both rooms was a small ventilator grille. Each was about two feet square. Useless. The doors appeared to be of some light metal, painted to match the walls. Bond threw the whole weight of his body against one of them. It didn't give a millimetre. Bond rubbed his shoulder. The place was a prison — an exquisite prison. It was no good arguing. The trap had shut tight on them. Now the only thing for the mice to do was to make the most of the cheese.

Bond sat down at the breakfast table. There was a large tumbler of pineapple juice in a silver-plated bowl of crushed ice. He swallowed it down and lifted the cover off his individual hot-plate. Scrambled eggs on toast, four rashers of bacon, a grilled kidney and what looked like an English pork sausage. There were also two kinds of hot toast, rolls inside a napkin, marmalade, honey and strawberry jam. The coffee was boiling hot in a large Thermos decanter. The cream smelled fresh.

From the bathroom came the sound of the girl crooning 'Marion'. Bond closed his ears to the sound and started on the eggs.

Ten minutes later, Bond heard the bathroom door open. He put down his toast and marmalade and covered his eyes with his hands. She laughed. She said, 'He's a coward. He's frightened of a simple girl.' Bond heard her rummaging in the cupboards. She went on talking, half to herself. 'I wonder why he's frightened. Of course if I wrestled with him I'd win easily. Perhaps he's frightened of that. Perhaps he's really not very strong. His arms and his chest look strong enough. I haven't seen the rest yet. Perhaps it's weak. Yes, that must be it. That's why he doesn't dare take his clothes off in front of me. H'm, now let's see, would he like me in this?' She raised her voice. 'Darling James, would you like me in white with pale blue birds flying all over me?'

'Yes, damn you,' said Bond through his hands. 'Now stop chattering to yourself and come and have breakfast. I'm getting sleepy.'

She gave a cry. 'Oh, if you mean it's time for us to go to bed, of course I'll hurry.'

There was a flurry of feet and Bond heard her sit down opposite. He took his hands down. She was smiling at him. She looked ravishing. Her hair was dressed and combed and brushed to kill, with one side falling down the side of the cheek and the other slicked back behind her ear. Her skin sparkled with freshness and the big blue eyes were alight with happiness. Now Bond loved the broken nose. It had become part of his thoughts of her and it suddenly occurred to him that he would be sad when she was just an immaculately beautiful girl like other beautiful girls. But he knew it would be no good trying to persuade her of that. She sat demurely, with her hands in her lap below the end of a cleavage which showed half her breasts and a deep vee of her stomach.

Bond said severely, 'Now listen, Honey. You look wonderful, but that isn't the way to wear a kimono. Pull it up right across your body and tie it tight and stop trying to look like a call girl. It just isn't good manners at breakfast.'

'Oh, you are a stuffy old beast.' She pulled her kimono an inch or two closer. 'Why don't you like playing? I want to play at being married.'

'Not at breakfast time,' said Bond firmly. 'Come on and eat up. It's delicious. And anyway, I'm filthy. I'm going to shave and have a bath.' He got up and walked round the table and kissed the top of her head. 'And as for

playing, as you call it, I'd rather play with you than anyone in the world. But not now.' Without waiting for her
answer he walked into the bathroom and shut the door.

Bond shaved and had a bath and a shower. He felt
desperately sleepy. Sleep came to him in waves so that
from time to time he had to stop what he was doing and
bend his head down between his knees. When he came to
brush his teeth he could hardly do it. Now he recognized
the signs. He had been drugged. In the coffee or in the
pineapple juice? It didn't matter. Nothing mattered. All
he wanted to do was lie down on the tiled floor and shut
his eyes. Bond weaved drunkenly to the door. He forgot
that he was naked. That didn't matter either. Anyway
the girl had finished her breakfast. She was in bed. He
staggered over to her, holding on to the furniture. The
kimono was lying in a pile on the floor. She was fast
asleep, naked under a single sheet.

Bond gazed dreamily at the empty pillow beside her
head. No! He found the switches and turned out the
lights. Now he had to crawl across the floor and into his
room. He got to his bed and pulled himself on to it. He
reached out an arm of lead and jabbed at the switch on
the bed-light. He missed it. The lamp crashed to the floor
and the bulb burst. With a last effort Bond turned on his
side and let the waves sweep over his head.

The luminous figures on the electric clock in the double
room said nine-thirty.

At ten o'clock the door of the double room opened softly.
A very tall thin figure was silhouetted against the lighted
corridor. It was a man. He must have been six feet six tall.
He stood on the threshold with his arms folded, listening.
Satisfied, he moved slowly into the room and up to the bed
He knew the way exactly. He bent down and listened to
the quiet breathing of the girl. After a moment he reached

up to his chest and pressed a switch. A flashlight with a very broad diffused beam came on. The flashlight was attached to him by a belt that held it above the breast bone. He bent forward so that the soft light shone on the girl's face.

The intruder examined the girl's face for several minutes. One of his hands came up and took the sheet at her chin and softly drew the sheet down to the end of the bed. The hand that drew down the sheet was not a hand. It was a pair of articulated steel pincers at the end of a metal stalk that disappeared into a black silk sleeve. It was a mechanical hand.

The man gazed for a long time at the naked body, moving his chest to and fro so that every corner of the body came under the light. Then the claw came out again and delicately lifted a corner of the sheet from the bottom of the bed and drew it back over the girl. The man stood for another moment gazing down at the sleeping face, then he switched off the torch on his chest and moved quietly away across the room to the open door through which Bond was sleeping.

The man spent longer beside Bond's bed. He scrutinized every line, every shadow on the dark, rather cruel face that lay drowned, almost extinct, on the pillow. He watched the pulse in the neck and counted it and, when he had pulled down the sheet, he did the same with the area round the heart. He gauged the curve of the muscles on Bond's arms and thighs and looked thoughtfully at the hidden strength in the flat stomach. He even bent down close over the outflung open right hand and examined its life and fate lines.

Finally, with infinite care, the steel claw drew the sheet back up to Bond's neck. For another minute the tall figure stood over the sleeping man, then it swished softly away and out into the corridor and the door closed with a click.

XIV

COME INTO MY PARLOUR

THE electric clock in the cool dark room in the heart of the mountain showed four-thirty.

Outside the mountain, Crab Key had sweltered and stunk its way through another day. At the eastern end of the island, the mass of birds, Louisiana herons, pelicans, avocets, sandpipers, egrets, flamingoes and the few roseate spoonbills, went on with building their nests or fished in the shallow waters of the lake. Most of the birds had been disturbed so often that year that they had given up any idea of building. In the past few months they had been raided at regular intervals by the monster that came at night and burned down their roosting places and the beginnings of their nests. This year many would not breed. There would be vague movements to migrate and many would die of the nervous hysteria that seizes bird colonies when they no longer have peace and privacy.

At the other end of the island, on the guanera that gave the mountain its snow-covered look, the vast swarm of cormorants had passed their usual day of gorging themselves with fish and paying back the ounce of precious manure to their owner and protector. Nothing had interfered with *their* nesting season. Now they were noisily fiddling with the untidy piles of sticks that would be their nests — each pile at exactly sixty centimetres from the next, for the guanay is a quarrelsome bird and this sixty-centimetre ring represents their sparring space. Soon the females would be laying the three eggs from which their master's flock would be increased by an average of two young cormorants.

Below the peak, where the diggings began, the hundred or so negro men and women who were the labour force were coming to the end of the day's shift. Another fifty cubic yards of guano had been dug out of the mountainside and another twenty yards of terrace had been added to the working level. Below, the mountainside looked like terraced vineyards in Upper Italy, except that here there were no vines, only deep barren shelves cut in the mountainside. And here, instead of the stink of marsh gas on the rest of the island, there was a strong ammoniac smell, and the ugly hot wind that kept the diggings dry blew the freshly turned whitish-brown dust into the eyes and ears and noses of the diggers. But the workers were used to the smell and the dust, and it was easy, healthy work. They had no complaints.

The last iron truck of the day started off on the Decauderville Track that snaked down the mountainside to the crusher and separator. A whistle blew and the workers shouldered their clumsy picks and moved lazily down towards the high-wired group of Quonset huts that was their compound. Tomorrow, on the other side of the mountain, the monthly ship would be coming in to the deep-water quay they had helped to build ten years before, but which, since then, they had never seen. That would mean fresh stores and fresh goods and cheap jewellery at the canteen. It would be a holiday. There would be rum and dancing and a few fights. Life was good.

Life was good, too, for the senior outside staff—all Chinese negroes like the men who had hunted Bond and Quarrel and the girl. They also stopped work in the garage and the machine shops and at the guard posts and filtered off to the 'officers'' quarters. Apart from watch and loading duties, tomorrow would also be a holiday for most of them. They too would have their drinking and dancing, and there would be a new monthly batch of girls from 'inside'. Some 'marriages' from the last lot would continue for further months or weeks according to the taste of the 'husband', but for the others there would be a fresh choice. There would be some of the older girls who had had their babies in the creche and were coming back for a fresh spell of duty 'outside', and there would be a sprinkling of young ones who had come of age and would be 'coming out' for the first time. There would be fights over these and blood would be shed, but in the end the officers' quarters would settle down for another month of communal life, each officer with his woman to look after his needs.

Deep down in the cool heart of the mountain, far below this well-disciplined surface life, Bond awoke in his comfortable bed. Apart from a slight nembutal headache he felt fit and rested. Lights were on in the girl's room and he could hear her moving about. He swung his feet to the ground and, avoiding the fragments of glass from the broken lamp, walked softly over to the clothes cupboard and put on the first kimono that came to his hand. He went to the door. The girl had a pile of kimonos out on the bed and was trying them on in front of the wall mirror. She had on a very smart one in sky-blue silk. It looked wonderful against the gold of her skin. Bond said, 'That's the one.'

She whirled round, her hand at her mouth. She took it down. 'Oh, it's you!' She smiled at him. 'I thought you'd never wake up. I've been to look at you several times. I'd made up my mind to wake you at five. It's half past four and I'm hungry. Can you get us something to eat?'

'Why not.' Bond walked across to her bed. As he passed her he put his arm round her waist and took her with him.

He examined the bells. He pressed the one marked 'Room Service'. He said, 'What about the others? Let's have the full treatment.'

She giggled. 'But what's a manicurist?'

'Someone who does your nails. We must look our best for Doctor No.' At the back of Bond's mind was the urgent necessity to get his hands on some kind of weapon — a pair of scissors would be better than nothing. Anything would do.

He pressed two more bells. He let her go and looked round the room. Someone had come while they were asleep and taken away the breakfast things. There was a drink tray on a sideboard against the wall. Bond went over and examined it. It had everything. Propped among the bottles were two menus, huge double-folio pages covered with print. They might have been from the Savoy Grill, or the '21', or the Tour d'Argent. Bond ran his eye down one of them. It began with *Caviar double de Beluga* and ended with *Sorbet à la Champagne*. In between was every dish whose constituents would not be ruined by a deep freeze. Bond tossed it down. One certainly couldn't grumble about the quality of the cheese in the trap!

There was a knock on the door and the exquisite May came in. She was followed by two other twittering Chinese girls. Bond brushed aside their amiabilities, ordered tea and buttered toast for Honeychile and told them to look after her hair and nails. Then he went into the bathroom and had a couple of Aspirins and a cold shower. He put on his kimono again, reflected that he looked idiotic in it, and went back into the room. A beaming May asked if he would be good enough to select what he and Mrs Bryce could care to have for dinner. Without enthusiasm, Bond ordered caviar, grilled lamb cutlets and salad, and angels on horseback for himself. When Honeychile refused to make any suggestions, he chose melon, roast chicken à l'Anglaise and vanilla icecream with hot chocolate sauce for her.

May dimpled her enthusiasm and approval. 'The Doctor asks if seven forty-five or eight would be convenient.'

Bond said curtly that it would.

'Thank you so much, Mr Bryce. I will call for you at seven forty-four.'

Bond walked over to where Honeychile was being ministered to at the dressing table. He watched the busy delicate fingers at work on her hair and her nails. She smiled at him excitedly in the mirror. He said gruffly, 'Don't let them make too much of a monkey out of you,' and went to the drink tray. He poured himself out a stiff Bourbon and soda and took it into his own room. So much for his idea of getting hold of a weapon. The scissors and files and probes were attached to the manicurist's waist by a chain. So were the scissors of the hairdresser. Bond sat down on his rumpled bed and lost himself in drink and gloomy reflections.

The women went. The girl looked in at him. When he didn't lift his head she went back into her room and left him alone. In due course Bond came into her room to get himself another drink. He said perfunctorily, 'Honey, you look wonderful.' He glanced at the clock on the wall and went back and drank his drink and put on another of the idiotic kimonos, a plain black one.

In due course there came the soft knock on the door and the two of them went silently out of the room and along the empty, gracious corridor. May stopped at the lift. Its doors were held open by another eager Chinese girl. They walked in and the doors shut. Bond noticed that the lift was made by Waygood Otis. Everything in the prison was de luxe. He gave an inward shudder of distaste. He noticed the reaction. He turned to the girl. 'I'm sorry, Honey. Got a bit of a headache.' He didn't want to tell her that all this luxury play-acting was getting him down, that he hadn't the smallest idea what it was all about, that he knew it was bad news, and that he hadn't an inkling of a plan of how to get them out of whatever situation they were in. That was the worst of it. There was nothing that depressed Bond's spirit so much as the knowledge that he hadn't one line of either attack or defence.

The girl moved closer to him. She said, 'I'm sorry, James. I hope it will go away. You're not angry with me about anything?'

Bond dredged up a smile. He said, 'No, darling. I'm only angry with myself.' He lowered his voice: 'Now, about this evening. Just leave the talking to me. Be natural and don't be worried by Doctor No. He may be a bit mad.'

She nodded solemnly. 'I'll do my best.'

The lift sighed to a stop. Bond had no idea how far down they had gone — a hundred feet, two hundred? The automatic doors hissed back and Bond and the girl stepped out into a large room.

It was empty. It was a high-ceilinged room about sixty feet long, lined on three sides with books to the ceiling. At first glance, the fourth wall seemed to be made of solid blue-black glass. The room appeared to be a combined study and library. There was a big paper-strewn desk in one corner and a central table with periodicals and newspapers. Comfortable club chairs, upholstered in red leather, were dotted about. The carpet was dark green, and the lighting, from standard lamps, was subdued. The only odd feature was that the drink tray and sideboard were up against the middle of the long glass wall, and chairs and occasional tables with ashtrays were arranged in a semi-circle round it so that the room was centred in front of the empty wall.

Bond's eye caught a swirl of movement in the dark glass. He walked across the room. A silvery spray of small fish with a bigger fish in pursuit fled across the dark blue. They disappeared, so to speak, off the edge of the screen. What was this? An aquarium? Bond looked upwards. A yard below the ceiling, small waves were lapping at the glass. Above the waves was a strip of greyer blue-black, dotted with sparks of light. The outlines of Orion were the clue. This was not an aquarium. This was the sea itself and the night sky. The whole of one side of the room was made of armoured glass. They were under the sea, looking straight into its heart, twenty feet down.

Bond and the girl stood transfixed. As they watched, there was the glimpse of two great goggling orbs. A golden sheen of head and deep flank showed for an instant and was gone. A big grouper? A silver swarm of anchovies stopped and hovered and sped away. The twenty-foot tendrils of a Portuguese man-o'-war drifted slowly across the window, glinting violet as they caught the light. Up above there was the dark mass of its underbelly and the outline of its inflated bladder, steering with the breeze.

Bond walked along the wall, fascinated by the idea of living with this slow, endlessly changing moving picture. A big tulip shell was progressing slowly up the window from the floor level, a frisk of demoiselles and angel fish and a ruby-red moonlight snapper were nudging and rubbing themselves against a corner of the glass and a sea centipede quested along, nibbling at the minute algae that must grow every day on the outside of the window. A long dark shadow paused in the centre of the window and then moved slowly away. If only one could see more!

Obediently, two great shafts of light, from off the 'screen', lanced out into the water. For an instant they searched independently. Then they converged on the departing shadow and the dull grey torpedo of a twelve-foot shark showed up in all its detail. Bond could even see the piglike pink eyes roll inquisitively in the light and the slow pulse of the slanting gill-rakers. For an instant the shark turned straight into the converged beam and the white half-moon mouth showed below the flat reptile's head. It stood poised for a second and then, with an elegant, disdainful swirl, the great swept-back tail came round and with a lightning quiver the shark had gone.

The searchlights went out. Bond turned slowly. He expected to see Doctor No, but still the room was empty. It looked static and lifeless compared with the pulsing mysteries outside the window. Bond looked back. What must this be like in the colours of day, when one could see everything perhaps for twenty yards or more? What must it be like in a storm when the waves crashed noiselessly against the glass, delving almost to the floor and then sweeping up and out of sight. What must it be like in the evening when the last golden shafts of the sun shone into the upper half of the room and the waters below were full of dancing motes and tiny water insects? What an amazing man this must be who had thought of this fantastically beautiful conception, and what an extraordinary engineering feat to have carried it out! How had he done it? There could only be one way. He must have built the the glass wall deep inside the cliff and then delicately removed layer after layer of the outside rock until the divers could prise off the last skin of coral. But how thick was the glass? Who had rolled it for him? How had he got it to the island? How many divers had he used? How much, God in heaven, could it have cost?

'One million dollars.'

It was a cavernous, echoing voice, with a trace of American accent.

Bond turned slowly, almost reluctantly, away from the window.

Doctor No had come through a door behind his desk.

He stood looking at them benignly, with a thin smile on his lips.

'I expect you were wondering about the cost. My guests usually think about the material side after about fifteen minutes. Were you?'

'I was.'

Still smiling (Bond was to get used to that thin smile), Doctor No came slowly out from behind the desk and moved towards them. He seemed to glide rather than take steps. His knees did not dent the matt, gunmetal sheen of his kimono and no shoes showed below the sweeping hem.

Bond's first impression was of thinness and erectness and height. Doctor No was at least six inches taller than Bond, but the straight immovable poise of his body made him seem still taller. The head also was elongated and tapered from a round, completely bald skull down to a sharp chin so that the impression was of a reversed raindrop — or rather oildrop, for the skin was of a deep almost translucent yellow.

It was impossible to tell Doctor No's age: as far as Bond could see, there were no lines on the face. It was odd to see a forehead as smooth as the top of the polished skull. Even the cavernous indrawn cheeks below the prominent cheek-bones looked as smooth as fine ivory. There was something Dali-esque about the eyebrows, which were fine and black and sharply upswept as if they had been painted on as make-up for a conjurer. Below them, slanting jet black eyes stared out of the skull. They were without eyelashes. They looked like the mouths of two small revolvers, direct and unblinking and totally devoid of expression. The thin fine nose ended very close above a wide compressed wound of a mouth which, despite its almost permanent sketch of a smile, showed only cruelty and authority. The chin was indrawn towards the neck. Later Bond was to notice that it rarely moved more than slightly away from centre, giving the impression that the head and the vertebra were in one piece.

The bizarre, gliding figure looked like a giant venomous worm wrapped in grey tin-foil, and Bond would not have been surprised to see the rest of it trailing slimily along the carpet behind.

Doctor No came within three steps of them and stopped. The wound in the tall face opened. 'Forgive me for not shaking hands with you,' the deep voice was flat and even. 'I am unable to.' Slowly the sleeves parted and opened. 'I have no hands.'

The two pairs of steel pincers came out on their gleaming stalks and were held up for inspection like the hands of a praying mantis. Then the two sleeves joined again.

Bond felt the girl at his side give a start.

The black apertures turned towards her. They slid down to her nose. The voice said flatly, 'It is a misfortune.' The eyes came back to Bond. 'You were admiring my aquarium.' It was a statement, not a question. 'Man enjoys the beasts and the birds. I decided to enjoy also the fish. I find them far more varied and interesting. I am sure you both share my enthusiasm.'

Bond said, 'I congratulate you. I shall never forget this room.'

'No.' Again a statement, perhaps with a sardonic inflection, of fact. 'But we have much to talk about. And so little time. Please sit down. You will have a drink? Cigarettes are beside your chairs.'

Doctor No moved to a high leather chair and folded himself down on to the seat. Bond took the chair opposite. The girl sat between them and slightly back.

Bond felt a movement behind him. He looked over his shoulder. A short man, a Chinese negro, with the build of a wrestler, stood at the drink tray. He was dressed in black trousers and a smart white jacket. Black almond eyes in a wide moon face met his and slid incuriously away.

Doctor No said, 'This is my bodyguard. He is expert in many things. There is no mystery about his sudden appearance. I always carry what is known as a walkie-talkie here,' he inclined his chin towards the bosom of his kimono. 'Thus I can summon him when he is needed. What will the girl have?'

Not 'Your Wife'. Bond turned to Honeychile. Her eyes were wide and staring. She said quietly, 'A Coca-Cola, please.'

Bond felt a moment of relief. At least she was not being got down by the performance. Bond said, 'And I would like a medium Vodka dry Martini — with a slice of lemon peel. Shaken and not stirred, please. I would prefer Russian or Polish vodka.'

Doctor No gave his thin smile an extra crease. 'I see you are also a man who knows what he wants. On this occasion your desires will be satisfied. Do you not find that it is generally so? When one wants a thing one gets it? That is my experience.'

'The small things.'

'If you fail at the large things it means you have not large ambitions. Concentration, focus — that is all. The aptitudes come, the tools forge themselves. "Give me a fulcrum and I will move the world" — but only if the desire to move the world is there.' The thin lips bent minutely downwards in deprecation. 'But this is chatter. We are making conversation. Instead, let us talk. Both of us, I am sure, prefer talk to conversation. Is the Martini to your liking? You have cigarettes — enough and the right sort to cosset your cancer? So be it. Sam-sam, put the shaker beside the man and another bottle of Coca-Cola beside the girl. It should now be eight-ten. We will have dinner at nine o'clock precisely.'

Doctor No sat slightly more upright in his chair. He inclined himself forward, staring at Bond. There was a moment's silence in the room. Then Doctor No said, 'And now Mister James Bond of the Secret Service, let us tell each other our secrets. First, to show you that I hide nothing, I will tell you mine. Then you will tell me yours.' Doctor No's eyes blazed darkly. 'But let us tell each other the truth.' He drew one steel claw out of the wide sleeve and held it upwards. He paused, 'I shall do so. But you must do the same. If you do not, these,' he pointed the claw at his eyes, 'will know that you are lying.'

Doctor No brought the steel claw delicately in front of each eye and tapped the centre of each eyeball.

Each eyeball in turn emitted a dull ting, 'These', said Doctor No, 'see everything.'

XV

PANDORA'S BOX

JAMES BOND picked up his glass and sipped at it thoughtfully. It seemed pointless to go on bluffing. His story of representing the Audubon Society was anyway a thin one which could be punctured by anyone who knew about birds. It was obvious that his own cover was in shreds. He must concentrate on protecting the girl. To begin with he must reassure her.

Bond smiled at Doctor No. He said, 'I know about your contact in King's House, Miss Taro. She is your agent. I have recorded the fact and it will be divulged in certain circumstances' — Doctor No's expression showed no interest – 'as will other facts. But, if we are to have a talk, let us have it without any more stage effects. You are an interesting man. But it is not necessary to make yourself more interesting than you are. You have suffered the misfortune of losing your hands. You wear mechanical hands. Many men wounded in the war wear them. You wear contact lenses instead of spectacles. You use a walkie-talkie instead of a bell to summon your servant. No doubt you have other tricks. But, Doctor No, you are still a man who sleeps and eats and defecates like the rest of us. So no more conjuring tricks, please. I am not one of your guano diggers and I am not impressed by them.'

Doctor No inclined his head a fraction. 'Bravely spoken, Mister Bond. I accept the rebuke. I have no doubt developed annoying mannerisms from living too long in the company of apes. But do not mistake these mannerisms for bluff. I am a technician. I suit the tool to the material. I possess also a range of tools for working with refractory materials. However,' Doctor No raised his joined sleeves an inch and let them fall back in his lap, 'let us proceed with our talk. It is a rare pleasure to have an intelligent listener and I shall enjoy telling you the story of one of the most remarkable men in the world. You are the first person to hear it. I have not told it before. You are the only person. I have ever met who will appreciate my story and also — ' Doctor No paused for the significance of the last words to make itself felt — 'keep it to himself.' He continued, 'The second of these considerations also applies to the girl.'

So that was it. There had been little doubt in Bond's mind ever since the Spandau had opened up on them, and since, even before then, in Jamaica, where the attempts on him had not been half-hearted. Bond had assumed from the first that this man was a killer, that it would be a duel to the death. He had had his usual blind faith that he would win the duel — all the way until the moment when the flame-thrower had pointed at him. Then he had begun to doubt. Now he knew. This man was too strong, too well equipped.

Bond said, 'There is no point in the girl hearing this. She has nothing to do with me. I found her yesterday on the beach. She is a Jamaican from Morgan's Harbour. She collects shells. Your men destroyed her canoe so I had to bring her with me. Send her away now and then back home. She won't talk. She will swear not to.'

The girl interrupted fiercely. 'I *will* talk! I shall tell everything. I'm not going to move. I'm going to stay with you.'

Bond looked at her. He said icily, 'I don't want you.'

Doctor No said softly, 'Do not waste your breath on these heroics. Nobody who comes to this island has ever left it. Do you understand? Nobody — not even the simplest fisherman. It is not my policy. Do not argue with me or attempt to bluff me. It is entirely useless.'

Bond examined the face. There was no anger in it, no obstinacy — nothing but a supreme indifference. He shrugged his shoulders. He looked at the girl and smiled. He said, 'All right, Honey. And I didn't mean it. I'd hate you to go away. We'll stay together and listen to what the maniac has to say.'

The girl nodded happily. It was as if her lover had threatened to send her out of the cinema and now had relented.

Doctor No said, in the same soft resonant voice, 'You are right, Mister Bond. That is just what I am, a maniac. All the greatest men are maniacs. They are possessed by a mania which drives them forward towards their goal. The great scientists, the artists, the philosophers, the religious leaders — all maniacs. What else but a blind singleness of purpose could have given focus to their genius, would have kept them in the groove of their purpose? Mania, my dear Mister Bond, is as priceless as genius. Dissipation of energy, fragmentation of vision, loss of momentum, the lack of follow-through — these are the vices of the herd.' Doctor No sat slightly back in his chair. 'I do not possess these vices. I am, as you correctly say, a maniac — a maniac, Mister Bond, with a mania for power. That' — the black holes glittered blankly at Bond through the contact lenses — 'is the meaning of my life. That is why I am here. That is why you are here. That is why here exists.'

Bond picked up his glass and drained it. He filled it again from the shaker. He said, 'I'm not surprised. It's the old business of thinking you're the King of England, or the President of the United States, or God. The asylums are full of them. The only difference is that instead of being shut up, you've built your own asylum and shut yourself up in it. But why did you do it? Why does sitting shut up in this cell give you the illusion of power?'

Irritation flickered at the corner of the thin mouth. 'Mister Bond, power is sovereignty. Clausewitz's first principle was to have a secure base. From there one proceeds to freedom of action. Together, that is sovereignty. I have secured these things and much besides. No one else in the world possesses them to the same degree. They *cannot* have them. The world is too public. These things can only be secured in privacy. You talk of kings and presidents. How much power do they possess? As much as their people will allow them. Who in the world has the power of life or death over his people? Now that Stalin is dead, can you name any man except myself? And how do I possess that power, that sovereignty? Through privacy. Through the fact that nobody *knows*. Through the fact that I have to account to no one.'

Bond shrugged. 'That is only the illusion of power, Doctor No. Any man with a loaded revolver has the power of life and death over his neighbour. Other people beside you have murdered in secret and got away with it. In the end they generally get their deserts. A greater power than they possess is exerted upon them by the community. That will happen to you, Doctor No. I tell you, your search for power is an illusion because power itself is an illusion.'

Doctor No said equably, 'So is beauty, Mister Bond. So is art, so is money, so is death. And so, probably, is life. These concepts are relative. Your play upon words does not shake me. I know philosophy, I know ethics, and I know logic — better than you do, I daresay. But let us move away from this sterile debate. Let us return to where I began, with my mania for power, or, if you wish it, for the illusion of power. And please, Mister Bond,' again the extra crease in the fixed smile, 'please do not imagine that half an hour's conversation with you will alter the pattern of my life. Interest yourself rather in the history of my pursuit, let us put it, of an illusion.'

'Go ahead.' Bond glanced at the girl. She caught his eyes. She put her hand up to her mouth as if to conceal a yawn. Bond grinned at her. He wondered when it would amuse Doctor No to crack her pose of indifference.

Doctor No said benignly, 'I shall endeavour not to bore you. Facts are so much more interesting than theories, don't you agree?' Doctor No was not expecting a reply. He fixed his eye on the elegant tulip shell that had now wandered half way up the outside of the dark window. Some small silver fish squirted across the black void. A bluish prickle of phosphorescence meandered vaguely. Up by the ceiling, the stars shone more brightly through the glass.

The artificiality of the scene inside the room — the three people sitting in the comfortable chairs, the drinks on the sideboard, the rich carpet, the shaded lights, suddenly seemed ludicrous to Bond. Even the drama of it, the danger, were fragile things compared with the progress of the tulip shell up the glass outside. Supposing the glass burst. Supposing the stresses had been badly calculated, the workmanship faulty. Supposing the sea decided to lean a little more heavily against the window.

Doctor No said, 'I was the only son of a German Methodist missionary and a Chinese girl of good family. I was born in Pekin, but on what is known as "the wrong side of the blanket". I was an encumbrance. An aunt of my mother was paid to bring me up.' Doctor No paused. 'No love, you see, Mister Bond. Lack of parental care.' He went on, 'The seed was sown. I went to work in Shanghai. I became involved with the Tongs, with their

illicit proceedings. I enjoyed the conspiracies, the bur-
glaries, the murders, the arson of insured properties. They
represented revolt against the father figure who had
betrayed me. I loved the death and destruction of people
and things. I became adept in the technique of crimin-
ality — if you wish to call it that. Then there was trouble. I
had to be got out of the way. The Tongs considered me too
valuable to kill. I was smuggled to the United States. I
settled in New York. I had been give a letter of introduction, in code, to one of the two most powerful Tongs in
America – the Hip Sings. I never knew what the letter
said, but they took me on at once as a confidential clerk.
In due course, at the age of thirty, I was made the
equivalent of treasurer. The treasury contained over a
million dollars. I coveted this money. Then began the
great Tong Wars of the late 'twenties. The two great
New York Tongs, my own, the Hip Sings, and our rival,
the On Lee Ongs, joined in combat. Over the weeks,
hundreds on both sides were killed and their houses and
properties burned to the ground. It was a time of torture
and murder and arson in which I joined with delight.
Then the riot squads came. Almost the whole police force
of New York was mobilized. The two underground armies
were prised apart and the headquarters of the two Tongs
were raided and the ringleaders sent to jail. I was tipped
off about the raid on my own Tong, the Hip Sings. A few
hours before it was due, I got to the safe and rifled the
million dollars in gold and disappeared into Harlem and
went to ground. I was foolish. I should have left America,
gone to the farthest corner of the earth. Even from the
condemned cells in Sing Sing the heads of my Tong
reached out for me. They found me. The killers came in
the night. They tortured me. I would not say where the
gold was. They tortured me all through the night. Then,
when they could not break me, they cut off my hands to

show that the corpse was that of a thief, and they shot me through the heart and went away. But they did not know something about me. I am the one man in a million who has his heart on the right side of his body. Those are the odds against it, one in a million. I lived. By sheer will-power I survived the operation and the months in hospital. And all the time I planned and planned how to get away with the money — how to keep it, what to do with it.'

Doctor No paused. There was a slight flush at his temples. His body fidgeted inside his kimono. His memories had excited him. For a moment he closed his eyes, composing himself. Bond thought, now! Shall I leap at him and kill him? Break off my glass and do it with the jagged stem?

The eyes opened. 'I am not boring you? You are sure? For an instant I felt your attention wandering.'

'No.' The moment had passed. Would there be others? Bond measured the inches of the leap: noted that the jugular vein was in full view above the neck of the kimono.

The thin purple lips parted and the story went on. 'It was, Mister Bond, a time for clear, firm decisions. When they let me out of the hospital I went to Silberstein, the greatest stamp dealer in New York. I bought an envelope, just one envelope, full of the rarest postage stamps in the world. It took weeks to get them together. But I didn't mind what I paid — in New York, London, Paris, Zurich. I wanted my gold to be mobile. I invested it all in these stamps. I had foreseen the World War. I knew there would be inflation. I knew the best would appreciate, or at least hold its value. And meanwhile I was changing my appearance. I had all my hair taken out by the roots, my thick nose made thin, my mouth widened, my lips sliced. I could not get smaller, so I made myself taller. I wore built up shoes. I had weeks of traction on my spine.

I held myself differently. I put away my mechanical hands and wore hands of wax inside gloves. I changed my name to Julius No — the Julius after my father and the No for my rejection of him and of all authority. I threw away my spectacles and wore contact lenses — one of the first pairs ever built. Then I went to Milwaukee, where there are no Chinamen, and enrolled myself in the faculty of medicine. I hid myself in the academic world, the world of libraries and laboratories and classrooms and campuses. And there, Mister Bond, I lost myself in the study of the human body and the human mind. Why? Because I wished to know what this clay is capable of. I had to learn what my tools were before I put them to use on my next goal — total security from physical weaknesses, from material dangers and from the hazards of living. Then, Mister Bond, from that secure base, armoured even against the casual slings and arrows of the world, I would proceed to the achievement of power — the power, Mister Bond, to do unto others what had been done unto me, the power of life and death, the power to decide, to judge, the power of absolute independence from outside authority. For that, Mister Bond, whether you like it or not, is the essence of temporal power.'

Bond reached for the shaker and poured himself a third drink. He looked at Honeychile. She seemed composed and indifferent — as if her mind was on other things. She smiled at him.

Doctor No said benignly, 'I expect you are both hungry. Pray be patient. I will be brief. So, if you recall, there I was, in Milwaukee. In due course, I completed my studies and I left America and went by easy stages round the world. I called myself "doctor" because doctors receive confidences and they can ask questions without arousing suspicion. I was looking for my headquarters. It had to be safe from the coming war, it had to be an island, it had to be entirely private, and it had to be capable of industrial development. In the end I purchased Crab Key. And here I have remained for fourteen years. They have been secure and fruitful years, without a cloud on the horizon. I was entertained by the idea of converting bird dung into gold, and I attacked the problem with passion. It seemed to me the ideal industry. There was a constant demand for the product. The birds require no care except to be left in peace. Each one is a simple factory for turning fish into dung. The digging of the guano is only a question of not spoiling the crop by digging too much. The sole problem is the cost of the labour. It was 1942. The simple Cuban and Jamaican labourer was earning ten shillings a week cutting cane. I tempted a hundred of them over to the island by paying them twelve shillings a week. With guano at fifty dollars a ton I was well placed. But on one condition — that the wages remained constant. I ensured that by isolating my community from world inflation. Harsh methods have had to be used from time to time, but the result is that my men are content with their wages because they are the highest wages they have ever known. I brought in a dozen Chinese negroes with their families to act as overseers. They receive a pound a week per man. They are tough and reliable. On occasion I had to be ruthless with them, but they soon learned. Automatically my people increased in numbers. I added some engineers and some builders. We set to work on the mountain. Occasionally I brought in teams of specialists on high wages. They were kept apart from the others. They lived inside the mountain until their work was done and then left by ship. They put in the lighting and the ventilation and the lift. They built this room. Stores and furnishings came in from all over the world. These people built the sanatorium façade which will cover my operations in case one day there is a shipwreck or the Governor of

Jamaica decides to pay me a call.' The lips glazed into
a smile. 'You must admit that I am able, if I wish, to
accord visitors a most fragrant reception — a wise precaution for the future! And gradually, methodically,
my fortress was built while the birds defecated on top of
it. It has been hard, Mister Bond.' The black eyes did
not look for sympathy or praise. 'But by the end of last
year the work was done. A secure, well-camouflaged
base had been achieved. I was ready to proceed to the
next step — an extension of my power to the outside world.'

Doctor No paused. He lifted his arms an inch and
dropped them again resignedly in his lap. 'Mister Bond,
I said that there was not a cloud in the sky during all
these fourteen years. But one was there, all the time,
below the horizon. And do you know what it was? It
was a bird, a ridiculous bird called a roseate spoonbill!
I will not weary you with the details, Mister Bond. You
are already aware of some of the circumstances. The two
wardens, miles away in the middle of the lake, were
provisioned by launch from Cuba. They sent out their
reports by the launch. Occasionally, ornithologists from
America came by the launch and spent some days at the
camp. I did not mind. The area is out of bounds to my
men. The wardens were not allowed near my compounds.
There was no contact. From the first I made it clear to
the Audubon Society that I would not meet their representatives. And then what happens? One day, out of a
clear sky, I get a letter by the monthly boat. The roseate
spoonbills have become one of the bird wonders of the
world. The Society gives me formal notification that they
intend to build a hotel on their leasehold, near the river
up which you came. Bird lovers from all over the world
will come to observe the birds. Films will be taken. Crab
Key, they told me in their flattering, persuasive letter,
would become famous.'

'Mister Bond,' the arms were raised and dropped back.
Irony gathered at the edges of the set smile. 'Can you
believe it? This privacy I had achieved! The plans I had
for the future! To be swept aside because of a lot of old
women and their birds! I examined the lease. I wrote
offering a huge sum to buy it. They refused. So I studied
these birds. I found out about their habits. And suddenly
the solution was there. And it was easy. Man had always
been the worst predator on these birds. Spoonbills are
extremely shy. They frighten easily. I sent to Florida for
a marsh buggy — the vehicle that is used for oil prospect-
ing, that will cover any kind of terrain. I adapted it to
frighten and to burn — not only birds, but humans as well,
for the wardens would have to go too. And, one night in
December, my marsh buggy howled off across the lake.
It smashed the camp, both wardens were reported killed —
though one, it turned out, escaped to die in Jamaica — it
burned the nesting places, it spread terror among the
birds. Complete success! Hysteria spread among the
spoonbills. They died in thousands. But then I get a
demand for a plane to land on my airstrip. There was to
be an investigation. I decide to agree. It seemed wiser. An
accident is arranged. A lorry goes out of control down the
airstrip as the plane is coming in. The plane is destroyed.
All signs of the lorry are removed. The bodies are
reverently placed in coffins and I report the tragedy. As
I expected, there is further investigation. A destroyer
arrives. I receive the captain courteously. He and his
officers are brought round by sea and then led inland.
They are shown the remains of the camp. My men suggest
that the wardens went mad with loneliness and fought
each other. The survivor set fire to the camp and escaped
in his fishing canoe. The airstrip is examined. My men
report that the plane was coming in too fast. The tyres
must have burst on impact. The bodies are handed over.

It is very sad. The officers are satisfied. The ship leaves. Peace reigns again.'

Doctor No coughed delicately. He looked from Bond to the girl and back again, 'And that, my friends, is my story — or rather the first chapter of what I am confident will be a long and interesting tale. Privacy has been re-established. There are now no roseate spoonbills, so there will be no wardens. No doubt the Audubon Society will decide to accept my offer for the rest of their lease. No matter. If they start their puny operations again, other misfortunes will befall them. This has been a warning to me. There will be no more interference.'

'Interesting,' said Bond. 'An interesting case history. So that was why Strangways had to be removed. What did you do with him and his girl?'

'They are at the bottom of the Mona Reservoir. I sent three of my best men. I have a small but efficient machine in Jamaica. I need it. I have established a watch on the intelligence services in Jamaica and Cuba. It is necessary for my further operations. Your Mister Strangways became suspicious and started ferreting about. Fortunately, by this time, the routines of this man were known to me. His death and the girl's were a simple matter of timing. I had hoped to deal with you with similar expedition. You were fortunate. But I knew what type of a man you were from the files at King's House. I guessed that the fly would come to the spider. I was ready for you, and when the canoe showed up on the radar screen I knew you would not get away.'

Bond said, 'Your radar is not very efficient. There were two canoes. The one you saw was the girl's. I tell you she had nothing to do with me.'

'Then she is unfortunate. I happen to be needing a white woman for a small experiment. As we agreed earlier, Mister Bond, one generally gets what one wants.'

Bond looked thoughtfully at Doctor No. He wondered if it was worth while even trying to make a dent in this impregnable man. Was it worth wasting breath by threatening or bluffing? Bond had nothing but a miserable two of clubs up his sleeve. The thought of playing it almost bored him. Casually, indifferently he threw it down.

'Then you're out of luck, Doctor No. You are now a file in London. My thoughts on this case, the evidence of the poisoned fruit and the centipede and the crashed motor car, are on record. So are the names of Miss Chung and Miss Taro. Instructions were left with someone in Jamaica that my report should be opened and acted upon if I failed to return from Crab Key within three days.'

Bond paused. The face of Doctor No was impassive. Neither the eyes nor the mouth had flickered. The jugular vein throbbed evenly. Bond bent forward. He said softly, 'But because of the girl, and only because of her, Doctor No, I will strike a bargain. In exchange for our safe return to Jamaica, you may have a week's start. You may take your aeroplane and your packet of stamps and try to get away.'

Bond sat back. 'Any interest, Doctor No?'

XVI

HORIZONS OF AGONY

A VOICE behind Bond said quietly, 'Dinner is served.'

Bond swung round. It was the bodyguard. Beside him was another man who might have been his twin. They stood there, two stocky barrels of muscle, their hands buried in the sleeves of their kimonos, and looked over Bond's head at Doctor No.

'Ah, nine o'clock already.' Doctor No rose slowly to his feet. 'Come along. We can continue our conversation in more intimate surroundings. It is kind of you both to have listened to me with such exemplary patience. I hope the modesty of my cuisine and my cellar will not prove a further imposition.'

Double doors stood open in the wall behind the two white-jacketed men. Bond and the girl followed Doctor No through into a small octagonal mahogany panelled room lit by a central chandelier in silver with storm glasses round the candles. Beneath it was a round mahogany table laid for three. Silver and glass twinkled warmly. The plain dark blue carpet was luxuriously deep. Doctor No took the centre high-backed chair and bowed the girl into the chair on his right. They sat down and unfolded napkins of white silk.

The hollow ceremony and the charming room maddened Bond. He longed to break it up with his own hands — to wind his silk napkin round Doctor No's throat and squeeze until the contact lenses popped out of the black, damnable eyes.

The two guards wore white cotton gloves. They served the food with a suave efficiency that was prompted by an occasional word in Chinese from Doctor No.

At first, Doctor No seemed preoccupied. He slowly ate through three bowls of different soup, feeding himself with a spoon with a short handle that fitted neatly between the pincers. Bond concentrated on hiding his fears from the girl. He sat relaxed and ate and drank with a forced good appetite. He talked cheerfully to the girl about Jamaica — about the birds and the animals and the flowers which were an easy topic for her. Occasionally his feet felt for hers under the table. She became almost gay. Bond thought they were putting on an excellent imitation of an engaged couple being given dinner by a detested uncle.

Bond had no idea if his thin bluff had worked. He didn't give much for their chances. Doctor No, and Doctor No's story, exuded impregnability. The incredible biography rang true. Not a word of it was impossible. Perhaps there were other people in the world with their private kingdoms — away from the beaten track, where there were no witnesses, where they could do what they liked. And what did Doctor No plan to do next, after he had squashed the flies that had come to annoy him? And if — when — he killed Bond and the girl, would London pick up the threads that Bond had picked up? Probably they would. There would be Pleydell-Smith. The evidence of the poisoned fruit. But where would Bond's replacement get with Doctor No? Not far. Doctor No would shrug his shoulders over the disappearance of Bond and Quarrel. Never heard of them. And there would be no link with the girl. In Morgan's Harbour they would think she had

been drowned on one of her expeditions. It was hard to
see what could interfere with Doctor No — with the second
chapter of his life, whatever it was.

Underneath his chatter with the girl, Bond prepared
for the worst. There were plenty of weapons beside his
plate. When the cutlets came, perfectly cooked, Bond
fiddled indecisively with the knives and chose the bread
knife to eat them with. While he ate and talked, he edged
the big steel meat knife towards him. An expansive
gesture of his right hand knocked over his glass of
champagne and in the split second of the crash his left
hand flicked the knife into the deep sleeve of his kimono.
In the midst of Bond's apologies and the confusion as he
and the bodyguard mopped up the spilled champagne,
Bond raised his left arm and felt the knife slip back to
below his armpit and then fall inside the kimono against
his ribs. When he had finished his cutlets he tightened the
silk belt round his waist, shifting the knife across his
stomach. The knife nestled comfortingly against his skin
and gradually the steel grew warm.

Coffee came and the meal was ended. The two guards
came and stood close behind Bond's chair and the girl's.
They stood with their arms crossed on their chests, impassive, motionless, like executioners.

Doctor No put his cup softly down on its saucer. He laid
his two steel claws down on the table in front of him. He
sat a fraction more upright. He turned his body an inch
in Bond's direction. Now there was no preoccupation in
his face. The eyes were hard and direct. The thin mouth
creased and opened. 'You have enjoyed your dinner,
Mister Bond?'

Bond took a cigarette from the silver box in front of
him and lit it. He played with the silver table-lighter. He
smelled bad news coming. He must somehow pocket the
lighter. Fire might perhaps be another weapon. He said

easily, 'Yes. It was excellent.' He looked across at the girl. He leant forward in his chair and rested his forearms on the table. He crossed them, enveloping the lighter. He smiled at her. 'I hope I ordered what you like.'

'Oh yes, it was lovely.' For her the party was still going on.

Bond smoked busily, agitating his hands and forearms to create an atmosphere of movement. He turned to Doctor No. He stubbed out his cigarette and sat back in his chair. He folded his arms across his chest. The lighter was in his left armpit. He smiled cheerfully. 'And what happens now, Doctor No?'

'We can proceed to our after-dinner entertainment, Mister Bond.' The thin smile creased and vanished. 'I have examined your proposition from every angle. I do not accept it.'

Bond shrugged his shoulders. 'You are unwise.'

'No, Mister Bond. I suspect that your proposition is a gold brick. People in your trade do not behave as you suggest. They make routine reports to their headquarters. They keep their chief aware of the progress of their investigations. I know these things. Secret agents do not behave as you suggest you have done. You have been reading too many novels of suspense. Your little speech reeked of grease-paint and cardboard. No, Mister Bond, I do not accept your story. If it is true, I am prepared to face the consequences. I have too much at stake to be turned from my path. So the police come, the soldiers come. Where are a man and a girl? What man and what girl? I know nothing. Please go away. You are disturbing my guanera. Where is your evidence? Your search warrant? The English law is strict, gentlemen. Go home and leave me in peace with my beloved cormorants. You see, Mister Bond? And let us even say that the worst comes to the worst. That one of my agents talks, which is highly improbable (Bond remembered the fortitude of Miss Chung). What have I to lose? Two more deaths on the charge sheet. But, Mister Bond, a man can only be hanged once.' The tall pear-shaped head shook gently from side to side. 'Have you anything else to say? Any questions to ask? You both have a busy night ahead of you. Your time is getting short. And I must get my sleep. The monthly ship is putting in tomorrow and I have the loading to supervise. I shall have to spend the whole day down on the quay. Well, Mister Bond?'

Bond looked across at the girl. She had gone deathly pale. She was gazing at him, waiting for the miracle he would work. He looked down at his hands. He examined his nails carefully. He said, playing for time, 'And then what? After your busy day with the bird dung, what comes next on your programme? What is the next chapter you think you're going to write?'

Bond didn't look up. The deep quiet authoritative voice came to him as if it was coming down from the night sky.

'Ah, yes. You must have been wondering, Mister Bond. You have the habit of inquiry. It persists even to the last, even into the shadows. I admire such qualities in a man with only a few hours to live. So I will tell you. I will turn over the next page. It will console you. There is more to this place than bird dung. Your instincts did not betray you.' Doctor No paused for emphasis. 'This island, Mister Bond, is about to be developed into the most valuable technical intelligence centre in the world.'

'Really?' Bond kept his eyes bent on his hands.

'Doubtless you know that Turks Island, about three hundred miles from here through the Windward Passage, is the most important centre for testing the guided missiles of the United States?'

'It is an important centre, yes.'

'Perhaps you have read of the rockets that have been going astray recently? The multi-stage SNARK, for instance, that ended its flight in the forests of Brazil instead of the depths of the South Atlantic?'

'Yes.'

'You recall that it refused to obey the telemetred instructions to change its course, even to destroy itself. It developed a will of its own?'

'I remember.'

'There have been other failures, decisive failures, from the long list of prototypes — the ZUNI, MATADOR, PETREL, REGULUS, BOMARC — so many names, so many changes, I can't even remember them all. Well, Mister Bond,' Doctor No could not keep a note of pride out of his voice, 'it may interest you to know that the vast majority of those failures have been caused from Crab Key.'

'Is that so?'

'You do not believe me? No matter. Others do. Others who have seen the complete abandonment of one series, the MASTODON, because of its recurring navigational errors, its failure to obey the radio directions from Turks Island. Those others are the Russians. The Russians are my partners in this venture. They trained six of my men, Mister Bond. Two of those men are on watch at this moment, watching the radio frequencies, the beams on which these weapons travel. There is a million dollars' worth of equipment up above us in the rock galleries, Mister Bond, sending fingers up into the Heavyside Layer, waiting for the signals, jamming them, countering beams with other beams. And from time to time a rocket soars up on its way a hundred, five hundred miles into the Atlantic. And we track it, as accurately as they are tracking it in the Operations Room on Turks Island. Then, suddenly, our pulses go out to the rocket, its brain is confused, it goes mad, it plunges into the sea, it destroys itself, it roars off at a tangent. Another test has failed. The operators are blamed, the designers, the manufacturers. There is panic in the Pentagon. Something else must be tried, different frequencies, different metals, a different radio brain. Of course,' Doctor No was fair, 'we too have our difficulties. We track many practice shoots without being able to get through to the brain of the new rocket. But then we communicate urgently with Moscow. Yes, they have even given us a cipher machine with our own frequencies and routines. And the Russians get thinking. They make suggestions. We try them out. And then, one day, Mister Bond, it is like catching the attention of a man in a crowd. Up in the stratosphere the rocket acknowledges our signal. We are recognized and we can speak to it and change its mind.' Doctor No paused. 'Do you not find that interesting, Mister Bond, this little sideline to my business in guano? It is, I assure you, most profitable. It might be still more so. Perhaps Communist China will pay more. Who knows? I already have my feelers out.'

Bond lifted his eyes. He looked thoughtfully at Doctor No. So he *had* been right. There *had* been more, much more, in all this than met the eye. This was a big game, a game that explained everything, a game that was certainly, in the international espionage market, well worth the candle. Well, well! Now the pieces in the puzzle fell firmly into place. For this it was certainly worth scaring away a few birds and wiping out a few people. Privacy? Of course Doctor No would have to kill him and the girl. Power? This was it. Doctor No had really got himself into business.

Bond looked into the two black holes with a new respect. He said, 'You'll have to kill a lot more people to keep this thing in your hands, Doctor No. It's worth a lot of money. You've got a good property here — a better one than I thought. People are going to want to cut themselves a piece of this cake. I wonder who will get to you first and kill you. Those men up there', he gestured towards the ceiling, 'who were trained in Moscow? They're the technicians. I wonder what Moscow is telling them to do? You wouldn't know that, would you?'

Doctor No said, 'You persist in underestimating me, Mister Bond. You are an obstinate man, and stupider than I had expected. I am aware of these possibilities. I have taken one of these men and made him into a private monitor. He has duplicates of the ciphers and of the cipher machine. He lives in another part of the mountain. The others think that he died. He watches on all the routine times. He gives me a second copy of all the traffic that passes. So far, the signals from Moscow have been innocent of any sign of conspiracy. I am thinking of these things constantly, Mister Bond. I take precautions and I shall take further precautions. As I said, you underestimate me.'

'I don't underestimate you, Doctor No. You're a very careful man, but you've got too many files open on you. In my line of business, the same thing applies to me. I know the feeling. But you've got some really bad ones. The Chinese one, for instance. I wouldn't like to have that one. The F.B.I. should be the least painful — robbery and false identity. But do you know the Russians as well as I do? You're a "best friend" at the moment. But the Russians don't have partners. They'll want to take you over — buy you out with a bullet. Then there's the file you've started with my Service. You really want me to make that one fatter? I shouldn't do it if I were you, Doctor No. They're a tenacious lot of people in my Service. If anything happens to me and the girl, you'll find Crab Key's a very small and naked little island.'

'You cannot play for high stakes without taking risks,

Mister Bond. I accept the dangers and, so far as I can, I have equipped myself against them. You see, Mister Bond,' the deep voice held a hint of greed, 'I am on the edge of still greater things. The Chapter Two to which I referred holds the promise of prizes which no one but a fool would throw away because he was afraid. I have told you that I can bend the beams on which these rockets fly, Mister Bond. I can make them change course and ignore their radio control. What would you say, Mister Bond, if I could go further? If I could bring them down into the sea near this island and salvage the secrets of their construction. At present American destroyers, far out in the South Atlantic, salvage these missiles when they come to the end of their fuel and parachute down into the sea. Sometimes the parachutes fail to open. Sometimes the self-destruction devices fail to operate. No one on Turks Island would be surprised if every now and then the prototype of a new series broke off its flight and came down near Crab Key. To begin with, at least, it would be put down to mechanical failure. Later, perhaps, they would discover that other radio signals besides theirs were guiding their rockets. A jamming war would start. They would try and locate the origin of the false signals. Directly I found they were looking for me, I would have one last fling. Their rockets would go mad. They would land on Havana, on Kingston. They would turn round and home on Miami. Even without warheads, Mister Bond, five tons of metal arriving at a thousand miles an hour can cause plenty of damage in a crowded town. And then what? There would be panic, a public outcry. The experiments would have to cease. The Turks Island base would have to close down. And how much would Russia pay for that to happen, Mister Bond? And how much for each of the prototypes I captured for them? Shall we say ten million dollars for the whole operation? Twenty million?

It would be a priceless victory in the armaments race. I could name my figure. Don't you agree, Mister Bond? And don't you agree that these considerations make your arguments and threats seem rather puny?'

Bond said nothing. There was nothing to say. Suddenly he was back in the quiet room high up above Regent's Park. He could hear the rain slashing softly against the window and M's voice, impatient, sarcastic, saying, 'Oh, some damned business about birds ... holiday in the sun'll do you good ... routine inquiry.' And he, Bond, had taken a canoe and a fisherman and a picnic lunch and had gone off — how many days, how many weeks ago? — 'to have a look'. Well, he had had his look into Pandora's Box. He had found out the answers, been told the secrets — and now? Now he was going to be politely shown the way to his grave, taking the secrets with him and the waif he had picked up and dragged along with him on his lunatic adventure. The bitterness inside Bond came up into his mouth so that for a moment he thought he was going to retch. He reached for his champagne and emptied the glass. He said harshly, 'All right, Doctor No. Now let's get on with the cabaret. What's the programme — knife, bullet, poison, rope? But make it quick, I've seen enough of you.'

Doctor No's lips compressed into a thin purple line. The eyes were hard as onyx under the billiard ball forehead and skull. The polite mask had gone. The Grand Inquisitor sat in the high-backed chair. The hour had struck for the *peine forte et dure*.

Doctor No spoke a word and the two guards took a step forward and held the two victims above the elbows, forcing their arms back against the sides of their chairs. There was no resistance. Bond concentrated on holding the lighter in his armpit. The white-gloved hands on his biceps felt like steel bands. He smiled across at the girl.

'I'm sorry about this, Honey. I'm afraid we're not going to be able to play together after all.'

The girl's eyes in the pale face were blue-black with fear. Her lips trembled. She said, 'Will it hurt?'

'Silence!' Doctor No's voice was the crack of a whip. 'Enough of this foolery. Of course it will hurt. I am interested in pain. I am also interested in finding out how much the human body can endure. From time to time I make experiments on those of my people who have to be punished. And on trespassers like yourselves. You have both put me to a great deal of trouble. In exchange I intend to put you to a great deal of pain. I shall record the length of your endurance. The facts will be noted. One day my findings will be given to the world. Your deaths will have served the purposes of science. I never waste human material. The German experiments on live humans during the war were of great benefit to science. It is a year since I put a girl to death in the fashion I have chosen for you, woman. She was a negress. She lasted three hours. She died of terror. I have wanted a white girl for comparison. I was not surprised when your arrival was reported. I get what I want.' Doctor No sat back in his chair. His eyes were now fixed on the girl, watching her reactions. She stared back at him, half hypnotized, like a bush mouse in front of a rattlesnake.

Bond set his teeth.

'You are a Jamaican, so you will know what I am talking about. This island is called Crab Key. It is called by that name because it is infested with crabs, land crabs — what they call in Jamaica "black crabs". You know them. They weigh about a pound each and they are as big as saucers. At this time of year they come up in thousands from their holes near the shore and climb up towards the mountain. There, in the coral uplands, they go to ground again in holes in the rock and spawn their broods. They march up in armies of hundreds at a time. They march through everything and over everything. In Jamaica they go through houses that are in their path. They are like the lemmings of Norway. It is a compulsive migration.' Doctor No paused. He said softly, 'But there is a difference. The crabs devour what they find in their path. And at present, woman, they are "running". They are coming up the mountainside in their tens of thousands, great red and orange and black waves of them, scuttling and hurrying and scraping against the rock above us at this moment. And tonight, in the middle of their path, they are going to find the naked body of a woman pegged out — a banquet spread for them — and they will feel the warm body with their feeding pincers, and one will make the first incision with his fighting claws and then ... and then ...'

There was a moan from the girl. Her head fell forward slackly on to her chest. She had fainted. Bond's body heaved in his chair. A string of obscenities hissed out between his clenched teeth. The huge hands of the guard were like fire round his arms. He couldn't even move the chair-legs on the floor. After a moment he desisted. He waited for his voice to steady, then he said, with all the venom he could put into the words, 'You bastard. You'll fry in hell for this.'

Doctor No smiled thinly. 'Mister Bond, I do not admit the existence of hell. Console yourself. Perhaps they will start at the throat or the heart. The movement of the pulse will attract them. Then it will not be long.' He spoke a sentence in Chinese. The guard behind the girl's chair leant forward and plucked her bodily out of the chair as if she had been a child and slung the inert body over his shoulder. Between the dangling arms the hair fell down in a golden shower. The guard went to the door and opened it and went out, closing it noiselessly behind him.

For a moment there was silence in the room. Bond thought only of the knife against his skin and of the lighter under his armpit. How much damage could he do with the two pieces of metal? Could he somehow get within range of Doctor No?

Doctor No said quietly, 'You said that power was an illusion, Mister Bond. Do you change your mind? My power to select this particular death for the girl is surely not an illusion. However, let us proceed to the method of your departure. That also has its novel aspects. You see, Mister Bond, I am interested in the anatomy of courage — in the power of the human body to endure. But how to measure human endurance? How to plot a graph of the will to survive, the tolerance of pain, the conquest of fear? I have given much thought to the problem, and I believe I have solved it. It is, of course, only a rough and ready method, and I shall learn by experience as more and more subjects are put to the test. I have prepared you for the experiment as best I could. I gave you a sedative so that your body should be rested and I have fed you well so that you may be at full strength. Future — what shall I call them — patients, will have the same advantages. All will start equal in that respect. After that it will be a question of the individual's courage and powers of endurance.' Doctor No paused, watching Bond's face. 'You see, Mister Bond, I have just finished constructing an obstacle race, an assault course against death. I will say no more about it because the element of surprise is one of the constituents of fear. It is the unknown dangers that are the worst, that bear most heavily on the reserves of courage. And I flatter myself that the gauntlet you will run contains a rich assortment of the unexpected. It will be particularly interesting, Mister Bond, that a man of your physical qualities is to be my first competitor. It will be most interesting to observe how far you get down the course I have devised. You should put up a worthy target figure for future runners. I have high expectations of you. You should go far, but when, as is inevitable, you have finally failed at an obstacle, your body will be recovered and I shall most meticulously examine the physical state of your remains. The data will be recorded. You will be the first dot on a graph. Something of an honour, is it not, Mister Bond?'

Bond said nothing. What the hell did all this mean? What could this test consist of? Would it be possible to survive it? Could he conceivably escape from it and get to the girl before it was too late, even if it was only to kill her and save her from her torture? Silently Bond gathered his reserves of courage, steeling his mind against the fear of the unknown that already had him by the throat, focusing his whole will on survival. Somehow, above all else, he must cling to his weapons.

Doctor No rose and stepped away from his chair. He walked slowly to the door and turned. The menacing black holes looked back at Bond from just below the lintel of the door. The head was inclined a fraction. The purple lips creased back. 'Run a good race for me, Mister Bond. My thoughts, as they say, will be with you.'

Doctor No turned away and the door closed softly behind the long thin gunmetal back.

XVII

THE LONG SCREAM

THERE was a man on the lift. The doors were open, waiting. James Bond, his arms still locked to his sides, was marched in. Now the dining-room would be empty. How soon would the guards go back, start clearing away the dinner, notice the missing things? The doors hissed shut. The liftman stood in front of the buttons so that Bond could not see which he had pressed. They were going up. Bond tried to estimate the distance. The lift sighed to a stop. The time seemed rather less than when he had come down with the girl. The doors opened on to an uncarpeted corridor with rough grey paint on the stone walls. It ran about twenty yards straight ahead.

'Hold it, Joe,' said Bond's guard to the liftman. 'Be right with you.'

Bond was marched down the corridor past doors numbered with letters of the alphabet. There was a faint hum of machinery in the air and behind one door Bond thought he could catch the crackle of radio static. It sounded as if they might be in the engine-room of the mountain. They came to the end door. It was marked with a black Q. It was ajar and the guard pushed Bond into the door so that it swung open. Through the door was a grey painted stone cell about fifteen feet square. There was nothing in it except a wooden chair on which lay, laundered and, neatly folded, Bond's black canvas jeans and his blue shirt.

The guard let go of Bond's arms. Bond turned and looked into the broad yellow face below the crinkly hair. There was a hint of curiosity and pleasure in the liquid brown eyes. The man stood holding the door handle. He said, 'Well, this is it, bud. You're at the starting gate. You can either sit here and rot or find your way out on to the course. Happy landings.'

Bond thought it was just worth trying. He glanced past the guard to where the liftman was standing beside his open doors, watching them. He said softly, 'How would you like to earn ten thousand dollars, guaranteed, and a ticket to anywhere in the world?' He watched the man's face. The mouth spread in a wide grin to show brownish teeth worn to uneven points by years of chewing sugar-cane.

'Thanks, Mister. I'd rather stay alive.' The man made to close the door. Bond whispered urgently, 'We could get out of here together.'

The thick lips sneered. The man said, 'Shove it!' The door shut with a solid click.

Bond shrugged his shoulders. He gave the door a cursory glance. It was made of metal and there was no handle on the inside. Bond didn't waste his shoulder on it. He went to the chair and sat down on the neat pile of his clothes and looked round the cell. The walls were entirely naked except for a ventilation grille of thick wire in one corner just below the ceiling. It was wider than his shoulders. It was obviously the way out into the assault course. The only other break in the walls was a thick glass porthole, no bigger than Bond's head, just above the door. Light from the corridor filtered through it into the cell. There was nothing else. It was no good wasting any more time. It would now be about ten-thirty. Outside, somewhere on the slope of the mountain, the girl would already be lying, waiting for the rattle of claws on the grey coral. Bond clenched his teeth at the thought of the pale body spreadeagled out there under the stars. Abruptly he stood up. What the hell was he doing sitting still. Whatever lay on the other side of the wire grille, it was time to go.

Bond took out his knife and the lighter and threw off the kimono. He dressed in the trousers and shirt and stowed the lighter in his hip pocket. He tried the edge of the knife with his thumb. It was very sharp. It would be better still if he could get a point on it. He knelt on the floor and began whittling the rounded end on the stone. After a precious quarter of an hour he was satisfied. It was no stiletto, but it would serve to stab as well as cut. Bond put the knife between his teeth and set the chair below the grille and climbed on to it. The grille! Assuming he could tear it off its hinges, the frame of quarter-inch wire might straighten into a spear. That would make a third weapon. Bond reached up with crooked fingers.

The next thing he knew was a searing pain up his arm and the crack of his head hitting the stone floor. He lay, stunned, with only the memory of a blue flash and the hiss and crackle of electricity to tell him what had hit him.

Bond got to his knees and stayed there. He bent his head down and shook it slowly from side to side like a wounded animal. He noticed a smell of burning flesh. He lifted his right hand up to his eyes. There was the red smear of an open burn across the inside of his fingers. Seeing it brought the pain. Bond spat out a four-letter word. Slowly he got to his feet. He squinted up at the wire grille as if it might strike at him again, like a snake. Grimly he set the chair upright against the wall. He picked up his knife and cut a strip off the discarded kimono and tied it firmly across his fingers. Then he climbed up again on to the chair and looked at the grille. He was meant to get through it. The shock had been to soften him up — a taste of pain to come. Surely he had fused the blasted thing. Surely they would have switched off the current. He looked at it only for an instant, then the fingers of his left hand crooked and went straight up to the impersonal wire mesh. His fingers went through the wire rim and gripped.

Nothing! Nothing at all — just wire. Bond grunted. He felt his nerves slacken. He tugged at the wire. It gave an inch. He tugged again and it came away in his hand and dangled down from two strands of copper flex that disappeared into the wall. Bond pulled the grille loose from the flex and got down from the chair. Yes, there was a join in the frame. He set to work unravelling the mesh. Then using the chair as a hammer, he straightened the heavy wire.

After ten minutes, Bond had a crooked spear about four feet long. One end, where it had originally been cut by the pliers, was jagged. It would not pierce a man's clothes, but it would be good enough for the face and neck. By using all his strength and the crack at the bottom of the metal door, Bond turned the blunt end into a clumsy crook. He measured the wire against his leg. It was too long. He bent it double and slipped the spear down a trouser leg. Now it hung from his waistband to just above the knee. He went back to the chair and climbed up again and reached, nervously, for the edge of the ventilator shaft. There was no shock. Bond heaved up and through the opening and lay on his stomach looking along the shaft.

The shaft was about four inches wider than Bond's shoulders. It was circular and of polished metal. Bond reached for his lighter, blessing the inspiration that had made him take it, and flicked it on. Yes, zinc sheeting that looked new. The shaft stretched straight ahead, featureless except for the ridges where the sections of pipe joined. Bond put the lighter back in his pocket and snaked forward.

It was easy going. Cool air from the ventilating system blew strongly in Bond's face. The air held no smell of the sea — it was the canned stuff that comes from an air-conditioning plant. Doctor No must have adapted one of the shafts to his purpose. What hazards had he built into it to test out his victims? They would be ingenious and painful — designed to reduce the resistance of the victim. At the winning post, so to speak, there would be the *coup de grâce* — if the victim ever got that far. It would be something conclusive, something from which there would be no escape, for there would be no prizes in this race except oblivion — an oblivion, thought Bond, he might be glad to win. Unless of course Doctor No had been just a bit too clever. Unless he had underestimated the will to survive. That, thought Bond, was his only hope — to try to survive the intervening hazards, to get through at least to the last ditch.

There was a faint luminosity ahead. Bond approached it carefully, his senses questing in front of him like antennae. It grew brighter. It was the glint of light against the end of the lateral shaft. He went on until his head touched the metal. He twisted over on his back. Straight above him, at the top of fifty yards or so of vertical shaft, was a steady glimmer. It was like looking up a long gun barrel. Bond inched round the square bend and stood upright. So he was supposed to climb straight up this shining tube of metal without a foothold! Was it possible? Bond expanded his shoulders. Yes, they gripped the sides. His feet could also get a temporary purchase, though they would slip except where the ridges at the joints gave him an ounce of upward leverage. Bond shrugged his shoulders and kicked off his shoes. It was no good arguing. He would just have to try.

Six inches at a time, Bond's body began to worm up the shaft — expand shoulders to grip the sides, lift feet, lock knees, force the feet outwards against the metal and, as the feet slipped downwards with his weight, contract shoulders and raise them a few inches higher. Do it again, and again and again and again. Stop at each tiny bulge where the sections joined and use the millimetre of extra support to get some breath and measure the next lap. Otherwise don't look up, think only of the inches of metal that have to be conquered one by one. Don't worry about the glimmer of light that never grows brighter or nearer. Don't worry about losing your grip and falling to smash your ankles at the bottom of the shaft. Don't worry about cramp. Don't worry about your screaming muscles or the swelling bruises on your shoulders and the sides of your feet. Just take the silver inches as they come, one by one, and conquer them.

But then the feet began to sweat and slip. Twice Bond lost a yard before his shoulders, scalding with the friction, could put on the brake. Finally he had to stop altogether to let his sweat dry in the downward draught of air. He waited for a full ten minutes, staring at his faint reflection in the polished metal, the face split in half by the knife between the teeth. Still he refused to look up to see how much more there was. It might be too much to bear. Carefully Bond wiped each foot against a trouser-leg and began again.

Now half Bond's mind was dreaming while the other half fought the battle. He wasn't even conscious of the strengthening breeze or the slowly brightening light. He saw himself as a wounded caterpillar crawling up a waste pipe towards the plug-hole of a bath. What would he see when he got through the plug-hole? A naked girl drying herself? A man shaving? Sunlight streaming through an open window into an empty bathroom?

Bond's head bumped against something. The plug was in the plug-hole! The shock of disappointment made him slip a yard before his shoulders got a fresh grip. Then he realized. He was at the top! Now he noticed the bright light and the strong wind. Feverishly, but with a more desperate care, he heaved up again until his head touched. The wind was coming into his left ear. Cautiously he turned his head. It was another lateral shaft. Above him light was shining through a thick porthole. All he had to do was inch himself round and grip the edge of the new shaft and somehow gather enough strength to heave himself in. Then he would be able to lie down.

With an extra delicacy, born of panic that something might now go wrong, that he might make a mistake and plummet back down the shaft to land in a crackle of bone, Bond, his breath steaming against the metal, carried out the manœuvre and, with his last ounce of strength, jack-knifed into the opening and crumpled full length on his face.

Later — how much later? — Bond's eyes opened and his body stirred. The cold had woken him from the fringe of total unconsciousness into which his body had plunged. Painfully he rolled over on his back, his feet and shoulders screaming at him, and lay gathering his wits and summoning more strength. He had no idea what time it was or whereabouts he was inside the mountain. He lifted his head and looked back at the porthole above the yawning tube out of which he had come. The light was yellowish and the glass looked thick. He remembered the porthole in Room Q. There had been nothing breakable about that one, nor, he guessed, would there be here.

Suddenly, behind the glass, he saw movement. As he

watched, a pair of eyes materialized from behind the electric light bulb. They stopped and looked at him, the bulb making a yellow glass nose between them. They gazed incuriously at him and then they were gone. Bond's lips snarled back from his teeth. So his progress was going to be observed, reported back to Doctor No!

Bond said out loud, viciously, '—— them all,' and turned sullenly back on his stomach. He raised his head and looked forward. The tunnel shimmered away into blackness. Come on! No good hanging about. He picked up his knife and put it back between his teeth and winced his way forward.

Soon there was no more light. Bond stopped from time to time and used the lighter, but there was nothing but blackness ahead. The air began to get warmer in the shaft, and, perhaps fifty yards further, definitely hot. There was the smell of heat in the air, metallic heat. Bond began to sweat. Soon his body was soaked and he had to pause every few minutes to wipe his eyes. There came a right-hand turn in the shaft. Round it the metal of the big tube was hot against his skin. The smell of heat was very strong. There came another right-angled turn. As soon as Bond's head got round he quickly pulled out his lighter and lit it and then snaked back and lay panting. Bitterly he examined the new hazard, probing it, cursing it. His light had flickered on discoloured, oyster-hued zinc. The next hazard was to be heat!

Bond groaned aloud. How could his bruised flesh stand up to that? How could he protect his skin from the metal? But there wasn't anything he could do about it. He could either go back, or stay where he was, or go on. There was no other decision to make, no other shift or excuse. There was one, and only one, grain of consolation. This would not be heat that would kill, only maim. This would not be the final killing ground — only one more test of how much he could take.

Bond thought of the girl and of what she was going through. Oh well. Get on with it. Now, let's see....

Bond took his knife and cut off the whole front of his shirt and sliced it into strips. The only hope was to put some wrapping round the parts of his body that would have to bear the brunt — his hands and his feet. His knees and elbows would have to get along with their single covering of cotton fabric. Wearily he set to work, cursing softly.

Now he was ready. One, two, three ...

Bond turned the corner and forged forward into the heat stench.

Keep your naked stomach off the ground! Contract your shoulders! Hands, knees, toes; hands, knees, toes. Faster, faster! Keep going fast so that each touch on the ground is quickly taken over by the next.

The knees were getting it worst, taking the bulk of Bond's weight. Now the padded hands were beginning to smoulder. There was a spark, and another one, and then a worm of red as the sparks began to run. The smoke from the stuff smarted in Bond's sweating eyes. God, he couldn't do any more! There was no air. His lungs were bursting. Now his two hands shed sparks as he thrust them forward. The stuff must be nearly gone. Then the flesh would burn. Bond lurched and his bruised shoulder hit the metal. He screamed. He went on screaming, regularly, with each contact of hand or knee or toes. Now he was finished. Now it was the end. Now he would fall flat and slowly fry to death. No! He must drive on, screaming, until his flesh was burned to the bone. The skin must have already gone from the knees. In a moment the balls of his hands would meet the metal. Only the sweat running down his arms could be keeping the pads of stuff damp. Scream,

scream, scream! It helps the pain. It tells you you're alive. Go on! Go on! It can't be much longer. This isn't where you're supposed to die. You are still alive. Don't give up! You can't!

Bond's right hand hit something that gave before it. There was a stream of ice-cold air. His other hand hit, then his head. There was a tinny noise. Bond felt the lower edge of an asbestos baffle scrape down his back. He was through. He heard the baffle bang shut. His hands came up against solid wall. They quested to left and right. It was a right-angled bend. His body followed blindly round the corner. The cool air felt like daggers in his lungs. Gingerly he laid his fingers down on the metal. It was cold! With a groan Bond fell on his face and lay still.

Sometime later the pain revived him. Bond turned sluggishly over on his back. Vaguely he noticed the lighted porthole above him. Vaguely he took in the eyes gazing down on him. Then he let the black waves take him away again.

Slowly, in the darkness, the blisters formed across the skin and the bruised feet and shoulders stiffened. The sweat dried on the body and then on the rags of clothing, and the cool air soaked down into the overheated lungs and began its insidious work. But the heart beat on, strongly and regularly inside the tortured envelope, and the healing sorceries of oxygen and rest pumped life back into the arteries and veins and recharged the nerves.

Years later, Bond awoke. He stirred. As his eyes opened and met the other pair, inches away behind the glass, pain took him and shook him like a rat. He waited for the shock to die. He tried again, and then again, until he had measured the strength of his adversary. Then Bond, to hide himself away from the witness, turned over on his stomach and took the full blast of it. Again he waited, exploring his body for its reactions, testing the strength of the resolve that was left in the batteries. How much more could he take now? Bond's lips drew back from his teeth and he snarled into the darkness. It was an animal sound. He had come to the end of his human reactions to pain and adversity. Doctor No had got him cornered. But there were animal reserves of desperation left and, in a strong animal, those reserves are deep.

Slowly, agonizingly, Bond snaked a few yards away from the eyes and then reached for his lighter and lit it. Ahead there was only the black full moon, the yawning circular mouth that led into the stomach of death. Bond put back the lighter. He took a deep breath and got to his hands and knees. The pain was no greater, only different. Slowly, stiffly, he winced forward.

The cotton fabric at Bond's knees and elbows had burned away. Numbly his mind registered the moisture as his blisters burst against the cool metal. As he moved, he flexed his fingers and toes, testing the pain. Slowly he got the measure of what he could do, what hurt most. This pain is supportable, he argued to himself. If I had been in an aeroplane crash, they would only diagnose superficial contusions and burns. I would be out of hospital in a few days. There's nothing wrong with me. I'm a survivor from the crash. It hurts, but it's nothing. Think of the bits and pieces of the other passengers. Be thankful. Put it out of your mind. But, nagging behind these reflections, was the knowledge that he had not yet had the crash — that he was still on his way towards it, his resistance, his effectiveness reduced. When would it come? What shape would it take? How much more was he to be softened up before he reached the killing ground?

Ahead in the darkness the tiny red pin-points might have been an hallucination, specks before the eyes as a result of exhaustion. Bond stopped and screwed up his eyes. He shook his head. No, they were still there. Slowly he snaked closer. Now they were moving. Bond stopped again. He listened. Above the quiet thumping of his heart there was a soft, delicate rustling. The pin-points had increased in number. Now there were twenty or thirty, shifting to and fro, some quickly, some slowly, all over the circle of blackness ahead. Bond reached for his lighter. He held his breath as he lit the little yellow flame. The red pin-points went out. Instead, a yard ahead of him, very narrow mesh wire, almost as fine as muslin, blocked the shaft.

Bond inched forward, the lighter held before him. It was some sort of a cage with small things living in it. He could hear them scuttling back, away from the light. A foot away from the mesh he dowsed the light and waited for his eyes to get used to the dark. As he waited, listening, he could hear the tiny scuttling back towards him, and gradually the forest of red pin-points gathered again, peering at him through the mesh.

What was it? Bond listened to the pounding of his heart. Snakes? Scorpions? Centipedes?

Carefully he brought his eyes close up to the little glowing forest. He inched the lighter up beside his face and suddenly pressed the lever. He caught a glimpse of tiny claws hooked through the mesh and of dozens of thick furry feet and of furry sacklike stomachs topped by big insect heads that seemed to be covered with eyes. The things plopped hurriedly off the wire on to the tin and scurried back and huddled in a grey-brown furry mass at the end of the cage.

Bond squinted through the mesh, moving the light back and forward. Then he dowsed the light, to save fuel, and let the breath come through his teeth in a quiet sigh.

They were spiders, giant tarantulas, three or four inches long. There were twenty of them in the cage. And somehow he had to get past them.

Bond lay and rested and thought while the red eyes gathered again in front of his face.

How deadly were these things? How much of the tales about them were myth? They could certainly kill animals, but how mortal to men were these giant spiders with the long soft friendly fur of a borzoi? Bond shuddered. He remembered the centipede. The touch of the tarantulas would be much softer. They would be like tiny teddy bears' paws against one's skin — until they bit and emptied their poison sacs into you.

But again, would this be Doctor No's killing ground? A bite or two perhaps — to send one into a delirium of pain. The horror of having to burst through the mesh in the darkness — Doctor No would not have reckoned with Bond's lighter — and squash through the forest of eyes, crushing some soft bodies, but feeling the jaws of the others lance home. And then more bites from the ones that had caught in the clothing. And then the creeping agony of the poison. That would have been the way Doctor No's mind would have worked — to send one screaming on one's way. To what? To the final fence?

But Bond had the lighter and the knife and the wire spear. All he needed was the nerve, and infinite, infinite precision.

Bond softly opened the jaws of the lighter and pulled the wick out an inch with his thumb and fingernail to give a bigger flame. He lit it and, as the spiders scuttled back, he pierced the thin wire mesh with his knife. He made a hole near the frame and cut down sideways and round. Then he seized the flap of wire and wrenched it out of the frame. It tore like stiff calico and came away in one piece. He put the knife back between his teeth and snaked through the opening. The spiders cowered before the flame of the lighter and crowded back on top of each other. Bond slid the wire spear out of his trousers and jabbed the blunt, doubled wire into the middle of them. He jabbed again and again, fiercely pulping the bodies. When some of the spiders tried to escape towards him he waved the light at them and smashed the fugitives one by one. Now the living spiders were attacking the dead and wounded and all Bond had to do was bash and bash into the writhing, sickening mess of blood and fur.

Slowly all movement slackened and then ceased. Were they all dead? Were some shamming? The flame of the lighter was beginning to die. He would have to chance it. Bond reached forward and shovelled the dead mess to one side. Then he took his knife from between his teeth and reached out and slashed open the second curtain of wire, bending the flap down over the heap of pulped bodies. The light flickered and became a red glow. Bond gathered himself and shot his body over the bloody pile of corpses and through the jagged frame.

He had no idea what bits of metal he touched or whether he had put his knee or his foot among the spiders. All he knew was that he had got through. He heaved himself yards on along the shaft and stopped to gather his breath and his nerve.

Above him a dim light came on. Bond squinted sideways and upwards, knowing what he would see. The slanting yellow eyes behind the thick glass looked keenly down at him. Slowly, behind the bulb, the head moved from side to side. The eyelids dropped in mock pity. A closed fist, the thumb pointing downwards in farewell and dismissal, inserted itself between the bulb and the glass. Then it was withdrawn. The light went out. Bond turned his face back to the floor of the shaft and rested his forehead on the cool metal. The gesture said that he was coming into the last lap, that the observers had finished with him until they came for his remains. It took an extra ounce of heart out of Bond that there had been no gesture of praise, however small, that he had managed to survive so far. These Chigroes hated him. They only wanted him to die, and as miserably as possible.

Bond's teeth ground softly together. He thought of the girl and the thought gave him strength. He wasn't dead yet. Damn it, he wouldn't die! Not until the heart was torn from his body.

Bond tensed his muscles. It was time to go. With extra care he put his weapons back in their places and painfully began to drag himself on into the blackness.

The shaft was beginning to slope gently downwards. It made the going easier. Soon the slope grew steeper so that Bond could almost slide along under the momentum of his weight. It was a blessed relief not to have to make the effort with his muscles. There was a glimmer of grey light ahead, nothing more than a lessening of the darkness, but it was a change. The quality of the air seemed to be different. There was a new, fresh smell to it. What was it? The sea?

Suddenly Bond realized that he was slipping down the shaft. He opened his shoulders and spread his feet to slow himself. It hurt and the braking effect was small. Now the shaft was widening. He could no longer get a grip! He was going faster and faster. A bend was just ahead. And it was a bend downwards!

Bond's body crashed into the bend and round it. Christ, he was diving head downwards! Desperately Bond spread his feet and hands. The metal flayed his skin. He was out of control, diving, diving down a gun barrel. Far below there was a circle of grey light. The open air? The sea? The light was tearing up at him. He fought for breath. Stay alive, you fool! Stay alive!

Head first, Bond's body shot out of the shaft and fell through the air, slowly, slowly, down towards the gun-metal sea that waited for him a hundred feet below.

XVIII

KILLING GROUND

Bond's body shattered the mirror of the dawn sea like a bomb.

As he had hurtled down the silver shaft towards the widening disc of light, instinct had told him to get his knife from between his teeth, to get his hands forward to break his fall, and to keep his head down and his body rigid. And, at the last fraction of a second when he glimpsed the up-rushing sea, he had managed to take a gulp of breath. So Bond hit the water in the semblance of a dive, his outstretched clenched fists cleaving a hole for his skull and shoulders, and though, by the time he had shot twenty feet below the surface, he had lost consciousness, the forty-mile-an-hour impact with the water failed to smash him.

Slowly the body rose to the surface and lay, head down, softly rocking in the ripples of the dive. The water-choked lungs somehow contrived to send a last message to the brain. The legs and arms thrashed clumsily. The head turned up, water pouring from its open mouth. It sank. Again the legs jerked, instinctively trying to get the body upright in the water. This time, coughing horribly, the head jerked above the surface and stayed there. The arms and legs began to move feebly, paddling like a dog, and, through the red and black curtain, the bloodshot eyes saw the lifeline and told the sluggish brain to make for it.

The killing ground was a narrow deep water inlet at the base of the towering cliff. The lifeline towards which Bond struggled, hampered by the clumsy spear in his trouser-leg, was a strong wire fence, stretched from the rock walls of the inlet and caging it off from the open sea. The two-feet squares of thick wire were suspended from a cable six feet above the surface and disappeared, algae encrusted, into the depths.

Bond got to the wire and hung, crucified. For fifteen minutes he stayed like that, his body occasionally racked with vomiting, until he felt strong enough to turn his head and see where he was. Blearily his eyes took in the towering cliffs above him and the narrow vee of softly breathing water. The place was in deep grey shadow, cut off from the dawn by the mountain, but out at sea there was the pearly iridescence of first light that meant that for the rest of the world the day was dawning. Here it was dark and gloomy and brooding.

Sluggishly Bond's mind puzzled over the wire fence. What was its purpose, closing off this dark cleft of sea? Was it to keep things out, or keep them in? Bond gazed vaguely down into the black depths around him. The wire strands vanished into nothingness below his clinging feet. There were small fish round his legs below the waist. What were they doing? They seemed to be feeding, darting in towards him and then backing away, catching at black strands. Strands of what? Of cotton from his rags? Bond shook his head to clear it. He looked again. No, they were feeding off his blood.

Bond shivered. Yes, blood was seeping off his body, off the torn shoulders, the knees, the feet, into the water. Now for the first time he felt the pain of the sea water on his sores and burns. The pain revived him, quickened his mind. If these small fish liked it, what about barracuda and shark? Was that what the wire fence was for, to keep

man-eating fish from escaping to sea? Then why hadn't
they been after him already? To hell with it! The first
thing was to crawl up the wire and get over to the other
side. To put the fence between him and whatever lived in
this black aquarium.

Weakly, foothold by foothold, Bond climbed up the wire
and over the top and down again to where he could rest
well above the water. He hooked the thick cable under his
arms and hung, a bit of washing on a line, and gazed
vaguely down at the fish that still fed from the blood that
dripped off his feet.

Now there was nothing much left of Bond, not many
reserves. The last dive down the tube, the crash of impact
and the half-death from drowning had squeezed him like
a sponge. He was on the verge of surrender, on the verge
of giving one small sigh and then slipping back into the
soft arms of the water. How beautiful it would be to give
in at last and rest — to feel the sea softly take him to its
bed and turn out the light.

It was the explosive flight of the fish from their
feeding ground that shook Bond out of his death-
dreaming. Something had moved far below the surface.
There was a distant shimmer. Something was coming
slowly up on the landward side of the fence.

Bond's body tautened. His hanging jaw slowly shut and
the slackness cleared from his eyes. With the electric shock
of danger, life flooded back into him, driving out the
lethargy, pumping back the will to survive.

Bond uncramped the fingers that, a long time ago, his
brain had ordered not to lose his knife. He flexed his
fingers and took a fresh grip of the silver-plated handle.
He reached down and touched the crook of the wire spear
that still hung inside his trouser-leg. He shook his head
sharply and focused his eyes. Now what?

Below him the water quivered. Something was stirring

in the depths, something huge. A great length of lumin-
escent greyness showed, poised far down in the darkness.
Something snaked up from it, a whiplash as thick as
Bond's arm. The tip of the thong was swollen to a narrow
oval, with regular budlike markings. It swirled through
the water where the fish had been and was withdrawn.
Now there was nothing but the huge grey shadow. What
was it doing? Was it ... ? Was it tasting the blood?

As if in answer, two eyes as big as footballs slowly swam
up and into Bond's vision. They stopped, twenty feet
below his own, and stared up through the quiet water at
his face.

Bond's skin crawled on his back. Softly, wearily, his
mouth uttered one bitter four-lettered word. So this was
the last surprise of Doctor No, the end of the race!

Bond stared down, half hypnotized, into the wavering
pools of eye far below. So this was the giant squid, the
mythical kraken that could pull ships beneath the waves,
the fifty-foot-long monster that battled with whales, that
weighed a ton or more. What else did he know about
them? That they had two long seizing tentacles and ten
holding ones. That they had a huge blunt beak beneath
eyes that were the only fishes' eyes that worked on the
camera principle, like a man's. That their brains were
efficient, that they could shoot backwards through the
water at thirty knots, by jet-propulsion. That explosive
harpoons burst in their jellied mantle without damaging
them. That ... but the bulging black and white targets of
the eyes were rising up towards him. The surface of the
water shivered. Now Bond could see the forest of tentacles
that flowered out of the face of the thing. They were
weaving in front of the eyes like a bunch of thick snakes.
Bond could see the dots of the suckers on their undersides.
Behind the head, the great flap of the mantle softly opened
and closed, and behind that the jellied sheen of the body

disappeared into the depths. God, the thing was as big as a railway engine!

Softly, discreetly, Bond snaked his feet and then his arms through the squares in the wire, lacing himself into them, anchoring himself so that the tentacles would have either to tear him to bits or wrench down the wire barrier with him. He squinted to right and left. Either way it was twenty yards along the wire to the land. And movement, even if he was capable of it, would be fatal. He must stay dead quiet and pray that the thing would lose interest. If it didn't ... Softly Bond's fingers clenched on the puny knife.

The eyes watched him, coldly, patiently. Delicately, like the questing trunk of an elephant, one of the long seizing tentacles broke the surface and palped its way up the wire towards his leg. It reached his foot. Bond felt the hard kiss of the suckers. He didn't move. He dared not reach down and lose the grip of his arms through the wire. Softly the suckers tugged, testing the amount of yield. It was not enough. Like a huge slimy caterpillar, the tentacle walked slowly on up the leg. It got to the bloody, blistered kneecap and stopped there, interested. Bond's teeth gritted with the pain. He could imagine the message going back down the thick tentacle to the brain: Yes, it's good to eat! And the brain signalling back: then get it! Bring it to me!

The suckers walked on up the thigh. The tip of the tentacle was pointed, then it splayed out so that it almost covered the width of Bond's thigh and then tapered off to a wrist. That was Bond's target. He would just have to take the pain and the horror and wait for the wrist to come within range.

A breeze, the first soft breeze of early morning, whispered across the metal surface of the inlet. It raised small waves that slapped gently against the sheer walls of the cliff. A wedge of cormorants took off from the guanera, five hundred feet above the inlet, and, cackling softly, made out to sea. As they swept over, the noise that had disturbed them reached Bond — the triple blast of a ship's siren that means it is ready to take on cargo. It came from Bond's left. The jetty must be round the corner from the northern arm of the inlet. The tanker from Antwerp had come in. Antwerp! Part of the world outside — the world that was a million miles away, out of Bond's reach — surely out of his reach for ever. Just round that corner, men would be in the galley, having breakfast. The radio would be playing. There would be the sizzle of bacon and eggs, the smell of coffee ... breakfast cooking....

The suckers were at his hip. Bond could see into the horny cups. A stagnant sea smell reached him as the hand slowly undulated upwards. How tough was the mottled grey-brown jelly behind the hand? Should he stab? No, it must be a quick hard slash, straight across, like cutting a rope. Never mind about cutting into his own skin.

Now! Bond took a quick glance into the two football eyes, so patient, so incurious. As he did so the other seizing arm broke the surface and shot straight up at his face. Bond jerked back and the hand curled into a fist round the wire in front of his eyes. In a second it would shift to an arm or shoulder and he would be finished. Now!

The first hand was on his ribs. Almost without taking aim, Bond's knife-hand slashed down and across. He felt the blade bite into the puddingy flesh and then the knife was almost torn from his grip as the wounded tentacle whipped back into the water. For a moment the sea boiled around him. Now the other hand let go the wire and slapped across his stomach. The pointed hand stuck like a leech, all the power of the suckers furiously applied. Bond screamed as the suckers bit into his flesh. He slashed madly, again and again. God, his stomach was being torn out! The wire shook with the struggle. Below him the water boiled and foamed. He would have to give in. One more stab, this time into the back of the hand. It worked! The hand jerked free and snaked down and away leaving twenty red circles, edged with blood, across his skin.

Bond had no time to worry about them. Now the head of the squid had broken the surface and the sea was being thrashed into foam by the great heaving mantle round it. The eyes were glaring up at him, redly, venomously, and the forest of feeding arms was at his feet and legs, tearing the cotton fabric away and flailing back. Bond was being pulled down, inch by inch. The wire was biting into his armpits. He could even feel his spine being stretched. If he held on he would be torn in half. Now the eyes and the great triangular beak were right out of the water and the beak was reaching up for his feet. There was one hope, only one!

Bond thrust his knife between his teeth and his hand dived for the crook of the wire spear. He tore it out, got it between his two hands and wrenched the doubled wire almost straight. He would have to let go with one arm to stoop and get within range. If he missed, he would be torn to shreds on the fence.

Now, before he died of the pain! Now, now!

Bond let his whole body slip down the ladder of wire and lunged through and down with all his force.

He caught a glimpse of the tip of his spear lancing into the centre of a black eyeball and then the whole sea erupted up at him in a fountain of blackness and he fell and hung upside down by the knees, his head an inch from the surface of the water.

What had happened? Had he gone blind? He could see nothing. His eyes were stinging and there was a horrible fish taste in his mouth. But he could feel the wire cutting into the tendons behind his knees. So he must be alive! Dazedly Bond let go the spear from his trailing hand

and reached up and felt for the nearest strand of wire. He got a hold and reached up his other hand and slowly, agonizingly, pulled himself up so that he was sitting in the fence. Streaks of light came into his eyes. He wiped a hand across his face. Now he could see. He gazed at his hand. It was black and sticky. He looked down at his body. It was covered with black slime, and blackness stained the sea for twenty yards around. Then Bond realized. The wounded squid had emptied its ink sac at him.

But where was the squid? Would it come back? Bond searched the sea. Nothing, nothing but the spreading stain of black. Not a movement. Not a ripple. Then don't wait! Get away from here! Get away quick! Wildly Bond looked to right and left. Left was towards the ship, but also towards Doctor No. But right was towards nothing. To build the wire fence the men must have come from the left, from the direction of the jetty. There would be some sort of a path. Bond reached for the top cable and frantically began to edge along the swaying fence towards the rocky headland twenty yards away.

The stinking, bleeding, black scarecrow moved its arms and legs quite automatically. The thinking, feeling apparatus of Bond was no longer part of his body. It moved alongside his body, or floated above it, keeping enough contact to pull the strings that made the puppet work. Bond was like a cut worm, the two halves of which continue to jerk forward although life has gone and been replaced by the mock life of nervous impulses. Only, with Bond, the two halves were not yet dead. Life was only in abeyance in them. All he needed was an ounce of hope, an ounce of reassurance that it was still worth while trying to stay alive.

Bond got to the rock face. Slowly he let himself down to the bottom rung of wire. He gazed vaguely at the softly heaving sheen of water. It was black, impenetrable, as deep as the rest. Should he chance it? He must! He could do nothing until he had washed off the caking slime and blood, the horrible stale fish-smell. Moodily, fatalistically, he took off the rags of his shirt and trousers and hung them on the wire. He looked down at his brown and white body, striped and pock-marked with red. On an instinct he felt his pulse. It was slow but regular. The steady thump of life revived his spirits. What the hell was he worrying about? He was alive. The wounds and bruises on his body were nothing — absolutely nothing. They looked ugly, but nothing was broken. Inside the torn envelope, the machine was quietly, solidly ticking over. Superficial cuts and abrasions, bloody memories, deathly exhaustion — these were hurts that an accident ward would sneer at. Get on, you bastard! Get moving! Clean yourself and wake up. Count your blessings. Think of the girl. Think of the man you've somehow got to find and kill. Hang on to life like you've hung on to the knife between your teeth. Stop being sorry for yourself. To hell with what happened just now. Get down into the water and wash!

Ten minutes later, Bond, his wet rags clinging to his scrubbed, stinging body and his hair slicked back out of his eyes, climbed over the top of the headland.

Yes, it was as he had guessed. A narrow rocky track, made by the feet of the workers, led down the other side and round the bulge of the cliff.

From close by came various sounds and echoes. A crane was working. He could hear the changing beat of its engine. There were iron ship-noises and the sound of water splashing into the sea from a bilge pump.

Bond looked up at the sky. It was pale blue. Clouds tinged with golden pink were trailing away towards the horizon. Far above him the cormorants were wheeling round the guanera. Soon they would be going off to feed. Perhaps even now they were watching the scout groups far out at sea locating the fish. It would be about six o'clock, the dawn of a beautiful day.

Bond, leaving drops of blood behind him, picked his way carefully down the track and along the bottom of the shadowed cliff. Round the bend, the track filtered through a maze of giant, tumbled boulders. The noises grew louder. Bond crept softly forward, watching his footholds for loose stones. A voice called out, startlingly close, 'Okay to go?' There was a distant answer: 'Okay.' The crane engine accelerated. A few more yards. One more boulder. And another. Now!

Bond flattened himself against the rock and warily inched his head round the corner.

XIX

A SHOWER OF DEATH

Bond took one long comprehensive look and pulled back.

He leant against the cool face of rock and waited for his breathing to get back to normal. He lifted his knife close up to his eyes and carefully examined the blade. Satisfied, he slipped it behind him and down the waistband of his trousers up against his spine. There it would be handy but protected from hitting against anything. He wondered about the lighter. He took it out of his hip pocket. As a hunk of metal it might be useful, but it wouldn't light any more and it might scrape against the rock. He put it down on the ground away from his feet.

Then Bond sat down and meticulously went over the photograph that was in his brain.

Round the corner, not more than ten yards away, was the crane. There was no back to the cabin. Inside it a man sat at the controls. It was the Chinese negro boss, the driver of the marsh buggy. In front of him the jetty ran twenty yards out into the sea and ended in a T. An aged tanker of around ten thousand tons deadweight was secured alongside the top of the T. It stood well out of the water, its decks perhaps twelve feet above the quay. The tanker was called *Blanche*, and the *Ant* of Antwerp showed at her stern. There was no sign of life on board except one figure lolling at the wheel in the enclosed bridge. The rest of the crew would be below, battened away from the guano dust. From just to the right of the crane, an overhead conveyor-belt in a corrugated-iron housing ran out from the cliff-face. It was carried on high stanchions above the jetty and stopped just short of the hold of the tanker. Its mouth ended in a huge canvas sock, perhaps six feet in diameter. The purpose of the crane was to lift the wire-framed mouth of the sock so that it hung directly over the hold of the tanker and to move it to right or left to give even distribution. From out of the mouth of the sock, in a solid downward jet, the scrambled-egg-coloured guano dust was pouring into the hold of the tanker at a rate of tons a minute.

Below, on the jetty, to the left and to leeward of the drifting smoke of the guano dust, stood the tall, watchful figure of Doctor No.

That was all. The morning breeze feathered the deep-water anchorage, still half in shadow beneath the towering cliffs, the conveyor-belt thudded quietly on its rollers, the crane's engine chuffed rhythmically. There was no other sound, no other movement, no other life apart from the watch at the ship's wheel, the trusty working at the crane, and Doctor No, seeing that all went well. On the other side of the mountain men would be working, feeding the guano to the conveyor-belt that rumbled away through the bowels of the rock, but on this side no one was allowed and no one was necessary. Apart from aiming the canvas mouth of the conveyor, there was nothing else for anyone to do.

Bond sat and thought, measuring distances, guessing at angles, remembering exactly where the crane driver's hands and feet were on the levers and the pedals. Slowly, a thin, hard smile broke across the haggard, sunburned face. Yes! It was on! It could be done. But softly, gently, slowly! The prize was almost intolerably sweet.

Bond examined the soles of his feet and his hands. They would serve. They would have to serve. He reached back and felt the handle of the knife. Shifted it an inch. He stood up and took several slow deep breaths, ran his hands through his salt- and sweat-matted hair, rubbed them harshly up and down his face and then down the tattered sides of his black jeans. He gave a final flex to his fingers. He was ready.

Bond stepped up to the rock and inched an eye round. Nothing had changed. His guess at the distances had been right. The crane driver was watchful, absorbed. The neck above the open khaki shirt was naked, offered, waiting. Twenty yards away, Doctor No, also with his back to Bond, stood sentry over the thick rich cataract of whity-yellow dust. On the bridge, the watch was lighting a cigarette.

Bond looked along the ten yards of path that led past the back of the crane. He picked out the places he would put each foot. Then he came out from behind the rock and ran.

Bond ran to the right of the crane, to a point he had chosen where the lateral side of the cabin would hide him from the driver and the jetty. He got there and stopped, crouching, listening. The engine hurried on, the conveyor-belt rumbled steadily out of the mountain above and behind him. There was no change.

The two iron footholds at the back of the cabin, inches away from Bond's face, looked solid. Anyway the noise of the engine would drown small sounds. But he would have to be quick to yank the man's body out of the seat and get his own hands and feet on the controls. The single stroke of the knife would have to be mortal. Bond felt along his own collarbone, felt the soft triangle of skin beneath which the jugular pumped, remembered the angle of approach behind the man's back, reminded himself to force the blade and hold it in.

For a final second he listened, then he reached behind his back for the knife and went up the iron steps and into the cabin with the stealth and speed of a panther.

At the last moment there was no need to hurry. Bond stood behind the man's back, smelling him. He had time to raise his knife hand almost to the roof of the cabin, time to summon every ounce of strength, before he swept the blade down and into the square inch of smooth, brownish-yellow skin.

The man's hands and legs splayed away from the controls. His face strained back towards Bond. It seemed to Bond that there was a flash of recognition in the bulging eyes before the whites rolled upwards. Then a strangled noise came from the open mouth and the big body rolled sideways off its iron seat and crashed to the floor.

Bond's eyes didn't even follow it as far as the ground. He was already in the seat and reaching for the pedals and levers. Everything was out of control. The engine was running in neutral, the wire hawser was tearing off the drum, the tip of the crane was bending slowly forwards like a giraffe's neck, the canvas mouth of the conveyor-belt had wilted and was now pouring its column of dust between the jetty and the ship. Doctor No was staring upwards. His mouth was open. Perhaps he was shouting something.

Coolly, Bond reined the machine in, slowly easing the levers and pedals back to the angles at which the driver had been holding them. The engine accelerated, the gears bit and began to work again. The hawser slowed on the spinning drum and reversed, bringing the canvas mouth up and over the ship. The tip of the crane lifted and stopped. The scene was as before. Now!

Bond reached forward for the iron wheel which the driver had been handling when Bond had caught his first glimpse of him. Which way to turn it? Bond tried to the left. The tip of the crane veered slightly to the right. So be it. Bond spun the wheel to the right. Yes, by God, it was answering, moving across the sky, carrying the mouth of the conveyor with it.

Bond's eyes flashed to the jetty. Doctor No had moved. He had moved a few paces to a stanchion that Bond had missed. He had a telephone in his hand. He was getting through to the other side of the mountain. Bond could see his hand frantically jiggling the receiver arm, trying to attract attention.

Bond whirled the director wheel. Christ, wouldn't it turn any faster? In seconds Doctor No would get through and it would be too late. Slowly the tip of the crane arced across the sky. Now the mouth of the conveyor was spewing the dust column down over the side of the ship. Now the yellow mound was marching silently across the jetty. Five yards, four, three, two! Don't look round, you bastard! Arrh, got you! Stop the wheel! Now, *you* take it, Doctor No!

At the first brush of the stinking dust column, Doctor No had turned. Bond saw the long arms fling wide as if to embrace the thudding mass. One knee rose to run. The mouth opened and a thin scream came up to Bond above the noise of the engine. Then there was a brief glimpse of a kind of dancing snowman. And then only a mound of yellow bird dung that grew higher and higher.

'God!' Bond's voice gave back an iron echo from the walls of the cabin. He thought of the screaming lungs stuffing with the filthy dust, the body bending and then falling under the weight, the last impotent kick of the heels, the last flash of thought — rage, horror, defeat? — and then the silence of the stinking tomb.

Now the yellow mountain was twenty feet high. The stuff was spilling off the sides of the jetty into the sea. Bond glanced at the ship. As he did so, there came three blasts on its siren. The noise crashed round the cliffs. There came a fourth blast which didn't stop. Bond could see the watch holding on to the lanyard as he craned out of the bridge window, looking down. Bond took his hands off the controls and let them rip. It was time to go.

He slipped off the iron seat and bent over the dead body. He took the revolver out of the holster and looked at it. He smiled grimly — Smith & Wesson ·38, the regular model. He slipped it down inside his waistband. It was fine to feel the heavy cold metal against his skin. He went to the door of the cabin and dropped down to the ground.

An iron ladder ran up the cliff behind the crane to where the conveyor-housing jutted out. There was a small door in the corrugated iron wall of the housing. Bond scrambled up the ladder. The door opened easily, letting out a puff of guano dust, and he clambered through.

Inside, the clanking of the conveyor-belt over its rollers was deafening, but there were dim inspection lights in the stone ceiling of the tunnel and a narrow catwalk that stretched away into the mountain alongside the hurrying river of dust. Bond moved quickly along it, breathing shallowly against the fishy ammoniac smell. At all costs he must get to the end before the significance of the ship's siren and of the unanswered telephone overcame the fear of the guards.

Bond half ran and half stumbled through the echoing, stinking tunnel. How far would it be? Two hundred yards? And then what? Nothing for it but to break out of the tunnel mouth and start shooting — cause a panic and hope for the best. He would get hold of one of the men and wring out of him where the girl was. Then what? When he got to the place on the mountainside, what would he find? What would be left of her?

Bond ran on faster, his head down, watching the narrow

breadth of planking, wondering what would happen if he missed his footing and slipped into the rushing river of guano dust. Would he be able to get off the belt again or would he be whirled away and down until he was finally spewed out on to the burial mound of Doctor No?

When Bond's head hit into the soft stomach and he felt the hands at his throat, it was too late to think of his revolver. His only reaction was to throw himself down and forward at the legs. The legs gave against his shoulder and there was a shrill scream as the body crashed down on his back.

Bond had started the heave that would hurl his attacker sideways and on to the conveyor-belt when the quality of the scream and something light and soft about the impact of the body froze his muscles.

It couldn't be!

As if in answer, sharp teeth bit deeply into the calf of his right leg and an elbow jabbed viciously, knowledgeably, backwards into his groin.

Bond yelled with the pain. He tried to squirm sideways to protect himself, but even as he shouted 'Honey!' the elbow thudded into him again.

The breath whistled through Bond's teeth with the agony. There was only one way to stop her without throwing her on to the conveyor-belt. He took a firm grip of one ankle and heaved himself to his knees. He stood upright, holding her slung over his shoulder by one leg. The other foot banged against his head, but half-heartedly, as if she too realized that something was wrong.

'Stop it, Honey! It's me!'

Through the din of the conveyor-belt, Bond's shout got through to her. He heard her cry 'James!' from somewhere near the floor. He felt her hands clutch at his legs. 'James, James!'

Bond slowly let her down. He turned and knelt and

reached for her. He put his arms round her and held her tightly to him. 'Oh Honey, Honey. Are you all right?' Desperately, unbelieving, he strained her to him.

'Yes, James! Oh, yes!' He felt her hands at his back and his hair. 'Oh, James, my darling!' she fell against him, sobbing.

'It's all right, Honey.' Bond smoothed her hair. 'And Doctor No's dead. But now we've got to run for it. We've got to get out of here. Come on! How can we get out of the tunnel? How did you get here? We've got to hurry!'

As if in comment, the conveyor-belt stopped with a jerk.

Bond pulled the girl to her feet. She was wearing a dirty suit of workmen's blue dungarees. The sleeves and legs were rolled up. The suit was far too big for her. She looked like a girl in a man's pyjamas. She was powdered white with the guano dust except where the tears had marked her cheeks. She said breathlessly, 'Just up there! There's a side tunnel that leads to the machine shops and the garage. Will they come after us?'

There was no time to talk. Bond said urgently, 'Follow me!' and started running. Behind him her feet padded softly in the hollow silence. They came to the fork where the side tunnel led off into the rock. Which way would the men come? Down the side tunnel or along the catwalk in the main tunnel? The sound of voices booming far up the side tunnel answered him. Bond drew the girl a few feet up the main tunnel. He brought her close to him and whispered, 'I'm sorry, Honey. I'm afraid I'm going to have to kill them.'

'Of course.' The answering whisper was matter of fact. She pressed his hand and stood back to give him room. She put her hands up to her ears.

Bond eased the gun out of his waistband. Softly he broke the cylinder sideways and verified with his thumb that all six chambers were loaded. Bond knew he wasn't going to like this, killing again in cold blood, but these men would be the Chinese negro gangsters, the strong-arm guards who did the dirty work. They would certainly be murderers many times over. Perhaps they were the ones who had killed Strangways and the girl. But there was no point in trying to ease his conscience. It was kill or be killed. He must just do it efficiently.

The voices were coming closer. There were three men. They were talking loudly, nervously. Perhaps it was many years since they had even thought of going through the tunnel. Bond wondered if they would look round as they came out into the main tunnel. Or would he have to shoot them in the back?

Now they were very close. He could hear their shoes scuffing the ground.

'That makes ten bucks you owe me, Sam.'

'Not after tonight it won't be. Roll them bones, boy. Roll them bones.'

'No dice for me tonight, feller. I'm going' to cut maself a slice of de white girl.'

'Haw, haw, haw.'

The first man came out, then the second, then the third. They were carrying their revolvers loosely in their right hands.

Bond said sharply, 'No, you won't.'

The three men whirled round. White teeth glinted in open mouths. Bond shot the rear man in the head and the second man in the stomach. The front man's gun was up. A bullet whistled past Bond and away up the main tunnel. Bond's gun crashed. The man clutched at his neck and spun slowly round and fell across the conveyor-belt. The echoes thundered slowly up and down the tunnel. A puff of fine dust rose in the air and settled. Two of the bodies lay still. The man with the stomach shot writhed and jerked.

Bond tucked his hot gun into the waistband of his

trousers. He said roughly to the girl, 'Come on.' He reached for her hand and pulled her after him into the mouth of the side tunnel. He said, 'Sorry about that, Honey,' and started running, pulling her after him by the hand. She said, 'Don't be stupid.' Then there was no sound but the thud of their naked feet on the stone floor.

The air was clean in the side-tunnel and it was easier going but, after the tension of the shooting, pain began to crowd in again and take possession of Bond's body. He ran automatically. He hardly thought of the girl. His whole mind was focused on taking the pain and on the problems that waited at the end of the tunnel.

He couldn't tell if the shots had been heard and he had no idea what opposition was left. His only plan was to shoot anyone who got in his way and somehow get to the garage and the marsh buggy. That was their only hope of getting away from the mountain and down to the coast.

The dim yellow bulbs in the ceiling flicked by overhead. Still the tunnel stretched on. Behind him, Honey stumbled. Bond stopped, cursing himself for not having thought of her. She reached for him and for a moment she leaned against him panting. 'I'm sorry, James. It's just that ...'

Bond held her to him. He said anxiously, 'Are you hurt, Honey?'

'No, I'm all right. It's just that I'm so terribly tired. And my feet got rather cut on the mountain. I fell a lot in the dark. If we could walk a bit. We're nearly there. And there's a door into the garage before we get to the machine shop. Couldn't we go in there?'

Bond hugged her to him. He said, 'That's just what I'm looking for, Honey. That's our only hope of getting away. If you can stick it till we get there, we've got a real chance.'

Bond put his arm round her waist and took her weight. He didn't trust himself to look at her feet. He knew they

must be bad. It was no good being sorry for each other.
There wasn't time for it if they were to stay alive.

They started moving again, Bond's face grim with the
extra effort, the girl's feet leaving bloody footsteps on the
ground, and almost immediately she whispered urgently
and there was a wooden door in the wall of the tunnel
and it was ajar and no sound came from the other side.

Bond took out his gun and gently eased the door open.
The long garage was empty. Under the neon lights the
black and gold painted dragon on wheels looked like a
float waiting for the Lord Mayor's Show. It was pointing
towards the sliding doors and the hatch of the armoured
cabin stood open. Bond prayed that the tank was full and
that the mechanic had carried out his orders to get the
damage fixed.

Suddenly, from somewhere outside, there was the sound
of voices. They came nearer, several of them, jabbering
urgently.

Bond took the girl by the hand and ran forward. There
was only one place to hide — in the marsh buggy. The
girl scrambled in. Bond followed, softly pulling the door
shut behind him. They crouched, waiting. Bond thought:
only three rounds left in the gun. Too late he remembered
the rack of weapons on the wall of the garage. Now the
voices were outside. There came the clang of the door being
slid back on its runners and a confusion of talk.

'How d'ya know they were shootin'?'

'Couldn't been nuthen else. I should know.'

'Better take rifles. Here, Joe! Take that one, Lemmy!
An' some pineapples. Box under da table.'

There was the metallic noise of bolts being slid home
and safety catches clicked.

'Some feller must a gone nuts. Couldn't ha been da
Limey. You ever seen da big pus-feller in da creek?
Cheessus! An' da rest of da tricks da Doc fixed up in da

tube? An' dat white gal. She cain't have been in much shape dis mornin'. Any of you men bin to have a look?'

'Nossir.'

'No.'

'No.'

'Haw, haw. I'se sho surprised at you fellers. Dat's a fine piece of ass out dere on de crab walk.'

More rattling and shuffling of feet, then, 'Okay let's go! Two abreast till we gets to da main tunnel. Shoot at da legs. Whoever's makin' trouble, da Doc'll sure want him to play wit.'

'Tee-hee.'

Feet echoed hollowly on the concrete. Bond held his breath as they filed by. Would they notice the shut door of the buggy? But they went on down the garage and into the tunnel and the noise of them slowly faded away.

Bond touched the girl's arm and put his finger to his lips. Softly he eased open the door and listened again. Nothing. He dropped to the ground and walked round the buggy and went to the half-open entrance. Cautiously he edged his head round. There was no one in sight. There was a smell of frying food in the air that brought the saliva to Bond's mouth. Dishes and pans clattered in the nearest building, about twenty yards away, and from one of the further Quonsets came the sound of a guitar and a man's voice singing a calypso. Dogs started to bark half-heartedly and then were silent. The Dobermann pinschers.

Bond turned and ran back to the end of the garage. No sound came from the tunnel. Softly Bond closed the tunnel door and locked and bolted it. He went to the arms-rack on the wall and chose another Smith & Wesson and a Remington carbine. He verified that they were loaded and went to the door of the marsh buggy and handed them in to the girl. Now the entrance door. Bond put his shoulder to it and softly eased it wide open. The corrugated iron rumbled hollowly. Bond ran back and scrambled through the open hatch and into the driver's seat. 'Shut it, Honey,' he whispered urgently and bent and turned the ignition key.

The needle on the gauge swung to Full. Pray God the damned thing would start up quickly. Some diesels were slow. Bond stamped his foot down on the starter.

The grinding rattle was deafening. It must be audible all over the compound! Bond stopped and tried again. The engine fluttered and died. And again, and this time the blessed thing fired and the strong iron pulse hammered as Bond revved it up. Now, gently into gear. Which one? Try this. Yes, it bit. Brake off, you bloody fool! Christ, it had nearly stalled. But now they were out and on the track and Bond rammed his foot down to the floor.

'Anyone after us?' Bond had to shout above the noise of the diesel.

'No. Wait! Yes, there's a man come out of the huts! And another! They're waving and shouting at us. Now some more are coming out. One of them's run off to the right. Another's gone back into the hut. He's come out with a rifle. He's lying down. He's firing!'

'Close the slot! Lie down on the floor!' Bond glanced at the speedometer. Twenty. And they were on a slope. There was nothing more to get out of the machine. Bond concentrated on keeping the huge bucking wheels on the track. The cabin bounced and swayed on the springs. It was a job to keep his hands and feet on the controls. An iron fist clanged against the cabin. And another. What was the range? Four hundred? Good shooting! But that would be the lot. He shouted, 'Take a look, Honey! Open the slot an inch.'

'The man's got up. He's stopped firing. They're all looking after us — a whole crowd of them. Wait, there's something else. The dogs are coming! There's no one with them. They're just tearing down the track after us. Will they catch us?'

'Doesn't matter if they do. Come and sit by me, Honey. Hold tight. Mind your head against the roof.' Bond eased up on the throttle. She was beside him. He grinned sideways at her. 'Hell, Honey. We've made it. When we get down to the lake I'll stop and shoot up the dogs. If I know those brutes I've only got to kill one and the whole pack'll stop to eat him.'

Bond felt her hand at his neck. She kept it there as they swayed and thundered down the track. At the lake, Bond went on fifty yards into the water and turned the machine round and put it in neutral. Through the oblong slot he could see the pack streaming round the last bend. He reached down for the rifle and pushed it through the aperture. Now the dogs were in the water and swimming. Bond kept his finger on the trigger and sprayed bullets into the middle of them. One floundered, kicking. Then another and another. He could hear their snarling screams above the clatter of the engine. There was blood in the water. A fight had started. He saw one dog leap on one of the wounded ones and sink its teeth into the back of its neck. Now they all seemed to have gone berserk. They were milling around in the frothing bloody water. Bond emptied his magazine among them and dropped the gun on the floor. He said, 'That's that, Honey,' and put the machine into gear and swung it round and began rolling at an easy speed across the shallow lake towards the distant gap in the mangroves that was the mouth of the river.

For five minutes they moved along in silence. Then Bond put a hand on the girl's knee and said, 'We should be all right now, Honey. When they find the boss is dead there'll be panic. I guess some of the brighter ones will try and get away to Cuba in the plane or the launch. They'll worry about their skins, not about us. All the same, we'll not take the canoe out until it's dark. I guess it's about ten by now. We should be at the coast in an hour. Then we'll rest up and try and get in shape for the trip. Weather looks all right and there'll be a bit more moon tonight. Think you can make it?'

Her hand squeezed his neck. 'Of course I can, James. But what about you? Your poor body! It's nothing but burns and bruises. And what are those red marks across your stomach?'

'Tell you later. I'll be okay. But you tell me what happened to you last night. How in hell did you manage to get away from the crabs? What went wrong with that bastard's plan? All night long I could only think of you out there being slowly eaten to death. God, what a thing to have dreamed up! What happened?'

The girl was actually laughing. Bond looked sideways. The golden hair was tousled and the blue eyes were heavy with lack of sleep, but otherwise she might just be coming home from a midnight barbecue.

'That man thought he knew everything. Silly old fool.' She might have been talking about a stupid schoolteacher. 'He's much more impressed by the black crabs than I am. To begin with, I don't mind any animal touching me, and anyway those crabs wouldn't think of even nipping someone if they stay quite still and haven't got an open sore or anything. The whole point is that they don't really like meat. They live mostly on plants and things. If he was right and he did kill a black girl that way, either she had an open wound or she must have died of fright. He must have wanted to see if I'd stand it. Filthy old man. I only fainted down there at dinner because I knew he'd have something much worse for you.'

'Well, I'm damned. I wish to heaven I'd known that. I thought of you being picked to pieces.'

The girl snorted. 'Of course it wasn't very nice having my clothes taken off and being tied down to pegs in the ground. But those black men didn't dare touch me. They just made jokes and then went away. It wasn't very comfortable out there on the rock, but I was thinking of you and of how I could get at Doctor No and kill him. Then I heard the crabs beginning to run — that's what we call it in Jamaica — and soon they came scurrying and rattling along — hundreds of them. I just lay still and thought of you. They walked round me and over me. I might have been a rock for all they cared. They tickled a bit. One annoyed me by trying to pull out a bit of my hair. But they don't smell or anything, and I just waited for the early morning when they crawl into holes and go to sleep. I got quite fond of them. They were company. Then they got fewer and fewer and finally stopped coming and I could move. I pulled at all the pegs in turn and then concentrated on my right hand one. In the end I got it out of the crack in the rock and the rest was easy. I got back to the buildings and began scouting about. I got into the machine shop near the garage and found this filthy old suit. Then the conveyor thing started up not far away and I thought about it and I guessed it must be taking the guano through the mountain. I knew you must be dead by then,' the quiet voice was matter of fact, 'so I thought I'd get to the conveyor somehow and get through the mountain and kill Doctor No. I took a screwdriver to do it with.' She giggled. 'When we ran into each other, I'd have stuck it into you only it was in my pocket and I couldn't get to it. I found the door in the back of the machine shop and walked through and into the main tunnel. That's all.' She caressed the back of his neck. 'I ran along watching my step and the next thing I knew was your head hitting me in the stomach.' She giggled again. 'Darling, I hope I didn't hurt you too much when we were fighting. My nanny told me always to hit men there.'

Bond laughed. 'She did, did she?' He reached out and caught her by the hair and pulled her face to him. Her mouth felt its way round his cheek and locked itself against his.

The machine gave a sideways lurch. The kiss ended. They had hit the first mangrove roots at the entrance to the river.

XX

SLAVE-TIME

'YOU'RE quite sure of all this?'

The Acting Governor's eyes were hunted, resentful. How could these things have been going on under his nose, in one of Jamaica's dependencies? What would the Colonial Office have to say about it? He already saw the long, pale blue envelope marked 'Personal. For Addressee Only', and the foolscap page with those very wide margins: 'The Secretary of State for the Colonies has instructed me to express to you his surprise ...'

'Yes, sir. Quite sure.' Bond had no sympathy for the man. He hadn't liked the reception he had had on his last visit to King's House, nor the mean comments on Strangways and the girl. He liked the memory of them even less now that he knew his friend and the girl were at the bottom of the Mona Reservoir.

'Er — well we mustn't let any of this get out to the Press. You understand that? I'll send my report in to the Secretary of State by the next bag. I'm sure I can rely on your ...'

'Excuse me, sir.' The Brigadier in command of the Caribbean Defence Force was a modern young soldier of thirty-five. His military record was good enough for him to be unimpressed by relics from the Edwardian era of Colonial Governors, whom he collectively referred to as 'feather-hatted fuddy-duddies'. 'I think we can assume that Commander Bond is unlikely to communicate with anyone except his Department. And if I may say so, sir, I submit that we should take steps to clear up Crab Key without waiting for approval from London. I can provide a platoon ready to embark by this evening. H.M.S. *Narvik* came in yesterday. If the programme of receptions and cocktail parties for her could possibly be deferred for forty-eight hours or so...' The Brigadier let his sarcasm hang in the air.

'I agree with the Brigadier, sir.' The voice of the Police Superintendent was edgy. Quick action might save him from a reprimand, but it would have to be quick. 'And in any case I shall have to proceed immediately against the various Jamaicans who appear to be implicated. I'll have to get the divers working at Mona. If this case is to be cleaned up we can't afford to wait for London. As Mister — er — Commander Bond says, most of these negro gangsters will probably be in Cuba by now. Have to get in touch with my opposite number in Havana and catch up with them before they take to the hills or go underground. I think we ought to move at once, sir.'

There was silence in the cool shadowy room where the meeting was being held. On the ceiling above the massive mahogany conference table there was an unexpected dapple of sunlight. Bond guessed that it shone up through the slats of the jalousies from a fountain or a lily pond in the garden outside the tall windows. Far away there was the sound of tennis balls being knocked about. Distantly a young girl's voice called, 'Smooth. Your serve, Gladys.' The Governor's children? Secretaries? From one end of the room King George VI, from the other end the Queen, looked down the table with grace and good humour.

'What do you think, Colonial Secretary?' The Governor's voice was hustled.

Bond listened to the first few words. He gathered that

Pleydell-Smith agreed with the other two. He stopped listening. His mind drifted into a world of tennis courts and lily ponds and kings and queens, of London, of people being photographed with pigeons on their heads in Trafalgar Square, of the forsythia that would soon be blazing on the bypass roundabouts, of May, the treasured housekeeper in his flat off the King's Road, getting up to brew herself a cup of tea (here it was eleven o'clock. It would be six o'clock in London), of the first tube trains beginning to run, shaking the ground beneath his cool, dark bedroom. Of the douce weather of England: the soft airs, the 'heat' waves, the cold spells — 'The only country where you can take a walk every day of the year' — Chesterfield's Letters? And then Bond thought of Crab Key, of the hot ugly wind beginning to blow, of the stink of the marsh gas from the mangrove swamps, the jagged grey, dead coral in whose holes the black crabs were now squatting, the black and red eyes moving swiftly on their stalks as a shadow — a cloud, a bird — broke their small horizons. Down in the bird colony the brown and white and pink birds would be stalking in the shallows, or fighting or nesting, while up on the guanera the cormorants would be streaming back from their breakfast to deposit their milligramme of rent to the landlord who would no longer be collecting. And where would the landlord be? The men from the S.S. *Blanche* would have dug him out. The body would have been examined for signs of life and then put somewhere. Would they have washed the yellow dust off him and dressed him in his kimono while the Captain radioed Antwerp for instructions? And where had Doctor No's soul gone to? Had it been a bad soul or just a mad one? Bond thought of the burned twist down in the swamp that had been Quarrel. He remembered the soft ways of the big body, the innocence in the grey, horizon-seeking eyes, the simple lusts and desires, the reverence for superstitions and instincts, the childish faults, the loyalty and even love that Quarrel had given him — the warmth, there was only one word for it, of the man. Surely he hadn't gone to the same place as Doctor No. Whatever happened to dead people, there was surely one place for the warm and another for the cold. And which, when the time came, would he, Bond, go to?

The Colonial Secretary was mentioning Bond's name. Bond pulled himself together.

'... survived is quite extraordinary. I do think, sir, that we should show our gratitude to Commander Bond and to his Service by accepting his recommendations. It does seem, sir, that he has done at least three-quarters of the job. Surely the least we can do is look after the other quarter.'

The Governor grunted. He squinted down the table at Bond. The chap didn't seem to be paying much attention. But one couldn't be sure with these Secret Service fellows. Dangerous chaps to have around, sniffing and snooping. And their damned Chief carried a lot of guns in Whitehall. Didn't do to get on the wrong side of him. Of course there was something to be said for sending the *Narvik*. News would leak, of course. All the Press of the world would be coming down on his head. But then suddenly the Governor saw the headlines: 'GOVERNOR TAKES SWIFT ACTION ... ISLAND'S STRONG MAN INTER-VENES ... THE NAVY'S THERE!' Perhaps after all it would be better to do it that way. Even go down and see the troops off himself. Yes, that was it, by jove. Cargill, of the *Gleaner*, was coming to lunch. He'd drop a hint or two to the chap and make sure the story got proper coverage. Yes, that was it. That was the way to play the hand.

The Governor raised his hands and let them fall flat

on the table in a gesture of submission. He embraced the conference with a wry smile of surrender.

'So I am overruled, gentlemen. Well, then,' the voice was avuncular, telling the children that just this once ... 'I accept your verdict. Colonial Secretary, will you please call upon the commanding officer of H.M.S. *Narvik* and explain the position. In strict confidence, of course. Brigadier, I leave the military arrangements in your hands. Superintendent, you will know what to do.' The Governor rose. He inclined his head regally in the direction of Bond. 'And it only remains to express my appreciation to Commander — er — Bond, for his part in this affair. I shall not fail to mention your assistance, Commander, to the Secretary of State.'

Outside the sun blazed down on the gravel sweep. The interior of the Hillman Minx was a Turkish bath. Bond's bruised hands cringed as they took the wheel.

Pleydell-Smith leant through the window. He said, 'Ever heard the Jamaican expression "rarse"?'

'No.'

' "Rarse, man" is a vulgar expression meaning — er — "stuff it up". If I may say so, it would have been appropriate for you to have used the expression just now. However,' Pleydell-Smith gave a wave of his hand which apologized for his Chief and dismissed him, 'is there anything else I can do for you? You really think you ought to go back to Beau Desert? They were quite definite at the hospital that they want to have you for a week.'

'Thanks,' said Bond shortly, 'but I've got to get back. See the girl's all right. Would you tell the hospital I'll be back tomorrow? You got off that signal to my Chief?'

'Urgent rates.'

'Well, then,' Bond pressed the self-starter, 'I guess that's the lot. You'll see the Jamaica Institute people about the girl, won't you? She really knows the hell of a lot about the natural history side of the island. Not from books either. If they've got the right sort of job … Like to see her settled. I'll take her up to New York myself and see her through the operation. She'd be ready to start in a couple of weeks after that. Incidentally,' Bond looked embarrassed, 'she's really the hell of a fine girl. When she comes back … if you and your wife … You know. Just so there's someone to keep an eye on her.'

Pleydell-Smith smiled. He thought he had the picture. He said, 'Don't worry about that. I'll see to it. Betty's rather a hand at that sort of thing. She'll like taking the girl under her wing. Nothing else? See you later in the week, anyway. That hospital's the hell of a place in this heat. You might care to spend a night or two with us before you go ho — I mean to New York. Glad to have you — er — both.'

'Thanks. And thanks for everything else.' Bond put the car into gear and went off down the avenue of flaming tropical shrubbery. He went fast, scattering the gravel on the bends. He wanted to get the hell away from King's House, and the tennis, and the kings and queens. He even wanted to get the hell away from the kindly Pleydell-Smith. Bond liked the man, but all he wanted now was to get back across the Junction Road to Beau Desert and away from the smooth world. He swung out past the sentry at the gates and on to the main road. He put his foot down.

The night voyage under the stars had been without incident. No one had come after them. The girl had done most of the sailing. Bond had not argued with her. He had lain in the bottom of the boat, totally collapsed, like a dead man. He had woken once or twice and listened to the slap of the sea against the hull and watched her quiet profile under the stars. Then the cradle of the soft swell

had sent him back to sleep and to the nightmares that
reached out after him from Crab Key. He didn't mind
them. He didn't think he would ever mind a nightmare
now. After what had happened the night before, it would
have to be strong stuff that would ever frighten him again.

The crunch of a nigger-head against the hull had woken
him. They were coming through the reef into Morgan's
Harbour. The first quarter moon was up, and inside the
reef the sea was a silver mirror. The girl had brought the
canoe through under sail. They slid across the bay to
the little fringe of sand and the bows under Bond's head
sighed softly into it. She had had to help him out of the
boat and across the velvet lawn and into the house. He
had clung to her and cursed her softly as she had cut his
clothes off him and taken him into the shower. She had
said nothing when she had seen his battered body under
the lights. She had turned the water full on and taken soap
and washed him down as if he had been a horse. Then
she led him out from under the water and dabbed him
softly dry with towels that were soon streaked with blood.
He had seen her reach for the bottle of Milton. He had
groaned and taken hold of the washbasin and waited for it.
Before she had begun to put it on him, she had come
round and kissed him on the lips. She had said softly,
'Hold tight, my darling. And cry. It's going to hurt,' and
as she splashed the murderous stuff over his body the tears
of pain had run out of his eyes and down his cheeks
without shame.

Then there had been a wonderful breakfast as the
dawn flared up across the bay, and then the ghastly drive
over to Kingston to the white table of the surgery in the
emergency ward. Pleydell-Smith had been summoned. No
questions had been asked. Merthiolate had been put on
the wounds and tannic ointment on the burns. The
efficient negro doctor had written busily in the duty

report. What? Probably just 'Multiple burns and contusions'. Then, with promises to come into the private ward on the next day, Bond had gone off with Pleydell-Smith to King's House and to the first of the meetings that had ended with the full-dress conference. Bond had enciphered a short signal to M via the Colonial Office which he had coolly concluded with: 'REGRET MUST AGAIN REQUEST SICK LEAVE STOP SURGEONS REPORT FOLLOWS STOP KINDLY INFORM ARMOURER SMITH AND WESSON INEFFECTIVE AGAINST FLAME-THROWER ENDIT.'

Now, as Bond swung the little car down the endless S-bends towards the North Shore, he regretted the gibe. M wouldn't like it. It was cheap. It wasted cipher groups. Oh, well! Bond swerved to avoid a thundering red bus with 'Brownskin Gal' on the destination plate. He had just wanted M to know that it hadn't quite been a holiday in the sun. He would apologize when he sent in his written report.

Bond's bedroom was cool and dark. There was a plate of sandwiches and a Thermos full of coffee beside the turned-down bed. On the pillow was a sheet of paper with big childish writing. It said, 'You are staying with me tonight. I can't leave my animals. They were fussing. And I can't leave you. And you owe me slave-time. I will come at seven. Your H.'

In the dusk she came across the lawn to where Bond was sitting finishing his third glass of Bourbon-on-the-rocks. She was wearing a black and white striped cotton skirt and a tight sugar-pink blouse. The golden hair smelled of cheap shampoo. She looked incredibly fresh and beautiful. She reached out her hand and Bond took it and followed her up the drive and along a narrow well-trodden path through the sugar cane. It wound along for quite a way through the tall whispering sweet-scented jungle. Then there was a patch of tidy lawn up against thick

broken stone walls and steps that led down to a heavy
door whose edges glinted with light.

She looked up at him from the door. 'Don't be
frightened. The cane's high and they're most of them out.'

Bond didn't know what he had expected. He had
vaguely thought of a flat earthen floor and rather damp
walls. There would be a few sticks of furniture, a broken
bedstead covered with rags, and a strong zoo smell. He
had been prepared to be careful about hurting her
feelings.

Instead it was rather like being inside a very large tidy
cigar-box. The floor and ceiling were of highly polished
cedar that gave out a cigar-box smell and the walls were
panelled with wide split bamboo. The light came from a
dozen candles in a fine silver chandelier that hung from
the centre of the ceiling. High up in the walls there were
three square windows through which Bond could see the
dark blue sky and the stars. There were several pieces of
good nineteenth-century furniture. Under the chandelier
a table was laid for two with expensive-looking old-
fashioned silver and glass.

Bond said, 'Honey, what a lovely room. From what you
said I thought you lived in a sort of zoo.'

She laughed delightedly. 'I got out the old silver and
things. It's all I've got. I had to spend the day polishing
it. I've never had it out before. It does look rather nice,
doesn't it? You see, generally there are a lot of little
cages up against the wall. I like having them with me.
It's company. But now that you're here ...' She paused.
'My bedroom's in there,' she gestured at the other door.
'It's very small, but there's room for both of us. Now
come on. I'm afraid it's cold dinner — just lobsters and
fruit.'

Bond walked over to her. He took her in his arms and
kissed her hard on the lips. He held her and looked down

into the shining blue eyes. 'Honey, you're a wonderful girl. You're one of the most wonderful girls I've ever known. I hope the world's not going to change you too much. D'you really want to have that operation? I love your face — just as it is. It's part of you. Part of all this.'

She frowned and freed herself. 'You're not to be serious tonight. Don't talk about these things. I don't want to talk about them. This is my night with you. Please talk about love. I don't want to hear about anything else. Promise? Now come on. You sit there.'

Bond sat down. He smiled up at her. He said, 'I promise.'

She said, 'Here's the mayonnaise. It's not out of a bottle. I made it myself. And take some bread and butter.' She sat down opposite him and began to eat, watching him. When she saw that he seemed satisfied she said, 'Now you can start telling me about love. Everything about it. Everything you know.'

Bond looked across into the flushed, golden face. The eyes were bright and soft in the candlelight, but with the same imperious glint they had held when he had first seen her on the beach and she had thought he had come to steal her shells. The full red lips were open with excitement and impatience. With him she had no inhibitions. They were two loving animals. It was natural. She had no shame. She could ask him anything and would expect him to answer. It was as if they were already in bed together, lovers. Through the tight cotton bodice the points of her breasts showed, hard and roused.

Bond said, 'Are you a virgin?'

'Not quite. I told you. That man.'

'Well ...' Bond found he couldn't eat any more. His mouth was dry at the thought of her. He said, 'Honey, I can either eat or talk love to you. I can't do both.'

'You're going over to Kingston tomorrow. You'll get plenty to eat there. Talk love.'

Bond's eyes were fierce blue slits. He got up and went down on one knee beside her. He picked up her hand and looked into it. At the base of the thumb the Mount of Venus swelled luxuriously. Bond bent his head down into the warm soft hand and bit softly into the swelling. He felt her other hand in his hair. He bit harder. The hand he was holding curled round his mouth. She was panting. He bit still harder. She gave a little scream and wrenched his head away by the hair.

'What are you doing?' Her eyes were wide and dark. She had gone pale. She dropped her eyes and looked at his mouth. Slowly she pulled his head towards her.

Bond put out a hand to her left breast and held it hard. He lifted her captive, wounded hand and put it round his neck. Their mouths met and clung, exploring.

Above them the candles began to dance. A big hawk-moth had come in through one of the windows. It whirred round the chandelier. The girl's closed eyes opened, looked at the moth. Her mouth drew away. She smoothed the handful of his hair back and got up, and without saying anything took down the candles one by one and blew them out. The moth whirred away through one of the windows.

The girl stood away from the table. She undid her blouse and threw it on the floor. Then her skirt. Under the glint of moonlight she was a pale figure with a central shadow. She came to Bond and took him by the hand and lifted him up. She undid his shirt and slowly, carefully took it off. Her body, close to him, smelled of new-mown hay and sweet pepper. She led him away from the table and through a door. The filtering moonlight shone down on a single bed. On the bed was a sleeping-bag, its mouth laid open.

The girl let go his hand and climbed into the sleeping-bag. She looked up at him. She said, practically, 'I bought this today. It's a double one. It cost a lot of money. Take those off and come in. You promised. You owe me slave-time.'

'But ...'

'Do as you're told.'

87

EKTACHROME BY NATIONAL GEOGRAPHIC PHOTOGRAPHER B. ANTHONY STEWART

National Geographic on

INDIANS OF THE AMERICAS

a Color-illustrated Record

**Hopi Heads Symbolize
the Beauty and Antiquity
of a Priceless Turquoise Necklace**

A thousand years ago some lucky Indian
of ancient Pueblo Bonito prized
this necklace of 2,500 hand-drilled beads.
Found buried with four ear pendants
under 15 feet of New Mexico sand, it was
an outstanding discovery of
the National Geographic Society's
Pueblo Bonito Expeditions of 1921–1927.
The background painting by W. Langdon Kihn,
illustrator of Part I of this volume,
portrays later dwellers in the region.
Girl's hairdo represents a squash blossom;
old wife wears her hair in braids.

National Geographic on

INDIANS OF THE

A Volume in the
National Geographic Story of Man *Library*

Illustrated with full-color reproductions of 149 paintings by
W. LANGDON KIHN and H. M. HERGET
and eight contemporary Indian painters; 113 photographs in natural color
by JUSTIN LOCKE, LUIS MARDEN, KIP ROSS, RICHARD H. STEWART, and
others; 130 black-and-white photographs, maps, drawings, and diagrams.

Foreword by **JOHN OLIVER LA GORCE**
Vice Chairman of the Board, National Geographic Society

WASHINGTON, D. C.

THE

AMERICAS

a Color-illustrated Record

MATTHEW W. STIRLING

Director, Bureau of American Ethnology, Smithsonian Institution, 1928–57, and Leader of National Geographic Society-Smithsonian Expeditions to Mexico, Panama, and Ecuador.

With contributions by HIRAM BINGHAM, Leader of National Geographic Society-Yale University Peruvian Expeditions; O. F. COOK, former botanist, U. S. Department of Agriculture; ANDREW ELLICOTT DOUGLASS, Professor of Astronomy and Dendrochronology, University of Arizona, Leader of National Geographic Society Tree Ring Expeditions; CLIFFORD EVANS, Associate Curator, Division of Archeology, U. S. National Museum; NEIL M. JUDD, former Curator, Division of Archeology, U. S. National Museum, Leader of National Geographic Pueblo Bonito Expeditions; DONALD B. MARSH, Bishop of the Arctic, PHILIP AINSWORTH MEANS, late authority on Andean civilizations; SYLVANUS GRISWOLD MORLEY, Director of Carnegie Institution Chichén Itzá Project, 1924–40; FROELICH G. RAINEY; Director, University of Pennsylvania Museum; FRANK H. H. ROBERTS, JR., Director, Bureau of American Ethnology; DOROTHY DUNN, BETTY J. MEGGERS, and others.

NATIONAL GEOGRAPHIC SOCIETY

NATIONAL GEOGRAPHIC PHOTOGRAPHER GUY STARLING

Dr. La Gorce Shows His Weapon Collection to a Sioux Visiting the Society's Headquarters

THIS IS THE INDIAN OF THE AMERICAS: The Navajo artist bent over his work of silver; Tarascan girls at a village fountain; the Eskimo battling a polar bear; the bow-and-arrow stalker in Guiana jungles; the ancient Maya priest decked in writhing quetzal plumes.

Here he is hunting, warring, here at play laughing, here sacrificing a human as a jagged obsidian blade descends in a grim pagan rite. From Indians crouched about a Texas hearth 37,000 years ago to those working riveting hammers in mid-20th century America, Indian life crowds upon these pages.

Indians dancing, worshiping, scalping, planting, raiding, clowning, mourning. Indians founding empires, feasting in golden halls, grubbing for roots. The Indian as medicine man and canoe builder, astronomer and horse thief, as food giver, warm friend . . . and deadly foe.

These things are revealed not in the words of armchair scholars but of doing men: the scientist who goes to live among a primitive jungle tribe or joins in a thrilling whale hunt; the professor who scales Andean cliffs to discover a lost city; the bishop who covers two and three-quarters million square miles of arctic diocese.

Since its birth in 1888 the National Geographic Society has contributed much to knowledge of the American past. Research expeditions have carried The Society's flag to Mexico, Panama, Peru; from Cape Horn to the bleak northland tundra of Southampton Island. Here are expedition leaders' exciting accounts: Matthew W. Stirling discovers the New World's oldest dated work of man, throws light on La Venta, or Olmec, culture, explores Panama's past by dugout and helicopter; Neil M. Judd reconstructs ancient life at Pueblo Bonito; Andrew Ellicott Douglass tracks down the "missing link" in the tree ring chronology of the Southwest; Hiram Bingham relives his historic discovery of Machu Picchu.

Two notable artists commissioned by The Society created an incomparable pictorial record under the guidance of Franklin L. Fisher, late Illustrations Editor of the *National Geographic Magazine*. W. Langdon Kihn is represented by 103 paintings of the North American Indian, H. M. Herget by 37 paintings of the Maya, Aztec, and Inca empires. Works of eight contemporary Indian artists are also included.

Explorers, scientists, writers, artists, photographers, cartographers, the wealth of Society materials all have contributed to this comprehensive volume. Its contents are as new as the latest find, as up-to-date as the remarkable carbon-14 dating technique which brings scientific accuracy to bear on prehistoric eras where only conjecture served before.

The Society's appreciation goes to each contributor, to Dr. Stirling for his counsel through the book's long months of preparation, and to Melville Bell Grosvenor, my successor as Editor of the *National Geographic Magazine,* whose conception and able direction were most valuable. Special thanks are due Merle Severy, who skillfully compiled and edited the text; Andrew Poggenpohl, who arranged the illustrations; and other members of the *National Geographic Magazine* staff for their part in creating a work in which every member of The Society may take pride.

November, 1958   JOHN OLIVER LA GORCE

KODACHROME BY JUSTIN LOCKE

Huehueteotl, Ancient God of Fire, looks down the ages at a modern Indian miss. This wrinkled, hunchbacked, leering god, wearing an incense burner as a hat, was discovered in 1941 at Cerro de las Mesas in Veracruz. Huehueteotl is one of many archeological treasures brought to light in Mexico by nine National Geographic Society-Smithsonian Institution expeditions led by Dr. Stirling.

• CONTENTS

FOREWORD *by John Oliver La Gorce*

Part I • INDIANS OF NORTH AMERICA, A HISTORICAL PANORAMA
by Matthew W. Stirling • Paintings by W. Langdon Kihn

Part II • ANCIENT LIFE IN THE NEW WORLD

INDIANS OF

NORTH AMERICA

A HISTORICAL PANORAMA

BY MATTHEW W. STIRLING

PAINTINGS BY W. LANGDON KIHN

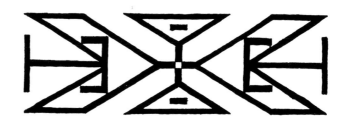

PAINTING BY W. LANGDON KIHN

Fierce, Stalwart, Free Stood the American Warrior. Chief One Bull fought Custer. Resplendent in Sioux trappings at 91, this nephew and adopted son of Sitting Bull evokes the Indian's indomitable spirit.

CHAPTER I

AMERICA'S FIRST SETTLERS THE INDIANS

"ARE THESE THINGS not a dream?" wondered battle-scarred conquistadores as they gazed upon temples, causeways, magnificent cities of the Aztecs. Many a Spanish don following Cortés to Mexican shores in 1519 expected to find naked savages living in primitive state.

Imagine their surprise to discover a flourishing people whose civilization outglittered their own. Palaces filled with gold, silver, and jade art made their heads swim. Tenochtitlán's canals eclipsed those of Venice. Cholula's great pyramid outbulked those along the Nile.

The quill of Bernal Díaz del Castillo, soldier-chronicler of Cortés's conquest of New Spain, scratched to a stop. How could he describe "things that had never been heard of or seen before, not even dreamed about"?

In Peru the conquerors came upon wonders equally staggering. The Chimu capital of Chan-Chan surpassed Assyria's Nineveh, Ur of the Chaldees, Babylon, even mighty Carthage. The imperial highway of the Incas, knifing three thousand miles down the ice-crested Andes, tunneling through living rock, spanning dizzy river chasms, marching mile after mile across burning desert, made Rome's Appian Way seem a garden path. Spanish eyes popped to see terraced irrigation systems soar into the clouds.

Even 20th century man, smug with the awareness of his own technical accomplishments, marvels at ancient Peruvian walls. Twenty-ton cut stones were fitted without mortar so that even today, countless earthquakes later, a slip of paper cannot be edged into the joints. Skyscraper towns rose in North American Pueblo lands centuries before New York's skyline took on its jagged look.

Today's surgeons are astounded by delicate brain operations successfully performed by Indians of the Andes in pre-Columbian days when Old World doctors were still prescribing ground unicorn horn and lioness milk. Indeed, aboriginal American knowledge of calendar, astronomy, and mathematics put medieval Europe's savants to shame. Ancestors of the Maya used the zero a thousand years before the Arabs.

Half the world feeds on the potato. Millions owe their subsistence to corn, and manioc, and beans—all foods first cultivated by American aborigines. The traditional Thanksgiving turkey dinner is all Indian. Rarely do we sit down to *any* meal without paying homage to the Indian.

Drink hot chocolate, munch peanuts or chew gum at a ball game, light a cigarette and you are indebted to the Indian. Speed along the highway and you are riding on rubber from the Indian. Speed too fast and the doctor will ease the pain of your injuries with cocaine—also In-

Sioux Mass for Attack as Custer Marches to His Fate. Surprise, confusion grip the tepee camp stretched three miles along tree-lined Little Bighorn River. Cooking fires still burn; women hustle children away from flying hoofs and brandished weapons. It is June 25, 1876. On this crucial day Sioux and Cheyenne, embittered by white encroachment on their sacred treaty-protected hunting grounds in the Black Hills of Dakota, lashed out, annihilated a cavalry column led by famed Indian fighter General George Armstrong Custer. The event rocked the nation.

At daybreak Custer's Crow scouts spied the smoke of Sioux fires, but did not realize that 12,000 to 15,000 Indians were gathered there. Custer split his 7th U.S. Cavalry into three wide-spreading columns, then rode at the head of some 225 troopers down barren ravines toward the Sioux camp.

Here whooping Indians rally as dust marks Custer's approach. While Sitting Bull "made medicine" to invoke aid of the gods, Chiefs Crazy Horse and Gall led more than 2,500 warriors to the attack. Custer made his stand on a grassy knoll behind his dead horses. The Indians squirmed near, then made a last howling charge. They took no prisoners, left the bodies where they fell. Several miles away, Reno's and Benteen's men in the other two columns, unaware of Custer's fate, beat off attacks a second day before the Indians, sighting a relief column, melted into the hills. Crazy Horse surrendered next spring, but Sitting Bull and Gall escaped into Canada, to return later under amnesty.

To re-create the scene of Custer's fight, artist W. Langdon Kihn went over the Montana battlefield, now a National Monument, with Sitting Bull's nephew, One Bull (page 12), who fought that day.

15

Returning Deerslayer Treads a Wooded Path. Plains Indians once lived in eastern woodlands. When white men drove them from the prairies some again took to forests in western mountains. Their buffalo herds slaughtered, they used canvas from the trader instead of hides to cover tepees.

dian. White man conquered the tropics with the aid of the Indian's quinine.

Who is our benefactor? The man profiled on the Indian Head nickel? The fearless mounted warrior of the movies —tall, eagle-nosed, wearing a feather headdress, living in a tepee?

This man is an American Indian, true. But so is the short, flat-nosed Wai Wai living in a palm-thatched Guiana hut. And the stocky Eskimo, builder of Arctic igloos.

We picture the whooping, hard-riding Sioux. We see the war-painted brave crouched behind a ledge, ready to ambush a covered wagon train with tomahawk, bow and arrow. We label our con-

ception "*the* American Indian," forgetting that accident placed this single type of aborigine astride our path of westward expansion. Sharp conflict fixed the image in our national memory. Bowing to stereotype, today's Eastern States Indian dons the Western Plains headdress his fathers never knew, so people will know he's Indian.

Of course, none are true Indians in the sense Columbus took them to be— inhabitants of India. Nor are they "redskins." Fondness for painting themselves with red ocher or red vegetable paints led the American aborigines to be called redskins by early explorers, fur traders, and colonists.

16

Thus arose the erroneous idea that the Indian's skin is naturally red, or copper-colored. Actually it is brown, sometimes shading almost to white.

If not real Indians, or redskins; if not the Lost Tribes of Israel, or refugees from sunken Atlantis, who are these people? Whence did they come?

Roll back the centuries to when the last great ice sheet still covered much of the northern portion of the globe, to perhaps 40,000 years ago. Let imagination carry you to bleak Alaskan shores. Before you a land bridge extends through the fog to what is now East Cape, Siberia. Over this bridge comes a venturesome Asiatic wanderer, a prehistoric Columbus of name unknown. He carries a stone-tipped spear. Perhaps tracking an animal has led him first to set foot on American soil.

Years whirl by. Glaciers melt. The sea rises to engulf the bridge. A strip of water separates the two continents. But migrants still come. They cross the ice, or paddle over in skin boats, just as Eskimos sometimes do today.

These first comers push southward into more hospitable climes and more productive lands. To roving hunters in quest of game, this vast virgin territory seems a paradise. No human enemies bar their way. Deer, elk, bison abound. The giant ground sloth with its sluggish habits proves an easy victim. The mighty mammoth and American camel—also to become extinct—provide meat for the hunter. He leaves ingeniously flaked stone knives and projectile points at camp sites to be found centuries later together with the bones of his prey.

Luring Moose from Forest Depths, a Chippewa hunter simulates their mating call. When a bull appears phantomlike at water's edge, a lucky shot means feasts of venison.

Through many centuries Asiatic people, responding to population pressure from the south and west, found this natural route into the Americas, just as successive streams of European immigration later penetrated inland from the Atlantic seaboard. So completely did these Asiatics establish themselves that, when the Europeans arrived, the two continents and practically all adjacent islands were occupied from the Arctic coast to Tierra del Fuego.

Wherever early white explorers went, they found signs of Indian achievement. The Indian was not only a skilled agriculturist, astronomer, engineer, builder of great empires. He was an adept weaver

Gallant Ally, Bitter Foe

Sacagawea, loyal Shoshoni girl who trekked 4,000 wilderness miles with Lewis and Clark, symbolizes the Indian's helping hand. At right, high on Columbia River banks 200 miles from the Pacific, she stands, infant on back, beside her husband Charbonneau, the interpreter, as Dalles Indians show the expedition leaders a way through the white water in 1805. Friendly, too, were the nomadic Cree of northern woodlands (bottom right). They trapped furs for the trader, their birchbark canoes served the explorer, their women often married French voyageurs. But relentless pressure from European settlers prodded most tribes into war. Some groups, after defeat, resented reservation life and broke out to return to ancestral lands. One such revolt occurred in 1872 when Modoc (below) entrenched themselves in a natural lava fortress in northern California. There they made a bitter last stand, held out for four months, inflicted heavy losses on attacking U. S. troops.

18

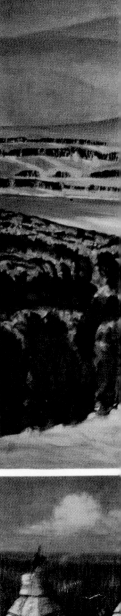

of textiles and basketry, and a maker of artistic pottery without aid of the potter's wheel.

True, although the Indian devised a hand loom, he was deficient in mechanical inventions. For example, he never discovered the keystone arch nor the practical use of the wheel. But he made up for this in the higher arts.

He was an excellent orator and dramatist. His poetry is filled with fine imagery, a deep appreciation of nature, and it reflects his often beautiful religious philosophy. Singing and dancing were highly developed. Works in sculpture, modeling, painting by aboriginal American artists take their places beside the masterpieces of all time.

The Indian was fond of games of chance and skill. Not only man-to-man competition in foot racing and wrestling, but sports requiring team play and mass participation were widespread. Lacrosse (page 22), a game since taken over by the white man, was a favorite among woodlands tribes east of the Mississippi. Maya youth played ball in the court at Chichén Itzá (page 203).

The European explorers also found an amazing range of cultures—from complex urban social organizations down to the most primitive, where the only recognizable unit was the family. Whatever his environment or stage of social development, the Indian learned Nature's secrets and found how best he could turn them to his ends.

Thus wandering bands of primitive Shoshoni, living in the parched deserts of the Great Basin, found food in the region's sparse and spiny plants, in grasshoppers, and fly larvae scraped from the surface of alkaline lakes. They made nets to trap the fleet jack rabbit and, for lack of better material, built their rude shelters of brush.

The diversity in aboriginal culture is illustrated most strikingly by languages. North of Mexico alone, at the time of the conquest, there were more than 50 unrelated linguistic stocks, and 700 distinct dialects. These dialects differed from one another as English differs from German or French, and the linguistic stocks have no common vocabulary or grammatical structure. This shows that many peoples of different origin had been isolated for long periods.

All these native American languages were capable of expressing abstract thought and subtle shades of meaning, their vocabularies were extensive, and the grammatical structure intricate and systematic. However, phonetic writing had never developed in the New World.

The principal linguistic stocks north of Mexico are the Eskimauan, which includes the entire Arctic coast from Alaska to Greenland; Athapascan, which includes Alaska and most of interior Canada west of Hudson Bay, and reappears in Arizona, New Mexico, and western Texas; Algonquian, which spans southern Canada from the Rocky Mountains to the Atlantic, thrusting south of the Great Lakes to Tennessee; the Iroquoian, which includes the St. Lawrence Valley and Lake Erie and Lake Ontario regions, south to northern Georgia.

The Shoshonean stock includes the Great Basin and northern Texas; the Siouan takes in most of the Great Plains and parts of the Carolinas and Virginia. The Muskhogean stock extends over most of Mississippi, Alabama, Georgia, and Florida.

Many lesser stocks dot the map of North America, the Pacific coast region being astonishingly diverse in this respect. And the linguistic situation south of the border is just as complex.

The varieties in physical type were not so great nor so striking as the cultural differences. All American Indians can be classified generally as of Mongoloid stock, to which the people of eastern Asia also belong. All have straight or slightly wavy black hair and brown

A War Whoop Rings Out. The Iroquois leader, hideous in war paint, signals the attack. The farmer drops plow for gun. Seldom could the isolated settler and his family survive the surprise raid. One tragic dawn in 1704, savages fell upon sleeping Deerfield, Massachusetts, killing 49 villagers, taking 111 others captive to French Canada. The colonial era was not one of continuous border warfare but of periodic outbreaks when Indians went on the warpath to defend their lands or to take scalps and thus gain prestige. Many massacres by Indians were to avenge attacks made upon them.

21

Lacrosse, Council Fires, Missionaries Shaped Iroquois Life

An Iroquois brave leaps high to catch the stuffed deerskin ball. Villages, even tribes competed in lacrosse, as much the national game of Indians east of the Mississippi as baseball is with modern Americans. But when they met in war council, in full regalia, tribal representatives of the five-nation Iroquois Confederacy might argue for grimmer conflict, perhaps against an old chief's plea for peace (right).

Christian peace was the message Jesuit missionaries early sought to bring to these warlike tribes of northeastern forests. Alone and unarmed (lower right), they wrote a heroic chapter in American history. Many a pioneer priest suffered unspeakable tortures. Yet they systematically learned the Indians' own beliefs the better to convert them, and despite hostility and every hardship continued to work among them for more than a century.

22

PAINTINGS BY W. LANGDON KIHN

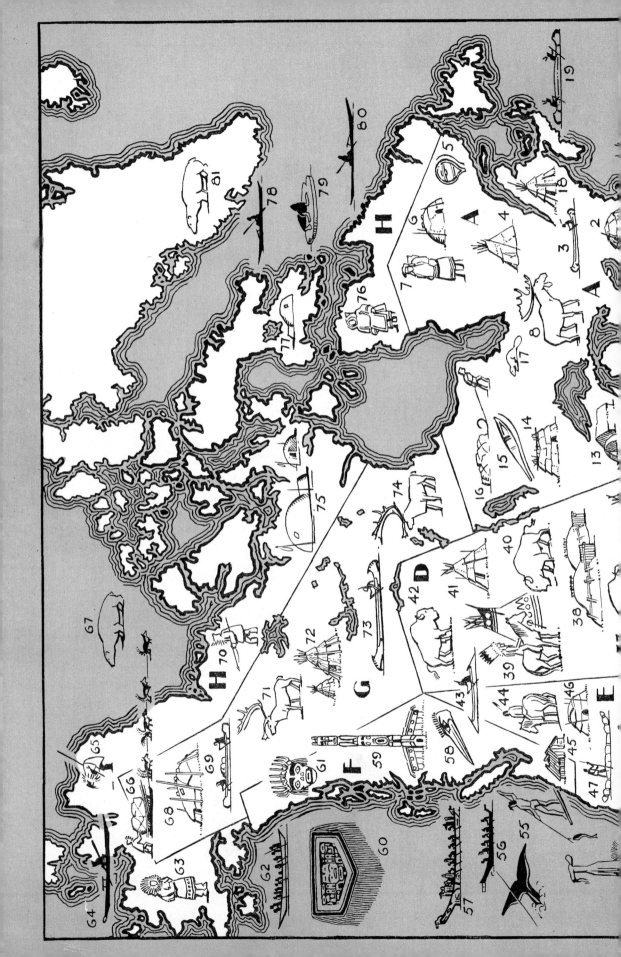

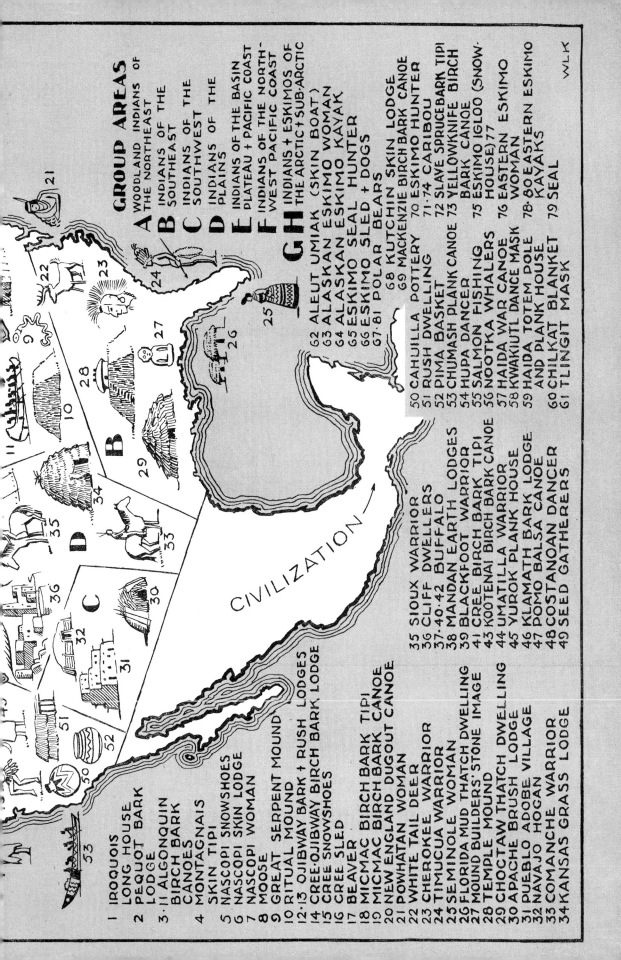

GROUP AREAS

A WOODLAND INDIANS OF THE NORTHEAST

B INDIANS OF THE SOUTHEAST

C INDIANS OF THE SOUTHWEST

D INDIANS OF THE PLAINS

E INDIANS OF THE BASIN PLATEAU + PACIFIC COAST

F INDIANS OF THE NORTH-WEST PACIFIC COAST

GH INDIANS + ESKIMOS OF THE ARCTIC + SUB-ARCTIC

CIVILIZATION

WLK

1 IROQUOIS LONG HOUSE
2 PEQUOT BARK LODGE
3-11 ALGONQUIN BIRCH BARK CANOES
4 MONTAGNAIS SKIN TIPI
5 NASCOPI SNOWSHOES
6 NASCOPI SKIN LODGE
7 NASCOPI WOMAN
8 MOOSE
9 GREAT SERPENT MOUND
10 RITUAL MOUND
12-13 OJIBWAY BARK + RUSH LODGES
14 CREE-OJIBWAY BIRCH BARK LODGE
15 CREE SNOWSHOES
16 CREE SLED
17 BEAVER
18 MICMAC BIRCH BARK TIPI
19 MICMAC BIRCH BARK CANOE
20 NEW ENGLAND DUGOUT CANOE
21 POWHATAN WOMAN
22 WHITE TAIL DEER
23 CHEROKEE WARRIOR
24 TIMUCUA WARRIOR
25 SEMINOLE WOMAN
26 FLORIDA MUD THATCH DWELLING
27 MOUND BUILDERS' STONE IMAGE
28 TEMPLE MOUND
29 CHOCTAW THATCH DWELLING
30 APACHE BRUSH LODGE
31 PUEBLO ADOBE VILLAGE
32 NAVAJO HOGAN
33 COMANCHE WARRIOR
34 KANSAS GRASS LODGE

35 SIOUX WARRIOR
36 CLIFF DWELLERS
37-40-42 BUFFALO
38 MANDAN EARTH LODGES
39 BLACKFOOT WARRIOR
41 CREE BIRCH BARK TIPI
43 KOOTENAI BIRCH BARK CANOE
44 UMATILLA WARRIOR
45 YUROK PLANK HOUSE
46 KLAMATH BARK LODGE
47 POMO BALSA CANOE
48 COSTANOAN DANCER
49 SEED GATHERERS

50 CAHUILLA POTTERY
51 RUSH DWELLING
52 PIMA BASKET
53 CHUMASH PLANK CANOE
54 HUPA DANCER
55 SALMON FISHING
56 NOOTKA WHALERS
57 HAIDA WAR CANOE
58 KWAKIUTL DANCE MASK
59 HAIDA TOTEM POLE AND PLANK HOUSE
60 CHILKAT BLANKET
61 TLINGIT MASK

62 ALEUT UMIAK (SKIN BOAT)
63 ALASKAN ESKIMO WOMAN
64 ALASKAN ESKIMO KAYAK
65 ESKIMO SEAL HUNTER
66 ESKIMO SLED + DOGS
67-81 POLAR BEARS
68 KUTCHIN SKIN LODGE
69 MACKENZIE BIRCH BARK CANOE
70 ESKIMO HUNTER
71-74 CARIBOU
72 SLAVE SPRUCEBARK TIPI
73 YELLOWKNIFE BIRCH BARK CANOE
75 ESKIMO IGLOO (SNOW-HOUSE)77
76 EASTERN ESKIMO WOMAN
78-80 EASTERN ESKIMO KAYAKS
79 SEAL

Proud, Fearless Mohawk Chief wears silver earrings bartered from white traders. He dons eagle headdress only on formal occasions, as when he sits with the Federal Council of the Iroquois. The Mohawks, early established in the Mohawk Valley, New York's gateway to the West, got firearms from Dutch traders about 1614 to help them gather furs. Possessing these weapons spurred the warlike tribe's rise to power. They extended their sway from Susquehanna to St. Lawrence. They terrorized Algonquian enemies, striking deep into French Canada.

The Mohawks sided with British against American in the Revolutionary War, were driven from their ancestral home, and later settled on Canadian lands assigned to them by the Crown. Today more than 4,500 Mohawks live on reservations in Ontario and Quebec. Some 400 others make their home in New York City, where they help build Manhattan's skyscrapers (page 421).

eyes. Complexion is generally dark.

The principal differences are in facial features, head form, and stature. The Indians east of the Mississippi and in the Great Plains were usually tall and stalwart in build, often exhibiting the aquiline nose we so commonly associate with the typical Indian face. This type also prevails in western and southern South America.

On the other hand, the Indians of Middle America and the Amazon Basin are shorter in stature and darker in complexion, with broader and flatter noses.

Seven times as many people live in New York City today as occupied all North America north of Mexico when Columbus arrived. Ethnologists estimate the total population of this area was then about 1,150,000.

Of this number 846,000 lived within the limits of the present United States, 220,000 in Canada, 72,000 in Alaska, and 10,000 in Greenland. The greatest concentrations were in the southeastern United States and in California, areas whose mild climate and abundant food supply could support large populations.

After these enterprising people had discovered America, populated it, and developed their interesting and diverse cultures, all that remained was for the Europeans to discover the Indians.

NORTHEASTERN WOODLANDS INDIANS

When Norsemen visited the New England coast during the first two decades of the 11th century, their all too brief descriptions of the savages, or *skraellings*, indicate an Algonquian people whose Northeastern Woodlands culture changed but little during the next few centuries.

The Norsemen described the Indians as swarthy, ferocious in aspect, with ugly hair, big eyes, and broad cheeks. They were clad in skin clothing, armed with bows and arrows, and used stone axes. They navigated the rivers in birchbark canoes and eagerly traded their furs for strips of red flannel to bind their heads.

They expressed keen surprise at the Vikings' iron tools and were terror-stricken at the bellow of Thorfinn's bull, brought over for breeding.

The Norsemen also described "self-sown wheatfields," but it is impossible to say whether

these were fields of cultivated maize or of wild rice.

No records have been preserved of subsequent Norsemen visits to America, but possibly the Basques, Normans, and Bretons explored this region by mid-15th century in search of fishing grounds. At any rate, soon after John Cabot sighted Cape Breton in 1497, Basques established

This Seneca Warrior, stern and dignified, suggests a James Fenimore Cooper character. Indians of the Eastern Woodlands, together with many northern Plains tribes, were fine physical specimens. The metal blade on this brave's war club and silver band around his head came from white men, probably in exchange for furs such as adorn his garments.

In mid-17th century the Seneca burst out from ancestral lands in the Lake Seneca region of western New York, spread their conquering mantle westward to Lake Erie and south along the Allegheny River into Pennsylvania, and became the most populous nation of the Iroquois Confederacy. Today over 3,000 tribesmen dwell on reservations in New York State.

PAINTINGS BY W. LANGDON KIHN

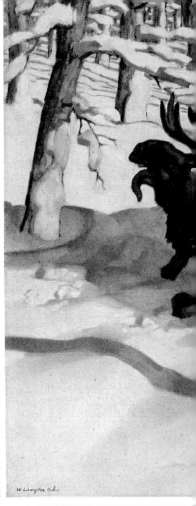

PAINTINGS BY W. LANGDON KIHN

Prowess as Hunter, Fisher, Warrior Spelled Prestige for the Red Man

With his last arrow, a snowshoed Penobscot Indian (above) takes aim at the moose he has trailed through wintry woods. His quarry, largest of the deer family, has bogged down, weak from wounds and plowing through heavy drifts. No longer can forest monarch stand off or escape the hunter relentlessly closing in with reinforced bow. Indians of the Penobscot River Valley in Maine lived near the sea during summer; in winter they moved inland to hunt game. On the success of the chase hung the tribe's survival.

Great Lakes Indians (top left) spear fish through holes in the ice. Bundled in Eskimolike furs, they chopped openings in the ice with stone hatchets and erected shelters over them. The man crouching under the tent at right dangles a lure with one hand and waits patiently, spear in the other. A woman with a basket makes her rounds, collecting the catch.

Indian tribes often went to war to defend hunting and fishing rights, so vital to their existence. Drums beat, painted braves (left) chant war songs as they dance after smoking the pipe of battle. The leader carries a war banner of eagle feathers. A scalp adorns the third man's lance. Among the Chippewa any brave could instigate a raid by sending a messenger with tobacco to ask warriors to join the party. Those willing smoked the pipe, then assembled for a feast given by the leader. They danced every night until the eve of departure, when a dog-meat feast closed the festivities. Chippewa warred mainly against their hereditary enemies, the Sioux, driving them onto the Plains.

29

Beneath a Towering Elm, William Penn and the Delawares Pledge Eternal Peace

Benjamin West's painting captures the feeling of brotherly love in 1683 when the founder of Pennsylvania forged a bond of friendship with the Indians at Shackamaxon, now a city park in Philadelphia. Penn's men trade bolts of cloth and chests of goods for land under this compact, to remain in force "as long as water flows and the sun shines and grass grows."

Voltaire called Penn's treaty the only one "never sworn to and never broken." It and others made by the fair-dealing Penn long spared the infant Quaker commonwealth the terrors of Indian warfare suffered by other English colonies along the eastern seaboard.

a permanent fishing settlement on Newfoundland. By 1578 some 150 French vessels were trading with the coastal Indians from Newfoundland to the mouth of the Potomac.

The Spaniards, meanwhile established in Florida, cast covetous eyes on the fur trade of the northern Atlantic coast. In 1565 Pedro Menéndez de Avilés wrote from St. Augustine that more than 2,000 buffalo skins had been canoed down the Potomac to Chesapeake Bay by Indians, and there traded to the French.

Thus, when English colonists arrived at Jamestown and Plymouth, the whites were already a familiar story to Indians of the Atlantic seaboard.

The first European settlements in the northeast were confined to a comparatively narrow coastal strip, but their presence was felt by tribes of the interior long before the white man appeared in person. The pressure created by the arrival of the French, the English, and the Dutch forced the westward withdrawal of the contact tribes. This caused conflicts with those whose territory was invaded. When these people were forced back in turn, established tribal territory again was dislocated. Finally the Siouan tribes living in the western Great Lakes region were pushed out from shaded woodlands into the sunlight of open plains. Their mode of existence changed with their new environment.

The conquest of the New World by the Spaniards is a story of the quest for gold. The conquest of northeastern North America is a story of French and English rivalry for control of the fur trade. Since furs were to be had only through friendly native allies, the European rivals soon took sides with the Indians.

When Champlain sought to colonize the St. Lawrence region early in the 17th century, it was only natural that he made friends with the Algonquians who occupied that territory. This alliance inevitably brought the French into conflict with the Iroquois, hereditary enemies of the Algonquians.

What Champlain had no means of knowing was that the agricultural and semi-sedentary Iroquois possessed a genius for political and military organization which, combined with their warlike traditions, was destined to give them the upper hand in conflict with native rivals.

When the English undertook to aid the Iroquois in their struggle, they allied themselves with the side that represented the balance of power. So it came about that North America is now basically English instead of French.

In contrast to English practice, the Roman Catholic French desire to convert the natives to Christianity was a leading factor in stimulating exploration. In 1615 Champlain sent missionaries into the St. Lawrence territory, first the Récollets, a Franciscan order. Then in 1625 the Jesuits came, pursuing their calling under almost unbelievably difficult conditions, with an unselfish courage and perseverance unsurpassed in the history of religion (page 23).

Because the Jesuits made a particular point of studying the natives and recording their customs, we have for the St. Lawrence and Great Lakes region a thorough knowledge of the aboriginal tribes before they had become greatly altered by contact with the Europeans.

Of all the North American tribes none were fiercer, more intelligent, more independent than the Iroquois (pages 21-23). Surrounded by Algonquian enemies, they lived in palisaded villages east and south of Lake Erie and Lake

Ontario, where they controlled the region between the Hudson and Ohio Rivers.

At the beginning of American history, they were only a weak remnant on the verge of extermination by their Algonquian neighbors. But at this critical juncture the Dutch furnished them with firearms, and so they were able to hold their own.

Increasing their strength further under the leadership of Dekanawida and Hiawatha, an Iroquois confederation was established among the Mohawk, the Onondaga, the Seneca, the Oneida, and the Cayuga. This confederation, known to the French as the "Long House" and to the English as the "Five Nations," was a unique experiment among American Indians and strongly influenced our own democratic type of government. Typical in many ways of Northeastern Woodlands culture were the customs and beliefs of the Iroquois.

The good Fathers found the Indians difficult to convert, for the entire background and philosophy of Christianity ran counter to native Indian beliefs.

(Continued on page 41)

AMERICA THROUGH 16TH CENTURY EYES   →

In the century after Columbus made his historic landfall, Europe knew only that a totally new world existed beyond the rim of the western ocean. What its people were like, how they lived, remained to be learned.

Thus the first pictures to be published of America stirred intense excitement. Imagine the effect today if The National Geographic Magazine were to publish authentic photographs of people on another planet, their settlements, their way of life.

The two artists who first depicted America were Jacques le Moyne de Morgues and John White. They painted what they saw on these shores at different places and times, but their work appeared almost simultaneously, in 1590 and 1591, when the Walloon engraver Theodore De Bry reproduced the paintings in two volumes that were to launch his vast publishing project, *Grands et Petits Voyages*.

Le Moyne, in 1564, took part in an ill-fated attempt to establish a French Huguenot colony in Spanish Florida. The Spanish a year later stormed the Huguenots' Fort Caroline, and Le Moyne with a few others barely escaped to a French ship.

White, as one of Sir Walter Raleigh's colonists, made three voyages from England to "Virginia," in 1585, 1587, and 1590. On the second he went as governor of the settlement on Roanoke Island; when he reluctantly sailed away for supplies, he left his daughter and his granddaughter, Virginia Dare, first English child born in the New World. He never saw them again, for when he returned the "Lost Colony" had disappeared, leaving the single enigmatic word "Croatoan" carved on a tree.

At no small peril both Le Moyne and White went boldly among the brown-skinned natives they found in this incredible new land. Le Moyne was commissioned to chart all Florida; his map (page 59) was accurate about places the French visited, but he accepted many unreliable names and positions from the Indians.

John White described Indian celebrations around fires on Virginia's shore (opposite), when warriors had "escaped any great danger by sea or lande, or be returned from the warr . . . in token of joye." His water colors showed the Indians living in neat towns, raising corn, pumpkins, and *uppowoc* (tobacco), and hunting deer in the adjoining forest. "When they go to battle they paynt their bodyes in the most terrible manner that they can devise," White said of the "lordes of Virginia."

Le Moyne spoke approvingly of the Florida Indians' storing their crops in public granaries. He painted their chiefs adorned with elaborate tattoos and headdresses. At times he was prone to exaggerate: his "crocodrilles," or alligators, are fantastic in size. Yet despite that fancy which sometimes clouds the detailed reporting in both men's drawings, these remain important documents of New World life.

"When They Be Returned from the Warr . . . They Make Merrie about the Fyer." John White depicts the Indians' "manner of prainge with rattels" and singing—"a strange custome, and worth the observation."

"Howses of the Towne of Secota Have Gardens . . . Wherin Groweth Tobacco (E)." Indians dance around curiously carved posts (C), feast in the street (D), hunt and cavort in this neatly arrayed town on the Pamlico River (L) in present North Carolina. Crouching in a hut (F), a watchman "maketh continual cryes and noyse" to frighten marauding "fowles and beastes" from ripening corn. Space was left between rows (H), "otherwise one stalke would choke the growthe of another." Pumpkins (I) grow near by.

"The Towne of Pomeiooc . . . Compassed Abowt with Poles Stucke Faste in the Grownde." Only the chief and his nobles occupied houses, which were built of poles tied together and covered with mats. These turned up to admit light. The chief's dwelling (B) and the temple (A) were the largest, "builded rownde and covered with skynne mattes." Feasts and celebrations were held in the middle of the village. When streams were too distant, Indians dug ponds for water (C). Open towns like near-by Secota (opposite) were described by White as "commonlye fayrer" than those huddled inside palisades, such as Pomeiooc.

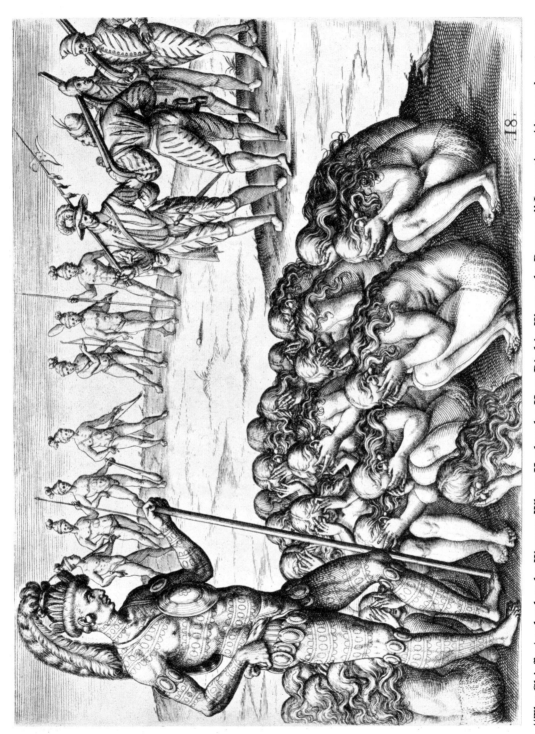

"The Chieffe Applyed to by Women Whose Husbandes Have Died in Warr or by Dysease." Lamenting widows seek sustenance, vengeance for their fallen warriors, permission to remarry after a proper time. Le Moyne's colonists (right) shoulder muskets and halberd.

36

"The Manner of Makinge Their Boates in Virginia is Verye Wonderfull." John White saw Indians fell trees by building fires close to the roots (upper right), then burn off tops and boughs. Lacking iron tools, they hollowed out trunks by fire and scraping with shells.

ENGRAVINGS BY THEODORE DE BRY

"Broylinge Their Fishe over the Flame . . . They Take Good Heed that They Bee Not Burntt." Two shadlike fish sizzle atop a wooden grill, two beside the fire. New catch includes garfish and small hammerhead shark. Virginia's Indians ate their fish at once; Florida's cured them for later use.

"Their Manner of Killynge Crocodrilles." As the reptile comes openmouthed to attack, the Indians shove a pointed pole down its throat, turn it over and assault its soft underbelly with clubs and arrows. From riverbank huts (left) Indians watch for their prey.

ENGRAVINGS BY THEODORE DE BRY

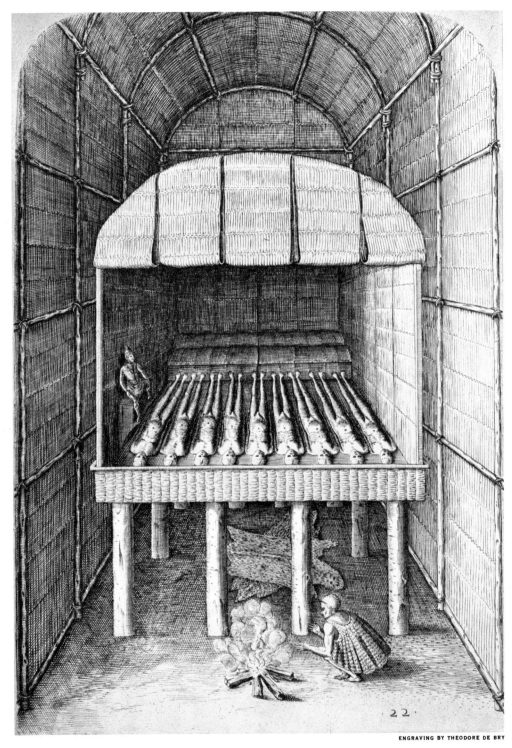

"The Tombes of the Weroans or Cheiffe Lordes." John White describes Virginia Indians preserving bodies of departed chiefs for veneration. They were drawn and skinned; their flesh, "clene taken from the bones," was dried in the sun. The skeleton, covered with its own tanned skin, was placed on a scaffold, the flesh in mats at its feet. Beside it the Indians "sett their idol Kiwasa [left] . . . for they are persuaded that the same doth kepe the dead bodyes . . . that nothinge may hurt them." Priest keeping vigil sleeps on deerskins beneath scaffold.

The fundamental idea of Christianity —immortality, with conduct during life determining the soul's reward or punishment—was incomprehensible to the aborigines, who gave little thought to the hereafter and did not mix ethics with religion. Moral principles of good and evil were not sharply defined and any such spirit abode as a "happy hunting ground," or an Indian hell, was foreign to native thought until missionaries implanted the idea.

Dreams or visions, induced by fasting or drugs, wherein he regularly saw and spoke with individuals known to be dead, amply proved to the Indian that soul and afterlife existed. Offerings placed with the dead manifested this belief. The souls of the dead, however, were usually feared and often extreme measures were taken to prevent their return.

Among the Huron, the body was placed in a flexed position in a bark coffin erected upon a scaffolding in the woods near the village, along with offerings of food and ornaments. Every 12 years, at the great feast of the dead, all bodies of tribal members who had died in the interim were removed from their original burial scaffolds by relatives. With demonstrations of affection, the bones were cleaned and wrapped with the finest robes, then conveyed to the village where they were displayed for a short time together with new offerings. From here the bones were carried to a huge common burial pit in which on the designated day all bones of the tribal dead were deposited with great ceremony (page 51).

Neither did Indians clearly comprehend the idea of a personified ruling deity. The loosely organized democratic tribes were unacquainted with a highly centralized type of government. Therefore the political analogy of a ruling god held no meaning for them.

The Indian's religion was entirely practical and designed to help him, not in the future, but in the immediate present. Thus when he thought himself plagued by an evil spirit, the obvious way to rid himself of his difficulty was to propitiate that spirit with offerings. His attention thus was fixed equally upon friendly and unfriendly forces. The missionaries, of course, interpreted this attitude as worship of the Devil.

Underlying all this was the mystic conception of an impersonal supernatural force which permeates all nature and animates all phenomena which control the destiny of man. This force, akin to the life principle, is called *manito* by the Algonquian, *pokunt* by the Shoshoni, and *orenda* by the Iroquois. Early white travelers, not comprehending the real nature of this idea, usually translated it as "The Great Spirit."

Among the American aborigines were many secret societies and groups which appeared in public only in elaborate masks and costumes in which they represented various deities, some of whose powers they supposedly acquired through this sacred paraphernalia. Characteristic is the Iroquois Society of Faces, which is still active (page 54).

The Indian's imagination peopled forest and lake with strange beings. Hunters having odd experiences attributed these to encounters with weird semi-human "faces," which occasionally appeared to them in dreams. These faces were supposedly empowered to cure various diseases. The man who dreamed of a face was instructed in his dream to carve a likeness of it as a mask, thus making him a healer while wearing it and singing the proper curing songs. If not treated respectfully and given occasional offerings of tobacco and ashes, the faces would produce the diseases they could cure.

The variety of faces is large. Some are black, some red, some white; some are young, and some old. Most are deformed and twisted. One with a broken and twisted nose had a mountain fall on his

Singing Menominee Gamblers stake blankets, pipes—even wives—on a flip of the red-and-white disks. They bet, then the man who is to "shoot" begins a song in which the others join. Suddenly the player strikes the bowl; the dice fly upward. How they land determines how many small wooden counters he wins. The final winner of all counters takes the stakes, including the saddle (foreground), perhaps even the watching wife. In some tribes losers became slaves of the winner.

PAINTINGS BY W. LANGDON KIHN

Making Medicine Against Death, an Iroquois shaman in fur cape shakes his shell rattle and chants a curing song. A beam of sunlight, coming through the smoke hole in the top of the lodge, lights the face of the dying warrior, whose wife grieves by the bedside. Ritualistic objects litter the floor. Fantastic masks with human hair are set on the lodgepole to frighten away spirits causing the illness. As controller of supernatural forces the medicine man played a powerful role in tribal life.

43

PAINTING BY W. LANGDON KIHN

Master Canoe Makers Were the Chippewa. Stakes outline the craft's shape. The builders place thick, pliable sheets of birch bark inside, bend edges upward and fasten them to wooden gunwales. Next they install bent cedar ribs (right foreground), fasten thwarts to brace the canoe, then sew the bark with strings from spruce roots. Spruce gum makes seams watertight. In versatility, the portable bark canoe outshone the ponderous dugout (page 46). Territory of the Chippewa, once one of the largest Indian tribes north of Mexico, extended from Lake Huron westward to the Dakotas.

face. Other disease spirits owe their mis-shapen features to their constant conflict with the Life God, who bested them in these encounters.

In spring and fall, when sickness is common, the Society of Faces go en masse through all homes of the community, shaking their turtle-shell rattles, making weird cries, and talking with a curious nasal twang. Thus they frighten away the invading disease spirits.

Both the Iroquois and the Algonquians believe in a masked cannibal called "Long Nose," who kidnaps children. Youngsters are never disciplined by corporal punishment. Fear that Long Nose will carry them off in his huge pack basket usually insures their good behavior.

The fabric of the Indian's religion was woven about his intimate observations of Nature. Each day he saw the sun rise in the east and set in the west, obliterating the stars which guarded the heavens at night. He noticed the regularity of the waxing and waning of the moon. He watched the procession of the equinoxes with the accompanying complex phenomena of the seasons: regular migrations of animals, birds, and fish; the annual growth cycles of plants and trees; heat and cold, rain and sunshine, lightning, wind, and snow.

At times Nature was lavish with her favors; often she denied man his wants. Now and then disease struck with unseen weapons and laid him low. All these things required explanation so that man might know how to produce more favors from Nature and make life more tolerable.

Lacking knowledge of physics, astronomy, and meteorology, the Indian personalized the various striking features of Nature. Among the Iroquois, the alternation of the seasons symbolized the perpetual struggle between the Life God and "Stony Coat," the god of ice and winter, whose function was to destroy. The adventures of these supernatural beings with Indian culture heroes form the intricate substance of a rich mythology wherein are explained, often in allegorical language, all things the Indian has pondered.

Since the Indians considered that the coming of each kind of food was brought about by supernatural causes, it was the custom to offer the first of each type obtained to the particular spirit supposed to control it.

A joyous occasion was the annual gathering of sap from budding maple trees in early March. With the rigors of winter behind them and the full prospects of spring and summer ahead, this was a happy season—a time of renewed activity, the "commencement" season (page 47).

The Menominee have a charming legend which explains the story of maple sugar. When man was new he did not know how to obtain the sap. One day the old grandmother, Nokomis, showed Manabusha, the great culture hero and friend of man, how to tap the trees and collect the sap. But the sap came out in the form of pure, thick syrup.

"This," thought the wise Manabusha, "is bad. The people will not have enough work if sugar is made so easily. It must be more difficult, to keep them occupied so they will not fall into idleness."

So Manabusha climbed to the top of the highest tree. With his hand he sprinkled water like rain over the trees, diluting the syrup so that it would flow from the trees in a watery sap.

Thereafter the Indians had to work hard to make sugar. Wood must be cut, bark vessels made, and the sap collected and boiled for several nights to reduce it to usable form.

By introducing the iron kettle, the French showed the Indians how to reduce further the sweet liquid, which the natives regarded as a beneficial medicine.

The *Jesuit Relations* tells how an early Father, hearing that a pagan Indian was near death, visited his wigwam to administer the rites of the Church. After baptizing him from a bark vessel standing in the room, he inquired of the wife what medicine the patient had been taking. The woman pointed to the vessel, and the priest discovered that he had performed the baptism with sweet maple sap.

"Fortunately," wrote the good Father, "I was able to secure water and perform the ceremony over again before the patient died."

The agricultural Indians of the Northeastern Woodlands used simple but effective methods of cultivation. Champlain tells that in place of plows they used a hardwood instrument shaped like a spade. The gardens were planted in May. They placed three or four kernels of Indian corn, or maize, and a few beans in rows at intervals of about three feet and heaped small hills of dirt over them. When the seed sprouted, the bean vines would climb the cornstalks, at the same time keeping the ground about the hills free from weeds.

Pumpkins and squash usually were planted in open areas fringing the corn patch, where vines would not be too much shaded by the tall corn plants. The

Iroquois believed that the guardian spirits of the three plants were sisters who desired to remain together.

The Iroquois name for maize means "our life." This veneration for corn was typical of all agricultural tribes of America, who regarded it as their principal means of subsistence. Many varieties of beans and corn were cultivated and there were numerous methods of preparing them as food. The aboriginal New England dish of succotash, a mixture of maize and beans, still retains its Indian name.

Garden care was mainly a woman's job, the men being too busy hunting at cultivating and harvesting time (pages 48-49).

Indian women have been described as drudges, beasts of burden, chattels, as virtual slaves of their husbands, and their existence a continuous round of backbreaking work, of childbearing, and dutiful waiting on their husbands' every whim. Such a picture is not characteristic.

In the old days Indian women worked hard, took pride in their work, lived, loved, and gossiped much as women do in all parts of the world. Since much of

When the Maple Sap Ran, Woodlands Indians tapped trees and brought the sap to a large trough. Women (above) hang kettles of green birch bark over embers to reduce the sap to syrup, which they pour into molds to harden. The family's right to certain groves of sugar maples carried from generation to generation.

With Fire and Stone Adzes, Massachusetts Indians (left) skillfully shape a dugout canoe by eye. The sturdy dugout predominated south of the limit of available birch. The Pilgrims at Plymouth met these Indians, living in bark-covered Quonset huts. Soon afterward they were virtually wiped out by the white man's smallpox.

their work was out of doors, their life was a healthy one.

The husband had no real authority over his wife's person and, while custom differed among tribes, the woman as a rule could leave her husband when she wished. Marriage, too, involved mutual consent as in our society. So-called wife purchases, when analyzed, are found to consist either of mutual exchange of gifts by the families or as compensation to the bride's family for loss of her services.

47

Four Scalps on Warpath! the painted warrior boasts to his somber-faced brother. Crimson-dyed horsehair, like a plumed Roman helmet, adorns the scalplock of this member of the Sauk and Fox.

This combined tribe, originally of Great Lakes canoe and farming peoples, migrated to Kansas after the Black Hawk War of 1832, in which Abraham Lincoln served as captain of volunteers. There they adopted the horse and prairie ways.

War, to the Indian, was as much a game as a way to wield power or to wreak vengeance on an enemy. Killing a foe merited less than taking unnecessary risks in battle. Touching an enemy with finger or coup stick in the midst of combat was the warrior's proudest feat.

Eagle feathers worn in certain ways, as by the man at right, were badges of honor denoting rank or prestige. His bear-claw necklace is punctuated with trader's beads.

48

Wild Rice, Cultivated Corn, crops
that sustained Indian life, were harvested
by women. Corn, gift of the American
aborigine, ranks as one of the world's
great bounties. It saved Jamestown and
Plymouth from famine, grew wherever
there was good soil and enough water.

Below, Iroquois women husk the tasseled ears which earlier they had gathered in baskets on their backs. Corn was
roasted or boiled while green, parched
and pounded into meal when dry. Indians ate mush, hominy, and corn dump-
lings. They knew corn soup, succotash,
and popcorn. From dried husks they
made moccasins, masks, and dolls. Corn-
cob fires, nearly smokeless, warmed tepee and lodge.

Chippewa wives (lower left) reap wild
rice, flailing the kernels into baskets in
their birchbark canoe. Rice grew along
shores in the Lake Superior region. Shortly before harvest time, women paddled
through the fields tying rice stalks into
looped bundles to protect the ripening
grain from the birds, wind, and rain.

49

Among such groups as the Iroquois, women had an important voice in tribal councils (page 23), and the right to nominate candidates for the chieftaincy of clan or tribe. A mother could even forbid her son to go on the warpath.

Indeed, records show that often white women taken captive in Indian raids later refused an opportunity to return to pioneer life. They had found living among the Indians more pleasant.

Misconceptions of the Indian woman's role arose when visitors saw the wife busily working while the man, if home, reclined lazily, seemingly with nothing to do. They overlooked the fact that his were the more strenuous pursuits: hunting, fishing, warfare, the clearing of land.

By ingenuity the Indian learned to hunt game over winter's heavy snow and in summer travel the waterways of his Woodlands home, a region of lakes and rivers. The snowshoe and canoe were two of his most useful inventions.

Snowshoes varied in form and construction, depending upon whether they were to be used in the woods or in the open, on hard or soft snow, but all were constructed on the same principle. A strip of ash was steamed and bent into shape and webbed with a netting of rawhide strips, moose intestine, twine, or sinew. When caught by a sudden snowstorm, the Indian quickly made an emergency pair by bending a frame of green willow and webbing it with bark strips.

The dugout canoe, hollowed from a log by fire and stone adzes, was used by most tribes south of the St. Lawrence (page 46). More ingenious and practical was the portable bark-covered canoe, widespread in the Woodlands region (page 44). Birch, spruce, or elm bark, and occasionally moose hide, covered a light cedar frame. Somewhat fragile, the craft was so light that one man could easily carry it across even a long portage. Early explorers adopted the birchbark canoe and with it penetrated to distant parts of the country.

The birchbark canoe was as necessary to the Woodlands Indian as the automobile is to us today. The nomadic Algonquian tribes of the northeast continually transported themselves and their equipment by this means. These wandering groups, seeking food, established themselves at different places as the seasons varied.

Hunting, fishing, and seed-gathering were their principal means of obtaining food. In a region where game still is relatively abundant, it was much more so before the coming of the white man and his firearms. Deer, moose, and caribou were plentiful; geese, ducks, and swans abounded, as did many other forms of bird and animal life.

Yet the Indian was often hard pressed to obtain enough food throughout the year. In summer he found it difficult, with his stone-headed arrows, to stalk and kill larger animals. When chance afforded, moose, deer, and caribou were driven into the water and shot from canoes while they swam. In winter, hunters with snowshoes ran down the heavy beasts floundering through the snow (page 29). It was also easier then to track down rabbits and other small game.

Fishing was highly important to a people living in a region of rivers and lakes. Quantities of fish were obtained through weirs and fish traps set across the streams, particularly when salmon were migrating in the coastal rivers, and in spring when sturgeon moved from lakes into streams. Spearing, shooting with bow and arrow, and jigging with lures and barbless hooks were also practiced.

In winter, fish were speared through holes cut in the ice (page 28). In summer, the usual spear-fishing method was for two men to go out in a canoe at night. The man in the stern paddled while the other speared fish attracted by the light of a bark torch in the bow. Fish were preserved by smoking and drying.

A Huron Family Buries Its Loved Ones. Skulls and bones on their backs, mournful Indians journey to the feast of the dead held every 12 years by the Huron, a tribe which lived southeast of Georgian Bay, in Ontario, Canada. Bodies were taken from scaffolds and carried, often many miles, to a common burial pit and there laid to rest amid cries of lament. "Nothing has ever better pictured for me the confusion there is among the damned," wrote the Jesuit Brébeuf of the assembled nation's din. By firelight, tribesmen scattered corn over the remains and burial offerings, and covered the pit with fur robes. Visitors received gifts, and the ceremony ended with a feast.

51

IMPACT OF THE WHITE MAN

During the waning days of Indian domination, great and valiant heroes emerged. Many foresaw that the white man's encroachment, if allowed to continue, meant disruption of the native manner of living and eventual extermination of the Indian.

The Eastern Woodlands area had its share of such men. Some, like Cornplanter, famous Seneca chief, believed that the Indian should make friends with the white men, save himself by imitating them, and subsist in open competition with them. In his old age Cornplanter regretted having taken this course.

Others believed that it was impossible for the Indian to make such basic changes, and that his only salvation was to resist and repel the invader. A famous exponent of this theory was Metacom, known to the English as King Philip. He was a Wampanoag, the son of Massasoit, whose friendly acts made possible the success of the Plymouth Colony.

For ten years Metacom quietly organized the Indians of New England, and in 1675, declared war upon the whites. During the ensuing year 52 of 90 English towns were attacked, and 12 completely destroyed. But for the treachery of some followers, Metacom would have driven the whites from New England. He was killed when colonists night-raided his Rhode Island swamp hideaway on August 12, 1676, ending "King Philip's War."

More than a century later the final desperate stand of Indian against white man in the northeastern United States was made under the leadership of Tecumseh (page 55). One of the ablest of all Indian warriors, he was noted for his humane character. Among other acts, he persuaded his tribe, the Shawnee, to abandon torturing prisoners, a basic practice of Indian warfare at the time.

Tecumseh vigorously opposed the white man's advance and denied the U. S. Government's right to purchase land from a single tribe on grounds that the vast woodland was common hunting territory belonging to all tribes. When the Government ignored his contention, he

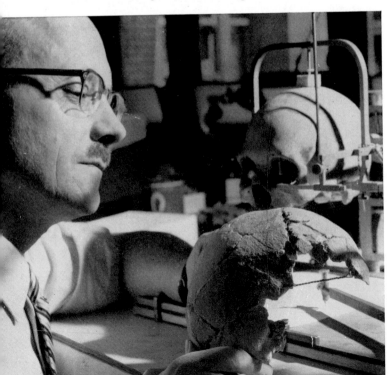

America's Oldest Inhabitant

Twelve or more millenniums ago a pre-Folsom man roamed our western plains. He was quenching his thirst near present-day Midland, Texas, when ravenous animals may have pounced upon him. Dr. T. Dale Stewart of the Smithsonian Institution pieced the ancient man's skull together. Here he compares it with the strikingly similar one of a modern Indian.

The skull, oldest human remains yet found in the Americas, was dated by measuring its fluorine absorption compared to that of fossil bones of now extinct animals found at the same water-hole site. Tests revealed them to be about the same age.

Hearths at Lewisville, Texas, suggest habitation 37,000 years ago.

SCIENCE SERVICE

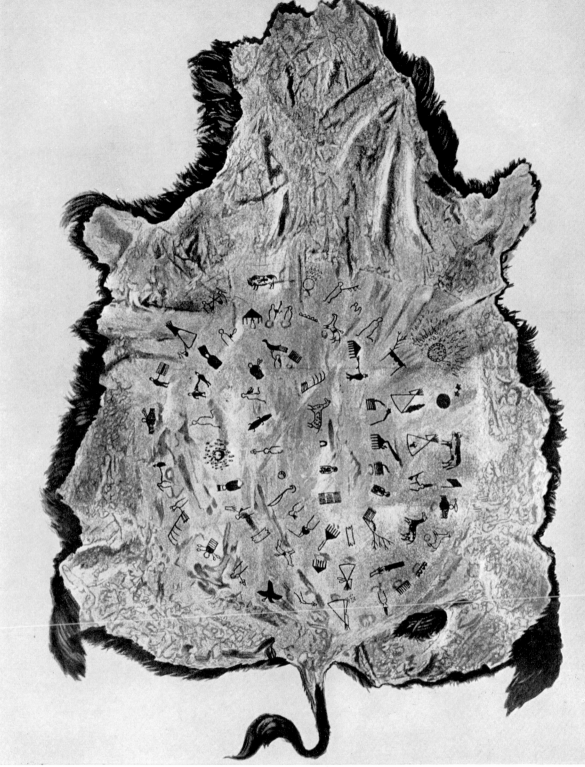

Buffalo Robe Calendar records 71 winters among the Dakota Sioux. Lone Dog, the artist, noted the passing years with symbols of important events spiraling counterclockwise out from center. His winter count begins in 1800 with 30 parallel lines in three columns at center. Each line stands for a Dakota slain by the Crows that year. Directly above, a spotted figure marks a smallpox epidemic. A horseshoe indicates shod mounts stolen from white men by the Dakotas, whose horses lacked shoes. Meteorite shower (left) is 1833–34, when "the stars fell." A cow (right) denotes 1868–69, when Texas longhorns entered Dakota country. Blacked-out sun attended by stars shows the eclipse of 1869.

formed a great confederacy of practically all Indians east of the Mississippi in hope of making the Ohio River the permanent boundary line between the two races. Tecumseh's purpose was defeated when followers precipitated the Battle of Tippecanoe in 1811, before plans of organization were complete.

The warrior then allied himself with the British against the Americans and was commissioned a brigadier general in the British Army, commanding 2,000 Indian allies. In 1813 he protected Proctor's retreat, following Perry's victory at Lake Erie, forcing Proctor to make a stand against the Americans near Chatham, Ontario. In the battle that followed, the Americans under Harrison won and Tecumseh was killed.

He had a premonition of this disaster and laid aside his British uniform, dressing in native costume for the fight. The death of Tecumseh removed the last serious obstacle in the path of white expansion and sealed the doom of native life in the eastern United States.

Another Indian whose career paralleled Tecumseh's was Thayendanegea, known to the whites as Joseph Brant. One of the first prominent Indians to read and write English, he was a Mohawk chief, born in 1742, active in border wars of the 18th century.

He fought with the British in Pontiac's war of 1763. Later he was commissioned a British colonel and, with his native troops, took an active part in famous raids against American settlements in 1779. His sister became the wife of Sir William Johnson.

As with many other peoples, most noted Indians owe their prominence to military activities. This should not, however, produce an unbalanced picture of Indian life. Warfare against the whites was inevitable because of the pressure of white expansion.

The Indian's method of fighting differed vastly from the mass tactics of the Europeans. His tech-

Nightmares in Wood, these carved masks represent supernatural beings seen in dreams by men of the Iroquois Society of Faces. Shaking huge turtle-shell rattles, members of the secret cult danced through the village to drive out demons of disease. The society still flourishes, but today when Iroquois don their grotesque masks to go from house to house chasing spirits they ride in automobiles.

PAINTINGS BY W. LANGDON KIHN

nique was to scatter forces, placing emphasis on concealment, surprise, and ambush. Not until the colonists adopted Indian fighting methods could they cope with them.

Two practices connected with warfare in the Northeastern Woodlands area have been prominent in literature. One was the torturing of prisoners, the other the taking of scalps. Both customs appear to have originated with the Iroquois and to have spread from them. European rivals in the northeast offered bounties to their Indian allies for enemy scalps, Indian or white. With this stimulus, the practice of scalping spread rapidly and widely. Bounties for the scalps of hostile Indians in the West were offered as late as the middle of the last century.

Probably no misunderstanding led to so much ill feeling and bloodshed between Indians and whites as the difference in their concepts concerning land ownership.

In America, the land within tribal boundaries was regarded as belonging to the tribe. Neither the Indian individual nor the family possessed vested rights in land, although each family might appropriate or have assigned to it, for cultivation or gathering, that required for its own needs. Thus it was impossible for any chief, family, or any section of a tribe legally to sell or give away any part of the tribal holdings.

Naturally any such treaties and transfers of rights had no significance to the early Indians. The first white settlers either were not aware of this fact or found it convenient to ignore it. Inevitably the Indians considered themselves ousted when the white men took possession of their lands.

Typical of the Indian attitude was the speech Toohulhulsote, a Nez Percé, made when the whites tried to

Tecumseh, Shawnee Chief, foresees death and discards British uniform and medal for native buckskins. A brigadier general in the War of 1812, he has accused the British of cowardice in retreating before the Americans. He will persuade his allies to stand on the Thames River, Ontario, and himself perish in that battle.

Born in 1768 near present Springfield, Ohio, Tecumseh early gained renown in border wars of the Northwest Territory. His father and two brothers died fighting the whites. Tecumseh's own death in 1813 shattered the last hope of a united Indian stand against the juggernaut of white expansion.

Paradoxically, a bronze bust of Tecumseh spells luck for midshipmen at the U.S. Naval Academy.

force his people to leave their home in the Wallowa Valley for a distant reservation.

"The earth," he said, "is our mother, and her body should not be disturbed by the hoe or the plow. Men should subsist by the spontaneous productions of Nature. The sovereignty of the earth cannot be sold or given away."

"We never have made any trade. Part of the Indians have given up their land. I never did. The earth is part of my body, and I never gave up the earth. So long as the earth will keep me, I wish to be let alone."

Early explorers, accustomed to European ideas of regal descent and individual political power, applied such terms as king, queen, or princess to members of the simply organized democratic village tribes of eastern America. This was absurd.

The idea of a legal executive head, though entirely foreign to these Indians, was fostered by the colonists because it helped them to do business, particularly to buy land.

Inherited rank was also an alien idea, for the most part. Even the so-called "chief" among many tribes was recognized as leader only because of his personal exploits or recognized ability. He had no actual authority, his rule being purely advisory but backed by custom. In certain groups, such as the Iroquois and some Pueblo tribes, it was the rule to select chiefs from a particular clan, although in practice such positions were usually elective.

The outstanding instance of despotism was among the Natchez and neighboring tribes of the lower Mississippi. However, submission to the chief's will was apparently voluntary and based upon religion.

Among the Natchez a caste system developed based on heredity, and on the northwest coast a caste distinction did

History in the Flesh. Jacob Lone Tree, eight-year-old Winnebago Indian, reads of doughty deeds of his Great Lakes ancestors. His classmate is fascinated to find a real Indian boy with savage roach cut in a Wisconsin school. The Winnebago fought under Tecumseh in the War of 1812.

Yakima Chief Visits Warrior Son. In tribal regalia father rides out to inspect son's iron steed on a firing range near Yakima, Washington. Indians fought bravely in two world wars and in Korea.

arise, based on property. But among American Indians generally, ideas of caste and individual wealth were absent.

The breakdown of native culture was inevitable once the white man had entrenched himself in the New World.

The first disaster was the introduction of smallpox, measles, and chicken pox, diseases to which the Indians had developed no resistance. Whole tribes were swept away, others decimated. The white man's alcohol likewise did much to break down Indian pride and spirit.

More devastating in the long run was the psychological effect of the contact of two conflicting cultures.

Tribal organization was based on kinship, which carried with it the obligation of mutual assistance and protection.

Typically, inheritance was reckoned through one side of the family, the mother's, and children came under the mother's clan. Our system of bilateral descent, conversely, puts children directly under parental authority and removes the feeling of oneness with the clan.

The new culture also obliterated the basic occupations of tribal life. The division of labor between the sexes was so strongly fixed by custom that when the encroachment of the white man destroyed the game, fenced off hunting grounds, and removed the possibility of aboriginal warfare, the balance was completely destroyed. The woman's work remained, but the man, left with nothing to do, could only loaf about. No longer was there place for the hunter, warrior, weaponmaker.

The woman, besides tending household and fields, also was a potter, usually the weaver of textiles and baskets, and the dresser of skins. These skilled arts, which permitted full development of the individual, vanished with the coming of metal kitchen utensils and machine-woven cloth. Readjustment has been slow and painful.

Today the blood of the American Indian flows in the veins of many of our leading citizens. His contributions to civilization, toward the betterment of mankind are met on every hand, but his story as a separate people now is a subject of history and a record of the past.

SOUTHEASTERN INDIANS

POCAHONTAS, DAUGHTER OF POWHATAN, holds a special place in American legend. How she persuaded her warlike father to spare the life of Capt. John Smith when he was held captive by the Indians is a story known to everyone. She was then a girl of 12. The year, 1608.

This episode (page 62), questioned by some because Smith did not mention it in his writings until years later, fits with what we know of the character of both Pocahontas and her father.

Her real name was Matoaka ("playful"). John Smith says she was called Pocahontas because "the savages did think that, did we know her real name, we should have the power of casting an evil eye upon her." This belief was widespread.

Powhatan, whose real name was Wahunsonacock, was founder of the Powhatan confederacy, typical of Algonquian tribal groups along the south-central Atlantic seaboard. These Indians were at their peak when Smith and his followers first entered Chesapeake Bay.

About this same time the Iroquois confederacy began in the North. But whereas the Iroquois tribes banded together through mutual consent, the Powhatan confederacy was based on conquest, treachery, and personal despotism.

With the arrival of the Jamestown colonists in 1607, Powhatan began to receive a bitter dose of his own medicine. The English, by superior force of arms, seized the Indians' winter supplies of corn, reducing them to near starvation.

In 1613, the colonists, knowing Powhatan's affection for Pocahontas, decoyed her aboard a ship and held her hostage to prevent Powhatan warring against them. During her captivity she was

Le Moyne's Map presents a 16th century European conception of the American "Province of Florida." Whalelike sea monster cruises offshore; Appalachian streams yield gold, silver, and copper. Indian hearsay named and located most villages, rivers, lakes, and forests.

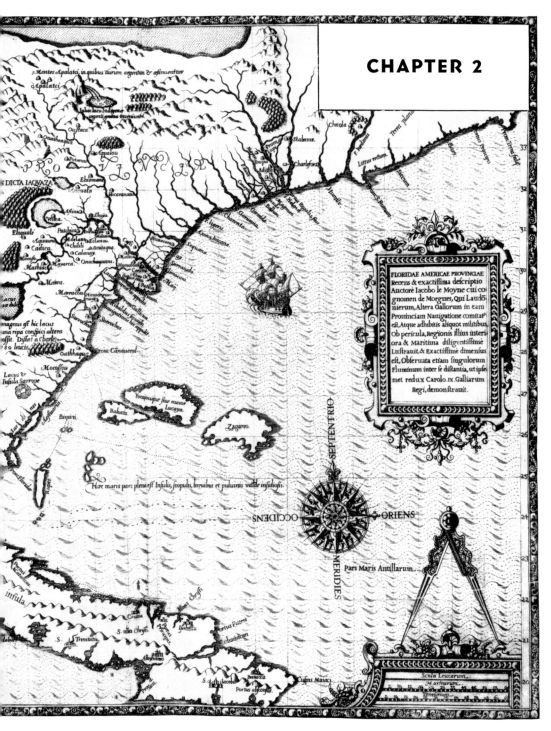

CHAPTER 2

FLORIDAE AMERICAE PROVINCIAE
Recens & exactiſſima deſcriptio
Auctoré Iacobo le Moyne cui cognomen de Morgues, Qui Laudonierum, Altera Gallorum in eam
Prouinciam Nauigatione comitaᵗ
eſt. Atque adhibitis aliquot militibus,
Ob pericula, Regionis illius interiora & Maritima diligentiſſimé
Luſtrauit.& Exactiſſimé dimenſus
eſt, Obſeruata etiam ſingulorum
Fluminum inter ſe diſtantia, ut ipſe
met redux Carolo.ix.Galliarum
Regi, demonſtrauit.

converted to Christianity, met and married John Rolfe, "an honest Gentleman, and of good behavior." In 1616 she and Rolfe voyaged to England where she was received as a princess, had her portrait painted (basis of the Kihn portrait, page 61), and was presented to the King and Queen. As a result of this marriage Powhatan kept peace with the English.

The Jamestown colonists were surprised to receive from England a royal gift for the old reprobate, consisting of a crown, scarlet cape, elaborate bedroom set, pitcher, basin, and other costly items, with orders to hold a coronation.

Hearing of the English King's fine present, Powhatan considered it a trap, and replied that if the English wished to make him a present they would have to bring it to him. This was no simple undertaking, since Powhatan was on a hunting trip almost a hundred miles away by canoe and wilderness trail.

But the English had their orders and, after a long and toilsome journey, they reached the forest camp of the suspicious chief. The cumbersome bed was hauled up on the stream bank, the basin and pitcher set beside it.

Powhatan was persuaded to accept the scarlet cloak, "but a fowle trouble there was to make him kneele to receave his crowne. He, neither knowing the majestie nor meaning of a Crowne, nor bending of the knee, indured so many perswasions, examples, and instructions, as tired them all."

The English finally resorted to strategy. Two stout soldiers grasped Powhatan by the shoulder and bore down heavily, pressing him behind the knees so that he was forced to kneel. Three others pushed the crown onto his head. This was the signal for firing a ceremonial volley, at which the terrified "king" leaped up and attempted to flee for his life.

He was restrained, however, and when convinced he was to be put to no further compulsions, gave to Captain Newport his old moccasins and mantle. The mantle still is in the Ashmolean Museum in Oxford, England, but there is no record of what happened to the luxurious bedroom suite left under the Virginia trees.

Through Powhatan's affection for his daughter Pocahontas, open warfare was deferred for some time. In 1622, however, four years after Powhatan's death, Opechancanough, his brother, attacked the now scattered colonists, killing 347 men, women, and children.

Another more devastating attack followed 22 years later. But retaliation was so severe that in 1646 the colony's Assembly reported the Indians to be "so routed and dispersed that they are no longer a nation, and we now suffer only from robbery by a few starved outlaws."

More successful in resisting the white men were the warlike Calusa, who occupied southern Florida. These were the first Southeastern Indians to meet the Europeans, a century before Jamestown, possibly more.

Among gold-seeking Spanish adventurers in the Antilles soon after Columbus were slavers, who found it easy to decoy trusting natives onto their ships and then sail off with them. But the Indians made poor slaves.

Some of these slavers must have visited the Florida coast well before the first recorded visit, that of Ponce de León in 1513. Maps of the peninsula were published in Europe before this date. More convincing evidence is the murderous reception Florida Indians gave Spanish mariners. Such conduct would be unlikely at their first meeting with whites.

Of powerful physique, these Calusa were the fiercest fighters in the New World. Ponce de León, seeking the "Fountain of Youth," was attacked by 80 canoes and forced to withdraw after an all-day battle. Eight years later they beat off his colonizing expedition of 1521, grievously wounding him with an arrow.

These near-naked warriors dismembered slain enemies, apparently sacrificed captives en masse, even were said to be cannibals. Killing and plundering, they drove back all European attempts to enter their country until foreign epidemic diseases thinned their ranks. By late 18th century they had ceased to exist as a tribe. The few survivors were absorbed among the late-arriving Seminole.

The Calusan linguistic stock, together with its north Florida neighbor, the Timucuan, was related to Muskhogean,

PAINTING BY W. LANGDON KIHN

Pocahontas, Powhatan's "Dearest Jewell and Daughter," proudly wears a turkey-feather robe.
With features from a portrait of 1616, this shows the Indian "princess" before she "renounced idolatree."

King Powhatan comands Ct Smith to be flayne, his daughter Pokahontas beggs his life his thankfullnefs and how he fubiected 39 of their kings. reade & hiftory.

Pocahontas Saves Capt. John Smith. His head rests upon a stone, the executioners' clubs are about to descend, when Pocahontas intervenes, begs for his life, places her head upon Smith's. Relenting, Powhatan adopted Smith into the tribe. So went Smith's own account, which appeared with this drawing by an unknown artist in his *Generall Historie of Virginia, New England, and the Summer Isles,* published in 1624. Today a few Pamunkey descendants of the once-feared Powhatan confederacy maintain tribal life near Richmond, Virginia. They have occupied this same reservation since 1677.

leading stock of the entire Southeast (group area map, page 24).

Typical Muskhogean-speaking peoples were tribes comprising the great Creek confederacy, which occupied the territory now Georgia and Alabama; the Choctaw, who lived in central and southern Mississippi (page 68); the Hitchiti of western Georgia; and the later Seminole.

Southeastern tribes in general were agriculturists. Each household had its garden plot a hundred feet square or more. They used wooden hoes and planting sticks to weed and cultivate these gardens, and made forest clearings by girdling the larger trees and felling the smaller ones with stone axes. They planted four varieties of corn, the principal crop.

They also raised pumpkins, beans, squash, sunflower seeds, tobacco, and gourds from which many utensils were made. They ate wild fruits, roots, and berries, supplemented by fish and game.

A custom of Southeastern Indians which impressed early travelers was their ceremonial use of "black drink." This strong tea, made by boiling leaves of the shrub *Ilex cassine* in water, was purgative, emetic, and a caffeine stimulant.

The Creeks drank the sacred beverage before council meetings to "invigorate the mind and body and prepare for thought and debate." It also played a role in their busk, or green corn ceremony, a New Year's celebration.

The Creeks conceived the new year as beginning in July or August with the ripening of the first crops, particularly maize. This celebration lasted eight days in large centers, four in smaller towns. The sacred number 4, or its multiples, was prominent in rituals.

The ceremony, centering in the plaza, was punctuated by singing, drinking the black drink, and dancing in which both men and women took part.

Climax was the lighting of the sacred fire, four logs aligned with the cardinal points. All other fires had earlier been put out and the hearths swept clean. Now new fires were laid and kindled from the sacred fire.

Preparing for the busk, the Creeks provided themselves with new clothing, new pottery and other household equipment. Houses were swept, sprinkled with clean sand, and the whole town put in order. Left-over food, clothing, equipment was burned; old pottery broken and cast away.

This material renovation symbolized the moral and spiritual renovation, the new life which was to begin the new year spotlessly pure. This concept, reminiscent of ancient Mexico, probably came from the Temple Mound cult, so widespread through the Southeast.

The Mound Builders have long been the subject of romantic, speculative writings picturing them variously as ancient, non-Indian, and highly civilized. Who were these mysterious builders of great earthworks which our own ancestors found buried in the forests from Great Lakes to Gulf of Mexico?

The roots of this culture sink deep into the past. Javelin points found in the Southeast are similar to those that occur in the high Plains together with remains of now extinct mammoth, camel, and giant bison. While no such association has yet been discovered in the East, the makers of these flaked stone points

Temple Mound Artistry is revealed in this realistically carved stone pipe found near Spiro, Oklahoma. Tobacco burned inside the hollow head; smoke was drawn through an aperture in the rear.

NATIONAL GEOGRAPHIC PHOTOGRAPHER B. ANTHONY STEWART

Ritual Made Life Go Round in Mound-building Days

Stocky, pearl-decked Hopewell women beat a rhythmic tattoo as priests perform a harvest ritual atop the mound (right). Tribal dignitary in foreground wears copper-covered antlers, holds a ceremonial mask in one hand, a spear in the other, tipped with obsidian. The burial mound, erected over the ashes of prominent dead, is in its primary stage. Succeeding mantles of earth will give it a tall domed shape. Near present Hopewell, Ohio, the Burial Mound culture, A.D. 500–1300, reached its zenith. Temple Mound period followed.

The chief of a Temple Mound tribe (lower right) greets his elder brother, the sun, and shows him his course across the heavens. Temples and chief's lodge were built on great flat-topped earth mounds. Probably inspired by Mexican example, this sun-worshiping cult flourished in rich agricultural lands of the Southeast from the 14th through the 17th centuries. The Spanish explorer De Soto, on his way to discover the Mississippi River in 1541, saw Temple Mound building at its peak.

Not all ceremonies took place atop mounds. Excavations near Macon, Georgia, reveal a peculiar council chamber hollowed out of red clay; only domed roof shows above ground. In this ceremonial earth lodge, about A.D. 1400, Macon warriors (below) plan an ambush of their enemies. They sit fifty strong around the circle. Before each seat a receptacle holds pipe, tobacco, magical charms. Raised platform represents an eagle, sacred to Southeastern forest dwellers. Kneeling figure wears a roach headdress. Powwow follows strict ceremonial procedure, for rite makes might. These may have been ancestors of the historic Creeks.

64

Ohio's "Great Serpent" Slithers Through a Smiling Countryside. Indian mounds in animal or bird form dot the upper Mississippi and Great Lakes area. Largest, this remarkable effigy mound loops 1,330 feet from coiled tail at left to head at right. Some scientists see jaws open to seize an egg. Others say oval is aboriginal way to portray snake's heart; the body once continued beyond.

were probably contemporary with western hunters of 20,000 years ago.

The first Southeasterners of whom we have adequate knowledge came into the region about 7000 B.C. This is revealed by carbon-14 dating at Russell Cave in Jackson County, Alabama. This method determines the age of organic remains by measuring the amount of radioactive carbon they contain.

These first sparse residents were a long-headed hunting, fishing, and food gathering people who lived in scattered villages along rivers and the seacoast where shellfish were available.

During this period, the Eastern Archaic, people did not dispose of their garbage, but let it accumulate where they lived. As the refuse piled higher, they continued to build their houses on it.

They buried their dead in this same refuse pile, together with offerings of bone, stone, or shell implements, spears, animal-teeth necklaces, red body paint, basketry, and other objects for the departed's use in the hereafter. Crude clay bowls appear after pottery making was introduced to the region about 1200 B.C.

The Burial Mound period—second major era of Southeastern prehistory—commences about A.D. 500, when a wave of new people and ideas came into the lower Mississippi Valley from the west and spread rapidly to the north and east.

Rather than displacing the Archaic people, these newcomers merged with them, profoundly changing their way of life. They brought agriculture, probably with corn the leading crop. Tubular smoking pipes show that tobacco was in use. Polished stone celt replaced the grooved ax of the Archaic. Copper tools and ornaments came in from the mineral-rich Lake Superior region.

A new and elaborate cult of the dead is reflected in the burial mounds built over conical log tombs of important persons. This cult reached its highest development in the Ohio Valley in the so-called Hopewell period (page 65).

About A.D. 1300 this Burial Mound culture gave way to a new civilization brought in from the southwest by a round-headed people who deformed their skulls. Bow and arrow replaced the spear.

Their pottery showed more variety in form and decoration.

This is called the Temple Mound period, from the great ceremonial centers these people built. Around a rectangular court stood huge flat-topped mounds (page 65). These served not for burials, but as elevated foundations for mat or thatch temples dedicated to sun worship, a concept derived from Mexico. Ritualistic objects, traded from afar, were the most elaborate of the entire mound-building era.

A sacred fire burned perpetually in a clay-lined fire pit tended by old men. The fire was believed to be of solar origin. If allowed to go out, disaster would befall the tribe, and only human sacrifice would appease the deity.

As in Mexico, these temples were destroyed at intervals and new ones built.

Peaceful Pursuits Contrast with Grim Taensa War Trophies

Priests leave their temple past skulls mounted on poles (bottom right). The Taensa temple, crowning a Mississippi earth mound contains the bones of departed chiefs, despotic representatives of the sun on earth. Inside, four old men tend a perpetual fire in the sun god's honor. Stylized eagles perch atop the thatch.

Corn was staff of life for the Choctaw of the Louisiana bayou country (below). Expert agriculturists, they practiced head binding, and used hickory bow and blowgun.

Rifle makes a successful deer hunt for the Seminole family (right) whose dugout glides through placid waters of Florida's Everglades. Roseate spoonbill wings overhead. But peace was a luxury for the Seminole. Their name, first used about 1775, means "runaway" or "separatist" in Creek. They migrated from Georgia and Alabama to Florida, raided Georgia, harbored runaway slaves. This led Andrew Jackson to invade Spanish Florida in 1818; it was annexed a year later. Attempts to remove the tribe west in 1835 sparked the costliest Indian war in U.S. history, decimated the 5,000 Seminole. Although seven generals failed to conquer the tribe completely, most survivors were sent to Oklahoma. Today some 900 live in Florida.

68

PAINTINGS BY W. LANGDON KIHN

As many as a dozen temples successively enlarged a single mound site.

What dramatic and colorful ceremonies must have taken place at Cahokia in southern Illinois, at Etowah in Georgia, and Moundville in Alabama, when this Temple Mound period reached its peak between 1550 and 1650! It marked the highest development achieved by Indians north of Mexico.

Representative of this culture were the Natchez of Mississippi and the related Taensa (page 68).

The Natchez government was a true theocracy. The supreme god lived in the sun. His kinsman came to earth, taught the people religion, organized their society, then turned himself into a stone to be revered in their temple.

Members of the ruling Sun clan had a divine right to extravagant honors from the commoners, or stinkards, as they were called. The children of noblewomen inherited their mother's rank, but children of common women fell one grade below their father's. A man could raise his status by certain means, but only to the lower grade of nobles.

Ceremonies at the death of a "Sun" lasted several days and were conducted with great pomp. The climax came when a score or more persons were put to death so that their spirits might accompany their lord in the other world. Victims—mainly the Sun's wives—were given tobacco pills to numb their senses, then strangled by a cord.

Others volunteered for sacrifice to honor their leader. Parents gained merit by offering children under three.

Natchez power was shattered in early 18th century wars with the French, who in 1731 sold 450 survivors into slavery. The mound-building period was at an end.

After 1700 the Southeastern tribes scattered widely and shrank in numbers. The final blow came in the 1830's when the Government forcibly removed most of the survivors west of the Mississippi, ending the real aboriginal life of once the most populous native region in the United States.

An abundance of colorful accounts by explorers and missionaries reveals native customs changing under Spanish, French, English, and American rule. Yet in no section of the States is it harder to trace tribes than in the Southeast. Tribes merged, split, were exterminated. Others, like the Shawnee, wandered widely.

Linguistic diversity, too, illustrates the multiple origin of the region's natives.

Mealtime in the Everglades

Seminole women (right) prepare food on a split-log table in Florida's Big Cypress Reservation. The Seminole preserve more of their original ways than any other Indian group in the Southeast. But enameled kitchenware on table and in palm-thatched storage attic behind symbolizes white man's influence. Flowing dress and pompadour hairdo, now so typically Seminole, were adapted from the Gibson Girl costume of the 1890's. Gay decorations, such as adorn the child's dress at left, came in with the sewing machine. Bottle and nipple feeding spotted fawn came from the general store.

NATIONAL GEOGRAPHIC PHOTOGRAPHER
WILLARD R. CULVER

There was not only the dominant Muskhogean, and offshoots of Algonquian stock, but the Caddoan, which reflects southern Plains culture.

The Iroquoian language was represented mainly by the important Cherokee tribe of the southern Appalachians, and by the Tuscarora confederation of North Carolina. The far-flung Siouan stock included the Biloxi of Mississippi, the Cheraw and Catawba of the Carolinas, and several central Virginia tribes.

The Yuchi of the upper Savannah River spoke a language unrelated to any other. Along the Mississippi, the Attacapan, Chitimachan, Tunican, and Natchezan were also small independent groups.

Remnants of Creeks, Hitchiti, and Yuchi from Alabama and Georgia, joined by runaway Negro slaves, became the Seminole tribe, which did not exist before the American Revolution. In the early 1800's they overran Florida, relentlessly pursued by United States troops.

When the tribe resisted Government efforts to remove them to Oklahoma, fighting culminated in the Second Seminole War. Begun in 1835 by Osceola, famous Seminole leader, it lasted nearly eight years, cost the Government 1,500 soldiers, and resulted in most Seminole being moved west of the Mississippi.

A few escaped to the swamps. Today their colorful descendants live in the Everglades, the only Southeastern group to retain much of their native culture.

Eagle Calf, Montana Blackfoot Indian, Dons War Bonnet of Ermine Tails, Owl and Eagle Feathers

CHAPTER 3

INDIANS OF OUR WESTERN PLAINS

FOUR HUNDRED YEARS AGO the nomad rulers of an empire of grass that rolled, almost treeless, across North America from Mississippi River to the Rocky Mountains, saw their first horses.

In July, 1541, a Wichita tribe in central Kansas stood dumbstruck as 30 pale-skinned warriors in shining armor, astride great pawing war beasts, rode into a tepee village they called "Quivira" or "Eldorado" and, in angry frustration, looked vainly about for objects of gold. Coronado had come as far north as he would go into a seemingly endless and empty continent.

Although the Spanish knew it not, the lonely expanses stretching north, east, west, and south would someday rank among the richest agricultural lands on earth. They belonged then, however, to aboriginal peoples on the verge of giving up farming for hunting. Over the next three centuries the horse would shape a new way of life for Plains Indians. To them it was a far more important "find" than any such throne of gold as the Spaniard sought.

The picture of human occupation of the Great Plains during the centuries immediately before the discovery of America by Europeans is obscure. We do know, however, that various agricultural peoples encroached on the Plains from the south and from the Northeastern Woodlands. As they moved into the open prairies, they saw huge buffalo herds, elk, and antelope, and the possibility of obtaining food by hunting became obvious.

Gradually most of them began to leave their permanent villages during the hunting season to follow the buffalo. They brought back quantities of dried meat and hides.

When Coronado's horsemen crossed the Plains, they met hunting parties using large wolflike dogs as beasts of burden. The dogs carried 40- to 50-pound packs or were hitched to the travois, basically two light poles that dragged on the ground behind (page 94).

Crude as was this primitive device, it marked the beginning of nomadic life for the Plains Indian. Dogs as burden bearers and the sledlike travois are traits that probably came from the far north.

Not for almost a century after Coronado did the horse appear out of the south in any numbers. But when it came it worked a revolution. As a mount, it enabled the Indian to hunt buffalo farther afield and with far greater prowess. As a beast of burden, it outcarried man and dog combined. In the languages of most Plains tribes, having no word for this new animal, they called the horse "big dog."

By 1750, Indian and horse had met all across the Plains. When the great era of white westward movement began about the middle of the last century, the nomadic, warlike life of mounted prairie tribes was at full flower.

These were the Indians met by trappers and explorers on their way to the Rockies, Mormons on their trek to Great Salt Lake, covered wagoners on the Oregon Trail, California-bound forty-niners.

From a Crag, Piegan Braves Scout a Montana Plain

Oddly, most of these tribes had, like the white man, come to the Plains from elsewhere and in quite recent times. As late as 1700, for example, the Cheyenne and Arapaho were still farmers living in permanent villages in present-day Minnesota.

The Dakota, or Siouan tribes, living still farther east in the Woodlands, were feeling strong pressure behind them from the Chippewa, who had been given guns by the French. Driven by the Chippewa, the Dakota forced the Cheyenne and Arapaho westward across the Missouri and finally to the base of the Rockies. The Dakota themselves, and some of the Chippewa, moved out onto prairie lands.

Similar pressure from the Ohio River region forced other Woodland tribes onto the Plains. The expanding white settlement along the Atlantic seaboard set up a pressure impetus that traveled from tribe to tribe, spreading them three-quarters of the way across the continent.

Northern and eastern parts of the Plains were peopled that way, many tribes keeping habits of ancestors who came from forests east of the Mississippi. Among these were the Kansa, the Mis-

souri, the Iowa, the Osage, and the Quapaw. Southern tribes, such as the Wichita and Pawnee, seem to have occupied their lands for a much longer time. Their tribal territories remained much as they were when Coronado came.

Some Plains tribes evidently brought with them from the northeast knowledge of the conical tent. With buffalo-hide covering in place of bark, the tent or tepee—simple, knock-down, and portable—proved extremely useful to earth-lodge peoples when they began following the buffalo for part of the year. With the introduction of the horse, the Indian could increase the size of his tent as well as his hunting range.

Most characteristic dwelling of the Plains Indians, however, was the earth lodge (page 91). Before Coronado, the central Plains were dotted with earth-lodge villages of agricultural peoples. Remains of these settlements may still be seen from North Dakota through Kansas.

The earth lodge was airy, clean, and admirably suited to the severe winters of the northern Plains. Early white settlers merely modified this Indian dwelling in building their long-lasting sod houses on the prairie.

Grass houses of the Caddo, Wichita, and Waco were very similar (page 87), although the walls were steeper and lacked a sod covering, made unnecessary by the milder climate of the southern Plains.

Typical of the farming earth-lodge tribes were the Mandan, whom the French explorer La Vérendrye visited in 1738. They then had six villages, each protected by encircling palisades and a deep ditch. The French were much impressed by these fortifications, which they saw must be impregnable to other Indians.

The Mandan were probably the earliest

arrivals of the village-dwelling tribes of the upper Missouri. Later the Hidatsa, or Minataree as they are sometimes called, moved in from the east. Although they spoke a different tongue, they generally adopted Mandan ways.

Still later, an offshoot of the Hidatsa moved westward across the Plains, gradually abandoned the earth lodge, and took up the nomadic life of the tepee. Ranging near the headwaters of the Cheyenne and the Yellowstone in the eastern Rockies, they became known as the Crow. In similar fashion, the Comanche, Kiowa, Arapaho, and Cheyenne have definite traditions of splitting off from agricultural earth-lodge peoples.

From the south, a Pawnee group drifted northward to become earth-lodge neighbors of the Mandan. These were the Arikara, one of the most warlike of upper Missouri tribes.

The artist George Catlin described the chief Mandan village in 1833: "In ranging the eye over the village from where I am writing, there is presented to the view the strangest mixture and medley of unintelligible trash (independent of the living beings that are in motion) that can possibly be imagined.

"On the roofs of the lodges, besides the groups of living, are buffaloes' skulls,

Bison Butt Down Indian Horses in Snorting Fury. Daring braves pick off stampeding prey as one unseated hunter teeters atop horse and charging beast. Buffalo gave Plains Indians food, clothing, shelter, buffalo-chip fuel. Their sinew was turned against them as part of the hunter's bow. Lewis and Clark saw "immence hirds . . . not less than 10 thousand buffaloe within a circle of 2 miles." George Catlin, Pennsylvania artist-ethnologist who recorded this hunt, lived among the Indians in the 1830's.

skin boats, pots and pottery, sleds and sledges—and suspended on poles, erected some 20 feet above the doors of their lodges, are displayed in a pleasant day, the scalps of warriors, preserved as trophies; and thus proudly exposed as evidence of their warlike deeds.

"In other parts are raised on poles the warriors' pure and whitened shields and quivers, with medicine bags attached; and here and there a sacrifice of red cloth, or other costly stuff, offered up to the Great Spirit, over the door of some benignant chief, in humble gratitude for the blessings which he is enjoying.

"Such is a part of the strange medley that is before and around me; and amidst them can be seen in the distance, the green and boundless, treeless, bushless prairie; and on it, and contiguous to the palisade which encloses the village, a hundred scaffolds on which their 'dead live,' as they term it."

The Mandan and other settled tribes on the Plains—Caddo, Pawnee, Arikara, and Hidatsa—knew how to make pottery. Probably this art came into the Plains from the Eastern Woodlands.

Spanish explorers compared the Caddo's ware with the best in Spain. In 1833, the German traveler, Prince Maximilian, wrote of the Missouri pottery: "The clay is of a dark slate color and burns a yellowish red, very similar to what is seen in the burnt tops of the Missouri hills. This clay is mixed with flint or granite,

Plains Indians Danced to the Sun, Gambled on the Turn of a Moccasin

Arapaho Sun Dancers, headed by seven-foot White Owl (left), face the sacred medicine bundle on its four-legged stand at the start of one of the most solemn ceremonies of the Plains tribes. To them, as to the Aztecs, the sun reigned supreme. Dancers gazed open-eyed at their fiery deity. The central pole symbolized an enemy. This was to be struck with feather-tipped coup sticks, here held in the mouth.

In former times self-torture played a prominent part in the Sun Dance. Celebrants pierced breast or back with wooden skewers attached to the pole by thongs, then writhed until the flesh gave way and dropped them to the ground. Another test was to attach buffalo skulls to the thongs and drag the heavy skulls around the dance ground. The deeper the skewers, the more valiant the dancer. Often they were imbedded so firmly that other dancers had to sit on the buffalo heads to tear the skewers loose.

Gambling often gripped the Indian with an intensity rivaling religious fervor. Below, Sioux warriors watch the man manipulate the moccasins. High stakes swung on this sport, which resembled the old pea-and-shell game. The gamblers wear beaded shirts fringed with ermine tails. Milk teeth of the elk adorn the dress of the wife, whose baby naps in a portable cradle ornamented with bright beads. Ladderlike frames propped behind the men are lazy-backs, back rests which took the place of chairs. Beds line the tepee's dew cloth beneath painted, feathered war trappings. Center fire drives away wintry chill.

PAINTINGS BY W. LANGDON KIHN

77

reduced to powder by the action of fire.

"The workwoman forms the hollow inside of the vessel by means of a round stone which she holds in her hand while she works and smooths the outside with a piece of poplar bark. When the pot is made, it is filled and surrounded with dry shavings, and then burnt, when it is ready for use."

Fortunately for our knowledge of the Mandan, not only Catlin and Maximilian but such travelers as Lewis and Clark, Brackenridge, and Bradbury visited them early in the 19th century, for in the spring of 1837 they were struck by a smallpox epidemic (page 90). When the disease abated, only 23 men, 40 women, and 60 or 70 children were left of the 1,800 souls that before had composed the nation. Those few that recovered, disfigured almost beyond recognition, were soon absorbed in other tribes. The Mandan ceased to exist.

The white man's coming struck the Plains Indian hard in many such ways. So, too, did the tough, far-ranging Indian of the open prairie strike a deep impression, often terror, in the hearts of white travelers, and lastingly etch his image in the Nation's imagination.

His powerful physique, feathered warbonnet, and prominent hooked nose still remain as mind's-eye features of all American Indians. His body paint ran to dramatic vermilions, yellows, and black. His hair sometimes hung in two braids,

PAINTING BY W. LANGDON KIHN

Snow Masks Horse Thief

Covered by a howling, driving blizzard, the intruder readies his rawhide lariat as he stealthily approaches a mount tied near its owner's tepee. Stealing horses was an honorable pursuit among the Plains Indians. The successful thief not only got the horse, but his fellow tribesmen's acclaim for exposing himself to danger.

If caught, he was killed, just as white men killed horse thieves in early days of the West. Chief honor— a greater coup—came from taking a mount tied near a tepee, far riskier than taking one hobbled in an open field.

sometimes in a forelock down over the nose, and sometimes stood stiffly erect, as in the forelock of the Crow.

The Plains Indian loved war regalia. A party of Plains warriors, bronzed and painted, naked except for breechcloth, weapons, and ornaments, riding at full gallop with bodies low to their horses' withers, eagle feathers flying, and the terrifying war cry ringing across the prairie, made a spectacular impression upon enemies. And the Indian knew it.

I have talked with old warriors and seen the reminiscent gleam come into their eyes when describing old encounters. They spoke with undisguised admiration of their foes' appearance as they galloped past. Brilliant uniforms and martial music of bygone European armies never glamorized warfare more than the feathers, paint, and war cries of the Plains Indian.

The mounted Indian usually rode bareback; nowhere in the world did more expert horsemen develop. Their roving equestrian life engendered a warlike spirit. Transcending its original primary purpose of vengeance or protection, warfare developed into a glorified game, a way of gaining honor and prestige, excitement and adventure.

Like any game, it acquired definite rules and a scoring system. The ultimate object became exposing oneself to risk and danger rather than killing enemies, which was secondary.

Score was kept by "counting coup"—a point system for brave exploits. Highest honor came from touching an enemy in combat with the hand; next was to touch him with bow or a coup stick carried for the purpose. It gave greater honor to spear and dismount a foe than to shoot him with bow and arrow or gun.

Also important were such feats as capturing an enemy's gun, taking a scalp, or stealing horses from another tribe. Witnesses were desirable, but seldom did a man falsify his achievements.

The warrior painted a pictorial record of his exploits on his tepee or on the bare side of his buffalo robe. On certain occasions he could boast publicly of his deeds. If he had four coups or more, he was an "ace," and might then hold tribal positions of honor and leadership. He could wear certain feathers or paint his face in certain ways, and others knew at a glance what honors he held.

"Family connections" had nothing to do with an individual's standing in his group. Leadership or the so-called chieftaincies came not through inheritance but as reward for personal achievement. Indians did not even inherit family names. Even so, Plains tribesmen regarded names

79

Blackfeet Bring in Furs to Trade. Pitching their tepees outside the fort's log stockade, tribesmen unload rich pelts from back-packs, horses, and travois. The trader will barter for them in dry goods, tobacco, trinkets, vermilion for face paint, sometimes rifles. Favorite swap was rum for beaver.

80

It was at fur-company posts such as this, scattered across the Great Plains during the 19th century, that Indians and whites met when the West was growing up. Often, peace pipes extinguished, war parties attacked these outposts. Defenders swept the circling band with fire from corner blockhouses.

as valuable property, often possessing magical virtues. They could be sold, pawned, given away, or discarded at will. A boy usually took a new name on reaching manhood. A girl kept her first name throughout life. Marriage did not change it.

Frequently Indian names suggested by some exploit or incident sound curious to our ears. A prominent Kiowa gloried in the name "Stinking Saddle Blanket." To the Indians this implied that he was a man who rode so hard and far on the warpath that he did not have time to change his saddle!

Loose or mistaken translations of Indian names into English often produced curious results. The name of the famous Chippewa chief "Hole in the Day" should have been translated "Rift in the Sky." The well-known Dakota Sioux warrior "Young Man Afraid of His Horses" actually was "Young Man Whose Very Horses Are Feared."

Sitting Bull, the Hunkpapa Sioux leader, was so called because the hieroglyph of his name appeared to represent a seated buffalo. Actually, his name meant "The Bull in Possession."

Indians are far from devoid of a sense of humor.

Covered Wagons Dare Indian Domain. Banded together for mutual protection, a gold rush train crosses Sioux and Cheyenne country under the eye of Indian scouts. Soon comes the attack. The pioneers, hastily barricaded behind tight circle of wagons, will repel it, or leave their bones to bleach on the prairies.

The High Plains became part of the United States with the Louisiana Purchase of 1803. Next spring, Lewis and Clark "hoisted Sail and Set out in high Spirits" from St. Louis, explored the mighty Missouri, crossed the Continental Divide, boated down the Columbia River—the first Americans overland to the Pacific. Half a century later was the westward movement was at full flood; between 1843 and 1857 some 350,000 pioneers undertook the long trek. Their stirring tales of hostile tribesmen made the Plains Indian *the* American Indian in most people's minds.

Sioux Rainmakers Ride Under Darkening Skies. Storm clouds give thunderous answer to the ghostly Sioux Horse Dance, performed beneath an arching rainbow. Riders paint themselves the color of their horses. Man and mount wear hornlike feathers.

Four black horses represent the west; white, the north; sorrel, the east; buckskin, the south. Four virgins lead the procession wearing scarlet-dyed buckskin dresses. Wreaths of green sage crown scarlet-painted faces. Single eagle feathers hang from their braids. Beyond the black-hooded horsemen, six grandfathers sing.

Artist and spectators were drenched, but the downpour missed the performers, who carried out the ceremony in bright sunshine. The big, circular tepee encampment is typical of those Lewis and Clark saw when passing through Sioux, or Dakota, lands in 1804.

A Blackfoot, noted among his fellow tribesmen for stinginess, carried the name, "Johnny Belches When He Eats." He was much embarrassed by whites laughing at him when they heard it. Whereupon he formally requested the tribal council to bestow a new name on him.

Custom required him to furnish a feast for the gathering. So Johnny purchased, at minimum cost, a small, undernourished steer. The council met and, after keeping Johnny in suspense for a couple of days, finally called him in to announce that his cause was just. They had given him a new name.

Henceforth he was to be known as "Johnny Does Not Belch When He Eats."

Not only warfare could enhance a brave's prestige, but also generosity in aiding the needy. The man who gave away valuable horses, for example, was greatly admired.

Since the buffalo hunt was vital to the tribe, success as a hunter was a principal means of gaining prestige and honor. Buffalo hunting, however, was organized under strict leadership and regulation. When scouts reported buffalo in the vicinity, the village authorities assigned roles to the hunters, who remained under military discipline while the hunt lasted.

Blackfoot War Party Skirts the Skyline

Bands of feather-bonneted warriors often displayed themselves to foes before attacking. War was a game, and risk its spice. The Indian full knew his dramatic impression; he heightened it by warpaint and trappings. His fondness for pintos, or "painted" piebald horses, gave the Wild West its characteristic steed. Natural-born riders, the Plains Indians took the Spaniard's horse, and proved their prowess as mounted hunter and fighter beyond compare.

A swirl of warriors (left) marks the attack. They peel off, strike at the flanks, circle tighter and tighter, presenting the most fleeting of targets. Always best in a running fight, the Plains warrior guided his mount with his knees, leaving hands free for bow and arrow, lance or gun. He could hang alongside his horse's neck, body out of sight; he could shoot under the horse's belly, or swing onto or off his mount at full gallop. Near-naked, bareback riders swooped in to pick up dead or wounded tribemates, sparing them from enemy scalping or mutilation.

JOSEPH K. DIXON

Three methods of organized hunting prevailed. In the "surround" system, used principally in the south, horsemen stampeded the buffalo in a circle and shot them one by one from the edge of the herd (page 75).

In the northern Plains, where heavy winter snows often covered the ground, Indians built a strong corral with a narrow entrance, from which long winglike fences extended outward in a V shape. The animals were herded into the wings of the funnel. Men stationed along the sides kept them converging until they entered the enclosure where they could be easily killed.

Blackfoot and Crow hunters practiced a third basically similar method. Long converging wings led to the edge of a cliff. The animals were driven over and killed by the fall (page 95).

When the buffalo were scattered, the hunter frequently covered himself with an animal skin and stalked his quarry against the wind. Both lance and bow and arrow were used.

The short recurved bow of western tribes, made of wood or horn and backed with buffalo sinew, was extremely powerful. Observers often reported arrows passing entirely through a bison's body.

In early times flaked stone points tipped the arrows. Later, triangular iron points were introduced by the trader.

Bow and arrow proved more effective for short-range work on horseback than the single-shot rifle. Not until the very end of the 19th century did the bow give way completely to the handgun and repeating carbine.

To the women fell the task of preparing products of the hunt. Buffalo meat was cut into strips, hung on wooden frames, dried and smoked. Pounded with dried berries and wild cherries and mixed with fat, the dried meat became pemmican, a concentrated, nutritious food for long journeys.

Buffalo hides were staked out on the ground for the women to scrape, dry, and later make soft and pliable by dressing with buffalo brains, liver, and fat. The

Caddo Lodge, Blackfoot Tepee Housed Dwellers of the Plains

Grass huts of the sedentary Caddo tribe look as if they belonged on Samoa. Actually, these beehive dwellings (right) were typical of the southern Plains. They resembled the earth lodges to the north, but without heavy sod covering the thatch. Their rafter poles were bent in a rain-shedding dome, lashed at top as in the frame in the background. Some lodges had leather-hinged doors, others walls that stopped short of the ground.

Caddo warriors tattooed their bodies and shaved their heads, save for a roach on the scalp and long braid behind. This agricultural tribe boasted the finest potters of the Plains.

Admirably suited to wandering Blackfoot ways was the easily transported tepee (below). This restless, aggressive tribe, without pottery art, canoes, or agriculture, adopted the white man's horse and gun, spread over immense territory from Montana north into Saskatchewan, Canada. Women not only made and erected the tall tents, they owned them. If a brave had trouble with his wife, he couldn't order her out of the tepee, but had to leave himself.

A tepee began with three or four poles, depending on the tribe. These poles, lashed together about three feet from the small ends, were raised like a big tripod. Ten to 20 more poles then were laid up in a cone, with their tops locking one another. Such a frame stood firmly against high winds. The buffalo skin covering laced down the front, leaving a door flap at bottom. Two outside poles adjusted a smoke hole and ventilator opening at the top according to the direction of the wind.

High-peaked Moorish-type saddle on horse is a "woman's saddle." Men mostly rode bareback, or used a pad saddle with short stirrups.

86

hides could then be worked into tepee covers, robes, or dresses.

The dressed side of buffalo robes was often decorated by painting or simple geometric designs formed of dyed porcupine quills. When the white traders came, colored glass beads gradually replaced quillwork in clothing. Great Plains beadwork can usually be dated by the various types of beads brought in by traders at different times.

Before the coming of the whites, the Indian man's normal costume was a small skin apron attached to a belt. With traders also came the breechcloth, worn by passing it between the legs and tucking it under the belt, fore and aft, so that it hung down a little at each end. This, with moccasins, was the dress for ordinary occasions.

Long skin leggings, reaching from ankle to thigh and fastened to the belt, might be added, but apparently only extreme northern tribes wore shirts, introduced by Canadian Indians.

Plains Indians placed rawhide soles on their soft leather moccasins. This contrasted to Eastern Woodlands practice, where one-piece moccasins of soft leather were made. Southwestern and Mexican Indians wore sandals.

While near nudity characterized the men, women were more fully clothed. In most Plains tribes they wore a full-length sleeveless dress of elkskin or buckskin, the upper portion draping over the shoulders in the form of a cape. They also wore knee-high leggings, held by garters. Women of the Osage, Pawnee, and Cheyenne, on the other hand, wore a two-piece costume like that of eastern Indians, consisting of a skirt and cape.

Favorite "costume jewelry" was the milk teeth of the elk, perforated and attached by sinew or thread (page 77).

Except for fur caps sometimes used in

Smoke in the Sky! A war-party leader in full regalia, gripping steel tomahawk and rope rein, reads signals rising above the ridgeline. Smoke codes by day, signal fires by night carried messages long distances through clear skies of the Plains. Near tribal campgrounds, lookout points were manned constantly.

A simpler, more graceful, or more practical dwelling was never devised by man. A large tepee encampment of the western Plains around the middle of the last century was one of the most picturesque sights offered in the North American continent.

In tepee-dwelling tribes, the organized camp circle was a prominent feature. Each band, or family group, pitched its tepees in an assigned segment of the circle. The council tent stood in the center.

At regular intervals around the circle were the tepees of the police, appointed by the council to enforce regulations. These warriors were selected from men's societies or clubs, military or ceremonial in nature and generally named for animals. Many tribes organized their societies by age grades. A man "graduated" from one to another as he grew older. Some northern Plains tribes had similar women's societies which performed ceremonies helping to obtain game.

far-northern reaches of the Plains, no headgear was worn by either men or women.

In addition to producing clothing, the woman made, erected, and was responsible for transporting the tepee, which was considered her property.

The size, form, and construction of the tepee often varied with different tribes. A typical tepee took 10 or 12 buffalo hides to cover. These were rid of hair and tanned on both sides, then skillfully tailored to fit tightly over the conical framework of smooth, barkless poles. Among the Crow and Blackfoot, tepees were sometimes 50 feet in diameter.

Characteristically, political organization among Plains tribes was loose, so loose it is not always easy to say what constitutes a tribe.

There were seven divisions among the Dakota: the Yankton, Teton, Sisseton, Yanktonai, Mdewakanton, Wahpeton, and Wahpekute. All self-governing and independent, these groups were yet bound by a common language, thought of themselves as one people, and did not war with one another. The name Dakota means, in Sioux language, "Friends."

Like the Dakota units, the three independent Blackfoot groups—the Piegan, Blood, and Blackfoot—felt close affinity.

Yet the Hidatsa, an earth-lodge people, did not consider themselves strictly related to the tepee-dwelling Crow, even though both groups spoke the same language. Their customs differed too much.

Complicating the tribal picture were the many Plains languages.

Most prominent linguistic stock was the Siouan, whose dialects include Mandan, Hidatsa, Assiniboin, Crow, Dakota, Iowa, Kansa, Osage, Omaha, Oto, and Ponca. These languages reached the Plains from the east.

From the north came the Algonquian languages of the Cree, Plains Chippewa, Atsina, Blackfoot, Cheyenne, and Arapaho. From the northwest came Athapascan, represented on the Plains by the Sarsi and the Kiowa Apache.

On the western High Plains the Shoshonean stock includes the Northern and Wind River Shoshoni, the Bannock, the Ute, and the Comanche. The Caddoan dialects spoken by the Arikara, Pawnee, Caddo, and Wichita came from the south.

Perhaps it was this linguistic diversity, combined with nomadic habits, that led the Plains Indians to develop the most effective sign language ever devised. By graceful signs and gestures of fingers and hands they communicated as fluently as by oral speech.

So realistic were the gestures, so adept these sign talkers that even the uninitiated, with little practice, could follow the trend of conversation. Sign language became of great use to white trappers and traders, and later to military men.

Religious concepts of the Plains Indians were similar to those of American Indians in general. Most Plains tribes revered the sun as the pre-eminent deity, a concept evidently coming from the south. The most characteristic and widespread ceremony of the Plains was the Sun Dance (page 76).

The sky, the moon, the earth, and the wind were also personified as gods. Lesser supernatural beings were the ruling spirits of the buffalo and the bear, lightning, thunder, rain, and whirlwind. Numberless mythological beings were honored in a lengthy series of myths.

The term *wakonda* in the Siouan languages expresses the idea of supernatural force. Every man's goal was to acquire contact with some supernatural being. Prolonged fasting in some lonely place sometimes induced a vision in which he spoke with some animal, human in character. The animal who gave the revelation was thenceforth regarded as protector of the individual, who always carried with him on any dangerous or important undertaking a bundle containing skin or feathers or some other part of such an animal, together with additional objects related to the vision. A man not fortunate enough to have a vision of his own might purchase a bundle from a medicine man.

Some famous bundles became the property of societies or tribes and were made the central feature of ceremonies. Although these bundles acquired high value, they could be sold or transferred. Sacred songs, prayers, even entire ceremonies might be sold or borrowed.

Among the Skidi Pawnee, the two most important sky gods were the Morning Star and Evening Star. They represented respectively the male and female principle, and as such they were regarded as parents of the first human. There were two sacred bundles, the Skull bundle and the Morning Star bundle.

Human sacrifices were sometimes offered to the Morning Star. The ceremony, evidently southern in origin, represented a renewal of life on earth.

Sacrificial rites were held at irregular intervals, usually when the Morning Star appeared to some warrior in a dream, or when the star seemed unusually bright, or a comet arched near it in the sky.

For the ritual, a beautiful maiden was captured from a neighboring tribe, to be sacrificed as bride of the Morning Star.

Often the captive would be held for several months
without knowing her fate, until the proper season for
the ceremony arrived. During this time she was given
every comfort and treated with the greatest respect,
as befitted the prospective bride of a god (opposite).

When the day to begin the ceremony arrived, the
priest came to the chief's lodge and spread out the
contents of the medicine bundle as an altar. The girl
was brought into the lodge, undressed, and her entire body painted red. She and her male captor then
were dressed in costumes from the Morning Star
bundle. Preliminary ceremonies lasted three days,
with everything done to allay the girl's fears.

On the afternoon of the fourth day, a scaffold was
erected outside the village, consisting of five symbolically painted horizontal bars lashed between two
uprights. The right half of the girl's body was
painted red, the left half black, and a fan-shaped
eagle-feather headdress was attached to her hair.

She was led to the scaffold, the procession being
timed to the star's rising. If the girl mounted the

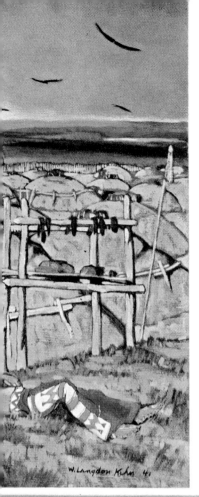

Smallpox Took Grisly Toll, Human Sacrifice But Few

Vultures circle, mourners wail from the domed roofs of their earth lodges. These are the only signs of life in the Mandan village (left), where the air hangs heavy with the stench of death. Epidemic smallpox, contracted from two diseased white men on a Missouri River trading boat, wiped out the Mandan in 1837. Indians, who had not known smallpox before the coming of the whites, had scant resistance and no way of combating it. The scourge spread like wildfire from village to village, tribe to tribe—to Arikara, Assiniboin, Blackfoot, Pawnee.

Among the Pawnee, the Skidi band (below) was the only Plains tribe to practice human sacrifice. In the smoke of a grass fire, a medicine man bathes the nude body of a young maiden, readying her for sacrifice as bride of the Morning Star. Soon she will be painted red and black, lashed to a sacred scaffold, and killed amid elaborate ritual (page 89).

Both Mandan and Pawnee built their strong, roomy earth lodges 30 to 60 feet in diameter, banking sod atop grass thatch over an ingenious post-and-rafter frame. Doorway tunnels usually faced east, direction of the rising sun, chief deity of many tribes. Skins curtained the openings. To harden floors, the earth was tamped and flooded with water; then dry grass was piled on it and set afire. Couches lined the wall. Covered with buffalo robes, they served as seats by day, beds by night. A fire burned in the center, beneath the smoke hole. Miniature cellars stored corn, dried meat, skins, extra clothing, and personal effects.

PAINTINGS BY W. LANGDON KIHN

Shoshoni Women Garbed as Men Parade Enemy Scalps. Drums thud. Scalps flutter like battle pennants atop tall poles. A war party has come home triumphant, bearing fresh scalps, trophies of great daring. Symbolizing victory, women bring forth all the tribe's old scalps, dried and mounted on hoops. In the scalp dance alone did women lead a tribal ritual or don warrior's apparel. These victory fetes took place among many tribes, even though scalp taboos and beliefs differed widely. Sometimes scalps were placed on buffalo chips and left on the battleground as sacrifice to the sun god. The Dakota destroyed theirs after a year in an impressive ceremony, releasing enemy spirits from earthly ties.

92

PAINTING BY W. LANGDON KIHN

Having served their ceremonial purpose, scalps might adorn a warrior's trappings or become bridle pendants. They might go into sacred medicine bundles, or they might simply be thrown away. Contrary to popular notion, a warrior's honors were measured not by his tally of scalps, but by counting coup (page 79). An Indian who killed or first struck an enemy (the higher honor) not always did the scalping; he might leave it to another in his party. Scalping was not practiced by all North American Indians, nor was it necessarily fatal. Some Plains tribes sought to overpower foes and scalp them alive, sending them mutilated back to their people as a gesture of defiance, a goad to new battle.

93

Blackfoot Hunters Stampede Bison Over Cliff's Edge

High above a circular tepee camp, a great herd is decoyed into a funnel of logs, rocks, and brush by mounted Indians disguised with buffalo robes. Suddenly blanket-waving beaters spring up (right). With a sound like thunder, the terrified bison sweep toward the mesa's rim; the decoys ride clear as best they can. Those animals not killed by the fall make easy targets for Indians waiting below.

Before the professional white hunter all but wiped out the American buffalo, vast herds darkened the Plains. Some experts estimated them to number more than sixty million. They roamed with the seasons and the grass, feeding always into the wind, wary yet vulnerable to Indians, cunning, swift, brave.

Buffalo sustained the Plains Indian; their pursuit became a way of life. Their flesh gave food, their blood drink. Buffalo chips fed prairie campfires. The hides housed the Indians, clothed them, gave them cooking vessels, shields, saddles, and warm robes.

Unlike the pig's squeal, not even the bison's beard was wasted: it decorated clothing, bows, and lances. Thick woolly bison hair stuffed "medicine balls." The ribs gave scrapers, arrowheads, and dice. Hoes were fashioned from shoulder blades; leg bones became knives, awls, and hammers. The skull made a fetish, porous hip bones saw use as paintbrushes, the horns yielded cups, bowls, spoons. Sinew made bowstrings and backed bows. From the scrotum came rattles; from the bladder, water bags. Even the tail found use as whip or fly swatter.

94

Back-pack and Dog Travois Carried the Buffalo Hunter's Loads Before the Horse Came

Coronado met bands, such as these wandering Kiowa (left), crossing the Kansas prairie in 1541. They left their villages to follow bison herds in long migrations, loading food and camp gear into women's packs and onto the light-poled travois dragged by their Huskylike dogs.

The first horses astounded the Indians. A century later the Spaniard's mounts were coming in numbers to the Western Plains. Escaped stallions sired wild herds that thrived on the endless grasslands. Horses swiftly changed Indian life. Wider hunting range, greater load-carrying capacity caused many tribes to abandon sedentary agriculture entirely for nomadic hunting.

In all their roving, Plains Indians strangely never used the great river highways that were to carry white explorers westward. Lacking canoe and keelboat, the Indians used only the bullboat for crossing larger streams. This crude craft consisted of buffalo hide stretched over a circular frame, an unwieldy bowl hard to paddle.

PAINTINGS BY W. LANGDON KIHN

95

scaffold of her own will, it was considered an especially favorable omen. She was lashed by the wrists to the scaffold, and as soon as the star appeared over the horizon, two men came from the east with flaming brands and touched her lightly on her armpits and groin. Four other men touched her symbolically with war clubs.

The man who had captured her then ran forward with the sacred bow and arrow from the Skull bundle and shot her through the heart. Simultaneously, another man struck her on the head with the club from the Morning Star bundle.

Then the Skidi Pawnee priest opened her breast with a flint knife and smeared his face with blood from her heart, while her captor caught some of the falling blood on dried meat. Every male in the tribe pressed forward to shoot an arrow into the girl's body, fathers or uncles pulling bows for boys too small to shoot by themselves. Then for three days, the entire village feasted and danced.

One of the most romantic episodes in Plains Indian history took place in 1818 in connection with this ceremony. The hero was a young Pawnee chief named Petalasharo, handsomest and most daring man in the tribe.

The girl had been lashed to the scaffold preparatory to the final act, when Petalasharo stepped forward, dramatically declaring that he intended to rescue the girl or lay down his life in the attempt. He leaped on the scaffold, cut the girl's bonds, and carried her through the astonished crowd to where two horses had been led. Placing her on one, mounting the other, he rode swiftly away. When safe from pursuit, he presented her with food, the horse she was riding, and sent her to her people, some 400 miles away.

Then Petalasharo returned to his village. His prominence and previous honors were such that no attempt was made to punish him. Probably most of his tribesmen admired the unprecedented feat. Thereafter other chiefs opposed human sacrifice in the Skidi Pawnee rituals.

As the white man pressed westward in ever-increasing numbers, taking up lands, building military posts and railroads, slaughtering the buffalo, the Plains Indian realized that unless this advance was checked he was doomed. The end of the buffalo herds meant the end of his free wandering life on ancestral hunting grounds.

Treaties failing, he felt armed resistance to be his only hope. Not accustomed to organized warfare, the Indian probably did not realize the futility of his stand. Yet his success against insuperable odds was remarkable. In his favor were his familiarity with the terrain, his fine physical condition, warlike tradition, excellent horsemanship, and above all, the fact that he was fighting to preserve a deeply loved homeland and ancestral way of life.

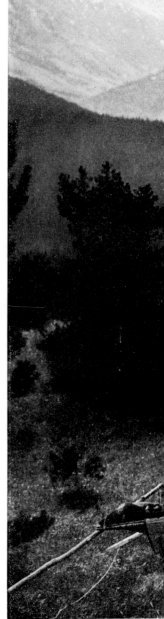

Nomads at Trail's End

White hunters, railroads, settlements doomed the bison and Plains Indian life, yet not until 1890 did fierce Sioux give up their battle against hopeless odds. Their image lives on. The Plains Indian, tall, hawk-nosed, with feather warbonnet, symbolizes all American Indians today. His features adorn currency and monuments. As fighter for liberty, he personifies an American ideal.

The white man's disregard of the strict rules by which the Indian fought put the latter under a handicap. Yet in the end it was disease and decimation of food supply rather than bullets and the numbers of his enemies that brought the Indian's inevitable downfall.

Gradually forced to adopt a way of life as a Government ward in reservations, the Plains Indian accepted his fate reluctantly, contesting every step of his further constriction. Such was the last outbreak of the Sioux and their allies, who slaughtered Custer's men on the Little Bighorn in Montana in 1876 (page 14).

But resistance was crushed, the Indian's spirit broken. Like a caged panther, his unused muscles grew soft and his eyes glowed with the memory of the freedom of a day which even he came to realize was forever gone.

With the passing of the hunt and the warpath, the rich ceremonies built around them lost their meaning. Indians yet living, who knew the old life, still are stirred by the old emotions. But younger generations, raised in a new world, find themselves between two cultures.

Blue of the Sky, Red of the Desert Color Navajo Life. Proudly this young mother, bedecked in silver and turquoise, comes to a tribal ceremony by covered wagon. The industrious Navajo, largest and one of the most adaptable of United States tribes today, herd sheep on dry New Mexico and Arizona tablelands, weave bright blankets, rugs, and work silver with traditional artistry.

CHAPTER 4

INDIAN TRIBES OF PUEBLO LAND

FRANCISCO VÁSQUEZ DE CORONADO in 1540 led his band of gold-hungry explorers into the rocky country near the headwaters of the Little Colorado River in what is now western New Mexico.

The conquistadores were fired by reports of Cabeza de Vaca and Fray Marcos de Niza, who had preceded them into that sun-seared land. Had not Fray Marcos himself seen from a distance the very city the guides said they were now approaching? Had he not stated that it appeared even more magnificent than rumors foretold?

Finally the great moment arrived. From a rise across the shallow valley, Coronado and his fellow Spaniards viewed the first of Seven Cities of Cíbola, drab against a background of arid hills.

The Spaniards were not impressed. Says Pedro de Castañeda, chronicler of the expedition:

"When they saw the first village, which was Cíbola, such were the curses that some hurled at Friar Marcos that I pray God may protect him from them. It is a little, crowded village, looking as if it had been crumpled all up together. There are ranch houses in New Spain which make a better appearance at a distance."

The conquistadores were in search of gold. They could not see or understand the other riches which lay behind these adobe walls, the wealth of a people who had intimate acquaintance with Nature and with Mother Earth, a people to whom religion and poetry were one. In the environment seemingly so unproduc-tive to the Spaniards, this race saw beauty with which to build their arts and ceremonies.

Wealth of a material sort these Indians neither had nor cared about. In the turquoise adorning their house entrances they saw the depths of clear waters and the sky's infinite space, and thus it repre-sented pure beauty. That turquoise might possess value of another sort never occurred to them. Among their possessions little else attracted the Spaniards.

Coronado's expedition was a failure, so far as its main purpose was concerned. Other fabled "cities of Cíbola" proved as disappointing as the first. No mines were discovered, no golden Inca halls.

The expedition's unfavorable reports discouraged further penetration for 40 years. Then, in the wake of later explorers, Spanish settlers drifted into the territory. As colonization mounted, the Pueblo Indians rebelled and drove out the white men in 1680.

The Spanish conquerors soon returned. Again in 1696 the Pueblos rose to expel the invaders, but after much bloodshed the uprising was put down. Since then the Pueblos, peacefully for the most part, have lived in their native manner down to the present day—remarkably unchanged after four centuries of white contact.

In probing the vast area we now call the Southwest, the Spaniards saw ruins of imposing settlements, apparently the work of an ancient people, long vanished. With the start of American occupation

Navajo Fire Dance Climaxes the Night Chants. Fire dancers, bodies painted white with clay to ward off heat, race around a blazing bonfire. Each clutches a burning brand, strikes the dancer ahead. Wildly they circle closer and closer to the leaping flames. One of the most impressive Indian ceremonies in North America, the Navajo Night Chants draw tribesmen from far and near. The many rituals, jugglery acts, prayers and songs under the stars combine the gaiety of a social gathering, the solemnity of a religious ceremony, the spectacle of tribal drama. Typical of Southwest ritual, clowns burlesque the priests, dance out of step, jest with blanket-wrapped onlookers. Left above: A Yaqui dancer, member of a fierce Mexican border tribe, pushes aside his mask.

Coronado Takes Hawikuh, Pueblo of the Zuni. Toledo blades, armor glint in the sun as conquistadores loot and kill in this "village of about 200 warriors . . . three and four stories high. The people of the whole district had collected here," says Castañeda's chronicle of 1540. "When they refused to have peace on the terms the interpreters extended to them, but appeared defiant, the Santiago [war cry] was given, and they were at once put to flight. The Spaniards then attacked the village, which was taken with not a little difficulty, since they held the narrow and crooked entrance." Coronado himself fell under a barrage of stones, was snatched from death by lieutenants. But Spanish fury conquered the pueblo in less than an hour. The troops found food they needed, but no gold, neither here nor in any of the legended Seven Cities of Cíbola. They departed, and the Zuni remained unmolested for 40 years.

about mid-19th century, some of these ruins were mapped. The world at large began to hear of them. "Cliff dwellers" became a household word.

These strange cities, it was said, might be 20 or 30 thousand years old! Perhaps a highly civilized non-Indian race built them, then grew effete and was vanquished by barbarians. Or perhaps the people were dwarfs, for their window-less dwelling places (actually storage granaries) were so small!

Thus fancy ran free until, after 1880, the spades of archeologists began to uncover the true prehistory of the Southwest. We now know that the "cliff dwellers" were early Pueblo agriculturists who built their amazing strongholds on cliffs for safety from hostile nomads. More is known today of the American

NATIONAL GEOGRAPHIC PHOTOGRAPHER WILLARD R. CULVER

Pueblos than of any comparable archeologic area in the world. In the tree-growth rings of wooden house beams, preserved in the dry stillness of the centuries, science has found a calendar that can date these sites more certainly than do cornerstone numerals carved by Romans date their edifices (Chapter 16).

The vast stage that mounted this Indian drama extends from southern Utah

Cliff Palace Crowds Below Mesa Verde's Rim

Largest of prehistoric cave villages in Mesa Verde National Park, Colorado, this ancient eight-story apartment house once sheltered at least 400 Indians from enemies and the elements. Here chanting black-eyed women ground corn on stone metates, while men clambered up perilous cliffside paths to till mesa-top fields and hunt game. Flat roofs are gone, but masonry walls of the 200 family rooms, 23 kivas, and storage bins have withstood seven centuries' wear. Two cowboys discovered the forgotten pueblo in 1888.

PAINTINGS BY W. LANGDON KIHN

Mesa Verde People Watch White-Painted Priests Emerge. Cliff dwellers cluster on stepped roof-tops beneath their four-story tower as masked members of a tribal society come forth for a public ceremony. Secret rites have concluded in the sacred kiva below. This circular windowless chamber, banned to women, represents the universe. The ceiling is the sky, the floor the earth. A hole at floor center symbolizes the passageway by which man first came from the underworld. The artist here recreates Cliff Palace (page 102) as it must have appeared in its stone-age heyday, long before the white man came to America. By Coronado's time these cliff villages were silent ruins. Archeologists believe a 24-year drought in the late 13th century, plus hostile nomads, spelled disaster to a great culture. This pueblo depended on crops grown above it on Mesa Verde—"green table" in Spanish.

and Colorado to northern Sonora and Chihuahua in Mexico. Its arid heartland is Arizona and New Mexico (group area map, page 24).

Centuries before Cabeza de Vaca and his cavaliers heard of the Seven Cities of Cíbola, there were people here of considerable culture. These first human occupants we know much about were the Basket Makers. But thousands of years before their arrival, much more primitive men hunted the mammoth, the camel, and the giant bison. Theirs was a different land and a different climate, as the last great glaciers thawed to the north. Of those Folsom and pre-Folsom people only scattered traces have been found, although more are discovered each year.

The Basket Makers first arrived about the start of the Christian era to occupy uplands of present-day New Mexico, Utah, and northern Arizona. These long-headed pioneers used spear throwers and lived in caves, probably also in brush shelters erected in the open. They knew no pottery, but made coiled baskets, fine square-toed sandals of woven cord, and twined yucca-fiber bags with colored decorations. So precious was good textile material that they hacked off their own hair for weaving.

Eventually these enterpris-

ing people either invented pottery making or, more likely, learned it from Mexican neighbors, and made the bow and arrow their principal weapon. They learned to make pit homes, artificial caves, digging out a cellar hole which they lined with mud or stones and roofed with a dome of poles covered with mats, brush, plaster, and earth. A smoke hole pierced the roof center and the room was entered through a tunnel in the side. In such subterranean homes they warded off winter cold.

About A.D. 500 a people shorter in stature invaded the country of the Basket Makers. The newcomers had round heads made even broader by their custom of lashing babies to hard cradleboards, which flattened the backs of their skulls. They wore round-toed sandals, and discovered or brought with them the use of cotton. With the Basket Makers, among whom they apparently settled, these were the ancestors of today's pueblo-dwellers.

At first they lived in circular pit houses

Turquoise Adorns a Zuni

Marked as a man of wealth, he represents the most numerous Pueblo tribe, which dwells near an arm of the Little Colorado River in western New Mexico.

Turquoise to him mirrors water and sky—sheer beauty. His ancestors, in the seven cities Coronado sought, made it into beads, rings, mosaics. Only in this century have Indian artisans mounted it in silver. Feathers plucked from the captive eagle embellish prayer sticks.

much like those of the Basket Makers, but gradually they began to build structures above ground with thick pole-and-plaster walls. Sometimes they joined these dwellings, making a house of several rooms.

In time these people built multi-unit community structures. Slabs of translucent selenite often served as window glass. Ceremonial chambers were circular in form, whereas at present they are usually rectangular.

Their agriculture became more intensive, their ceremonies more elaborate, their arts more specialized and localized as the culture advanced. Its greatest flowering came in the period from about A.D. 1050 to 1400. Early in this era the Pueblos built great apartment dwellings like Pueblo Bonito (page 111) and Chettro Kettle of Chaco Canyon. These are the most impressive structures ever erected by aborigines north of Mexico.

Just as these peaceful agriculturists were achieving their highest advance, warlike enemies appeared— fierce nomads from north and east. For protection many apartment dwellers deserted the open lands to build their pueblos on ledges and high open caves, such as the imposing Cliff Palace and Spruce Tree House of Mesa Verde (page 104).

Archeological evidence of these nomad invaders is scant. Even during the Spanish period they form a shadowy background, always elusive, always hostile to the settled Pueblo peoples. But these were the forebears of the second great group of Southwest Indian tribes. Among them were the Ute, the Kiowa, and the Comanche, who formed a link with the buffalo hunting tribes of the Great Plains; the Navajo, and the Apache, whose warlike exploits extended into fairly recent times under their famous chief Geronimo (page 115).

Fleet Hunters Run Down Rabbits. Prehistoric Hopi, forebears of present Pueblos, stun the nimble prey by hurling boomerang-like sticks. A line of Indians drives jackrabbits toward a net wall raised on open ground. As the trapped quarry frantically seek escape, barefoot runners race in, curved missiles ready. Hunting nets such as this have been found, well preserved, in northern Arizona caves. Similar roundups corralled antelope and turkeys. Then as now, the Hopi also farmed industriously.

Pima Woman Retains the Basket Makers' Skill. Seated in shade before a square adobe village house and domed igloolike hut, a Pima wife weaves willow strips, cattail, and devil's-claw into coiled basketry of ancient design. Chin tattooing enhances her beauty to her husband. He wears his hair even longer than hers, tying it off in a dangling bun. Nearly 2,000 years ago, the Hohokam, ancestors of these *rancheria* peoples, came to Basket Maker land.

PAINTINGS BY W. LANGDON KIHN

Towering Walls Guard the Havasupai, isolated deep in a gorge branching from Grand Canyon. Only two trails thread the sheer red sandstone cliffs, but today the remote tribe boasts telephones! Its 300 members farm hemmed-in garden-land turned green by the beautiful stream flowing through the canyon. From it comes the tribal name, Havasupai, "People of the Blue-green Water." Of old, they migrated in winter to the parched mesa above to hunt and gather pine nuts; now most remain year-round in their village (page 409).

These people are primarily hunters and seed gatherers who live in temporary villages or shelters. Most practice agriculture of sorts, probably learned from the Pueblos, for, despite hostility, the sedentary peoples and the nomads exchanged customs across the years.

Whence these wanderers came, anthropologists still can only guess. Linguistic evidence shows it must have been from afar. Navajo and Apache, for example, speak tongues of far-flung Athapascan stock, traceable to Canada.

No "vanishing Americans," the Navajo, largest of Indian tribes in the United States, number more than when the Spaniards came. Over 75,000, they occupy a huge territory in northeastern Arizona and northwestern New Mexico. With the Apache, they comprise over half the Southwest's present-day Indian population.

Contrasting both to the Pueblos and to the nomads are the tribes living along the Gila and lower Colorado Rivers in southwestern Arizona.

These stem from the same period as the early Pueblos, when another people, the Hohokam, invaded the semi-desert region south and west of the land of the Basket Makers. Like the Basket Makers, they were long-headed. They lived in square houses of poles and brush plastered with mud, and surrounded their villages with adobe walls. Expert farmers, the Hohokam built elaborate irrigation systems which made the desert bloom (page 112).

Just as prehistoric Pueblos

were direct ancestors of the modern Pueblo peoples, so were the Hohokam probable ancestors of present-day Pima, Papago, and other farm-village or *ranchería* tribes. Most speak dialects of Sonoran stock from Mexico, related to Aztec.

These cultural middlemen live, like the nomads, in single-family dwellings. But these are clustered in true villages. Like the Pueblos, they practice agriculture. Domestic crops, however, are supplemented with the nomad's wild plants: the mesquite bean, screw bean, yucca, agave, and the fruit of the giant saguaro cactus.

This two-way influence is also apparent in the Havasupai who, deep in precipitous Havasu Canyon (opposite), in the western end of Grand Canyon National Park, till their fields and live in what is probably the most isolated Indian settlement in the United States.

Until recently the Havasupai moved in winter to the high plateau where firewood is plentiful and where they could gather piñon nuts and hunt deer. Despite the introduction of cottages, they still cling by preference to their Navajo-like hogans (Chapter 20).

These, then, are the three native groups—nomads, village tribes, and Pueblos—that today occupy the Pueblo land of the Southwest. Mutually influenced to a considerable extent, their tribal patterns yet remain quite distinct.

Most dominant culturally, despite numbering only about 20,000 in all, are the Pueblo Indians. They live in 26 towns, most of them near the upper Rio Grande in New Mexico. Here compact communal houses of adobe brick, stone, or clay and rubble crowd together, each consisting of two or more set-back stories. This is the characteristic architecture responsible for the name the conquistadores gave the Indians—*pueblo,* the Spanish word for town.

To the east stand Picuris, Jemez, San Ildefonso, San Juan, Santa Clara, Nambe, Tesuque, Santo Domingo, San Felipe, Santa Ana, Chochiti, Zia, Taos, Sandia, and Isleta.

West of these, but still in the Rio Grande drainage, are the pueblos of Acoma and Laguna. Farther west, on the headwaters of the Little Colorado River, is the pueblo of Zuni.

In northeastern Arizona, also in the drainage of the Little Colorado, stand the seven Hopi villages. In this same group is the pueblo of Hano, settled in early historic times by immigrants from the Rio Grande region.

Despite the cultural homogeneity, no single tongue prevails among the various Pueblo tribes. There are several languages, of wholly different stocks. Zuni and affiliated villages, for instance, have one all their own.

Today, Taos and Zuni are the skyscrapers of Pueblo land. Taos dwellings reach five stories. Each of the five is smaller by the width of a room than the one below it, producing a rectangular terraced pyramid (page 414). At Santa Clara and Jemez, buildings face the four sides of a court, climb in terraces at front, end with a perpendicular wall in the rear. The great ruin in Chaco Canyon in New Mexico (page 111) varies this style by terracing back from a semicircular court.

Sometimes buildings climb away from both sides of a street, as at Acoma. The upper tiers are entered by ladders projecting through holes in the roof, although now side doors are becoming more common. Too, there is a growing tendency to build individual houses, after the European fashion.

Fireplaces usually are built in a corner of the room, and a hood over them carries the smoke to the chimney. In another corner, parallel with the wall, are the slab-lined mealing bins, with their stone metates for grinding corn (page 117). Tortillas are often baked on a stone slab as they were centuries ago (page 120).

From Pueblo Bonito to Zuni Stretches a Ghostly Line

High on the rim of Chaco Canyon in what is now northwestern New Mexico, ancient Pueblo hunters look down upon the fortress city their people built in the desert, centuries before Columbus. Four stories tall at outer wall, its apartments terrace back from an inner court, like a half-cut cheese. Smoke drifts from cooking fires. Ladders jut from roof holes of kivas, where tribal men's societies chant their rites.

Shown here at highest development, Pueblo Bonito shelters more than 1,200 inhabitants in some 800 rooms. Its wealth brings traders from afar. Envious nomad barbarians from the north attack. Eventually they will conquer, and this great communal city will crumble into rubble, covered by windblown sands until archeologists of National Geographic Society expeditions dig it free in the 1920's (Chapter 16).

Pueblo culture, however, survived, absorbing from and changing the nomads who came against it. Zuni, one of 26 modern pueblos, traces its heritage back to the ancient builders. Its rites (below) evoke the spirits of long-dead ancestors. In the famed Zuni Shalako, priests chant beside giant *kachina* images, "Behold us maned with buffaloes' dead manes and beaked with beaks beyond man's memory of birds." By Indian belief, spirits enter the images to honor the dead, provide game for hunters, and bless the hall, here festooned with blankets and skins.

110   PAINTINGS BY W. LANGDON KIHN

The material culture of the Indians has changed much more during American occupation than it did under the Spaniards. Yet, though these communities depend on farming, resistance to the introduction of farm machinery has been marked, because such devices interfere with the basis of traditional ceremonials.

At Isleta the newly erected town council house remained unfinished pending a long-drawn-out controversy as to whether an old-style or tin roof should be used. Eventually advocates of the tin roof won out. Now many houses of the eastern pueblos have tin roofs.

Factory-made stoves have now generally replaced the picturesque earthen dome-shaped oven, an Old World invention borrowed from Mexico during early historic times. Window frames with glass panes are also in general use.

The white man's alcohol, however, has had little effect on pueblo life. The Pueblo Indians were among the earliest advocates of prohibition in this country. Because the governing bodies saw the bad effect of alcohol on their people, most pueblos banned it. While the regulations have now relaxed in many of them, in others, such as Zuni, strict prohibition is still in force.

The standard drink of Pueblo aborigines was *atole*, a thin gruel of cornmeal. Now coffee has become the universal beverage, with bottled carbonated drinks a close second.

Although the potter's wheel was unknown in aboriginal America, early pottery of the Southwest was so good it could hold water indefinitely and be placed directly on the cooking fire.

The art so degenerated after the introduction of cheap metal kitchen utensils that the technically poor ware can be used only for decorative or ritual purposes. But the tourist demand for native

Ancient Engineers Bring Water to the Desert. Stone-age Hohokam carve irrigation canals to turn parched lands along the Gila and Salt Rivers of Arizona green with crops. Village houses, mud plaster over poles and brush, stand behind thick adobe walls, with ladders the only way across. Archeologists found ruins of one city nine miles from the nearest river. Its water flowed through a canal seven feet deep, 30 feet wide at top. Overall, Hohokam canals watered about 200,000 acres. Some have been restored to use today.

Medicine Men Work With Tribal Faith. Navajo "medicine," even today, invokes ancient curing ceremonies (lower left). Sunlight stabs down from the smoke hole in the hogan's roof, illuminating a kneeling woman. While a helper behind feathered prayer sticks shakes his rattle and chants, a masked shaman stalks across a beautifully wrought sand painting. Its curiously elongated figures, drawn in varicolored sands, are mythological beings. The "doctor" touches various symbols, then various parts of the patient's body. When the ritual ends, the sand painting is destroyed. With it, so the Navajo believe, goes the illness.

As corn dancers parade in Tewa pueblo of San Ildefonso (below), clowns caricature the solemn priests. A gray-painted jester cavorts in front of the sacred wand, decorated with feathers, sash, foxskin, and other sacred emblems. A chanting chorus keeps time to a beating tom-tom, an appeal to the gods for bountiful crops. Clowns often take part in Pueblo ceremony. They relieve the ritual's intense seriousness and keep onlookers from growing too sad. They safely break the most rigid taboos and play practical jokes on spectators.

PAINTINGS BY W. LANGDON KIHN

113

art products has sparked a revival, and frequently in artistic form and decoration the modern ware compares favorably with the ancient products.

At Zuni, black, white, and red pigments are used. In Hopi pottery making, yellow and black appear in designs revived from an earlier day. The famous ware of Santa Clara and San Ildefonso (page 117), however, utilizes a new technique, whereby patterns of dull black are produced on a glossy black surface.

Basketry, practiced in the Southwest long before pottery making, is now practically a lost art among the Pueblos, except the Hopi. The best Southwest basket makers of the present are the Pima (page 107) and the Apache.

So also, when machine-woven textiles were brought in by white traders, weaving was virtually abandoned, except in the Hopi and Zuni pueblos and by the Navajo. Of these, the Hopi male weavers are probably the most skillful, while the Navajo women have won greater fame.

The Navajo probably learned weaving from the Pueblos in the early 18th century and made a specialty of it after the introduction of sheep from Mexico. The finest Navajo weaving was done during the 19th century from yarn obtained by unraveling *bayeta*, a woolen trade cloth introduced by the Spaniards. These beautifully woven blankets were usually of two colors in simple broad stripes. The now-rare Navajo bayeta blankets are in demand by collectors.

About 1850, American traders introduced vegetable-dyed yarn imported from Saxony. This eliminated laborious unraveling of textiles for dyed thread, and greatly increased blanket production. When, in the 1870's, the Navajo began to produce rugs instead of ponchos, this spurred the art. About 1880 came brilliant and cheaper aniline-dyed Germantown yarns.

The modern era of Navajo weaving begins after 1890, when traders introduced the aniline dyes that enabled weavers to use native wool and produce rugs cheaper. As a result, Navajo weaving has become a major asset to the tribe's economy.

Of Navajo blankets the question is often asked, "What does this design mean?" Despite much talk of symbolism, and the explanations many an enterprising native artisan will obligingly give a prospective customer, the answer generally should be "Nothing." One might as well ask the meaning of designs on wallpaper or a patchwork quilt.

True, identifying names are given to certain designs or design elements, but the Indian potter, weaver, or jeweler, except where ritual objects are concerned, thinks of the decorative value of his creation, not of any secret meaning.

In the old days rarely was any pattern other than plain stripes used, with no significance apart from decorations intended. Modern times have brought complex and bizarre figures, many introduced by traders. Even designs from sand paintings (page 112) are used, an unthinkable heresy to Navajo priests of old. It is not even uncommon to see on a beautifully woven rug the words "Ivory Soap" or "Kleenex," copied from a cardboard box!

Designs have been borrowed, too, in silver working, another alien craft that has taken root among the Navajo. Except for a few scattered copper objects received in trade from Mexico, the Indian tribes of Pueblo land formerly knew nothing of metals or metalworking.

Finally, about the middle of the 19th century, a Mexican silversmith entered Navajo country. Soon the craft spread. Along with borrowed patterns, the first silver used by the Navajo consisted of coins obtained from Americans. Later, Mexican pesos—of a purer grade of silver and hence easier to work—were used exclusively. From these beginnings the Navajo have developed an art that has brought them world fame (page 417).

The dramatic topography of the Southwest had a profound effect upon the religious ideology of the tribes who made the region their home. It is a land of tremendous distances, of fantastic formations, of red cliffs and square-cut buttes.

The clear air is occasionally invaded by black storm clouds, the clamor of thunder, and the quick stab of lightning. The deep blue of the sky is painted at dawn and at sunset with colors which defy the brush of the painter.

As all this appeals to the modern artist and poet, so did it stimulate the imagination and poetic instincts of the Indian. In the rising thunderclouds he saw the advancing forms of the *kachinas*, bearing rain for his cornfield. In the rumble of the thunder he heard the beating of the wings of a mythical bird; the whirlwind was a wandering spirit.

To the Pueblo Indian, his people lived in the center of the universe. All nature was created for him and explained in rich mythology. His complete belief produced a deep affection for those deities who made life pleasant for him, particularly those directly concerned with his sustenance: the corn mother, the squash maidens, the rain gods who brought life-giving moisture, the hunting gods who helped him find game. He willingly performed lengthy ceremonies to please them.

PAINTING BY W. LANGDON KIHN

Geronimo, Dread Apache Raider, led the rebel Chiricahua off an Arizona reservation in 1881. For five years he struck white settlements, killed, burned, then vanished, often into Mexico's Sierra Madre. His surrender to General Nelson Miles ended the U.S. Army's most famous Indian hunt. In 1909, at 80, he died in Oklahoma, his name destined to be an American paratroop cry.

Snake Dancers, Potters, Weavers Characterize Pueblo Life Old and New

Rattlesnake gripped in teeth, a Hopi Snake Society dancer in full paint and regalia stamps across the ceremonial court at Walpi (below). A second priest distracts the reptile with feather whip, while the team's third member stoops to pick up another rattler. Hopi believe the venomous snakes, set free, will carry news of the ritual to pleased rain gods. Cloudbursts often follow!

At San Ildefonso (right) smoke billows from hot ashes as two women tong hand-shaped pottery from the primitive firing hearth. The craft is age-old, but the two-tone black decorative technique is new, developed here and at Santa Clara.

Hopi men, master Pueblo weavers, produce belts and sashes on an old-style lap loom (bottom right). The wife bends patiently, grinding corn meal. Kachina doll hangs beside deerskin, bringing luck to a dwelling differing little from Coronado's day. Basket of corn meal rests beside water jar in the wall niche.

116

Most conspicuous among the Pueblos is the kachina cult, concerned primarily with the control of weather, particularly the bringing of rain. The kachinas are supernatural beings, said to have been created at the time the first ancestors of man emerged from the underworld. Others say they represent spirits of man's early ancestors, residing in the west in some prominent mountain.

There are many varieties of kachina, each having its own curious features and costume and each concerned with some aspect of nature connected with the health and welfare of man.

The religion of the Indian is intimate and omnipresent. He feels himself as much a part of the supernatural world as are the nature gods of his own creation. No crisis of life, no activity affecting the welfare of individual or tribe is too trivial to have its place in religion, its special rite.

Ceremony attends the individual at birth, at marriage, during sickness, and at death. It precedes planting and harvest. War expeditions, journeys—all are fitted into the religious pattern. Nothing is haphazard, nothing left to fate.

The major part of a ritual is held in secrecy in the underground ceremonial chamber, or *kiva,* with only the initiated present. Many rites, often lasting several days, end in public performances.

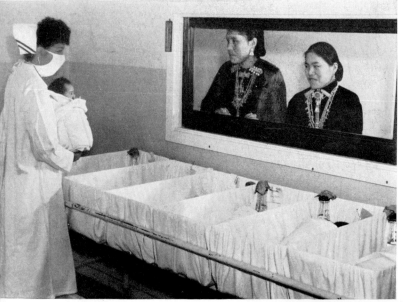

JERRY MC LAIN

In the Indian's poetic mind the kiva represents the universe, a sort of primitive planetarium. The roof and walls are the firmament, the floor is the earth. Around the walls are benches for members of the secret society, and beyond these are imaginary "cloud seats" where the gods watch ceremonies in their honor.

In the center of the floor a small hole represents the *sipapu,* the sacred place where emerged the ancestral twins from whom all mankind descended. Near

Navajo Nursery in an up-to-date Indian hospital is a far cry indeed from the ancient cradleboard (right). Not entirely forgotten, such tight-lashed conveyances of Indian offspring once uniformly flattened the backs of round Pueblo heads. Unlike white men's children, virtually all Indian babies are born with plentiful straight black hair.

H. ARMSTRONG ROBERTS

Sand-painted Circle Will Spirit Away Boy's Illness, so Navajo believe. The medicine man gestures swiftly; awestruck patient hides face behind bony knee. Through the strange symbols of colored sand and meal the priest summons forth healing spirits to remove the foreign substance in the sufferer's body, introduced perhaps by some witch. Itchings and skin diseases are considered by the Navajo's Pueblo neighbors to be malignant acts of the ant spirit. Thus, at Acoma, one prominent symbol is the horned toad, eater of ants. Pueblo sand paintings and curing rites resemble those of the Navajo. Few white men may witness these ceremonies, photographers almost never.

this is a larger opening covered with a plank, upon which the dancers stamp to signal denizens of the underworld that a ceremony is under way.

Masks and other sacred paraphernalia must be meticulously cared for between ceremonies by special keepers, lest ill luck and death descend on the village. Because of this fear Pueblo Indians are reluctant to part with ritual objects. Duplicates can be made and sold, however, since they acquire power only through elaborate ceremony.

An Acoma Indian described to me, with great emotion, the passing of the Scalp Society, formerly one of the most important in the pueblo. To be eligible for membership, an Acoma had to kill an enemy in combat and take his scalp.

American occupation made scalp-lifting impossible. Finally only a single aged member remained to care for the sacred materials. The headmen met in grave conference. Disaster threatened the community should the old man die, leaving the society's objects untended. They decided the society itself must be brought to an end before too late.

Thereupon the old man, carefully purifying himself, spent days in the kiva praying, making offerings, devitalizing the sacred masks and other objects of the ancient Scalp Society.

At last, the task completed, the aged scalp priest in the early morning hours carried the emasculated equipment of his beloved society up through the door of the kiva where it had been stored since before the conquistadores. All other villagers stayed hidden indoors.

Three times he descended from the rock with portions of his precious load, the last time just as the rising sun cast its ruddy hue on the summit of the Enchanted Mesa to the north. Then, bearing his burden to a point in the desert known only to himself, he buried all beneath the sands.

The sun was well above the horizon when he wearily climbed the age-old rock to enter the apparently deserted city. For him this was the end—he was unfrocked by his own will that his people might go on.

As the dwellers reappeared from their doorways and the unnatural silence ended, the old priest descended the ladder into the kiva. But now all was changed.

Until this moment he had always sat in the presence of the gods. He looked at the "cloud seats" around the painted walls. He felt nothing there. The kiva was empty.

Undoubtedly the most famous of all North American ceremonies is the Hopi Snake Dance, held in alternate years at most Hopi villages. For nine days, the Antelope Society and the Snake Society pray and dance for rain.

The dance at Walpi is considered most authentic. Certainly it is most colorful. At Walpi the snakes are gripped solely by the mouths of the celebrants, no hands, and the snake is held as near the middle as possible to allow its head more freedom of movement (page 116).

Ancient priests probably would roll over in their graves if they were to see the ceremony's modern setting. Visitors converge on the mesa. Indian vendors sell soda pop and chewing gum. Native policemen busily impound cameras and lay down rules to spectators. So famed has the dance become that it is scarcely possible to crowd everyone in.

Snakes are there, ready in ceremonial

Maize, Mainstay of Pueblo Life

With pronged wooden digging stick, a prehistoric Acoma farmer (above) cultivates his sun-baked field. Squash grows among the cornstalks. Behind rises the famous Rock of Acoma, a sandstone mesa 357 feet above the surrounding plain. Built upon it is Sky Village, oldest continually occupied settlement in the United States. This same tribe was raising corn, squash, and beans before the coming of the Spaniards, who introduced other crops, cattle and sheep.

Laguna breadmakers (left) turn blue cornmeal dough into *piki*, crisp, wafer-thin, and palatable as the tortillas of Mexican meals. The women feed their stove dry mesquite sticks. They then spread a thin paste of cornmeal and water, with a dash of wood-ash lye, over the hot stone slab. Indians of the Southwest concoct many different dishes of this basic bread, rolling it around meat, nuts, beans, and chili peppers. Today most use metal tops on their stoves. Except for the women's silver-mounted jewelry, this scene could be prehistoric.

PAINTINGS BY W. LANGDON KIHN

crocks in the kiva. Days before, members of the Snake Society go out in pairs to gather them, the first day to the north, the second day to the west, the third to the south, the fourth to the east. Most are rattlesnakes.

On the eighth day the first dance is held outside the kiva. On the ninth day the snakes are brought out to a bower on the plaza. Then the priests, first of the Antelope and then of the Snake Societies, come from their kivas and parade four times around, stamping a foot drum each time to notify the gods below that the ceremony has begun. The priests line up facing each other.

Three at a time, Snake Society priests go to the bower. One receives a snake, grasps it in his teeth. He dances down the plaza, while the second celebrant distracts the snake with a feather whip. Then the snake is dropped, to be picked up by the third priest. As each dancer drops his snake, he returns to the bower for another, and repeats the performance.

Spectators are ignored, unless it is to lash out at them with a snake to move them back, or in anger at one's wary kick at a loose snake.

Finally, when all the snakes have been danced with, the chief Snake priest pours cornmeal in the outline of a six-segmented circle, representing the four corners of the world, its zenith, and its nadir. The snakes are thrown into the circle, and women scatter more cornmeal on them.

Then, at a signal, the Snake priests rush in and with each hand grasp as many snakes as they can hold. With squirming burdens, they run from the pueblo down to the plain below, where the snakes are carried toward the four quarters of the compass and set free as messengers to bear news of the ceremony to the rain gods.

Why are the priests not bitten? The Hopi are neither immune, nor have the fangs or poison glands been removed. Chief secret of the dangerous dance is the Indians' skill in handling and distracting the snakes. Too, for several preceding days the snakes have been handled; this takes the edge off their aggressiveness. In the kivas, the snakes are allowed to strike, thus draining their venom. Dancers are sometimes bitten, but I have never known of serious results.

The ceremonial life of the village-dwelling tribes is less elaborate than that of the Pueblos. Their religious ideas center on the interpretation of dreams, particularly

Nomad and Pueblo Share a Starkly Beautiful Land

Nature's palette paints a vivid Southwestern scene as the Navajo sheepherder (above) pauses to let his flock browse high above the winding river. Sheep adopted from Spanish *rancheros* in the 18th century helped the Navajo wanderer wrest a living from his harsh, yet radiant land. Sheepherding gave rise to the Navajo weaving industry. Now atomic-age wealth in oil and uranium further bolsters the tribal economy.

Ornate silverwork adorns the Zuni women (left), who display "squash blossom" necklaces, common in Pueblo land. Coming first from Spanish Mexico, these actually represent pomegranates, a fruit early Indians had never seen. Circular or oval "concha" silver ornaments mounting native turquoise are also Zuni designs copied from the Navajo, who knew no metal craft before the mid-19th century. Zuni women have worn the same hand-woven black dress since pre-Columbian days.

PAINTINGS BY W. LANGDON KIHN

122

among such western tribes as the Yuma, Cocopa, and Mojave.

All Yuman tribes cremate the dead, thus releasing the spirit, otherwise believed to remain in the body. When an individual died in a house, the house and all his personal property were burned.

The cremation, held in the open, presents a wild, barbaric scene. As the flames of the funeral pyre rise, mourners wail and cry, tear their hair and scratch their faces. Women rip off their dresses and throw them in the flames. Others throw in offerings, often money, asking the departing spirit to take these to their own dead relatives and friends. Mourners then fast for four days.

Several village tribes hold a strange memorial service for the dead. The annual *Károk* of the Yuma climaxes in the public burning of images of the dead, also their personal effects. The names of the dead are never again spoken.

Today the white man's iron rails bisect the great American Southwest. Automobiles roar across the land on arrow-straight roads. But behind these narrow ribbons the great canyons remain unchanged from the days of the Basket Makers. Thunderheads rise with the same magnificence they displayed when Pueblo Bonito was in flower. The machine age has come to the desert, but it has touched the Indian more lightly than many realize.

The rain priests still make their elaborate calculations; the masked dancers perform their age-old ceremonies. When the rainstorm follows, soaking the parched cornfields, the Indian, gazing beyond the gasoline haze of the highway, offers quiet thanks, serene in the knowledge that above, below, and in the four world quarters his own gods still rule.

123

PAINTING BY W. LANGDON KIHN

Chief Joseph, the Xenophon of American Indians, led his Nez Percé warriors, women, and children through the Northwest in a 1,000-mile march comparable to the ancient Greek's retreat of the Ten Thousand. With U.S. troops ahead, behind, on his flank, this "greatest of Indian strategists" outfought them several times, finally was cut off, forced to surrender only 50 miles from Canada. The "Pierced Noses" lived in the Snake and Columbia River basins in present Idaho, Oregon, Washington.

CHAPTER 5

INDIANS OF THE FAR WEST

BETWEEN THE WASATCH RANGE of Utah and the foothills of the Sierra Nevada the traveler gazes down from his high-flying plane upon what seems to many a panorama of complete desolation —the Great American Desert.

Mile after mile of saline flats and sagebrush plains unfolds west of Great Salt Lake, where a century ago hundreds of covered wagon pioneers left their bones and those of their oxen to whiten along torturing trails.

The Great Basin was an implacable enemy to white men then. Even now, though crossed by railroads, airlines, and highways, much of it seems unfit for man or beast. Yet from this forbidding, inhospitable waste, before the white man's arrival, some 10,000 Indians wrested a living and in their way prospered.

They did this without agriculture, or tools save crude implements fashioned from sticks and stones, without even adequate clothing or shelter from the severe cold of winter or summer's blazing heat. Rarely in human annals can be found as striking an example of man's adapting to an unfriendly environment.

In long-past geologic ages the Great Basin was a region of lakes and lush forests. And so it was when man first entered the scene, we have learned through scattered excavations in caves and near old lake terraces. Now carbon-14 dating at Lewisville, Texas, suggests an antiquity for aboriginal Americans of 35,000 B.C. and beyond.

With passing centuries rainfall became scanty, winters extremely cold, summers hot. Food grew scarce through the parched and withered land. The Indian had to utilize every form of it he could get. Big game was scarce. Even bison, which had ranged most of Utah and northern Nevada until A.D. 1500, had retreated from the Great Basin.

Forests gone, the Indian used sagebrush to make rude shelters, often merely roofless semicircles, which served as windbreaks and gave only scant protection against rain and snow.

White travelers who had encountered the colorful Plains and Pueblo tribes expressed scorn for Indians of the Great Basin, who belong almost exclusively to one linguistic stock, the Shoshonean. Exaggerated descriptions pictured them as living at the level of animals, always half starved, hibernating without food like bears in caves, whence they emerged in the spring, crawling on hands and knees to eat grass.

To the disgust of early observers the Shoshoni ate crickets, lizards, snakes, gophers, and roots. However, since one's diet is largely a matter of custom, a Shoshoni might be just as annoyed at seeing a white man eat crab or lobster.

Nuts of the pine tree, or piñon, were the basic food. In southern areas, seeds of the mesquite bean, ground into flour, and the agave or century plant, roasted in stone-lined pits, also were favored.

Skillful basket weavers, the Great Basin tribes collected roots and the seeds of wild rye and other grasses in large conical carrying baskets and processed them in basketry trays (page 131).

Food collecting was often a community effort. When Mormon crickets or long-horn grasshoppers swarmed, the Indians encircled an area with converging fire. The singed insects accumulated in enormous piles in the center.

Group drives caught the abundant jack rabbits, good for food, and whose skins made winter robes. Nets of twisted grass were strung in a quarter-mile arc. Entire families spread out in a line, beat the brush and drove the rabbits before them into the barrier. The fast and wary antelope also were corralled and dispatched with bow and arrow.

The quest for food so preoccupied Great Basin tribes, living in widely scattered groups, that they had little time for dances or courtship. Most marriages resulted when families gathered at rare intervals to sing, dance, and gamble for a week

White Deerskins, Yellow Water Lilies, Gay Beads Marked Indian Life on Pacific Slopes

Hupa tribesmen (right) usher in the new year in the Trinity River Valley of northwest California by parading treasured albino deerskins on high poles. Chief dancers in the 10-day September ritual wear crowns of sea-lion tusks, carry sacred obsidian knives. Shell beads adorn dancers' necks; headdresses are of wolf pelt. Hupa hunters masked man odor by bathing and smoke, got within easy bowshot of game, disguised as deer. So well did they play the part that panthers sometimes pounced on them.

Oregon's Klamath Indians (below) harvest seedpods of the yellow water lily in long dugout canoes, sun-dry, pound, and winnow them into *wokas*, a highly prized food. The supply was enormous; Klamath Marsh alone had 15 square miles of solid water-lily growth. The hardy Klamath never took the warpath against whites, but raided other tribes for female slaves.

A Yakima girl (lower right) rides in beaded finery behind the high, decorated pommel of a Spanish-type saddle. Otterskins wrap her long braids; beaded cape is elkskin, her earrings are shell. The Yakima lived along the Columbia, Yakima, and Wenatchee Rivers in Washington.

PAINTINGS BY W. LANGDON KIHN

or two when food was plentiful. Since the two sexes were not always equal in number, a man might have two or more wives, a woman more than one husband. Taking sisters or brothers as plural spouses was considered a wise precaution against jealousy.

Not until about 1840 did white immigration into the Far West begin in earnest. Starting with caravans on the Oregon Trail, and the Mormon settlements around Great Salt Lake, it reached its peak in the California gold rush. The most direct routes traversed the heart of the Great Basin.

Tens of thousands of gold seekers crossed the desert during the rush years. Hollow-cheeked and red-eyed from heat and acrid dust, they cursed this "useless" country, scorned the "Diggers," as they contemptuously called the root-gathering natives. But when rich lodes of gold and silver were struck in western Nevada, miners stampeded back across the Sierras into the Basin.

With recently acquired horses and guns the Indians, particularly the Ute, put up stern resistance for a while. Then in 1869 the golden spike driven at Promontory Point, Utah, joined the last sections of the transcontinental railroad. Ranchers came. Grazing livestock reduced the edible plants. White settlers began cutting down for fuel the piñon trees, the red man's most important source of food. The aborigines had lost their sun-scorched kingdom.

In this period there grew to manhood in Mason Valley, Nevada, a Paiute of lowly origin who became known as Wovoka, "the Cutter." He never left his little native valley. Although industrious and of good character, he was distin-

Chumash Mariners Return from Sea. Bearskin-clad captain orders his craft carried above reach of tide or storm along California's Santa Barbara coast. With flint tools and patient skill, Chumash tribesmen built the New World's only planked canoes. Lacking big trees for dugouts, they split planks from driftwood. These they shaped and smoothed. Along the edges they drilled holes, "sewed" the planks together with fiber cords, calked the seams with asphalt. Keel, endposts, and a thwart amidships formed the frame; shells and paint gave decoration. Double-bladed paddles propelled the light craft, 12 to 25 feet in length, carrying 2 to 13 fishermen. Sail power was unknown to pre-Columbian Indians of North America.

Indian Nets Chinook from the Churning Columbia. Salmon, migrating upriver to spawn and die, leap up the thundering green-white curtain of Celilo Falls. Braced on ancestral fishing stand, clad only in breechclout, this Indian scoops up fish just as modern Indians in dungarees and crew shirts were later to do, by treaty right, from similar platforms at the same site. Lewis and Clark in 1805 portaged around the falls, noted stacks of salmon "neatly preserved." Salmon was the Columbia River Indians' chief food and commodity of trade.

Now reservoir waters backed up by the new Dalles Dam will bury Celilo Falls. The U.S. Government is paying the Warm Springs, Celilo, and Yakima tribes $23,700,000 for the loss of their traditional fishing grounds.

PAINTINGS BY W. LANGDON KIHN

guished neither in intellect nor aggressiveness. Yet in his early thirties he became one of the most influential Indians in North America. From Gulf of Mexico to Canadian border pilgrims came to his little dome-shaped tule hut. Wovoka was originator and prophet of the Ghost Dance movement, which excited great unrest among Western tribes.

About 1888 Wovoka, already a medicine man of repute, had his great revelation. While he lay ill with fever, an eclipse of the sun awed the Indians. Wovoka believed that his soul had traveled to the spirit world and there consulted with the Indian god who revealed to him that the Indians would regain their ancient inheritance and be rejoined by departed relatives and friends.

Wovoka said he was given a set of songs and dances for the Indians to practice to ready themselves for the great day of deliverance. He attributed no supernatural powers to himself, but considered that he had been chosen as prophet to herald the coming restoration.

The new movement spread like wildfire from Nevada to tribes east of the Rockies, and culminated in the killing of Sitting Bull and the massacre at Wounded Knee (South Dakota) in 1890.

Among the American Indians many such messianic movements arose in the wake of white domination, including the great Pontiac Conspiracy (1763–65).

First to describe aboriginal life in the Plateau area north of the Great Basin were Lewis and Clark, who arrived at the headwaters of the Missouri in 1805. There they noted many traits of buffalo-hunting Plains tribes among the northeastern Shoshoni, who had adopted the tepee, the rawhide container, and danced the characteristic Sun Dance.

Obtaining horses from the Shoshoni, Lewis and Clark pushed on through western Montana territory of the Flatheads. The name of this Salishan tribe was bestowed, not because they de-

formed their heads, but because, unlike their neighbors to the west, they left their skulls as Nature formed them—flat on top. Living on fish and game, the Flatheads built their houses underground, roofed with cedar-bark mats laid over poles and covered with earth.

Lewis and Clark found similar men's and women's pit houses among the Nez Percé, accommodating from 10 to 15 persons each, and community dwellings housing as many as 50 families. Each village had a large ceremonial or dance house.

The semi-dugout house in various forms appeared among tribes farther west—the Wallawalla, the Palus, the Umatilla, the Tenino, the Yakima (page 127), and the Klikitat. Typical of the Northwest, it extended well into California.

The Nez Percé tribes, occupying the valleys of the Snake River and the Columbia as far as The Dalles, were so named because French trappers reported that tribes in the vicinity pierced the nose to receive a shell ornament. The Nez Percé, so far as is now known, were never given to the practice!

They were courageous fighters. Rebelling at an order restricting them to a small reservation in Idaho, Chief Joseph, renowned among American Indian leaders (page 124), won several victories over United States troops, then led his people in 1877 in a masterful 1,000-mile retreat through Idaho and Montana.

Joseph's speech at the time of his surrender expresses the hopelessness that came to tribe after tribe as they retreated before the inexorable tide of the white man's advance.

"I am tired of fighting," he said. "Our chiefs are killed. Looking Glass is dead. Toohulhulsote is dead. The old men are all dead. It is the young men who say yes or no. He who led the young men is dead. It is cold and we have no blankets. The little children are freezing to death.

Paiute Subsist on a Lean Land. Roaming the arid reaches of the Great Basin, the Paiute lived a primitive existence unchanged for centuries. As these women are doing, they gathered and ground wild seeds into meal. Their few utensils, even water containers and cooking vessels, were baskets. Men kindle fire by friction before the crude brush hut. Child's hooded cradle lies in right foreground.

My people, some of them, have run away to the hills and have no blankets, no food. No one knows where they are —perhaps freezing to death. I want to have time to look for my children and see how many of them I can find. Maybe I shall find them among the dead.

"Hear me, my chiefs. I am tired. My heart is sick and sad. From where the sun now stands I will fight no more forever."

Unlike the forest-dotted, low-lying region east of the Mississippi, the Far West is a land of tremendous topographic diversity. Mount Whitney and Death Valley, highest and lowest points in the United States, are within sight of each other. Burning sands give way to verdant meadow and towering evergreen forest.

The Indians there were as diversified as the setting, whose rugged barriers circumscribed their movements.

Tribes living in the Columbia River region had, in their salmon runs, better food sources than tribes of the inhospitable Great Basin (page 128). Best off from the standpoint of abundant natural resources and genial climate were tribes dwelling between the Sierra Nevada-Cascade Range and the Pacific Coast.

Here, in one of the most complex ethnological areas in the New World, tribes of two chief linguistic stocks, Hokan and Penutian, lived under nearly perfect conditions for primitive man. Deer, elk, rabbits, and squirrels abounded. Marshes and lakes teemed with waterfowl, rivers and ocean with fish, and along the coast there were clams, mussels, abalones, crabs, and crayfish.

Tribes of extreme southern California—the Mohave, the Yuma, the Kamia, and the Diegueño—learned from tribes of northern Mexico and Pueblo tribes of the Southwest how to grow maize, beans, squash, and to make good pottery. Yet in the "Promised Land" of central California, now one of the world's most productive regions, agriculture was as unknown as famine.

Acorns were the Indian staff of life. These were gathered in the fall, ground and leached, then made into a thick soup cooked by hot stones dropped into a tight-woven basket.

In keeping with the mild climate, clothing was simple. Only in cold weather did the men wear as much as a skin wrapped around the hips. Women wore double aprons of fringed buckskin, shredded bark, grass, or fiber cordage: a small apron suspended from the waist in front, a larger one behind. As footwear, central tribes wore deerskin socks; southern tribes, sandals of twisted agave fiber.

California tribes produced no cloth. The nearest approaches to it were finger-woven fiber bags and twined

Indian Converts Dance Before Spanish Mission

Now extinct, the Costanoan tribe lived along the California coast from Monterey to the Golden Gate. They were early converts of the Mission of St. Francis, which gave the city of San Francisco its name. The original chapel founded by Spanish priests in 1776 still stands within the city, well-preserved. It is known today as Mission Dolores.

An artist with Russia's first round-the-world expedition, which touched here in 1805, sketched the scene which Mr. Kihn painted above. Indians, after Sunday Mass, dance in ancient tribal fashion while two friars look on. Vulture feathers made the dark ceremonial bonnets worn by the dancers.

robes made of twisted rabbitskin strips. As basket weavers, however, these tribes were without peer.

Basket weaving reached its peak among the Pomo, who produced the finest feathered baskets and practiced a wide variety of weaving techniques. The peace-loving Pomo were also chief minters for a large area, making currency from clamshells and magnesite. They counted, using a unit of 100 fours.

Many California tribes had hereditary chiefs. More powerful still were the medicine men. Some specialists in the cure and prevention of snake bite handled live rattlesnakes in their ceremonies. The bear doctor was feared, for he had the power to kill enemies by turning himself into a grizzly bear.

As among Indian tribes in general, the medicine man claimed his power from a vision, produced by fasting or drugs, in which he met and conversed with some animal who taught him how to contact the spirit world. His cure often was to suck out of the patient the invading object causing the disease. This might be a piece of flint, a live lizard, or a spider. He could cause death just as well, it was believed, by mixing poison with some part of his intended victim, such as a hair or a nail paring.

An old Indian woman of my acquaintance had a bag filled with toenail and fingernail parings she had saved all her life, fearing lest they fall into the hands of a person who might harm her.

The California Indians first became known to the white man in 1542 when Juan Rodríguez Cabrillo sailed among the channel islands and along the Santa Barbara coast. There he encountered the Chumash Indians, in many respects the most advanced of California's tribes.

Villages in this, the most densely populated section of California, consisted of dome-shaped communal houses accommodating 40 or 50 persons. Built of willow poles covered with tule mats, these large circular dwellings were unique in two respects. They were partitioned into rooms, and in these rooms were platform beds supported on posts.

Fine basket weavers and skillful wood carvers, the Chumash also made beautifully formed and polished pots and animal, bird, and fish carvings in soapstone. Most remarkable were their planked ocean-going canoes (page 129).

California Indians farther north were first described by Francis Fletcher, chaplain of Sir Francis Drake's *Golden*

Hind, which put in north of San Francisco in 1579. These were undoubtedly the coastal Miwok.

The natives received the Englishmen with elaborate ceremonies and loud wailings. The women tore out their hair and lacerated their bodies until they were covered with blood. Drake was crowned with an elaborate feather crown; yards of shell beads were placed around his neck. The puzzled Englishmen did not realize that the Indians considered them ancestors returned from the dead.

The first Franciscan mission in California was founded at San Diego in 1769. By 1823, twenty other missions stood north along the coast to beyond San Francisco. The Indians met the priests

Paiute Prophet Wovoka Spellbinds His People. In the campfire's eerie light, chanting men and women, wild eyes riveted on the figure at center, circle slowly, keeping time to ritual songs taught them by the prophet. Frenzy mounts. Swaying dancers crumple to the ground, sprawl in prolonged trances. Devotees ready themselves to be delivered from bonds, restored to their heritage, reunited with loved ones. Stemming from Wovoka's fevered revelation of 1888, the cult spread swiftly from tribe to tribe. Its message of hope fired deep longings of the Indians, defeated, confined to reservations, their culture, their ancestral way of life gone. It triggered the Sioux uprising of 1890.

PAINTINGS BY W. LANGDON KIHN

"Big Heads" Dance to Save the Earth. Arrayed in savage splendor, secret cult members meet before their round house for one of a vital series of ceremonies held October to May. They believed the world would disintegrate if dances ceased. This cult, originating among southern Wintun Indians, flourished in central California, and took the name of the Kuksu, or "Big Head," Dance. Pincushion-like headdresses measure four feet across; feathers or poppies tip the slender rods. Dancers carry flag, bird-bone whistle, magic staff, gourd rattle, and bow and deer-head quiver. Stamping on a foot drum, they will perform inside the ceremonial lodge. Boys became cult novices at an early age.

in peace, were forcibly converted to Christianity, made dependents of the missions (page 133), and held there by Spanish troops from near-by presidios. Discipline and strange tasks as well as the new religion drastically changed their lives.

In 1834 the Mexican Government took over the missions, making token provision for tribes settled around them. But the Indians had already lost the self-assurance that went with their own culture and had not learned to adapt to the new. Their health and spirits had begun to fail. They soon lost their restored lands, their numbers fell, and the mis-

sion tribes were on the way to extinction.

The 1849 gold rush concentrated in the north and along the Sierras where the missions had not penetrated. In early gold-rush days the Indians' lot was hard. Miners hunted them like wild game for sport. The Modoc, the Shasta, and other of the more warlike tribes resisted, but opposition was short-lived (page 18).

Following the mining came the State's amazing agricultural development. As the white population increased, many tribes became extinct; of others only a handful of survivors remains.

To white men California is a paradise gained. To the Indians, a paradise lost.

Memories of Past Days' Glory Show in This Niska Chief's Face as he wears the carved totem of his clan. A cannery worker in modern-day British Columbia, he poses in old-time regalia, holding dyed-feather wands, the eagle of his mythological origin crowning his head. Denim work shirt peeks from under blue wool blanket adorned with red-flannel design, rows of pearl buttons, wisps of swan's-down.

CHAPTER 6

INDIANS OF THE NORTH PACIFIC COAST

MOST ARISTOCRATIC of all Indians north of Mexico were the tribes which dwelt on our wild and beautiful North Pacific coast. Theirs was a civilization rivaled, above the Rio Grande, only by the Pueblo Indians of Arizona and New Mexico.

Their realism in dance and impersonation was matched by the skill of those who designed the masks and costumes. With their famous totem poles, Northwest Coast carvers and painters produced what many modern critics consider the finest art work ever developed by the American Indian.

Their art found further expression in the skillful weaving of baskets and blankets, stonework, and in the working of native copper and, later, silver. Yet of two developments usually considered as signs of an advanced culture—agriculture and pottery making—they had neither.

Unlike the vast majority of their North American kinsmen, these tribes did not develop democracy. Rather, they set much store by wealth, family connections, and possessing slaves. Social-climbing and crushing one's rivals in wealth and prestige became prime goals. In their celebrated *potlatch* ceremonies they carried "keeping up with the Joneses" to fantastic extremes.

Interestingly, the great impetus to this late-flowering culture came from the white man. In prehistoric times the amount of property a man could accumulate limited his ability to advance his status. But with the coming of the white man's fur trade and steel tools, the Indian's rather simple social system became greatly elaborated.

Like the introduction of the gun among Eastern Woodlands tribes, and the horse to the Plains, the fur-trade wealth pouring into the Pacific Northwest brought into high relief already existing cultural traits. Yet nowhere else did white influence have such spectacular effect. From Puget Sound to the Copper River Delta in southern Alaska, Indian culture burgeoned like the flare of a skyrocket before finally spluttering out.

Who were these fascinating tribes? Northernmost was the Tlingit, who came into contact with the Eskimo and the Ahtena Indians. Visited by Russians in 1741, they were the first Northwest Indians to encounter European civilization.

Next came the Haida, who extended from southern Prince of Wales Island down through the Queen Charlotte Islands; and the Tsimshian, who lived in the basins of the Nass and Skeena Rivers.

South of the Skeena River to the northern coast of Vancouver Island dwelt the Kwakiutl, whose territory was almost split in two by a Salishan tribe, the Bellacoola, who lived along Dean Channel and the Bella Coola River.

Southernmost tribe was the Nootka,

In the Frog Clan's Carved and Painted House, Tlingit Spin and Weave

While her companion rolls mountain goats' hair into thread, the weaver copies designs from the pattern board to her right. Unseen warp is of cedar-bark threads. On this simple crossbar "loom," without using shuttle, heddle, batten, or other such aid, Chilkat Tlingit produced masterpieces of finger weaving. A finished example is draped over the chief. Festive cedar-bark collar is worn by man at right. Drab trade goods supplanted the gay Chilkat blanket, but its weaving has been revived among this southeastern Alaska tribe.

settled along the deep-indented west coast of Vancouver Island.

Heavy rainfall and the tempering climatic influence of the Japan Current characterize the region. Forests of gigantic evergreen trees mantle rugged mountains that rise abruptly from the sea and march inland in an almost unbroken succession of ranges to the Rocky Mountains. A jagged chain of islands, separated by a maze of sea channels, skirts the entire coast.

In this crumpled realm of forest, mountain, and ocean, these warlike tribes, among the few in North America to wear body armor, jealously kept their independence and spoke unrelated languages. Yet their homeland constituted one of the most distinct cultural areas in North America (group area map, page 24). Their influence extended as far north and west as the Aleutians, as

far east as the Mackenzie River, and as far south as California.

Theirs was a maritime culture. Villages hugged the seacoast or main waterways, where the sea pushes fingers far into the mountains in sunken valleys, or fiords, and the great rivers cut their way through the barrier which isolates the coastal region from the interior. Fish and whales were the buffalo of Northwest tribes; seaweed, roots, and berries their maize; the gigantic ocean-going cedar canoe their horse.

Basic unit of exchange was the woolen trade blanket. The value of any object was expressed in blankets. In earlier times blankets of sea-otter fur were apparently used, but the complex financial system of these wealth-minded Indians probably did not develop until after the advent of the trade blanket.

For high-denomination bank notes, the Indians used curious large shield-shaped plaques of copper, painted and engraved, whose value spiraled higher and higher through sale and resale.

Aleut Women Weave Watertight Baskets, Split Strands with Fingernails

Beside the weaver, a tub of water keeps straw moist. Bearded man descends notched log ladder, of a kind used by Siberian tribes. Entrance to this barabara, or Asia-type pit house, was through a roof hole. Roof was sod over dry grass supported by driftwood poles. In this typical Aleutian Islands community house, each family had its matted-off quarters. As many as 150 people lived in a single underground dwelling up to 240 feet long, heated and lighted with seal- or whale-oil lamps of stone. Modern Aleuts live in frame houses.

PAINTINGS BY W. LANGDON KIHN

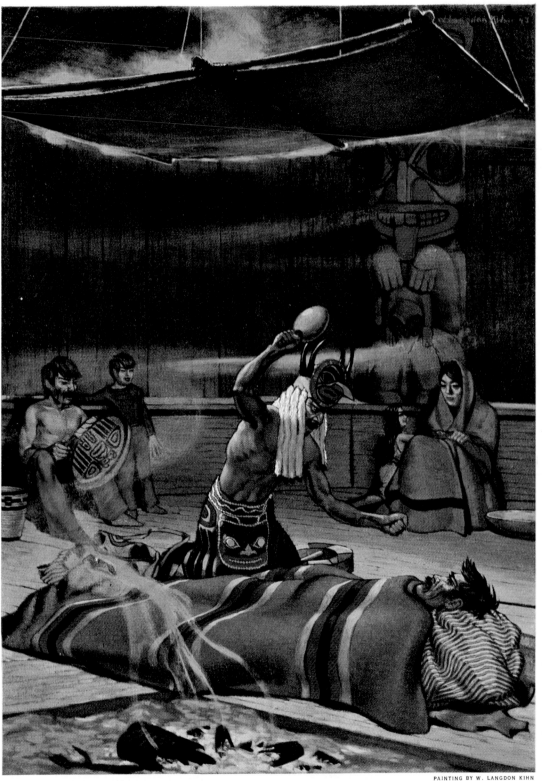

Shaman Wears Spirit Helper's Headdress, his earthly apprentice beats a drum. The Tlingit medicine man shakes his rattle, conjures away the malady. Bark mat below smoke hole shields fireplace from rain.

140

Purchase of a well-known copper constituted one of the most elaborate of Northwest Coast ceremonies. Coppers were always sold to rivals. If an offer to sell a copper was refused, this was an admission that the rival group could not raise sufficient wealth to make the purchase, and the group was correspondingly humiliated. Therefore, when a man accepted such an offer, all members of his group had to back him to the limit with loans of blankets. His wealth represented the holdings of the group.

Once the offer was accepted, details of the purchase were arranged in advance. The public sale, however, resembled an auction, with lavish display of the blankets offered in payment. The intended purchaser first made a low offer, at once accepted by the owner, who had to show how little he cared for money. But his friends vigorously protested and demanded more, citing previous sales. This continued until the agreed-on price was finally reached and the property transfer took place.

Each copper had a name, and its history and value were well known. In 1893 one copper worth 5,000 blankets was called "Making the House Empty of Blankets." Another valued at 6,000 blankets was named "Steelhead Salmon"—it glides out of one's hands like a salmon. A third copper worth 7,000 blankets was called "All Other Coppers Are Ashamed to Look at It."

Not only the sale of coppers, but the building of houses, the erection of totem poles, memorial services, the naming of children of important families, or their initiation into secret societies served as occasions for the big winter ceremonials of Northwest Coast tribes. Feasting and singing, spectacular costumed performances, and formal distribution of property marked these events.

Potlatch, the general name for such rites, is taken from the Chinook jargon, general trade language of the region, and is a corruption of the Nootka word *patshatl,* meaning "giving."

Details of the potlatch differed among the several tribes, but the underlying idea was always the same—to acquire rank and social status for the giver of the ceremony and his descendants. Not only did the giver gain much prestige by stripping himself of possessions, but he actually became potentially richer than before. Self-esteem dictated that when others gave potlatches they must return to him an even greater gift than the one they had received.

This complex ritual developed out of the widespread aboriginal custom of exchanging gifts as goodwill tokens. The obligation of a return gift gave rise to the white expression, "Indian giving."

Chiefs also rivaled one another in destroying property. At a formal feast to which a rival was invited, a chief might burn blankets, destroy a canoe, kill a slave, or break a copper. If the rival was not able to destroy quickly an equal or greater amount of property, his name was "broken," his prestige lost.

No modern diplomats were ever more sensitive to protocol than the prestige-seeking Northwest Coast Indians. Seating at formal feasts was carefully arranged according to rank, and aristocrats were ever alert to see that the family's prestige was maintained.

If a dignified person should slip and fall in the mud and thus be made to appear ridiculous, he could prevent any further reference to the incident by giving a small face-saving potlatch.

Similarly if his group received an accidental favor from the opposing group, such as the rescue of a drowning child, a potlatch would be given at once—not to express gratitude, but to prevent his group from being laughed at for loss of dignity.

Vengeance potlatches were given by an individual insulted by a member of a rival group, if the person delivering the insult was of equal rank. One ignored, as well as he could, insults from a person whose clan wealth was greater. Insults from individuals of lower social status were beneath notice. Since blood cannot be extracted from a turnip, where would be the profit in potlatching such a one?

The basic social fabric out of which these complex ceremonial systems developed was one of three social grades: aristocrats, commoners, and slaves.

The aristocrat inherited status through his mother's line, and was respected in proportion to the number and elaborateness of the potlatches he gave.

While the individual who had not inherited caste could gain approval by giving potlatches, aristocrats never accepted him as a social equal. They regarded him a newly rich social climber.

Derelictions of any individual reflected on the entire family group. Thus, when parents were too lazy or devoid of pride to give potlatches, or left orphaned children, a paternal uncle ceremonially adopted the youngsters to save the family name, thereby giving them the same status as his own children.

Slaves, obtained by war, purchase, or through debt, had no rights, were not permitted to marry, and were regarded as much the property of their owner as was his canoe. As a rule, these menials were badly treated, and might even be sacrificed at potlatches to the greater glory of their owners. Later, when white occupation made it difficult for the Indian to kill slaves, he made the same gesture of relinquishing property in a less dramatic way by freeing the slave.

All Northwest Coast tribes are divided into two or more groups which control marriage and descent. Among the Haida, everyone is born either a Raven or an Eagle. One must always marry in the opposite group; so when a man is a Raven, his wife and children are Eagles, since descent is reckoned only through the mother's family line.

While the southern Tlingit are divided into Ravens and Wolves, the Tsimshian have four groups: Eagles, Wolves, Ravens, and Killer Whales.

Among the Kwakiutl, the principal object of marriage was to acquire, through the wife, the clan crest and privileges for the expected children. This was achieved through a property exchange.

The husband paid the wife's father an agreed amount of property at marriage. The wife was then given to him as first installment on the return payment. When a child was born, the clan privileges were formally given, along with material property.

With this payment, the marriage was considered annulled, since the father had redeemed the payment made on his daughter. She could now stay with her husband or leave, as she chose. Sometimes the husband made a new payment so that he might retain a claim on her.

The ceremony in which the marriage money plus interest was returned to the son-in-law, along with delivery of the clan crest, was usually a part of one of the big winter potlatches. Dramatizations of mythological episodes in the clan tradition accompanied the ceremony.

Dr. Franz Boas, when among the Kwakiutl some 60 years ago, heard of a man punishing his father-in-law who had delayed repaying the purchase money and evaded giving his name to the son-in-law.

The son-in-law carved an image representing his wife and invited the populace to a feast. Placing a stone around the image's neck, he threw it into the sea. Thus he humiliated his father-in-law and indicated that he regarded the daughter as worthless.

Each clan was in effect an extended family, headed by a hereditary leader. Among the Tsimshian, Haida, and Tlingit, the heir was eldest son of the chief's eldest sister. Among the other tribes he was son of the chief. As symbol of the group, the chief had custody

A Tense Moment for the Nootka. Will the harpoon stay fixed in the sounding whale? Soon sealskin floats will be attached. One blow from the giant flukes will smash the frail canoe, or it may be towed for days before lances finish the beast. Bolder Nootka leaped with spears on wounded whales' backs. The successful hunt meant flesh and skin for food, intestines for oil containers, sinew for rope, blubber to be eaten or made into oil. Seals and porpoises were harpooned from canoes in similar manner.

143

Celebrants Arrive in Totem Pole Town for the Potlatch Ceremony. Richly attired clansmen, actors in masks crowd painted cedar canoes paddled by mustached slaves. Townspeople emerge from wooden community houses to cluster in welcome along water's edge beneath a forest of storied poles.

144

From Oregon to Alaska, the potlatch was winter's main social event. Hooded men impersonated legend-ary animals. Dancing, singing, feasting led up to extravagant giving or destruction of property in which the host impoverished himself and clan in a frenzied bid for prestige or to break a rival.

145

or berries came in season the chief would call on the group to build a fish trap or to hold a community berry gathering. The resulting food supply he used to give a general feast, during which he formally announced his hereditary right to the use of the spot, then told the group to go ahead and use it for themselves.

Violation of rights to such "owned" places was a frequent cause of wars. The desire to obtain prestige through war honors and to acquire captives for slaves was another motive. But revenge for real or fancied injuries was the most common reason these bellicose aborigines took up their bows and arrows, spears, copper knives, and stone-headed clubs and went into battle.

of the tribal wealth, lands, and produce.

Every foot of territory throughout the area, including coastal water, was "owned." This implied, rather than ownership of the land itself, the right to hunt, fish, and exploit products of the soil.

Usually the first seasonal harvest of stream and forest was given to the chief as token of his custodianship. When fish

As protective armor troops wore wooden helmets and sleeveless shirts either of rawhide in several thicknesses or of vertical wooden rods, tightly bound with stout twine.

The heads of slain enemies were generally taken as trophies. In later times, the Tlingit collected scalps, taking all the head hair and the ears. The much-valued war honors, unlike other honors,

Shaiks, Chief of the Tlingit, carries a Killer Whale staff of office. "Bear teeth" in his cedar head-dress are abalone shells. Human hair adorns hat and staff. His mustache belies the common misconception that American Indians had no facial hair. Most tribesmen zealously plucked it out. Hairs were coarser, scantier than among whites, but some tribal elders and, in the Pacific Northwest, young men as well, wore mustaches and beards.

PAINTINGS BY W. LANGDON KIHN

had to be earned and could not be transmitted through inheritance.

Captives did not always supinely accept their fate. A totem pole at one Tsimshian village has carved on it the figure of a woman holding a severed head. This commemorates an occasion when the Haida raided the Tsimshian and took a number of captives. One woman escaped and returned to her people. However, she first went to the trouble of killing and beheading her captor, bringing his head with her as souvenir.

The fact that this is recorded on a totem pole shows that it is over-simplification to say that totem poles were purely heraldic in nature and represented only the owner's mythologic genealogy. They might record any notable experience of the owner, such as being the first of his group to see a white man, or being converted to Christianity. One man carved on his pole a representation of the Tsar of Russia, to commemorate the sale of Alaska to the United States. Several Tlingit poles bore the likeness of Abraham Lincoln wearing top hat and beard.

There was nothing sacred or religious about totem poles. They represented the owner's claim to fame and were a means of displaying to the public his prestige and social standing. Sometimes, as a touch of vanity, the figure of the owner is shown holding a valuable possession to indicate his wealth. Again, a rival might be depicted in ridiculous light.

For example, a man of the Raven clan gave a potlatch to a rival of the Killer

147

Whale group, bestowing the usual gifts. The latter became a drunkard and could not return the gifts as required by social law. So the Raven man carved on his totem pole the figure of a Raven biting the dorsal fin of a Killer Whale. The impoverished Killer Whale representative could do nothing to offset the affront.

The wood-carving art of the North Pacific Coast was already fully developed by mid-18th century, as shown by the smaller objects collected by Captain Cook, Capt. George Dixon, Malaspina, and other explorers. But totem-pole descriptions begin to occur in travelers' writings only about the year 1790, by which time a few poles were standing in some Haida villages in the Queen Charlotte Islands. The custom probably did not originate much before this period.

The totem pole doubtless evolved from the practice of carving the front house post. With carving facilitated by iron tools introduced by the Russians about 1750, it is easy to see how the desire of the Haida or Tsimshian aristocrats to outdo one another in making bigger and better house posts would result, first, in a house post reaching above the roof of the house, and, finally, in one being erected as a detached mast.

Among the interior villages of the Tsimshian, poles sometimes more than 50 feet high were placed in a row, well in front of the houses. With the introduction of commercial paints, a rich palette of colors replaced the simple red, black, and white of the earliest poles.

Reaching its peak development between 1840 and 1880, totem-pole art rapidly declined when the native cultures began to break down as a result of ever-increasing contact with the whites.

Some specialists, to whom this carving art appears Asiatic in inspiration, have suggested that it may have been introduced by Polynesian or Asiatic crews of early European voyagers. Many such sailors, it is known, settled among the Indians.

Northwest Coast carvers and painters produced highly realistic designs. Some images or masks were actual portraits. Mostly, however, they preferred grotesque representation of semianimal or semihuman mythological beings.

A curious stylization developed wherein the artist dissected his subject, representing features symbolic of the creature he wished to portray.

The faces of a man, a killer whale, and a beaver, as carved on a totem pole or a box, might all look essentially alike. Erect ears on top of the head, however, showed beaver and killer whale to be animals. They were further distinguished by characteristic symbols: the dorsal fin of the killer whale, and the flat cross-hatched tail and long incisor teeth of the beaver.

Some of the carved masks used in dramatic performances were elaborate affairs, with movable parts attached to strings cleverly operated by the performers. Uncanny jugglery and sleight of hand also were part of these presentations, probably unequaled in their electrifying realism and dramatic power among American aborigines.

With performers elaborately costumed and masked to represent animals and legendary beings, these theatrical displays by secret societies dealt with mythological subject matter, supernatural "seizures," and miraculous restorations. Nevertheless they were more social than religious. A feature of many was the initiation of new members into the society.

In a typical initiation, the novice, captured by his hereditary spirit animal and taken to the forest, later was returned, apparently dead. Ceremonial attendants restored him to life. Such ceremonies usually lasted four days. Two described by mid-19th century travelers well illustrate the vividness of these displays.

"During the song and dance, which at first seemed to present nothing peculiar, a well-known slave . . . suddenly ceased dancing and fell down on the ground, apparently in a dying state, his face covered with blood.

"He did not move or speak, his head fell on one side, his limbs were drawn up, and he certainly presented a ghastly

Haida Raise a Totem Pole

Clan dignitaries, guests in ceremonial robes assemble as men strain at the ropes to erect a lofty memorial to a departed chief. Downward from the Eagle clan totem at the crest, the figures represent the chief himself, the Thunderbird, and one of the chief's ancestors. Projections on other poles symbolize fins of the Killer Whale.

Totem poles are not idols, but proclamations of prestige. Hollowed at back for easier handling, these painted masts represent months of carving by well-paid professionals. Standing them alone was a late development. Earlier poles formed part of the house framework, and were pierced by door openings.

Christianized Haida abandoned their villages around 1880, zealously cut down poles or sold them. At Tsimshian settlements on the upper Skeena River the totem-pole custom persisted until after 1900. Poles of recent vintage erected outside their proper region are imitations.

PAINTING BY W. LANGDON KIHN

Tattooed Widows Wail for a Chief Buried in a Canoe, his head toward the sea, his canoe rendered unfit for use. Earth burial was viewed with horror. Some tribes placed burial boxes on carved posts or hid them in caves; others cremated, burying only shamans. Slaves were sometimes sacrificed at funerals. Missionaries with great difficulty persuaded Northwest Coast Indians to adopt the white man's cemetery. Now one sees totemic animal symbols accompanied by Biblical verses on white-marble tombstones.

spectacle. While the dance raged furiously around the fallen man, the doctor, with some others, seized and dragged him to the other side of the fire round which they were dancing, placing his naked feet very near the flames.

"After this a pail of water was brought in, and the doctor, who supported the dying man on his arm, washed the blood from his face; the people beat drums, danced, and sang, and suddenly the patient sprang to his feet, none the worse for the apparently hopeless condition of the moment before.

"While all this was going on, I asked the giver of the feast whether it was real blood upon the man's face, and if he were really wounded. He told me so seriously that it was, that I was at first inclined to believe him, until he began to explain that the blood which came from the nose and mouth was owing to the incantations of the medicine man, and that all the people would be very angry if he did not afterwards restore him. . . .

"On the morning of December 13, another strange ceremony began, by the king's firing a pistol, apparently without a moment's warning, close to the ear of Satsat, who dropped down instantly as if shot dead on the spot.

"Upon this all the women set up a most terrible yelling, tearing out their hair by handfuls, and crying out that the prince was dead, when the men rushed in, armed with guns and daggers and inquiring into the cause of the alarm, followed by two of the natives covered with wolfskins, with masks representing the wolf's head. These two came in on all fours, and taking up the prince on their back, carried him out, retiring as they had entered.

"The celebration terminated with a shocking and distressing show of deliberate self-torment. These men, each with two bayonets run through their sides, between the ribs, walked up and down in the room, singing war songs, and exulting in their firmness and triumph over pain."

Details of costume differed somewhat among the various Northwest Coast tribes. Men as a rule wore their hair comparatively short, keeping it out of the eyes with a fur or cloth headband. Women wore their hair in two braids, and used ear and nose ornaments made of bone, wood, and abalone shell. Tlingit women beautified themselves by wearing, in slits in their lower lips, 3- or 4-inch wooden disks shaped like pulley wheels.

While the Kwakiutl and others painted their faces, the Haida practiced tattooing, favoring elaborate designs representing their family crests.

Two methods of deforming the head were practiced by Northwest Coast Indians. The Kwakiutl bound the head in infancy so that the skull grew upward and back in an elongated fashion. The Nootka placed a pad on an infant's forehead, flattening the front of the skull and causing it to slope backward from the eyebrows with "beautifying" effect.

Unlike most other American tribes, Northwest Coast Indians went barefoot the year round, wore raincoats (cedar-bark ponchos) in the wet season, and the old men went about entirely nude in summertime. Also, many men sported luxuriant mustaches.

Women once wore an apron made of shredded cedar bark, suspended by a belt of the same material (opposite). But the most conspicuous wearing apparel for both men and women was the blanket, woven from a mixture of mountain-goat wool, cedar bark, dogs' hair, and feathers. The weaving technique was about the simplest on the continent, but the results often were works of art (page 138).

A less elaborate blanket was made of soft cedar bark, the weft being simply turned across the warp. These blankets were usually trimmed with fur. Others were made of tanned sea-otter skins.

The earliest known blankets had simple designs, purely geometric in character. Complicated heraldic designs probably were not adopted until the general culture began to elaborate after contact with the whites. In this respect, the evolution of intricate patterns from simple beginnings parallels the known development of Navajo weaving.

With the coming of the white traders, woolen blankets gradually replaced the native types except for display purposes. Nowadays men wear shirt and trousers and women wear a dress under the blanket.

Whaling was an important industry of the Nootka of Vancouver Island and the Quileute and Makah who lived along the west coast of the Olympic Peninsula.

The Nootka pursued the whale in seagoing dugout canoes (page 143), frequently far from land. A whaling party usually numbered three to ten canoes, each about 30 feet long and manned by a crew of eight.

The whale-hunt leader, who inherited his position, acquired a helping spirit by praying in a special forest shrine containing wooden figures and the skulls of previous whale chiefs. To gain fortitude he wore clothing made from stinging nettles or thorny rose bushes. Wearing special adornments, such as scalps, was believed to bring additional supernatural power, for the whale was thought too powerful to be taken by human effort alone.

Whalers approached within a yard of the whale before thrusting the broad-pointed harpoon. They drove it as close to the head as possible to avoid the dangerous tail swipe of the wounded mammal. A long line of whale sinew was fastened to the detachable harpoon head. Inflated sealskin floats on the line served as drags and also marked the whale's position when it sounded.

Sometimes a whale would tow a canoe three or four days before it tired sufficiently to be killed with long lances. A daring lancer sometimes leaped on the whale as it was harpooned, drove his spear into its back, and stayed with the animal as it submerged. A respected, heritable Nootka name means "Stepping on a Whale."

Although tribes north along the coast were glad to make use of any whale carcass cast up on their shores, it was only with the Kodiak islanders and Aleuts that we again find expert whalers.

Aleut whaling ceremonies resembled those of the Nootka, but their boats—the closed kayak and the large, open umiak—were Eskimo. Also, they smeared the stone blades of their whale lances with poison from roots of the monkshood, which grows abundantly in the islands. A whale struck by such a lance died within two or three days and the carcass would wash ashore. Only whaling leaders knew the secret of preparing poison and they made the populace believe it got its magic potency from the fat of corpses.

The warlike inhabitants of the bleak and foggy Aleutian Islands, when first encountered by Russians in the 18th century, showed a combination of traits reflecting influences from the Eskimo, the eastern Siberian tribes, and tribes of the American Northwest.

In common with Northwest Coast people, the Aleuts had a social class system with slaves, wore rod armor in combat, and lived in large wooden communal houses (page 139).

The Aleut language is related to Eskimo, and like the Eskimo, the Aleut's principal weapons were javelins or harpoons, propelled by a throwing stick. Their aboriginal costume was Eskimo-like. The men wore long shirts of feathered birdskins, while women's similar garments were made from fur-seal or sea-otter skins. Light transparent raincoats with pointed hoods were made from strips of seal intestines, decorated at

Salmon Steak Broils Over an Indian Campfire. Winter's fillets dry on racks beneath massive canoe cedars flanking Alaska's Chilkat River. Fishing's easy harvest prevented famine, allowed leisure for winter's rich ceremonial life. Each spring salmon choked the rivers; also eulachon, or candlefish, source of the oil Indians lavished on dried meats, berries, other foods. Eulachon oil was foremost trade item of central Northwest Coast tribes with neighbors north and south and Athapascan tribes of the interior. Hudson Bay traders called these trade routes "grease trails."

the seams with feathers, and weatherproofed by hood and wrist drawstrings.

Because of the abundant food supply—sea mammals, fish, birds, birds' eggs, mollusks, berries and roots—the Aleutians were about as densely populated as any section of aboriginal America.

In 1740 there were probably 25,000 natives in the islands, but the effect of white contact was disastrous to them. In 1834, according to the missionary Veniaminoff, fewer than 2,500 remained. The smallpox epidemic in 1848 reduced them to about 900.

When the Japanese invaded the western islands in World War II, mystery surrounded the fate of those Aleuts living on Attu. When the Americans reoc-

cupied this island, all natives were gone. After the war, they were returned from Japan and resettled on Atka.

Time has brought many changes to the Aleutians and to the entire Pacific Northwest. The colorful cedar dugout has given way to the gasoline launch. The salmon cannery has set a new tempo of life. The hunter pursues deer and wild duck with rifle and shotgun. The sea otter, which once gave the Northwest Coast Indian his standard of value, is now almost extinct.

Some aged men and women still recall the old way of life. But the potlatch is gone, and the cherished coppers, and only a few rotting totem poles yet stand where many once were proudly raised.

King Islanders Paddle Home to Cliffside Village. These Bering Sea Eskimos venture in big walrus-skin umiaks across storm-swept waters to work as stevedores or trade ivory carvings in white man's Nome.

154

CHAPTER 7

NOMADS OF THE FAR NORTH

"I STEPPED FORWARD and took each of them by the hand . . ." wrote a young Scotsman in 1793, high in the Canadian Rockies. "This was the first time they had ever seen a human being of a complexion different from their own."

Thus Alexander Mackenzie, following the Peace River's headwaters westward, won friendship of awe-struck Indians in his historic journey to the Pacific. North West Company partner, one of the dauntless "Pedlars" who dared infringe on the fur-trading monopoly of the Hudson's Bay Company, Mackenzie was opening a way west, the first white man in an unknown maze of river and lake, forest and muskeg—the haunt of wandering, hardy peoples.

Before Mackenzie, explorers, missionaries, trappers, and birchbark-borne *voyageurs* had deeply penetrated the wilderness from the east, traveling freely among many of Canada's scattered Indian tribes. Ships of Russian sealers and British map makers had touched the northwest Pacific coast, meeting Indians of advanced culture. But no one yet had bridged east and west. Mackenzie was first to cross North America north of Mexico just as he was the first, four years earlier, to follow north-flowing water to the Arctic Ocean itself.

These journeys took the Scottish trader into lands of all three major native groups of the far north—Algonquian, Athapascan, and Eskimo (map, page 24).

Many times he followed the Nor'westers' fur trail from Montreal to his own Fort Chipewyan on Lake Athabaska, in what is now northeast Alberta. By waterway and portage it struck straight through country of Cree and Chippewa (page 44).

The Cree (page 19) were the largest and in many ways most typical of northern Algonquian tribes. They ranged south of Hudson Bay almost to the Great Lakes, east to the base of the Quebec-Labrador peninsula, and west to the northern Great Plains. There one branch, the Plains Cree, took on the typical Plains culture of their neighbors, the northern Blackfoot and the Assiniboin. True nomads, they moved their camps with seasonal migrations of game and fish. Woodland Cree, masters of light, portable, bark canoes, ranged far and wide on lakes and rivers. Their canoes and nets were sewn with vegetable-fiber twine, their conical tepees covered by skins or birch bark.

Cree men wore tight leather leggings to the hip, leather breechclouts, and moccasins. In winter they donned mittens and fur caps often hung with animal tails, and threw a fur robe over the shoulders. Women wore a knee-length skin dress, belted at the waist, adding detachable sleeves in winter.

In former times Cree men tattooed themselves, sometimes over the entire body, while their wives usually contented themselves with two or three simple lines on the face. Men of status usually took more than one wife; if a wife died, the widower married her sister.

Mackenzie said of the Cree: "Their eyes are black, keen and penetrating; their countenance open and agreeable...

"Of all the nations which I have seen on this continent, the Cree women are the most comely. Their figure is generally well proportioned, and the regularity of their features would be acknowledged by the most civilized people of Europe. Their complexion has less of that dark tinge which is common to those savages who have less cleanly habits."

A corpulent Cree, went another account, was "a much greater curiosity than a sober one."

Early traders said the Cree from childhood excelled in fraud and cunning in trade, but in all else were scrupulously honest and trustworthy. Amiable, extremely generous, they were of model behavior until liquor was introduced.

Before modern trade goods came in, the Cree used birch-bark or stone containers. They made arrowheads and axes of stone; knives, fishhooks, and awls of bone. The fur trader and his new and desired goods changed Cree life rapidly. Tribesmen diverted more energy to trapping fur animals. White man's disease struck. Smallpox, introduced in 1786, alone cut Cree numbers from 15,000 to about 3,000.

The first of all Canada's Indians to meet white settlers were the Micmac. French colonists who landed in "Acadia" —present-day Nova Scotia—in 1604 found the Micmac fairly densely settled there and in near-by regions. Fierce and warlike, these Algonquians early became good friends of the French and enemies of the British. Like their northern neighbors, the Nascapi, they painted their leather costumes in bright patterns.

More advanced in political organization than northern tribes, they gave their chiefs real authority. During historic times, the Micmac absorbed European ways, including some farming.

The Nascapi, by contrast, remain nomadic. They and the closely related Montagnais sparsely occupy the entire Quebec-Labrador peninsula, save only its north and west coasts. Basically Eastern Woodlands peoples, their customs have been much modified by severe climate and by contact with Labrador coast Eskimos, whom they once fought continually, but now fully associate with.

Early-day Nascapi lived in skin-covered conical tepees winter and summer, but Eskimo influence shows in the crude snowhouse they sometimes made over a frame of spruce boughs. And to the usual Algonquian leather breeches, leggings, moccasins, gloves, and fur cap, Nascapi added the Eskimo's long coat, decorating it with red, blue, yellow, and brown painted designs (page 160).

Their canoes and snowshoes were Eastern Woodlands, their toboggans Athapascan, their sleds Eskimo. Among southern Nascapi bands, men and women provided the pulling power, for neither horse nor dog was used.

Typical of northern tribes, the Nascapi set deadfalls for the flesh-eating bear, lynx, and cougar; snares for the herbivorous moose, caribou, deer, hares, rabbits, and ptarmigan; and shot caribou from ambush, or speared them from canoes while swimming (opposite).

These northern nomads preserve caribou flesh by drying, then pound it, and make it into pemmican, their basic food while roaming the interior in search of game. They live in alternate abundance and want. Sometimes after a long period of hunger followed by a successful caribou hunt, they gorge themselves sick with incredible quantities of meat.

Summer in the northland brings weather almost as warm as winters are cold. Sheets of surface water spawn hordes of mosquitoes; biting flies abound. No white traveler venturing into the Barren Grounds has failed to reserve his best eloquence for describing the insect pests. Flanking Hudson Bay,

Yellowknives Spear Swimming Caribou in Great Slave Lake. To slow their fleet prey, northland hunters drive reindeer into water, overtake them in swift birchbark canoes. The Yellowknife earlier lived along the Coppermine River, and prospered trading knives they made of yellow copper. White man's steel broke their monopoly, warfare thinned their ranks, and they moved south to better hunting grounds.

157

Summer Work of this provident Montagnais on Quebec's Pointe Bleue Reservation readies snowshoes for winter trapping rounds hundreds of miles north. This tribe and the neighboring Nascapi excel in snowshoe craft. For different uses, they make some almost round, some long and narrow, some with upturned toes. Taut moosehide web inside wooden frame keeps wearer from sinking in soft snow.

HOWELL WALKER, NATIONAL GEOGRAPHIC STAFF

the Yukon River across the mountains to the west, is homeland to the Athapascan-speaking Tanana, Kutchin, Hare, Yellowknife, Nahani, and Slave—trackers of caribou through scraggly spruce forests.

Geologically, this territory is an extension of the Great Plains to the south. What the buffalo was to Plains tribes the caribou is to Indians of the far north. Stalking, snaring, trapping customs the Athapascans share with Algonquian tribes to south and east. But they originated a massed hunting technique later adopted by buffalo hunters of the Plains.

In this community venture, throngs of Indians howling like wolves drive a caribou herd into a large circular corral with a funnellike entrance having wings, perhaps a mile apart. Trapped inside, the milling animals are shot.

Magical aid was normally sought by the hunter. One method, common also in parts of Asia, was to carve animal images on a caribou shoulder blade, then hold it over a fire until cracked by heat. The cracks pointed toward good hunting.

The Indians hunt mainly during late summer and in the winters, which are long and severe, although snowfall is not heavy. In early summer they fish for sal-

this bleak desert north of the tree line, summer grazing range of caribou and musk ox, extends 2,500 miles from Labrador to the delta of the Mackenzie River.

In summer Eskimo hunters penetrate this no man's land from the north, Indians from the south. These latter include the Chipewyan (page 161), Caribou-eaters, and Beaver, wandering tribes long tapped for fur by the "Company of Adventurers of England Trading into Hudson's Bay."

From Fort Chipewyan, Mackenzie explored his river flowing west out of Great Slave Lake. He had found the second longest stream in North America, from its source in the Rockies to its mouth on the Beaufort Sea.

This wide drainage basin, and that of

mon in Yukon headwaters, whitefish in the Mackenzie basin. These migrating fish are taken in nets or in basket traps, while natives hook lake trout up to 30 pounds in all seasons.

Of political organization among Athapascan groups one early explorer said: "The authority of the chief is limited, for the Indians are very unruly and not at all disposed to submit to authority.

"The chiefs are chosen either for their wisdom or courage, and not at all on account of birth. They have no insignia of office, and as for privileges they have all that they can take, and none that the others can withhold from them.

"The chiefs and old men are all who are entitled to speak in council, but any young man will not hesitate to get up and give his seniors the benefit of his wisdom."

In contrast to weak chiefs were the shamans, who could stir up winds, drive away a storm, foretell success or failure in hunting or warfare. The shaman could cure, he could kill. Any person harboring a grudge could hire him to send sickness into an enemy.

Punishment for crimes lay entirely in the hands of the offended. For adultery the woman alone was punished—beaten or cast off. For murder, the victim's relatives avenged his death. But if a shaman had been paid to kill him, the shaman was regarded innocent. Revenge was taken against the individual who paid him.

Brisk Weather, Brisk Business Mix at a Hudson's Bay Post. North beyond all trees on the inhospitable west coast of Quebec's Ungava Peninsula, the Port Harrison trader fights cold with caribouskin parka, warm gloves, and fur-lined cap while tending his unheated store. The Eskimo couple offers a fine catch of red, white, and silver fox pelts, worth many aluminum credit tokens, known as "made beavers." Several lie beside the order pad. With these the natives buy coffee, tea, tobacco, matches, traps, ammunition. Guns and steel traps came to Eskimo country with the first Hudson's Bay Company traders. Founded in 1670, the company long held a monopoly in Canada's fur trade.

RICHARD HARRINGTON

Hardy North Country Indians Roam Lands Locked in Snow

In winter camp in Quebec's Gulf of St. Lawrence district, early-day Nascapi (above) prepare for the trail. The man ices sled runners, his wife smoke-tans a caribou hide on a tripod over a half-smothered fire. Near-round snowshoes hanging on a dead snag offer wide support in soft snow, yet are easily maneuverable on upland trails. Bright designs band Nascapi skin clothing.

Northern tepees, not so tall and steep as the familiar Plains dwelling, were covered with skins or bark. Even when snow drifts high, fire inside maintains warmth. Amid conical Nascapi tepees, a dome-shaped lodge at center hints kinship with the igloo. Northern Nascapi bands adopted the Eskimo's dog, but this southern group puts human brawn to work pulling sleds.

Dogs and snub-nosed toboggans provide transport for old-time Chipewyan crossing treeless plains (right). Biting Hudson Bay winds whip snow past caribou-skin tepees pitched before the austere battlements of Fort Prince of Wales. Commanding the region's best harbor and a voyageur route to the Peace, Athabasca, and Mackenzie River country, this British outpost thrives on fur trade with Indians and Eskimos. Soon, in 1782, the French will destroy the fort, but some walls will remain in later Churchill, Manitoba, 20th century terminus of the Hudson Bay railway.

Chipewyan nomads ranged from Lake Athabasca to Hudson Bay, and north as far as Caribou Eskimo country. Through the long winter they followed the migrating caribou, whose hides provided shelter and fringed-leather clothing, whose flesh was their daily fare.

160

Typical of northern and western Athapascan tribes are the Kutchin. Formerly called the Loucheux, they live between the upper Yukon and the lower Mackenzie. Much of their territory lies north of the Arctic Circle, where winters of 50° F. below zero are followed by summers up to 90° F.

As with the Nascapi of Labrador, the dressed caribou-skin costume of the Kutchin somewhat resembles Eskimo dress. Their fringed coat had a pointed tail both in front and behind, the latter convenient for sitting on blocks of ice. Coats were embellished with porcupine quills dyed in different colors, and with rows of Dentalium shells. The finest porcupine-quill embroidery in America was that of the Athapascan tribes, who probably originated the art.

Kutchin trousers sometimes were in one piece with the moccasins. In winter a hood was attached to the coat, and detached mittens were worn, fastened Eskimo-like to a line passed over the neck. Women's clothing usually was more ample to allow room for a suckling baby under it, and there was no tail in front.

Kutchin women placed their infants in bark cradles (page 163). Most other northern tribes substituted the moss bag, a simple sack with a lining of moss which

Eskimo Comedians Mimic a Kutchin Dance. Laughter splits swarthy Alaskan faces as feather-shaking dancers jig to the beat of one-faced drums. Despite a bleak habitat, Eskimos are cheerful and fun-loving.

162

Artful Headdress, Soot Tattoos Beautify a Kutchin Mother. She cradles her baby in a chair-shaped bark basket. Bone beads, porcupine-quill embroidery, trimmed feathers adorn her caribou-skin costume.

163

W Langdon Kihn '48

could be changed frequently. Wives of north-woods traders adopted this practical device.

In winter, the Kutchin and their neighbors live typically in a gable-roofed log house. Logs are set vertically for walls, horizontally for the roof, which is made weatherproof with moss and turf. A hanging skin covers the door opening. When on the move, Kutchin live in dome-shaped structures of skins over poles.

A woman's life was no joy. Women, not dogs, pulled Kutchin sleds. When a new camp was selected, the men, arriving first, awaited the women dragging lodges and other paraphernalia, then lounged around while the women set up camp.

In addition to moving camp, the woman had to retrieve game killed by the male hunters and back-pack it home. She dried the meat in summer, made all clothing, dressed skins, repaired snowshoes, performed the camp drudgery. Her husband could beat her for disobedience. So severe was her lot—far harder than among most Indian tribes—that mothers often killed infant daughters to spare them a woman's life.

Men did the cooking. They always ate first, selecting the choicest items for themselves and throwing what was left on the ground for the women.

Although game was abundant at times, there were often

164

By Age-old Ingenuity the Eskimo Masters His Frozen World

In slanting light of the spring sun, Central Eskimos (left) prepare for their long inland migration. Caribou antlers top a heavy-laden sled. Ivory goggles with narrow eyeslits cut down reflected glare, prevent snow blindness. Harpoons jutting from the snow kill and tether wary mammals of icy seas. In bulging sealskins in foreground, oil and blubber are packed for the journey. White Arctic fox pelts hanging from the lance behind the woman will buy needed staples at the trading post.

From Coppermine east across the Canadian Arctic, such igloo villages as this one house Central Eskimos through long, dark, bitter cold winters. Unlike Alaskan and Greenland Eskimos, who use snow only for temporary shelter, these Hudson Bay people, in a region empty of wood or stone, build large snowblock dwellings that are marvels of engineering. Domed construction does away with inner frame. Clear panes of ice admit light. Long entrance tunnels keep out howling wind and marauding polar bear. Though temperature outside plunges far below zero, body heat, oil lamps, and cooking fires keep tight igloos warm—often above 60°F.

Families strip to the waist for indoor comfort (below). Cross-legged on a skin-draped snow platform, a man drills ivory with a bow-and-socket tool. Pipe-smoking woman tailors fur clothing. Another cooks with shallow stone dish over a seal-oil flame. Girl standing on fur-covered floor plays Eskimo version of cat's cradle.

PAINTINGS BY W. LANGDON KIHN

165

Igloos, Like Fallen Snowmen, Dot the Arctic Shore. Tethered dogs will soon form yelping teams as Central Eskimos set out to hunt on the ice. Except for the tent, this sealing camp on an island near Coppermine, Northwest Territories, could have been photographed a century ago. Each domed snow-house is home for about five persons. Early Eskimo invented sleds like the ladder-shaped one at left, and bred large dogs to pull them. The dog travois of Plains Indians probably came from the Eskimo.

periods of want and famine. Old people, sick or no longer able to care for themselves, were frequently abandoned by their families in the wilderness.

The Kutchin once practiced slavery. Slaves were either war captives or tribesmen without protecting friends or relatives. Most warlike of Athapascan tribes, the Kutchin fought with their Indian neighbors, and more often with the Eskimo. Mostly they were the aggressors. Their motive: to gain prestige, booty, and captives.

Indian women usually submitted docilely to their captors, but Eskimo women often bided their time in apparent submission, awaiting revenge.

Before a war party set out, a dance feast stirred up the proper military spirit. On the way to their objective the warriors killed every creature they encountered. But upon meeting their prospective victims, they would act as friends until their hosts were off guard. They then knifed men, women, and children, except such women as they wished for wives. For each victim he had thus killed in "warfare" a man tattooed a line on his arm.

Times of plenty saw many less grim pastimes than war. The Kutchin liked singing, dancing, and long stories; they gambled, using sticks for dice; they wrestled joyfully, or pitted men against women in a tug of war.

At the start of a tribal wrestling match the two smallest boys grapple. The winner then takes on the next larger boy, who rushes in before his opponent can get his breath. Thus the match continues without pause until the strongest men are wrestling. A better wrestler may throw three or four opponents until, exhausted, he in turn is thrown and leaves the field to his conqueror.

When the male champion has been determined, the women have their turn, the contest beginning with two little girls.

In winter the Kutchin play a dangerous game. Four trees, growing in the form of a square and about 30 feet apart, are selected, and two moose-skin thongs stretched diagonally between pairs of trees, forming an X about 20 feet above ground. Where they intersect a small leather platform about a foot square is attached. Participants stand on this tiny platform in turn and jump up and down.

Each time the player lands on the square the cords' elasticity throws him higher, until he is thrown more than 10 feet above the platform. The higher he bounces the more difficult it is to keep balance. The object is to see who can complete the greatest number of jumps before falling to the ground far below.

Of course each participant finally comes a cropper, to the hearty amusement of the spectators.

Cultural signposts among the Kutchin point in several directions. Hunting customs they share with Athapascan neigh-

Seal Carved in Ivory shows skill of a culture predating even the Old Bering Sea people of 2,000 years ago. This grotesque figurine comes from Ipiutak, long-buried town of 800 houses north of Bering Strait at Point Hope, Alaska. Log tombs yield human skulls set with carved walrus-ivory eyeballs, nose plugs, and mouthpieces. Coming from Asia, 160 miles away, these mysterious people excelled the practical Eskimo in artistry, but did not have seal-oil lamps, sleds, or slate tools. Later came the Eskimo wave that peopled the Arctic as far east as Greenland.

bors and Algonquian tribes. From the
Eskimo come tailored skin costumes, the
use of built-up sleds, wrestling as the favorite sport. Other Kutchin traits recall
the Tutchone, Tahltan, and Carrier
tribes of the south—in turn swayed by
the potlatch, slavery, and prestige -
through-wealth concepts of the spectacular Northwest Coast tribes.

Mackenzie opened Athapascan country. He traveled among the Kutchin. It
was the Carrier who led him at last to the
Pacific. But he reached another world,
too, in his journey down the Mackenzie
River to its mouth. There, facing sea ice,
on a quaking muskeg coast with perma-
frost not far beneath, he had come to the
land of the Eskimo.

Here live in many respects the most remarkable aborigines in the New World.
Spread thinly across some 6,000 miles of
Arctic coast and great islands from East
Cape, Siberia, to eastern Greenland,
these people for centuries have had to
adapt to a stark, cruel environment, or
die. Nowhere else in the world did a
primitive people extend themselves so
widely. Yet they show surprising uni-
formity in physical characteristics, language, and customs.

Although the Eskimo are unmistak-
ably of Asiatic origin, many ethnologists
refer to them not as "Indians" but as a
group apart. Nomenclature is unimportant, since the term "Indian" in any case
is arbitrary.

It would be easy to explain their indi-
viduality by saying that the Eskimo
were late arrivals from northern Asia
who spread rapidly along the uninhab-
ited Arctic coast, by-passing established
tribes. But archeology proves this is not
so. In Alaska extensive remains have
been found which date back 2,000 years
or more. These remains—not even the
earliest known—show that these ancient
people were true Eskimo who already
had developed an amazing culture.

Similar traits can be found as far west

as the Ob River and as far south as Lake
Baikal in central Asia. Along Siberia's
Arctic coast today several different
language and culture groups show descent from separate northward movements of ancient people from inner Asia
down the long rivers that flow to the
Arctic.

One of these movements reached the
shores of Bering Sea in easternmost Siberia. Here walrus, seal, fish, and birds
supplied the necessities of life.

Crossing Bering Strait in their skin-
covered boats, these people soon settled
in permanent villages on the Diomede
Islands, St. Lawrence Island to the
south, and on the Alaska coast. Sea-nur-
tured, they felt no need to penetrate the
American interior.

These Old Bering Sea people lived in
communities of small rectangular houses
excavated in the ground. Floors were of
stone, walls of driftwood and whale
bones laid horizontally between stakes,
roofs probably of wooden rafters covered
with turf. A long, low entrance tunnel
shielded the interior from cold.

They did not construct platforms in
their houses as did the later Eskimo.
They cooked their food in round-bot-
tomed pottery vessels, they carved plates
and spoons of driftwood. Open, shallow
pottery lamps gave heat and light.

Their skin-covered boats were the
kayak and the umiak, types still used by
the Eskimo (page 172).

They traveled overland with small,
low, heavy-runnered sledges, as well as
whalebone toboggans, both drawn by human power. The only dogs were a small-
sized breed apparently raised for food.

Chief weapon, and key possession of
these and later Eskimo, was the harpoon.
With detachable head of ivory or bone
fastened to line and float, this complex
spear proved indispensable for hunting
sea mammals. Since both form and decoration changed with different periods,
a prehistoric Eskimo site can be dated by

PAINTING BY W. LANGDON KIHN

Hunters and Huskies Battle Pain-maddened Polar Bear. Daring Eskimo lunges to spear 1,000-pound beast with knife lashed to a stick. His companion draws sinew-backed bow. Eskimos also hunted bear with fist-sized "death pills" temptingly strewn on sea ice. The frozen balls, containing sharpened whalebone pieces wound up like clocksprings inside strips of seal blubber, sprang open in bear's stomach.

169

Frozen Seas Hold the Eskimo Larder

Still as a statue, the Central Arctic hunter (left) waits above a seal's blow-hole, snowknife at his side. Hours may pass. Suddenly the harpoon flashes down. Seal- or caribou-skin clothing, usually fur side in, traps warm-air layer against body. Mukluks (skin boots) and a bearskin square keep feet from freezing on ice.

Seal in tow, Bering Strait hunter (right), returns to Little Diomede Island, skin boat on back. Boatless hunters paddle ice cakes across open leads in sea ice.

King Islanders (below) butcher a cow walrus on an ice floe. Besides flesh for food, the beast's fat feeds lamps, its hide covers boats, its sinew provides cordage. The walrus was hardware store to the Eskimo: shoulder blades made snow shovels, tusks became ice picks and sled runners, ivory was carved into harness swivels and buckles, tools, weapons, and images.

GONTRAN DE PONCINS
JUAN MUÑOZ (BELOW)   170

AUDREY AND FRANK MORGAN

the style of harpoon heads found in it.

These designs were made with sharp flint gravers; holes were drilled with an ingenious bow and socket technique. An ivory or wooden "mask" fitted over the Eskimo's mouth and held the upper end of the drill shaft. The bowstring was looped around the shaft. Moving the bow back and forth spun the drill rapidly.

Prospering for several centuries, the Old Bering Sea people inched south along the Alaskan coast, and north to where a group developed that archeologists call the Birnik people.

About a thousand years ago a sudden change and expansion took place. New traits and ideas from Siberia broke through the old conservatism. With them came the use of iron.

Decorative designs grew bolder, more rigid with iron engraving and carving tools. The art of flaking away stone to make ax, knife, or scraper gave way to ground-stone implements, usually of slate. Larger whaling harpoon heads came into use, and Eskimo ingenuity created bird arrows, bolas, and fishhooks.

The bird bola consisted of a number of ivory balls on strings. The hunter hurled it at birds. When any part of the bola struck a bird, the remainder whirled about, entangling it.

As the complex sinew-backed bow increased in power, archers began to wear wrist guards to protect them from the bowstring's rebound. For warfare, body armor of bone plates came into use.

With more food, population increased. Houses became larger. Population pressure began a strong eastward movement along the Arctic coast, a movement which did not stop until scattered groups fringed the entire coast as far as eastern Greenland in the north, Newfoundland in the south.

Archeologists call these Eskimo the Punuk in their Bering Sea habitat, the Thule in central and eastern Arctic.

The rapidity and vast extent of their population spread came partly because until they reached Hudson Bay they encountered no other humans along their line of migration. From there to Greenland, however, they met a long-settled people. These, the primitive Dorset, were related in some ways to the Eskimo.

171

The Dorset culture still remains a mystery. Although no trace of them has yet been found in the west, archeologists believe the Dorset stem from the Denbigh people, whose recently discovered remains in western and interior Alaska are the Arctic's earliest yet known.

Traveling eastward, the Dorset people finally settled north and east of Hudson Bay from Labrador to Greenland. They disappeared with the arrival of the Thule, being displaced, or merging with them.

Later, islands along the central Arctic coast were abandoned by the Thule. Within the last thousand years the land there has risen more than 30 feet, closing straits and shoaling the sea. Whales no longer visited the section. The Thule, largely dependent on whales for subsistence, moved to the mainland.

Excavations in western Greenland reveal that the Thule at Inugsuk traded with the Norse in the 13th century. This first archeological evidence of European influence provides a definite point of departure in dating Eskimo culture. Norse sagas and documents tell of much earlier Greenland meetings with Eskimos, the first American aborigines to meet the white man.

172

PAINTINGS BY W. LANGDON KIHN

Sled and Kayak Carry Eskimos on the Endless Search for Food

Beneath eerie curtains of the aurora borealis, Central Eskimos (above) trudge toward the coast to winter in snow houses and hunt food out across the ice. Men as well as dogs in fan-shaped harness haul sledges piled high with wood for trail fires, caribou meat, even a rakish kayak. Through dark months ahead, seal and walrus will become staff of life, existence on the sea ice a grim battle for survival.

At spring's end when sunlight floods the north country, Eskimos migrate inland in pursuit of caribou, and to fish in lakes and streams. On the Barren Grounds Eskimo and Indian have met and swapped traits over long centuries. Tailored skin clothing, the sled, other Eskimo inventions thus made their way south. The bark canoe of Eastern Woodlands may stem from the kayak.

The kayak (left) ranks high among Eskimo achievements. These tricky, one-man canoes are literally closed skin tubes. The hunter makes the one opening watertight by lacing his clothing over the manhole rim. Deft use of the double-bladed wooden paddle rights his craft when capsized, sometimes by rolling full circle.

Stalking walrus, the hunter leans forward, conceals himself behind the saillike blind mounted on the bow. He hurls his harpoon with a throw stick. Sinew line snakes out from tray on foredeck. Inflated sealskin buoys up the carcass while towing.

Unlike the kayak, the umiak—"woman's boat"—is a bulky open craft that can carry a sizable load. Ancient Eskimos propelled umiaks both by paddles and oars, the only instance of oars used by American aborigines. Outboard motors now do much of the work.

173

Greenland Madonna and Child. Woman's bead cape and hair bun show white man's influence. Child's furs, skin boat are traditional. Norse from Iceland settled on Greenland about A.D. 900. Of American aborigines, the Eskimo have had longest contact with Europeans, remain among the least affected. Despite vast spread, their culture is strikingly uniform; a Greenlander can converse with an Alaskan Eskimo.

Once the Arctic coast was settled, about A.D. 1000, minor local differences began to appear among the Eskimo. In modern times we classify them as Western, Central, and Eastern Eskimo.

The mind's-eye image most of us have when we say "Eskimo" is that of the Central Eskimo. How well we picture parka-clad men wandering far across the ice in search of breathing holes of seals, there to wait hours on end, spear in hand (page 170). The patience and skill of the Eskimo is proverbial, and his knowledge of the quarry's behavior unsurpassed.

Early in life, boys join their fathers on hunts, sharing their hardships in the severe climate. They learn to set nets of whalebone under the ice. On warm days when seals emerge to bask on the ice, they slither belly down across the hummocks, inching toward their wary prey, leaping up, hurling the harpoon.

Summers, when the family moves inland and lives in skin-covered tents, boys take part in caribou hunts and fish in lakes and rivers.

In the winter communities on the sea ice, they help their fathers build snowhouses, hemispherical in shape, with compact snow blocks locked with a key block at the dome's apex. Snow platforms edge the wall. Covered with furs, these are used for lounging and sleeping (page 165). Heating the newly built house forms a glaze of ice over the interior, making it strong and compact. Light comes in "windows" made of ice.

These igloos, considered so typical of the Eskimo, were used regularly only by the Central Eskimo, not by the early or later-day Alaska Eskimo.

The Eskimo's ingenuity is further illustrated in his stone or pottery lamp. In a woodless region, life on the sea ice would be impossible without it. In a bowl of stone or pottery, seal or whale oil burns from a wick of twisted moss or other absorbent. The lamp furnished light during the long winter night, it heated the almost airtight winter houses, it cooked the Eskimo's food.

In aboriginal times the Eskimo made fire by striking together two pieces of iron pyrites, driving a spark into tinder, or by friction produced with the bow drill.

Eskimo garb was also remarkably adapted to the severe climate. In the Eastern and Central groups the hooded coat was cut away at the sides and had a long tail down the back, looking for all the world like a modern full-dress coat. Knee-length trousers, skin hip boots, and mittens completed the costume.

Clothing was generally of caribou or seal skin. In Alaska garments were also tailored bird skins or skins of small mammals sewed together. Intestines of sea mammals made light rain gear; polar-bear fur, the best ice-free mittens.

Like their Indian neighbors to the south, the Eskimo have little if any political organization. Lacking chiefs, the family is the basic social unit. Again the most influential individuals are the shamans, who influence the leaders, interpret dreams, make or break up marriages, and foretell weather and the movements of game. The shaman is also the doctor.

When the Labrador Eskimo medicine man is called, he is blindfolded. The patient lies on his back on the ground. The shaman, when worked up to a proper state of frenzy, throws himself on his victim and begins to chase the evil from its hiding place. Meanwhile, the patient is on the receiving end of a series of violent blows and jerks.

As the spell develops, the shaman gives vent to hideous sounds, shouting as the evil spirit supposedly flees to another part of the body. After a time the shaman announces that he has ousted the spirit, placed it under his control.

If it escapes and again gets into the victim's body, the shaman continues until the patient either recovers or dies. If the former, the doctor's reputation is enhanced. If the latter, he merely blames his failure on outside interference. In any case he collects a substantial fee.

When a Labrador Eskimo is seriously ill, his relatives move him outside before death if possible. If he dies in the house, a hole must be cut in the side of the house, through which the body is removed. The hole is then closed to prevent the ghost of the departed from returning, as it would had the body been taken through the door.

The dead, wrapped in skins, are left near a rock or on a hilltop, covered with stones. The frozen ground prevents burial. For the same reason the Nascapi neighbors hang their dead from tree limbs when death occurs in winter.

Through the influence of the great fur-trading companies, by the mid-19th century both northland Indian and Eskimo had adopted many of the white man's ways. The Indian, ideal fur hunter, took to guns and steel traps, textile clothing, metal tools, and cooking utensils. Grad-

ually the canvas-covered or aluminum canoe replaced his birchbark craft; trader's canvas covered his tepee.

The Eskimo with his native mechanical genius now propels his boats with gasoline motors. The phonograph has become as important to the igloo as the blubber lamp. Skin clothing, especially in summer, has given way to European-style attire.

Missionaries following the traders did to the native's beliefs and ideas what the trader had done to his material culture. In remote regions, remnants of old ways are still strong; in others they have almost disappeared.

Tribal territories change and shrink as the white man continues his inexorable march. Gold miners, bush pilots, uranium prospectors press into the once lonely realm of the wandering aborigine. The click of the Geiger counter has become the new heartbeat of the north.

Only the old people remember the past, and, like mankind the world over, sigh and pine for "the good old days."

Indians of Our Western Plains
The National Geographic Magazine
JULY, 1944

Sioux Kinsmen Meet

In eagle-feather war bonnet, bear-claw necklace, and bone-bead breastplate, Chief Crazy Bull views the National Geographic Society's exhibit of Indian paintings by W. Langdon Kihn which lined Explorers Hall at The Society's Washington, D.C. headquarters.

Crazy Bull holds an eagle-feather fan; porcupine quill-work decorates his sleeve. He lingers before the portrait of his grim-featured Sioux relative, One Bull (page 12), witness to Custer's Last Stand.

How the artist came to paint One Bull's portrait, and his vivid account of 14 years in the field in search of the American Indian past is told in the following chapter.

NATIONAL GEOGRAPHIC PHOTOGRAPHER
JOHN E. FLETCHER

CHAPTER 8

PAINTING THE
NORTH AMERICAN INDIAN

BY W. LANGDON KIHN

FROST SETTLED ON THE DESERT as the Navajo fire dance ended. The first red sliver of the rising sun jutted into view; colorfully costumed Indians sang their haunting Bluebird Parting song, and then quietly drifted away. One small group remained, drinking coffee from a pot sitting on campfire coals.

Cold and lame from standing all night watching the dance (page 101), I took a tin cup from my car and walked over to help myself to the brew. As I stood quietly, sipping my hot drink, a stocky Navajo approached, glittering with turquoise earrings, silver-buttoned buckskin moccasins, sporting a wide-brimmed hat and fine blanket.

"How did you like our dance?" he asked.

"Great," I replied.

"I see you're from Connecticut," he went on, glancing at my license plate. "What part?"

"A little town you probably never heard of—Hadlyme."

"Sure," he replied promptly, "I know Hadlyme. I know the Connecticut River from Hartford to Saybrook."

"How come?" I asked.

"I went to Yale," he grinned.

That incongruous conversation in the middle of a desert wilderness scented by sweet smoke from burning piñon logs is one of many incidents I recall from 14 years during which I completed the 103 paintings on North American Indians in this book.

I began the project in 1935, humbled by its scope and its problems. No series of paintings on such a large scale had ever before been attempted. Except for a few isolated groups of Indians who still resist the white man's era, traces of aboriginal culture have almost vanished from North America.

With exhaustive research I set out to recapture the dress and paraphernalia of each main group of Indians at its historic peak. Obviously, I was slated to visit reservations, to watch ceremonies, and explore beautiful remote Shangri-Las where the American Indian had carved his destiny.

Often, as I traversed deep forests, wide plains, and mighty mountains that formed the backdrop for the American Indian, I turned my mind back through time. In my imagination I pictured strange families of a thousand years ago occupying stone and adobe dwellings carved from the golden rock walls of towering cliffs.

Or, facing the green-blue sea that washed a deserted totem pole village, I visualized a brightly painted war canoe laden with costumed warriors, stealthily skirting a spruce-jungle cove.

My wife and I would leave Connecticut in a car loaded with painting and camping equipment, books, and luggage and head for Indian country. I would choose a general area to study, such as the northern plains or southwest desert. From there on, we never knew exactly what to expect.

We put up where we could, sometimes boarding, sometimes camping. The Indians themselves, among whom I have many personal friends, often played host.

One thing that impressed me from the outset was the amazing tribal differences among American Indians. Just as each nation of the world has its own traits, so does each Indian tribe possess its unique personality. But common to all tribes is an ancient, deep-rooted, well-justified mistrust of the white man. Sometimes it was a difficult barrier to overcome.

On the Blackfeet Reservation in Montana I met a striking type of this colorful Algonquian tribe. Grabbing my interpreter, I told him to ask the prospect to pose. Ten dollars for posing was the immediate demand.

One dollar, I told my interpreter, was all I could pay.

The Indian spoke scornfully. "I know you white fella, smart fella. You make picture and take him back to New York town. Then you hang him up in big brick tepee. Pretty soon another white man come along and you sell him picture for ten dollar. I want ten dollar for posing."

I told him he was crazy; that if I made a dollar on my pictures I would be lucky.

"A dollar?" queried the Indian, a disconcerting glint in his eyes.

"That's right."

"All right," he said, "I'll buy picture for one dollar."

Generally, the Blackfeet seemed a happy, even-tempered people. My old friend Eagle Calf (page 72) kept me laughing with yarns like his story about Fish Wolf Robe.

Fish Wolf Robe returned from a sun dance in Canada in a secondhand Model T. When the tires blew out, he stuffed them with hay. He clattered up to Eagle Calf's tepee at midnight. That worthy went out in his long-sleeved, ankle-length union suit to see what the rumpus was about. When Fish saw Eagle Calf in the moonlight in his white undies, he thought he was a ghost. He yelled, and the last Eagle Calf saw of him that night was when he disappeared over the nearest hill.

A different type of people are the totem pole dwellers of the Northwest. These Indians are a suspicious lot, constantly involved in intrigue.

Many years ago I was painting on the Northwest Coast in the Indian village of Nootka, Vancouver Island. The picturesque cluster of frail wooden shacks, clinging precariously to rocky cliffs, housed Indian families that worked in the large pilchard cannery.

One morning I met an incredibly old man with a wizened face and one penetrating squint eye. He looked like a Chinese pirate. Calling the cannery owner's son, I requested him to ask the Indian if he would pose for me.

At first the old fellow would have none of it. But my friend insisted. A long parley ensued, in Chinook (a gibberish tongue, part Indian, part Spanish, English, French, and what not). Finally, the old Indian grinned and came along with me.

Afterwards the white boy described how he'd told the Indian I was a "Boston man" (American) who had come from "way back east in New York and Washington where all the big white chiefs live to paint famous Indian chiefs like you.

"This man hang his pictures in a big potlatch house," the boy continued. "He invite all big white chiefs to come see all big Indian chiefs. When they come

The Indian's Heroic Age Lives Again. W. Langdon Kihn puts final touches to his painting of a Columbia River Indian netting salmon (page 128), one of his 103 paintings in this book. New York-born Mr. Kihn began art studies at 15. Today more than 50 museums and galleries here and abroad have exhibited his work. Commissioned by The National Geographic Society to capture on canvas major North American Indian groups at high points in their history, he roamed from Florida to Alaska, from California to Labrador. By car, train, boat, canoe, horseback, and plane he probed some of the continent's most remote wildernesses. He visited chiefs and tribesmen, sketched costumes, jotted notes on ceremonies. His artistry and painstaking research have produced the most complete, authentic, and dramatic picture record of the North American Indian ever achieved.

and look around, they say 'Where's Sam?' And if you don't pose for this man there'll be no Sam."

Sam could not bear the thought of not having his picture hung in the white man's potlatch house.

I finished most pictures in my Connecticut studio using sketches and notes made in the field. Geronimo (page 115) and Chief Joseph (page 124) are composite pictures done from existing photographs. The features of Pocahontas (page 61) were taken from a portrait made of her in England in 1616.

Some canvases, mostly portraits, I painted on the spot. Sometimes these were of Indians who had supplied information. Occasionally subjects belonged to notable families.

For the better part of a day I went over the Little Big Horn battleground in Montana with One Bull (page 12).

The old warrior, a nephew of Sitting Bull, actually took part in the fight that wiped out General George A. Custer and his cavalry detachment in June, 1876. One Bull's firsthand recollections of the battle will not be heard again. In his nineties when I talked with him, he died a few years later.

I was also fortunate to meet and paint Chief Shaiks (page 147) at Wrangell, Alaska. He was the last descendant of a line of hereditary chiefs dating from the time of Russian occupation in the mid-18th century. Until his death, a year after he posed for me, Chief Shaiks remained an influential figure among the Tlingit.

One particular portrait, that of the Hopi girl with the "squash blossom" hairdo (frontispiece), proved to my satisfaction that most of the more primitive tribes are adjusting rapidly to what we call civilization. The Hopi are a tribe of the Pueblo, mild, soft-spoken Indians of the Southwest who live, dress, and conduct their ceremonies much as they did when Cabeza de Vaca and his Negro lieutenant Estevan found them more than 400 years ago.

Before the Hopi girl's last sitting as my model, she gave birth to a stillborn child. In earlier days, her people would have believed that I had somehow drawn the life out of the unborn child. Probably they would have killed me. I was thankful that their views on the matter were modified.

Indians that have been in close contact with us for generations now live much as we do. They have houses, autos, radios, jobs in all walks of life. Eskimos often power their primitive skin umiaks with outboard motors, many Navajos drive to fire dances in pickup trucks, and I once watched the christening of a plane which Indians at Oregon's Klamath Reservation had bought to patrol their forest reserve.

My last field trip traced the oldest migration routes in northwestern America, from Alaska's coast to the interior. In 18 hours' flying from Nome to the Mackenzie delta, we accomplished a trip that would have taken those early migrants from Asia years to complete.

We soared over high mountains and fertile valleys spotted with game. Landing at Fort Yukon on the Arctic Circle, we were met by a temperature of 93 degrees and myriads of mosquitoes. Soon after take-off, we plunged into the boiling smoke of a forest fire which blotted out the sun and forced us to skim low over the twisting Porcupine River.

After what seemed an anxious eternity, the smoke thinned, the mountains dwindled, and we slipped in to land at Old Crow, northernmost Indian outpost of Yukon Territory.

The isolated village contains a score of log cabins, a log trading post, a mission, and the log residence of the Royal Canadian Mounted Police. A jungle of spruce, poplar, alder, and willow hems in the community, adding to its remote atmosphere. The population of about 125 Kutchin Indians, formerly called the Loucheux, lives exclusively by hunting and trapping.

In such a setting I expected to find a people uninfluenced by the distant outside world. I anticipated ancient rituals from the pagan past. I looked for unique costumes, tuned my ears for Indian songs.

After a day or so, invited to a village dance, I accepted gladly, preparing myself for a flood of fascinating material. The rigors of the trip to Old Crow would now seem worthwhile—I thought.

A surprise was in store. The dance turned out to be a Hudson's Bay jig, a good deal like a New England square dance. The music consisted—not of chants, savage and insistent—but of English and Scottish tunes played on a fiddle and guitar by two Kutchin braves!

PART II

ANCIENT LIFE

IN THE

NEW WORLD

Yum Kax, God of Harvest, Sows Corn on the Earth Mother, adorned with serpent head-dress. His bright knitted bag holds grains of the Maya staff of life; his hat, resembling a bishop's miter, is a conventionalized ear of corn. Man's face fastened to the god's back may be a severed human head or a mask of stone or wood. More than 1,000 years ago a Maya sculptor fashioned the original of this scene on a 16-foot stela found in 1921 at Piedras Negras, Guatemala.

CHAPTER 9

THE MAYA OF YUCATAN

BY SYLVANUS GRISWOLD MORLEY

DURING THE EARLY YEARS of the Christian Era there developed in what is now northern Guatemala a civilization called the Maya.

This civilization, destined to become the most brilliant cultural expression of ancient America, was based upon agriculture, chiefly the raising of corn.

Because the early Maya were primarily farmers, they became interested in the phenomena of time, the passing of the seasons, the several stages of the farmer's year—when the forest should be felled, the dried wood and leaves burned, the corn planted, and harvested. All these were of vital concern, so their priests during the millennium before Christ turned to the study of time measurement and astronomy.

Although the Maya in their knowledge of the apparent movements of heavenly bodies—the sun, moon, Venus, and probably other planets as well—far excelled both the ancient Egyptians and Babylonians, their greatest intellectual achievement was the invention of a chronology, exact to the day within a period of 374,-400 years.

For the first time in human history, a system of chronology used numbers involving the concept of the abstract mathematical quantity of zero, one of the outstanding achievements of all time. All the essential elements of our modern arithmetic had been put to use by the ancient Maya 2,000 years ago, at least five centuries before the Hindus developed the fundamentals of Arabic notation in India (page 198).

By their accurate system, Maya priests were able to predict eclipses and the heliacal rising and setting of Venus. Of even greater importance to the Maya farmer, they had determined the length of the tropical year with as high a degree of accuracy as Pope Gregory XIII did a good thousand years later.

The excellent weather calculations of these astronomer-priests were largely responsible for the accumulation of food reserves. This growing wealth, in turn, meant more and more time off from the routine of keeping body and soul together, so that people were able to turn to other pursuits. Architecture, sculpture, painting, ceramics, jade engraving, weaving, and featherworking became highly esteemed by the ancient Maya.

Thus, during the fourth to eighth centuries of the Christian Era, there rose numbers of cities, with public buildings made of stone, decorated with stucco, and brilliantly painted.

There were lofty pyramids, surmounted by towering temples, progenitors of our modern skyscrapers; great monasteries for the numerous priesthood; probably palaces for the ruling caste; astronomical observatories; ball courts where a game like modern basketball was

Kneeling Penitent Makes Blood Offering to the Gods. Dressed in gorgeous raiment, he pulls a thick cord studded with thorns through a slit in his tongue. Maya priest with ceremonial staff supervises. Reddened cord and drops of blood fall into carved stone vase. Bloodletting from pierced ear lobes was also a common form of self-mutilation to express religious devotion. This scene was carved on the underside of a door lintel in a Yaxchilán temple. Some of the finest Classic Maya sculpture was created at this ceremonial center in the Usumacinta River Valley. Even today Lacandone Indian descendants of the Maya come to Yaxchilán to burn copal incense on ancient altars.

played; vapor baths, and other specialized masonry constructions. These buildings were arranged around large squares or plazas, or on top of artificially raised terraces sometimes of enormous extent.

In the plazas and on the terraces stood beautifully sculptured monuments, ranging from 5 to 25 feet in height. These were erected at five- or ten-year intervals to commemorate the principal astronomic events of the passing years, to set forth corresponding calendar corrections for the period, like our own leap-year corrections, and for other ceremonial and religious purposes.

This first florescence of the Maya culture I have called the Old Empire.* It

was the highest civilization, judged both by its intellectual and esthetic achievements, ever produced by the American Indian.

The Old Empire was probably not so much a political entity as a cultural unit, like the city-states of ancient Greece: Athens, Sparta and Corinth; or the city-states of Renaissance Italy: Venice Genoa, and Florence. The Maya constituted a loosely associated group of powerful communities enjoying a common and exceedingly homogeneous culture.

The Old Empire stretched from what

*Instead of Morley's "Old Empire" and "New Empire" concepts, archeologists today refer to Formative, Classic, and Mexican periods.

now is western Honduras to the highlands of central Chiapas, Mexico, always keeping to the Atlantic side of the Continental Divide. Thence it extended north across the heavily forested lowlands of northern Guatemala (the Department of Petén) and adjacent parts of the States of Chiapas and Tabasco, Mexico, on the west and British Honduras on the east, and still farther north into the Yucatán Peninsula (map, page 189).

Uaxactún, deeply buried in the jungle of northern Guatemala, is representative of Old Empire cities. Its peculiar importance lies in that it is the oldest center of Maya civilization.

The writer will never forget the day he discovered the oldest Maya monu-

ment, standing in its lonely court on the Acropolis of Uaxactún. As he came through the thick bush he caught sight of the tall shaft of stone leaning far to one side, with two columns of hieroglyphics engraved upon its back, so covered with dried moss and living lichens as to be all but indistinguishable.

Climbing up the back of the shaft, he fell to work cleaning off the dried moss which obscured the details of the inscription. Suddenly there literally flashed from the stone the number 8—three dots and one bar, as the ancient Maya wrote it—and beside it the sign for the baktun. Baktun 8.

Most older Maya monuments were erected in Baktun 9, a period extending

Religion Filled Youths' Lives in Maya Days. Noble maiden contemplates Yum Kax (page 182), one of many deities in the Maya pantheon. Her elaborate headdress, heavy bracelets, and rich-embroidered kirtle fringed with jade beads reveal her as a chieftain's daughter. To her, each day had its astrological significance, each event its patron god. Right: A young craftsman deftly depicts religious scenes on a graceful jar. No pre-Columbian Indians produced more artistically decorated ceremonial ware than the Maya. The potter's finest work went into the tombs of nobles.

From His Stately Throne, the Chief Bids Courtiers Be Silent. The artist re-creates a drama in stone from a Piedras Negras lintel, finest known specimen of Maya skill. While Europe languished in the Dark Ages, Indian pyramid builders carved such masterpieces as this, dating from A.D. 761.

186

Chief's extended arm, heads of squatting nobles were carved in the round. Natural poses, perfectly proportioned figures suggest Greek art; rich garments, fans, tassels show amazing realistic detail. Some 158 hieroglyphs form a border on the original, now in Museum of Archeology, Guatemala City.

Priests Sacrifice a Parrot. Copal resin burns on stone altar carved with sun god's face and serpent heads like gargoyles. Snakes dominate headdresses. The Maya did not seek charity from their gods. They willingly paid in human, animal, fruit and vegetable offerings for all favors granted.

from A.D. 176 to A.D. 571. Just as we start our calendar from the birth of Christ, the Maya began theirs from a date some 5,000 years ago which must have marked a great event in their mythological history. Instead of our millennium, century, decade, year, month, and day, they figured time in baktuns (144,-000 days), katuns (7,200 days), tuns (360 days), uinals (20 days), and kins (one day).

The date of this earliest monument— 8.14.10.13.15 (8 baktuns, 14 katuns, 10 tuns, 13 uinals, 15 kins)—falls A.D. 68!

Because this monument records a date in the Maya Baktun 8, the name Uaxactún was given to the city, the word

meaning in Maya *uaxac,* "eight," and *tun,* "stone"—stone eight.

Several years later the Carnegie Institution selected Uaxactún for extensive study and excavation. Frans Blom, of the Seventh Central American Expedition, in 1924 discovered that the arrangement of temples and pyramids on the east and west sides of the plaza in probably the oldest parts of Uaxactún formed a giant sundial for determining the equinoxes and solstices.

The priests of Uaxactún gave this information to the farmers, enabling them to regulate the different activities of their year; the felling and burning of

188

the bush, planting and harvesting, with ceremonies appropriate to each occasion.

Later excavations at Uaxactún revealed what is unquestionably one of the most magnificent examples of aboriginal American architecture extant—a silvery white, stucco-covered pyramid of exquisite proportions and perfect outline.

The northern half of the Yucatán peninsula, which I have called the New Maya Empire, was only a provincial region in Old Empire times. It did not reach its cultural zenith until the 12th, 13th, and 14th centuries.

One by one the cities of the Old Empire ceased to build new temples and palaces, ceased to erect sculptured stone monuments and hieroglyphic inscriptions setting forth their respective dates in the Maya era; ceased, in fact, to func-

tion as governmental and religious centers. Meanwhile the cities of Yucatán increased in prosperity and were becoming new fountainheads of Maya culture.

The common people of the Old Empire fell away, and finally the former centers of teeming population were abandoned. The forest returned, and again the jaguar, tapir, peccary, and deer stalked the courts where kings had ruled and priests performed their rites of human sacrifice.

Earthquakes, foreign conquest, civil war, recurrent epidemics of yellow fever and malaria, climatic changes bringing an increased rainfall so abundant that the land was no longer tillable by the Maya system of agriculture; intellectual and esthetic exhaustion following a long period of forced productivity; social disorganization, political decay, and gov-

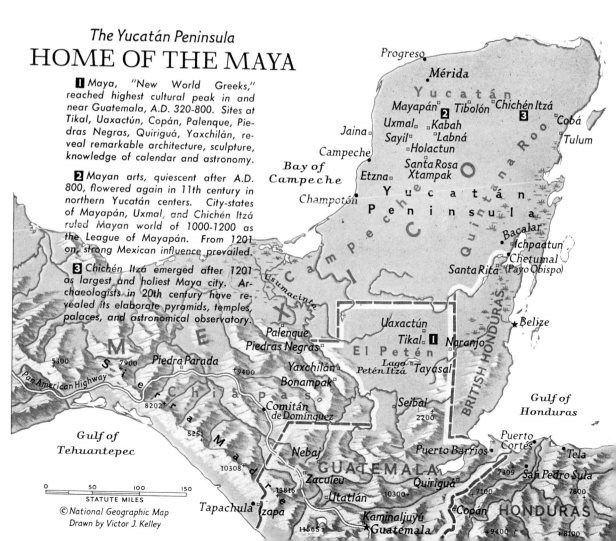

The Yucatán Peninsula
HOME OF THE MAYA

1 Maya, "New World Greeks," reached highest cultural peak in and near Guatemala, A.D. 320-800. Sites at Tikal, Uaxactún, Copán, Palenque, Piedras Negras, Quiriguá, Yaxchilán, reveal remarkable architecture, sculpture, knowledge of calendar and astronomy.

2 Mayan arts, quiescent after A.D. 800, flowered again in 11th century in northern Yucatán centers. City-states of Mayapán, Uxmal, and Chichén Itzá ruled Mayan world of 1000-1200 as the League of Mayapán. From 1201 on, strong Mexican influence prevailed.

3 Chichén Itzá emerged after 1201 as largest and holiest Maya city. Archaeologists in 20th century have revealed its elaborate pyramids, temples, palaces, and astronomical observatory.

STATUTE MILES
0   50   100   150

© National Geographic Map
Drawn by Victor J. Kelley

ernmental disintegration—all these have been assigned at one time or another by different writers as causes for the collapse of the Old Empire.

While some of these factors undoubtedly played their part in the Maya decline, especially social and governmental disorganization, I believe the chief cause was the law of diminishing returns.

Agriculture as practiced by the Maya consisted in felling a patch of forest at the end of the rainy season in December or January, in burning it toward the end of the dry season in March or April, and in planting it at the beginning of the rains early in May. This procedure had two drawbacks, both serious in consequence.

PAINTINGS BY H. M. HERGET

Noble and Priest went clothed in resplendent attire. Standing before a stucco-covered temple, a portly noble (above) displays contrasting skirt and tunic of heavy cloth. Olivella shells from oceans east and west cloak his upper arms. Hard palm wood forms his staff.

Ornate ceremonial bar identifies priest (right), whose flaming headdress has a carved wood frame. Grotesque head decorating his jaguar-fur skirt represents a Maya god. Small face mask peers from tasseled belt. Even the sandals are topped with jaguar skin. The painting interprets a figure carved on a mid-ninth century monument at Seibal, in northern Guatemala.

190

Masters of Calendar Lore Were the Maya Priests. Their massive pyramid temples dominated the ancient cities; their jaguar skins, jade, and quetzal plumes set them apart from the common people, whose lives they greatly influenced. Priests alone could fathom the Maya calendar, foretell the good or evil portents of each coming day, and determine the propitious time for sacred rites.

First, the corn harvested the second year from any field was only about two-thirds the first year's yield, while the third year's crop shrank still another third, due to the intense competition from weeds.

In practice the Maya find it easier, now as then, to clear forest and make a new cornfield than to fight the weeds a third year in the same field. Thus most available land must have lain fallow in the populous ancient times awaiting reforestation so it could be cleared again.

Today, depending upon the fertility of the region, this process of reforestation takes from three to ten years.

The second drawback was even more serious than the first. If the burnings are continued long enough, a point is reached where reforestation is retarded. Instead of woody growth returning to the abandoned cornfields, they become overgrown with grass. When this stage was reached, Maya agriculture was at an end.

Even today the modern Maya have no way of turning the stony soil, every-

191

Worshipers Throng Chichén Itzá, Holy City of the Maya. Priest and warrior, noble and commoner assemble for rites vital to their existence. Rising gleaming white from green Yucatán jungle, Maya cities were not abodes of the people, who lived in scattered villages, but great ceremonial centers, mostly open and undefended, and skirted by thatched homes of priesthood and nobility.

From their round, gargoyled observatory Chichén Itzá's astronomers scanned the sky. Narrow openings pierced thick walls, formed lines of sight on stars, sun, moon, and planets. In background: El Castillo (left), largest structure and chief sanctuary to Kukulcan, city's patron deity; Temple of the Warriors (right), named for sculptures of fighting men on the myriad pillars of its colonnade.

193

where interspersed with outcroppings of the native limestone. They have no hoes, picks, harrows, shovels, spades, or plows. Their only agricultural implements are the ax, the machete, or cutlass, with which they fell the forest, and the wooden planting stick with which they make holes in the ground and plant the corn. Their ancestors had only the stone ax and planting stick (page 201).

In ancient times the trees were killed by cutting a ring around the bark with a stone ax. When they had dried out they were burned standing.

I believe that by the eighth century the Old Empire region had been transformed from forest to vast man-made savannas. The ancient Maya priests surely must have foreseen what was impending and made many appeals to the gods to send more abundant crops. The Maya deities did not hearken to these prayers.

Long before affairs had reached this crisis in the south, the centers in Yucatán were increasing in size and power. An early Spanish chronicler, Father Bernardo de Lizana, mentions a tradition that the Maya entry into Yucatán was from the east and that at first only a few people came, for which reason this first immigration was called the *Cenial,* or "Little Descent." Later many people came from the west, which movement was called the *Nohenial,* or "Great Descent."

War Prisoners Learn Their Fate. Bound with rope, necklaces removed, faces scarred, ear ornaments torn out in degradation, they have played the game and lost. Now they face sacrifice. Those with hope gaze up as their unfettered leader supplicates the victorious war chief. Two haughty subchiefs hover by. A large sculpture found in four pieces at Piedras Negras depicts this rare early Maya martial scene. Carved with hard stone tools, it stands 10 feet 4 inches high, weighs 4 tons as restored in the Museum of Archeology, Guatemala City.

PAINTINGS BY H. M. HERGET

195

Maya on the Warpath, like later-day Indians, donned awesome regalia to frighten foes. Club-sword mounted with sharp obsidian, small round shield, served in hand-to-hand fighting. Bow and arrow came later to Yucatán.

Not bent on land conquest, the early Maya fought to gain captives for sacrifice. The sun, after its nightly descent into underworld, required blood to recover from ordeal. Thus needs of a theocratic society bred a warrior class.

To a certain extent this tradition agrees with the archeologic evidence. For there is a chain of dated cities extending from northeastern Petén up the east coast of the peninsula and thence inland (Ichpaatún, Tulum, Cobá, and Chichén Itzá) and another up the west side of the peninsula (Santa Rosa Xtampak, Etzna, Holactun, and Jaina). The eastern cities, with one exception, have earlier dates than the western ones.

There is strong evidence that the first Maya in Yucatán found people already settled there who may or may not have spoken the Maya language, but who certainly did not have Maya culture. They had no stone architecture, no chronology or calendar, no hieroglyphic writing and no typical Old Empire pottery. And herein lies the archeological catch.

If the Maya had found no previous occupants of the region, the pottery they made after reaching Yucatán would have been much the same as they had made in their former homes in the south. But such is not the case. H. B. Roberts, Carnegie Institution expert on Maya ceramics, found the pottery used throughout Yucatán in New Empire times entirely different from that used in the Old Empire region from whence they came. This pottery is related to the earlier wares on the Veracruz coast.

It is evident that a distinctive indigenous ceramic art had already been developed by inhabitants of Yucatán. The bearers of the Maya tradition simply took over native styles of pottery—much the easiest thing to do—but imposed architectural and other elements of their own culture.

Yucatán must have held not a few disappointments for these early adventuring Americans. It is at best but a parched land, limestone in formation, with no rivers or streams and only one or two lakes. Here and there about the country a few natural wells—great holes in the ground, sometimes several hundred feet in diam-

eter—have formed where the limestone crust has become undermined and has fallen through, exposing subterranean water. These the Maya called *cenotes,* and wherever they existed important population centers were established and flourished.

The place where Chichén Itzá was later to be founded was peculiarly favored, for here the waterless plain of Yucatán is pierced by two great natural wells within half a mile of each other. Under primitive conditions, this fact alone determined that an important city would one day grow up around them.

Chichén Itzá, destined to become holy city of the New Empire, seems to have been founded toward the end of the seventh century; Uxmal and Mayapán, other important cities of the north, perhaps 300 years later. Early in the 11th century these three Yucatán city-states established a confederacy called the League of Mayapán, dividing the country into three spheres of influence.

With the peaceful conditions which followed, the country prospered under wise leaders, and a true Maya Renaissance flowered and endured for two centuries.

The façades of the New Empire buildings, instead of being decorated with stucco, were elaborately sculptured with geometric designs, mask panels of the rain god and other decorative elements, and brilliantly painted. Sculpture as an independent art languished, being used chiefly as an adjunct to architecture.

Toward the end of the 12th century the League of Mayapán dissolved in a fierce quarrel between the rulers of Chichén Itzá and Mayapán. Uxmal, standing on the side lines, watched her former allies fight it out.

The "True Man" of Mayapán, as the ancient Maya called their ruler, Hunnac Ceel, finding himself hard pressed in the ensuing war, brought over foreign allies from the interior of Mexico (page 202). These were the Toltecs, whose power cen-

Into the Sacred Well Hurtles a Maiden, Sacrifice to the Rain God. Incense swirls upward.
Thousands throng holy Chichén Itzá and shower jeweled offerings into the abyss as the priests
perform their barbaric rite. From somber waters 20th century dredging has recovered identifiable
bones of 21 children, 13 men, 8 women; jade and other treasure, much of it deliberately smashed.

197

MAYA CALENDAR AND NUMERAL SYSTEM

FASCINATED BY MYSTERIES of time and astronomy, the Maya perfected a calendar and numeral system that rank as outstanding intellectual achievements.

No narratives of personal glories or national calamities fill their written records. Not even the homely record of weighing baskets of corn. Instead, strange and complex figures tell of the beginning and end of time cycles, predict the movement of heavenly bodies, correlate moon-month and sun-year, and chart dates for rituals honoring the gods.

Maya priest-scholars set forth an imaginative concept of time as a series of burdens carried on the backs of divine bearers. Each day brought by the sacred bearers held its own promise of happiness or misery, success or failure.

The thought was mystic but the chronology was as accurate as our own Gregorian calendar, and so precisely organized that no two days could be confused. One monument at Quiriguá calculates in stone a theoretical date 400,000,000 years ago!

As we do today, the Maya wrote figures in two distinct ways, comparable to Roman and Arabic numerals. Maya "Roman" numerals were dots and bars, as shown below. A dot stood for one; a bar, five. Combined, they reached 19—maximum number of days before the next time unit, the Maya 20-day month. Starting off the numeral system is the shell sign for zero.

For their "Arabic" system, from zero through 19, the Maya designed fantastic heads (right). These were of two kinds. Zero through 13 were represen-

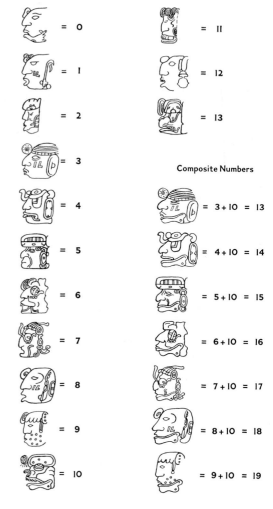

Composite Numbers

= 0	= 11
= 1	= 12
= 2	= 13
= 3	
= 4	= 3 + 10 = 13
= 5	= 4 + 10 = 14
= 6	= 5 + 10 = 15
= 7	= 6 + 10 = 16
= 8	= 7 + 10 = 17
= 9	= 8 + 10 = 18
= 10	= 9 + 10 = 19

ted by patron deities such as Death, Sun, and Rain. From the second number 13 on, the heads were composites. Each combined the skeleton jaw from number 10 with one of the other number signs, 3 through 9.

Thus the compound sign 13 consists of the jaw plus 3, the godhead whose band and disk oddly resemble the mirror worn by a modern physician.

In writing large numbers, the Maya multiplied by means of position, involving use of the zero. So accustomed are we to the zero that we hardly realize what an amazing concept it is. Try, for example, to multiply MCMLXXXIV times MCMLXXXIV!

Without their system, the Maya and their cultural forebears would have had to write impossibly complex combinations of higher figures. To calculate long time periods would have taken stone calendars the size of the Washington Monument!

With the zero, they were able to use a limited number of recurring symbols, giving them value accord-

= 0		= 12
= 1		= 13
= 2		= 14
= 3		= 15
= 4		= 16
= 5		= 17
= 6		= 18
= 7		= 19
= 8		
= 9		
= 10		
= 11		

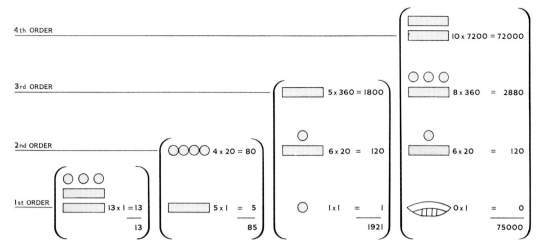

4th ORDER .... 10 x 7200 = 72000

3rd ORDER .... 5 x 360 = 1800 | 8 x 360 = 2880

2nd ORDER .... 4 x 20 = 80 | 6 x 20 = 120 | 6 x 20 = 120

1st ORDER | 13 x 1 = 13 | 5 x 1 = 5 | 1 x 1 = 1 | 0 x 1 = 0

13 | 85 | 1921 | 75000

ing to their position in an overall figure. This is similar to the way we indicate 1,255,378 by the decimal system of units, tens, hundreds, thousands, and so forth from right to left. But where our system progresses by tens, theirs mounted by twenties. Too, instead of writing numbers horizontally as we do, the Maya placed theirs one over the other.

The above chart gives examples of Maya dot-and-bar numbers through the first four orders of the time count. The figures represent days, beginning at the first order with 13 units (13 x 1).

At the second order, four dots are multiplied by 20 (the number of days in a Maya month) and added to five units, producing 85.

The third order brings an exception, the only one to break the even rise of Maya figures. At this point the multiple becomes 360 (that is, 1 x 20 x 18) instead of 400 (1 x 20 x 20). This deviation probably arose from the Maya wish to bring this count as near as possible to the length of the solar year.

With the fourth order, progression by twenties returns, providing a Maya 20-year period of 7,200 days. In the last column's grand total of 75,000 the final, all-important unit zero is obtained by the simple step, 0 x 1 equals 0.

The Maya calendar comprised two cycles: a sacred round of 260 days endlessly repeated, and the con-

ventional 365-day solar year. The cycles were interlocking, like teeth of two unequal cogwheels. As the wheels revolved and cogs meshed, each day took on a double identity.

From the religious count came 260 "day god" symbols, formed by combining numbers 1 through 13 with 20 names. The solar year provided a "month god" position for every day (such as our May 30). There were 18 full months of 20 days in the Maya year, plus an ill-omened fragment of five days.

The sequence of both sets of names and numbers was so staggered that it took 18,980 days or 52 years for the dual identities to duplicate. Hence the Maya 52-year cycle was a complete time unit in their calendar, as the century is in ours.

Pictured below are eight dates from the Maya solar-year cycle that correspond to some of our holidays or celebrations. In each hieroglyph, the number in bars and dots indicates position in the month, the sign at right the name of the Maya month.

These parallels are based on the Maya calendar of the 1560's described by Bishop Diego de Landa.

Two examples, 11 Zac and 12 Mol, show how the sculptors filled unused numeral spaces with decorative detail. Thereby the Maya reveal not only their artistry but the infinite care with which they fashioned in stone a monument to their philosophy of time.

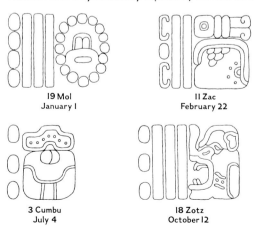

19 Mol
January 1

11 Zac
February 22

3 Cumbu
July 4

18 Zotz
October 12

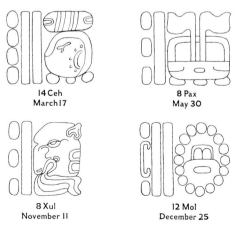

14 Ceh
March 17

8 Pax
May 30

8 Xul
November 11

12 Mol
December 25

tered at Tula, north of the Valley of Mexico. They probably spoke a tongue related to Nahuatl, language of the Aztecs. Possibly it was they who introduced the bow and arrow into Yucatán. This weapon may have had crucial effect in the conflict.

With the aid of his Mexican allies, Hunnac Ceel about 1200 defeated Chac Xib Chac, ruler of Chichén Itzá. Thus the Cocoms, ruling house of Mayapán, became leaders in the northern half of Yucatán Peninsula.

By the clever expedient of compelling all the other Maya chieftains to reside at Mayapán, the Cocom capital, and to administer their respective towns and villages through deputies, the successive Cocom rulers in effect held the other Maya chieftains in hostage while they pursued their tyrannical way.

Though the fragmentary pre-Span-

Grinding Corn and Weaving was women's work then as now. Child on back, a Maya woman patiently bends over stone muller and metate. She soaks dried kernels overnight to loosen hulls, then grinds grain to pasty dough for tortillas, toasts them on a hot griddle, keeps them warm in a gourd until served.

Nor has looming cloth (right) changed much since Maya days. Spanish conquerors mistook fine Indian garments for silk. Homes past and present were walled with saplings, roofed with thatch. Ancient Maya domesticated turkeys, bees, dogs, but had no beasts of burden. Sculptors ignored women in carvings, but pottery figurines reveal their daily life.

200

PAINTINGS BY H. M. HERGET

ish chronicles are silent on the point, it appears probable that Chichén Itzá was given to the Mexican allies as their share in the spoils of war. During the closing period of the city's history (13th to mid-15th centuries) strong Mexican influence is clearly reflected in the new architecture, art, customs and ideas.

This foreign influence from the distant Vale of Anahuac even gave to the Itzá people a new religion, for the conquerors brought with them the worship of the fair golden-haired god, Quetzalcoatl, the "Feathered Serpent," whom the Maya called Kukulcan and revered as patron deity.

Maya Seed Their Fields, armed with planting stick, bag, and gourd. Milpa (clearing) agriculture still survives, begins with dry-season felling and burning of forest trees. Stick planting follows. Ripened ears are bent over and left to dry on stalk. Gourd water bottle still refreshes Maya planter or hunter, corn comprises four-fifths of his family's diet. A sick Indian reveals his state by saying: "I ate only two tortillas this morning." Average Yucateco consumes 20 per meal. Maya also cultivate beans, squash, tubers, cacao, papaya, and avocado pear.

201

PAINTINGS BY H. M. HERGET

Bronzed Warriors Gaze on the City Their Forebears Conquered

Pre-Aztec Toltecs came from central Mexican highlands to aid Mayapán against the Itzá about A.D. 1200. Victorious, they took Chichén Itzá as war prize, made it flourish anew as holy city of Kukulcan, Mayan version of the Mexican deity Quetzalcoatl, the Feathered Serpent. They built the city's principal structures, including the temple (El Castillo) looming in distance. Their dramatic Sacred Well rite drew pilgrims from all parts of the Maya world. Their weapons and militaristic spirit changed Yucatán's once-serene ways.

The feathered serpent columns which guard the portals of many Chichén Itzá temples show Toltec influence. The Chac Mool statues of reclining human figures (page 215), the stone fretwork roof ornaments, the jaguar and eagle sculptures, the turquoise-crowned figures in the reliefs, the exquisite turquoise mosaic plaques, some hieroglyphics—all these are Mexican importations.

The Toltec aliens, remaking religion and architecture in 250 years' sway, put a strong Mexican stamp even on *tlachtli* (right), Maya game combining features of basketball and soccer. Using elbows, knees, and hips, but not hands, players sought to drive a solid rubber ball through a stone ring high on the opponents' wall. Shouts ricocheted in the enclosure. Tradition says spectators vanished when a player scored; the feat made him winner of their clothes and jewelry. One of Chichén Itzá's courts is larger than a modern football field.

Because it presents a blending of two such important native cultures of North America, the Maya and the Toltec, Chichén Itzá was selected by the Carnegie Institution as a center for intensive explorations begun in 1924. Many imposing structures have been revealed and a flood of light thrown upon the life of the New Maya Empire.

Chichén Itzá's two cenotes, or wells, are each about 200 feet in diameter, with their water level 70 feet below the ground. The city takes its name from them, Chichén Itzá meaning in Maya "The mouths of the wells of the Itzá."

One, the Xtoloc Cenote, or Lizard Well, in the center of the city, was used as water supply in ancient times. The other, at the northern end, served a more sinister purpose.

This was the Well of Sacrifice. Into its gloomy depths in times of great national necessity such as drought, tradition holds that young maidens were hurled at daybreak as living sacrificial victims (page 197).

The Spanish chronicles naïvely observe that if the girls managed to survive until midday, ropes were lowered to them and they were pulled out. Then they were questioned as to what the gods had told them was in store for the Itzá, whether an abundant year or famine. If the deities indicated the former, there was great

Massive Stone Rings carved with feathered snakes were goals for Maya youth. Players made offerings in temples at court's open ends to help put ball through 18-inch hole 24 feet above court floor. Courts also served as auditoriums. Less athletic descendants hold oranges for sale.

Jade-studded Jaguar Throne, found in 1936 in a secret chamber of Chichén Itzá's pyramid of Kukulcan, is a prized relic of ancient America. Carved from a single block, painted bright red, it has fangs of white stone. Flat back cradles large turquoise mosaic honoring the sun god.

Henequen, or Sisal, Is Green Gold of Yucatán. Ancient Maya wove fiber into cloth, rope, nets. With steel scraper, modern villager strips tough strands from 50 long, thick leaves a day. Wife separates fibers. Dried strands hang white from hammock behind her. Henequen, related to century plant, took its commercial name from Sisal, coast village near Mérida. A secondary industry, hunting chicle to make chewing gum, led to discovery of several jungle-buried Maya cities.

rejoicing. If the latter, stones were hurled into the well and the people fled with loud cries.

The spectacular nature of this cruel rite—maidens at the brink of the dark pool, the incensing of priests, the sides lined with waiting thousands, a push, perchance a startled cry, a splash below, and silence—all combined to arouse such interest in the ceremony that Chichén Itzá became Mecca of the Mayan World.

Pilgrims came from far and near to hurl treasures into the depths: jade earplugs, noseplugs, beads, plaques and pendants, copper bells and rings, carved bones, shells, elaborate wooden weapons, masses of sacred copal incense, goldwork from Costa Rica and beyond, cloisonné-

like pottery from northwestern Mexico.

Some of this material was recovered early in the 20th century by dredging and now is on exhibition at the Peabody Museum at Harvard University. Judging from the objects recovered, practically the entire cult of the Well of Sacrifice was of Mexican rather than Mayan origin.

More recent studies of bones found at the bottom of the well reveal—venerable traditions to the contrary—that not only girls, but infants and adult men and women were sacrificed.

The foreign rulers, with their new ideas, their new customs, their new religion, gave to the Itzá just that impetus which had been lacking at the end of the 12th century, when the culture stagnated.

All over the northern part of the city, which dates principally from this last period, temples and sanctuaries were rising to the new god, all adorned with highly realistic representations of the Feathered Serpent—in columns, balustrades, cornices, and bas-reliefs.

The so-called Castillo, which in fact is not a castle at all, but the principal temple of Kukulcan at Chichén Itzá, dates from this period. It covers an acre of ground and towers more than 100 feet above the level of the broad plaza at its base (page 192). Four balustraded stairways ascend its terraced sides, and the sanctuary on the summit is entered through a doorway flanked by feathered-serpent columns.

Other buildings of the Mexican period are the Tlachtli-ground or Ball Court (pages 203–05) and the Temple of the Jaguars, the Temple of the Tables, the High Priest's Grave, and the Caracol or Astronomical Observatory.

This observatory was a building of primary importance. The scientific life of the community centered here, and it is thought by some to be the most beautiful structure in the city (page 192). The round tower, 37 feet in diameter, is composed of two concentric circular passages which surround a solid core of masonry. A spiral stairway ascends inside the latter, emerging in a small chamber near the top, from which observations of important astronomic phenomena were made through small tunnellike passages.

Another enormous construction is the Group of the Thousand Columns. This vast architectural complex of pyramid-temples, colonnaded halls, sunken courts, terraces and platforms includes a central plaza more than five acres in extent.

The most imposing structure excavated at Chichén Itzá is the Temple of the Warriors, standing at the northwest corner of this Group of the Thousand Columns (page 193).

This truly magnificent building stands on a pyramid's broad summit. Approximately 70 feet square, it was originally 22 feet in height. A pair of great feathered-serpent columns, 15 feet high, divides the entrance into three doorways. The exterior walls are sculptured with alternating panels of grotesque human masks; conventionalized representations of Kukulcan, patron deity of the city; and of the serpent-bird, a fearsome mythological conception with the body, feet, and wings of a bird, the head of a serpent with forked tongue, and a human head issuing from its mouth.

The front chamber is a long colon-

School Days in Maya Land find young Yucatecos learning Mayan as well as Spanish. No hieroglyphs perplex them in the dimly lit classroom, for they write their ancient American tongue phonetically in A B C's. Girls are garbed in same spotless, embroidered Mother Hubbards their elders wear.

The Glory That Was Tulum Shines in Its Majestic Ruins. Back to the Caribbean, Tulum stands on a 40-foot cliff on Yucatán's east coast. A half-mile stone wall, thicker than its 15-foot height, protected three land sides. The five gateways were narrow, low, and dark to thwart invaders.

Archeologists find thrilling parallels to Greek architecture in Tulum's little Temple of Frescoes, foreground, with its carved figures of a plunging god. Behind the ceremonial square rises the lofty Palace. The Maya city flourished a dozen centuries ago, and again in the Mexican period.

naded hall; behind it is the sanctuary. The carved and painted columns still preserve their colors in practically their original brilliancy —red, blue, green, yellow, brown, black, and white. Enormous plumed serpents weave around the sides of both chambers.

Imagine the barbaric splendor of this building in its heyday, broad summit thronged with priests gorgeously robed in jaguar skins, feather cloaks, and embroidered cottons, half seen in clouds of swirling incense!

The buried temple proved a treasure house. Found lying on its back in a far corner of the outer hall, buried beneath rubble, was the Chac Mool—the reclining human figure which had originally stood before the portals of this temple. Its carving is almost perfectly preserved, except for the nose and part of the headdress, apparently battered off intentionally (page 215).

But the greatest discovery of all, the finest specimen ever recovered from the Maya area, was found under the floor of the sanctuary where the Atlantean altar had originally stood.

As an electric torch was flashed into the interior of a limestone jar

Quiriguá Stela Wears Bird-nest Beard

Eleven centuries have marked little change on the god's Buddha-like face. For each hotun, 1,800-day period in Maya reckoning, Quiriguáns erected such a sandstone shaft. Carved figures of gods front and back wear tall feather headdresses; near-naked bodies are heavily ornamented at waist, wrists, ankles. Hieroglyphs on sides record the period's astronomical events, calculate mythical dates of ages past.

Quiriguá lies in eastern Guatemala's fertile Motagua valley, now banana land. Ancients probably rafted stones to city when river was at flood. They carved boulders into tortoises, jaguars, sky monsters.

a beautiful ball of jade reflected the light. This proved to be an almost perfect sphere, two inches in diameter, highly polished. The Indian laborers at once identified it as a *sastun,* or conjuring stone, such as old Maya medicine men far back in the bush still use in their incantations and magic.

A carved jade pendant, pierced for hanging on a cord, some jade and shell beads, and some bones of a tiny bird, possibly a hummingbird, successively came to light. Still the jar guarded its most precious secret.

In the bottom there flashed forth the blue of turquoise, the first ever found in a Maya city. Brushing disclosed the scalloped edge of a turquoise mosaic, in perilously fragile condition.

Slowly and with infinite pains the sifted earth was removed until there lay revealed a mosaic plaque 8¾ inches in diameter. The wooden back to which the pieces of turquoise had been fastened had long since crumbled to dust. Indeed, upon this dust rested the mosaic, so that any blow would have shattered the arrangement of the more than 3,000 cut and highly

polished pieces. It took a skilled preparator, specially summoned from New York, three weeks to reset the mosaic on a new base. The completed plaque was later put on exhibition in the National Museum of Mexico.

It is amazing to think that Chichén Itzá reached her greatest development, her crowning glory as the holy city of the Maya only after fate had brought her under the heel of a foreign conqueror and the Itzán people had been made to feel the gall and bitterness of foreign rulers and a foreign religion. Yet never before had the city experienced such a building boom. In those two and a half centuries more buildings went up in the

Sacred Plume-giver to the Maya

Carvings, pottery from Maya and Aztec centers alike link the quetzal with worship, prove male fondness for the sweeping iridescent green tail feathers. Supplying the demand enriched highland Maya in the bird's limited habitat.

Crest and upper parts are green, belly crimson, as on these mounted specimens held by a Guatemalan woman. Quetzal is her country's symbol of liberty, appears on national coat of arms, stamps, and coins; gives its name to the Republic's equivalent of the dollar.

KODACHROMES BY LUIS MARDEN,
NATIONAL GEOGRAPHIC STAFF

city than had been built since its foundation, six centuries earlier.

But increasing oppression under the Mayapán dynasty, the Cocoms, backed by their powerful Mexican allies, finally goaded the Maya to desperation. In 1448, banded under the leadership of the Lord of Uxmal, Tutul Xiu, they attacked, captured, and sacked Mayapán. The ruler and all his family were slain, except one son, who was absent at the time, and the city was depopulated.

A curious result of this war of independence was that both vanquished and victors abandoned their former capitals and established themselves elsewhere.

The Cocoms, under the leadership of the single surviving royal son, founded their new capital of Tibolón, east of Mayapán. The Tutul Xiu, although victorious, abandoned Uxmal, where this dynasty had ruled for some five centuries, and founded a new capital at a place named Mani, meaning, "It is finished."

The Itzá not only abandoned Chichén Itzá but withdrew entirely from the peninsula, migrating southward into northern Guatemala, whence the Maya had come some six or seven centuries earlier. There, on a peninsula at the western end of Lake Petén Itzá, they established a new capital called Tayasal. And there in

Ancient Builders in Stone
left their mark on Yucatán. Ruin
at Uxmal (left), struggling to
escape Nature's cloak, is House
of the Pigeons; the many openings in this nine-gabled façade
resemble a vast dovecot. White
buildings of so-called Nunnery
in background enclose a spacious
court. Towering Temple of the
Magician is all but hidden behind
gable ruin to right of tree. Governor's Palace stands at far right.

Skill in cut-stone veneer shows
in famous arch at Labná (below).
Arcade sides converge at top,
are surmounted by flat capstone
in place of keystone unknown to
Maya builders. Such corbeled
arches served not as doorways
but as ceremonial gateways to
quadrangles walled by buildings.

KODACHROMES BY JUSTIN LOCKE

213

1525 the Itzá ruler, Canek, was visited by Hernán Cortés on the latter's heroic march from Puerto Mexico, on the edge of Maya country, across northern Guatemala and south to Honduras.

This last independent branch of the Maya managed to survive because of their extreme isolation for another century and a half until 1687 when they were finally conquered by the Spanish Captain General and Governor of Yucatán, Martín de Ursua y Arizmendi.

The modern Maya, who still comprise probably half the population of the peninsula, are cheerful, friendly, home-loving folk, endowed, in my opinion, with more likable qualities than any other Indian people.

They are short in stature, the men averaging about 5 feet 1 inch and the women only 4 feet 8 inches. All Maya have exceedingly broad heads, which is probably their most marked physical characteristic; their hands and feet are small and beautifully formed.

Add to this eyes nearer black than brown, a strong, well-formed, expressive mouth, and a skin of dark, golden brown with warm high lights, and you have one of America's handsomest native races.

The Maya home consists of a palm- or grass-thatched hut with sides of saplings, often daubed with mud. It is rectangular, with rounded ends, usually about 25 feet long, 10 to 12 feet wide, and 15 feet high to the ridgepole of the steeply sloping roof.

In typical houses there are no windows and only two doorways, in the middle of the long sides (page 206).

Everybody sleeps in this combination living room, bedroom, dining room, and chapel, frequently two to a hammock, with dogs lying beneath and occasionally a setting hen in a corner. The men and boys of the family eat in the main house, women and girls in the kitchen.

The Maya Indian is devout. He was in ancient times when, under the direction of his priests, he reared tremendous stone pyramids and temples to his gods. He was equally devout during the Spanish colonial period when, under the supervision of the Franciscan fathers, he built the enormous churches and spacious monasteries with their cloistered courts, and exchanged his own pagan deities for the white man's God.

Even today much of his own former religious beliefs colors his comprehension of the Church's teachings.

The Maya dances of today are not those of old pagan times. The latter were thought by early Franciscan fathers to be immoral, pertaining to the Devil, and they were speedily replaced by Spanish dances such as the *jarana* and *zapateo*.

But the chief business of the Maya man today, as it has been of his forefathers for century after century, is to raise corn for his family. And the chief occupation of his womenfolk today, just as it was a thousand years ago, is to prepare that corn into tortillas for the family's daily meals.

The way each goes about his or her task has remained practically unchanged throughout the centuries. The man now has a steel ax and machete to fell the forest, instead of ringing the trees with his stone ax. His wife, when she lives in a village, takes her own corn to the local mill and has it ground for a few centavos.

In remoter villages a few women have hand-turned grinders somewhat like a small coffee grinder, but the majority still use a stone slab with a stone grinder held in the hand (page 200).

From 75 to 85 percent of everything the average Maya eats is corn in one form or another. The remaining 15 to 25 percent consists of *frijoles* (beans), chili, chocolate, honey, squashes, a few native tubers, and fruits.

A study of Maya agriculture has established two interesting facts. First, the simple system of raising corn practiced today throughout the Yucatán Peninsula

Chac Mool Keeps a Secret. Giving ear to a modern Chichén Itzá lass, he is one of 12 of his stone-silent kind found in the Maya city. These heroic-size, half-reclining figures with knees drawn up, body resting partly on elbows, hands touching flat bowl on abdomen, lounged before temples or daises within to hold incense or offerings to the gods. Found also in several highland sites, they apparently originated with the Toltec invaders, possibly with a Bacchic cult of drunkenness.

would support at least two million people (three times its present population). Second, to support the average family of five, a Maya Indian has to work in his cornfield only about sixty days a year.

These facts explain the larger population of pre-Columbian times, and how the ancient Maya found time to build their many cities of cut stone.

An environment admirably suited to raising corn, which made the food quest relatively simple; a superabundance of excellent and easily quarried building limestone, which when burned gave them lime for mortar and also furnished a coarse marl gravel that served as sand; wise leaders, who developed a highly efficient governmental organization under which large public works were planned and successfully carried out; and finally, the Maya themselves, elevated and sustained by a lofty religious philosophy—these are the principal factors that made the Maya civilization the most brilliant cultural achievement of ancient America.

Today, silent are the temples, courts, and colonnades; gone the rulers, priests, and sacrificial victims; gone the artisans and builders; gone those humbler folk whose unremitting toil alone made all this pomp and pageantry possible—back to Mother Earth, enshrouded by the living green of tree and bush and flower.

But of a moonlit night, standing on the lofty terrace before the palace of the kings, the silent city of Chichén Itzá at your feet, temples and pyramids rising white and spectral above the dark forest, you will sense that breezes whispering through the trees bring stirring tales of other days, other men, and other deeds. He who would may listen then and hear.

215

El Rey, 30 Tons of Carved Lava, Gets His Colossal Face Scrubbed. Workmen called him el Rey because he was the King of 11 enormous heads found at three sites near the Bay of Campeche by Dr. Stirling, leader of the southern Mexico expeditions. All, like a football eleven, wear helmets. Flattened on back, the sculptures presumably stood against a high wall and are believed to be portraits in stone of leaders of the vanished La Venta culture. A marauding tribe, conquering the flat-nosed sculptors centuries ago, tried to destroy the heads but could only mar and topple them. This well-preserved 1945-season find at San Lorenzo needed only to have fragments restored to section above right eye.

CHAPTER 10

LA VENTA MAN

BY MATTHEW W. STIRLING

DEEP IN STEAMING SWAMPS near the coast of southern Mexico, a family of colossal stone heads stares inscrutably across abandoned plazas where the mysterious La Venta, or Olmec, people once performed barbaric rites.

I saw the first of these heads in 1938, but their existence had been known locally since 1858. Natives with visions of buried treasure excavated one of them, then dropped their spades in disappointment when only an immense carved face appeared. Erosion gradually reburied the head (page 224).

One day at the turn of the 20th century, a Mexican trudging in a tobacco field 15 miles from the almost forgotten head saw a piece of pale-green stone gleam in the dark moist earth. He picked up a small jadeite figurine about eight inches tall, and could not resist a smile.

The carving depicted a bald-headed Indian priest whose wide-open eyes radiate infectious good humor (page 218). This object was destined to become one of the most famous archeological finds in the New World. Curious-looking incised figures on the godlet's stomach eventually were deciphered as a date corresponding to 98 B.C.

The beautifully carved relic baffled archeologists. They called it the Tuxtla Statuette for its discovery site near San Andrés Tuxtla. Its carved glyphs were quite different from those on dated Maya monuments found far to the east in the Peninsula of Yucatán (Chapter 9).

Assuming the date was contemporary with the figurine, was it placed there by early Maya, or did some other group in the Veracruz region invent the calendar and later pass it on to the Maya?

These questions turned tantalizingly in my mind in 1938 as I set out on a long trail leading to the second answer and to the discovery of La Venta Man.

First, I sought the great stone head that had disappointed jungle treasure seekers so long ago. I swung onto a horse and jogged for eight jolting hours along a small tributary of the Papaloapan River to Hueypapa. Within a mile of the village of Tres Zapotes the weather-blackened head came into view, buried to its forehead in a plaza formed by four mounds. Brushing stubborn earth from its face, I saw for the first time its grim, sullen expression.

When I returned to Washington, D. C., staff members of the National Geographic Society examined my photographs of the colossal head and realized the potential importance of the Tres Zapotes site. We organized the first of nine expeditions into La Venta country cosponsored by the Society and the Smithsonian Institution. The field staff —besides my wife Marion and me— included Dr. and Mrs. C. W. Weiant and National Geographic Photographer

Cheerful Duck-billed Godlet, the Tuxtla Statuette, was plowed up in southern Mexico in 1902. It created an immediate stir. Bars and dots on the jolly figurine's stomach indicate a Maya calendar date for 98 B.C.—but the find was outside Maya territory, and earlier than any known Maya date. This enigma led to the discovery of La Venta culture. La Venta lapidaries usually depicted pudgy men with long heads, flattened noses, fleshy jowls and necks. This specimen of pale-green jadeite, in Smithsonian Institution, wears duck-bill mask on lower face; robe draped over shoulder represents folded wings of a bird.

Richard H. Stewart. With us in later seasons were Dr. Philip Drucker and Dr. Alexander Wetmore of the Smithsonian Institution and artist-naturalist Walter A. Weber.

On January 1, 1939, we single-filed into the heart of one of Mexico's most isolated backwashes. Long ago, a numerous and prosperous people pushed back the jungle to live in prosperity on the level plains and high ground at the foot of the Tuxtla Mountains. It was a friendly place: the earthen barrier sheltered them from lashing, Gulf-born hurricanes; abundant crops sprouted from rain-soaked tropical soil.

We set up camp near Tres Zapotes, a thriving farm village. At once we noted an interesting analogy. Its inhabitants were again wresting the rich soil from the jungle and planting the same crops grown by ancients—maize, beans, and squash. We found the Tres Zapoteans cheerful, honest, and hard-working, eager to wield our shovels.

We immediately began excavating the colossal head. Finally it stood fully exposed. We gazed at ten tons of perfectly proportioned workmanship, six feet high and 18 feet around.

Square, pug-nosed, and heavy featured, the face wears an expression of

Oldest Dated Work of Man so far known in the Western Hemisphere, this broken stone slab was discovered by the first Stirling-led National Geographic Society-Smithsonian Institution expedition into La Venta territory. Earlier Tuxtla Statuette find was only 15 miles away.

Delicate dot-dash symbols, interpreted by the Spinden correlation, read November 4, 291 B.C. The stone's reverse is carved with a weeping rain god. Weathering indicates this shattered stela lay on its back for centuries before being set up and re-used by a later people. If three more inches had broken off top or bottom, date could never have been determined!

American Prehistory in Cross Section. Workers slice through a temple mound at San Lorenzo, revealing the structure's stages of growth. Pottery, figurines, artifacts from the different time levels show evolution of style. La Venta mounds were forerunners of Maya and Aztec pyramids.

profound ill humor. It is incredibly life-like, strikingly dissimilar to any other American Indian sculpture that I had seen. Topped by an incongruous helmet, the sturdy face might easily have depicted a 20th century football player.

"How do you suppose it got here?" someone asked.

We knew that the nearest source for this massive basalt block was the base of Mount Tuxtla, 10 miles away. But none of us could imagine how ancient engineers, working without wheels or draft animals, could have performed the feat—and crossed the gorge between Tres Zapotes and mountain. The quarrying alone would be a prodigious task.

Our admiration for these artistic, ingenious people grew as workmen's spades uncovered other large carved stones, including a great open-mouthed jaguar deity representing the Earth Monster (page 228).

Grim suggestions of pagan bloodletting turned up in the heavy clay soil: a stone chest and a barrel-shaped piece of basalt with a shallow basin on top. We could envision high priests spilling human blood into the basin, transferring it to the stone storage chest as mankind's most precious offering to the gods. Indians of southern Mexico were practicing sacrifice of this nature when the Spaniards splashed ashore in Veracruz.

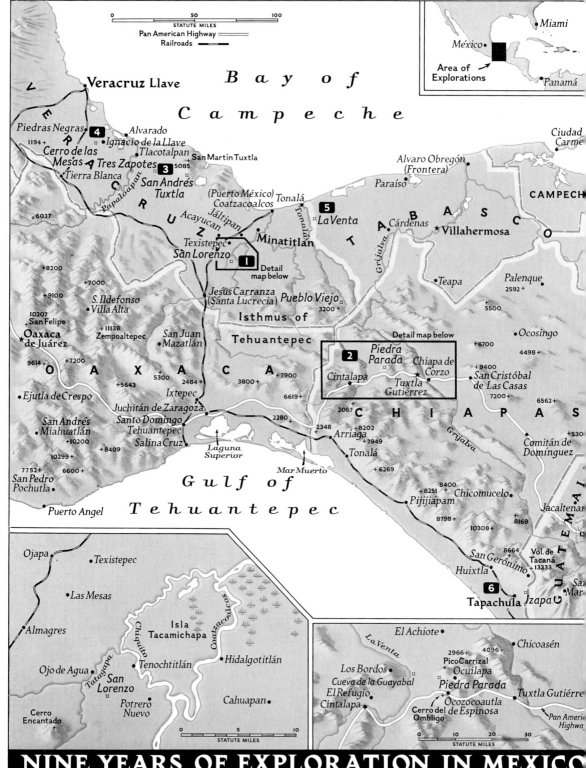

Miami

México

Area of
Explorations

Panamá

Ciudad
Carme

CAMPECH

Bay of

Campeche

Veracruz Llave

Piedras Negras
1194 +
Cerro de las
Mesas
Tierra Blanca

Alvarado
Ignacio de la Llave
Tlacotalpan
San Martín Tuxtla
Tres Zapotes 5085
San Andrés
Tuxtla

Alvaro Obregón
(Frontera)

Paraíso

Palenque
2592 +

(Puerto México)
Coatzacoalcos
Tonalá

La Venta

Cárdenas

Villahermosa

Papaloapan

Acayucan

Jáltipan

Minatitlán

Texistepec
San Lorenzo

Detail
map below

Teapa

+6037

+8200

+7000

Jesús Carranza
(Santa Lucrecia)

Pueblo Viejo
3200 +

5500

Ocosingo

Detail map below

+6700

4498 +

+9100
10207
San Felipe
Oaxaca
de Juárez

S. Ildefonso
Villa Alta
+11138
Zempoaltepec

San Juan
Mazatlán

Isthmus of
Tehuantepec

Piedra
Parada
Chiapa de
Corzo
Cintalapa
Tuxtla
Gutiérrez

+9400
San Cristóbal
de Las Casas
7200 +

9614 +

+7200

+5300

2484 +

3800 +

+7900

6619 +

2067 +

6562 +

+530

Ejutla de Crespo

San Andrés
Miahuatlán
+10200

+5643

Ixtepec
Juchitán de Zaragoza
Santo Domingo
Tehuantepec
Salina Cruz

2280 +

2348 +

Arriaga

8202
+7949

CHIAPAS

Grijalva

Comitán de
Domínguez

Laguna
Superior

Tonalá

+8409

7752 +
San Pedro
Pochutla
10299 +

6600 +

Mar Muerto

Gulf of

Mar Muerto

+6269

8400
+8251
8798 +

Chicomucelo

Pijijiápam

10308 +

8169

Jacaltenar

Puerto Angel

Tehuantepec

8664
+
San Gerónimo

Vol. de
Tacaná
+13333

Huixtla

Sa
Mar

Tapachula

Izapa

Ojapa

Texistepec

Las Mesas

Isla
Tacamichapa

El Achiote

Chicoasén

2966 +
PicoCarrizal
+ Ocuilapa
Piedra Parada

4096 +

Almagres

Ojo de Agua

San
Lorenzo
Potrero
Nuevo

Tenochtitlán

Hidalgotitlán

Cahuapan

Los Bordos
Cueva de la Guayabal
El Refugio
Cintalapa

Ocozocoautla
de Espinosa
Cerro del
Ombligo

Tuxtla Gutiérre

Pan Americ
Highwa

Cerro
Encantado

STATUTE MILES

STATUTE MILES

NINE YEARS OF EXPLORATION IN MEXICO

1 Here La Venta culture reached its height. Discovered were five colossal stone heads, two 9 feet high, and the remains of an ancient aqueduct.

4 A cache of carved jade, 782 pieces, was found at Cerro de las Mesas. Ceramics found at this site and at Tres Zapotes link a history chain from 300 B.C. to A.D. 1400.

2 Piedra Parada, heretofore unexplored archeologically, is in an area of stone structures, ball courts, and caves containing much pottery.

5 Ceremonial center of La Venta culture. Here were colossal heads, carved jade, and mosaic floors of jaguar motif. Tombs of priests held rich gifts of semi-precious stones.

3 Here were found the New World's oldest dated work, 291 B.C. (Spinden correlation), and cerami styles covering 200 B.C. to A.D. 1000

6 Exploration at Izapa reveale over thirty stone monuments an altars curiously carved with man beast figures. These indicate a pre La Venta period, as yet unstudied

Our explorations soon convinced us that our spades were cutting into the site of a great aboriginal city. Although tall tough grass and dense jungle camouflaged much of the land, we counted 50 ceremonial mounds in a stretch of two miles. The growing awareness that this was a hitherto unknown culture heightened our sense of expectancy.

On January 16, 1939, under broiling hot sun, I tramped to a distant section of our workings to examine a flat stone a workman had pointed out. Digging bared traces of a weathered design. The back appeared to be plain. The workmen were on their knees in the muddy excavation pit, carefully cleaning soil from the stone with their hands. Suddenly, one called out in Spanish.

"Chief! Here are numbers!"

Peering close, I saw that a beautifully carved row of bars and dots ran across the stone in low relief (page 218). These immediately suggested a Maya calendar date, something we all had hoped for but had not dared to expect.

The stone obviously was a fragment broken from a large stela, a slab bearing inscriptions. By good fortune, almost all the date was preserved on the section we found.

I copied the characters and hurried back to camp. Excited, we started to decipher the bars and dots. Checked and rechecked, the date was 6 Eznab 1 Uo.

November 4, 291 B.C.—oldest recorded date ever found in the New World!

Predating the Tuxtla Statuette by 193 years, carved a generation before Rome and Carthage launched the Punic Wars, it ranks as the Rosetta Stone of Middle American archeology.

For four months thatched huts by the colossal head were our not entirely com-

Tomb of Three Ancients at La Venta at first defied penetration because of its skillful stone fitting. Nine basaltic columns on each side, five at rear, supported roof. Sloping columns at front formed a ramp; when removed they revealed interior packed to roof with clay. Workers finally uncovered flagstone platform at rear of tomb. On it a layer of brilliant cinnabar held mere traces of human bones amid masterpieces of jade carving.

Under a 10-inch "clamshell" was an exquisite polished jade female figure with pleasant features and long hair. Near by were an ornate headdress, a frog, heart, flower, beads, and figurines—all in vivid green and translucent blue jade.

NATIONAL GEOGRAPHIC PHOTOGRAPHER
RICHARD H. STEWART

Largest Jade Find in the New World comes to light as Mrs. Stirling brushes away concealing earth. This thrilling moment reveals varied workmanship and colors, styles early and late, indicating pieces came from far and wide (page 230).

Zapotes. At a depth of 20 feet, sealed beneath a layer of volcanic ash, spaders penetrated a deposit of dark-colored earth filled with pottery fragments and figurines. The artifacts left little doubt that Tres Zapotes was one of the longest-inhabited sites in Veracruz State. Ceramic styles covered a span of 1,800 years, from a time several centuries before Christ's birth until shortly before the Spanish occupation.

A small mound yielded the second season's most exciting discovery: a group of pottery vessels covering figurines, among them wheeled toys (page 226). Previously it had been doubted that the principle of the wheel was known in the New World.

Now we started a new phase of exploration: side trips in southern Veracruz and neighboring territory, a rich archeological storehouse with a definite bearing on the interpretation of such classical high culture zones as the Maya of Central America, the Zapotecan of Oaxaca, and the Toltec and Aztec of the Valley of Mexico.

fortable home. We shared them with ants, ticks, mosquitoes, biting flies and plump worms. At times northers lashed camp, halting work and filling excavations with muddy water.

We found evidence that two distinct peoples had occupied the site in remote times. Near the surface rested charred bones in covered pottery vessels, an obvious sign of cremated burials. Deep beneath were direct interments in an entirely different type of pottery.

Still unanswered, however, was the riddle of the ancient Indians who lived and died on the place where we dug and walked.

We returned to Mexico early in 1940 to dig deeper into the secrets of Tres

We recalled that a Tulane University expedition, headed by Frans Blom and Oliver La Farge, had pressed in 1925 to La Venta, a village east of Tabasco State's Tonalá River. They photographed the top of a stone head, but lacked time to excavate. The stone might be a twin to our colossal head at Tres Zapotes.

Thus we set forth for La Venta, a remote pin point of a place destined to give its name to a rich prehistoric culture.

We boated up the wide river and into a small coffee-colored tributary mirroring immense webs of mangrove trees. Unseen monkeys chattered and quarreled in the upmost branches.

A pleasant surprise awaited us. An oil-prospecting team had pitched camp two days before at the derelict village of Blasillo. The hospitable Mexicans cleared a space for our cots in their storage tents and their Chinese cook placed a superb dinner before us.

Next morning, camp guides and carriers led us through foot-sucking thickets toward a dry, sandy rise in the heart of an expansive mangrove swamp. Patches of corn and bananas appeared. A half-hour of easier walking brought us to La Venta itself, a large clearing containing the homes of elderly Sebastián Torres and his two sons-in-law and their families.

The La Ventans generously vacated one of their houses for us. They speak Aztec among themselves, but they also know Spanish so we had no difficulty communicating with them.

A colossal stone head? No, they knew nothing about it.

Yes, there were several carved stones, perhaps a great many covered by jungle growth. But take care. Ghosts of Aztec emperor Montezuma and his court come out to dance and sing among the ruins on moonlit nights.

We soon stood on the jungle-tangled top of a huge

Red-painted Ear Plugs, Pointed Beard, and Satanic Leer of this life-size clay head found at Cerro de las Mesas reminded the Stirlings of a similar figure, page 227, unearthed a year earlier 50 miles southeast at Tres Zapotes. Below: Broken before burial, arms and legs of a fire god were found piled on a cross-decorated brazier, worn atop the hollow idol's head to hold hot coals. Prize jade cache lay near by.

KODACHROMES BY NATIONAL GEOGRAPHIC PHOTOGRAPHER RICHARD H. STEWART

mound 105 feet high. The pyramid sloped down to a rectangular base 100 yards square. North stood a sweeping enclosure walled by stone columns ten feet high. Windblown earth now filled the corral, but the formidable close-set pillars indicated that it once served as a sanctum. Three symmetrically placed smaller knolls loomed south of the main mound.

We were standing on the crest of a major ceremonial shrine.

Next day we began excavating two intricately carved stone altars. Before one, a workman uncovered 99 large jade beads arranged in the position of necklaces and armlets. The other altar was artistically the finest object we discovered. Five babies, carved with amusing realism, rest in the arms of adults. We dubbed them the "Quintuplets."

Stone after stone appeared from La Venta's sandy soil, but no sign of a giant head. We began to fear that the jungle had camouflaged it forever.

Excavating a jutting stone pillar occupied us for a week. To our surprise, the stela emerged 14 feet high, almost seven feet wide, and 34 inches thick. The delicate low-relief composition depicts two seven-foot adults apparently talking to each other. One is a handsome individual with aquiline nose and long, flowing beard. Both figures wear tall head-

"Kettle" Inspired Expeditions. What was trash to fortune-seeking Mexicans a century ago became treasure to modern archeologists. Excavation of colossal heads and other La Venta objects raised the curtain on a new culture and shed light on early American intellectual and artistic achievements formerly attributed to the Maya. All this stemmed from a seeming inverted kettle (above) once partially unearthed by Veracruzanos who hoped it held buried loot. Intrigued by accounts of giant heads bedded in clay to the eyebrows and cloaked by Mexican jungle, the National Geographic Society and the Smithsonian Institution in 1939 launched the first of nine expeditions that found the "missing link" of Middle American antiquity. A replica of one of the heads rests in National Geographic headquarters.

Right: Although the party worked only through the four-month dry season, unscheduled rains occurred. The excavation could not be drained. Bailing it by hand took two tedious days, had to be repeated three times one week.

224

Helmeted La Venta Enigma. Dr. Stirling kneels beside largest of five gigantic basalt heads found at La Venta. Time-worn and battle-scarred, the inscrutable face has lost lower jaw and most of its flat nose—probably the work of pre-Columbian vandals. But finely carved teeth remain intact. Engineers as well as sculptors, the mysterious La Ventans somehow transported 30-ton stones across rugged terrain from distant basalt sources. "Helmets" are believed a practical decorative touch serving in place of elaborate feathered headdresses fragile and difficult to carve.

225

Wheels for Toys, but not for Labor-saving. Earliest known New World use of wheels dates back 12 centuries to this smiling dog and laughing jaguar. Mounted on hollow tubes, they were found beside round disks at Tres Zapotes, suggesting that La Ventans inserted wooden axles and used the disks as wheels. Sole similar discovery prior to Dr. Stirling's was tiny coyotelike figures dating from about A.D. 1400 uncovered 13,000 feet high on Popocatepetl. Recent finds confirm pattern: all are in Mexico, all animal effigies in clay, all toys. Opposite: Like a character from Faust, this lifelike clay head with pointed beard and crafty grin ranks with best of ancient ceramic art.

dresses. Like other headdresses on La Venta statuary, none bears the ornamental bird plumes so widely used by related Indian cultures.

Another crew shoveling earth from a flat-topped stone north of La Venta's dominant mound disclosed an unusual base in the form of a head. Archaic style and aged appearance suggest it to be one of La Venta's oldest treasures.

A hole runs through this gaunt old altar, starting at the left ear and emerging at the mouth. It was not difficult to imagine a high priest speaking into the stone ear, his stentorian tones emerging awesomely as if by magic from the mouth itself!

A workman mentioned faintly recalling two other stones in the forest near by. He hacked through matted undergrowth. Suddenly we stumbled upon a large hemispherical pate almost smothered in vines. I looked at it closely and grinned. The eyes were covered and there was little else to judge by. But I knew this must be Blom's colossal head.

Excavated, the stone proved to be a good two feet taller than the colossal head at Tres Zapotes. But the two looked like brothers; both had the same broad nose, thick lips, helmetlike headdress, and dyspeptic expression.

A small boy approached. "Señor," he said, "I have seen some stones near the new *milpa* (maize field) where my papa is working."

In the forest a half mile away he pointed out three round stones bulging from the earth about 30 yards apart. Here were three more immense heads. Two bore a new sculptural feature, finely carved teeth (page 225). The fifth and last stone head unburied at La Venta showed its appreciation by displaying a foolishly happy, befuddled smile.

Among the 20 sculptured monuments excavated during our second season in Mexico were the finest specimens of stone carving ever brought to light in ancient America.

The National Geographic-Smithsonian expedition returned to La Venta several more seasons, firm in its conviction that this art represented in a pure form an ancient fountainhead of Middle American culture. Scattered examples of the art style previously had been called Olmec, after the legendary "rubber people" dwelling along the Veracruz coast.

While neither stone temples nor palaces stood at La Venta, the people who raised the huge stelas and statues were skilled engineers as well as artists. No igneous rock of the type from which the monoliths were carved exists closer than 50 miles from the swamp-enfolded island.

Geometry-minded La Ventans oriented their constructions to an imaginary line bisecting the summit of the central mound. To explore this line, we dug a deep wide trench. Alongside, workmen uncovered a vividly colored jaguar-mask mosaic 23 feet below topsoil. The ancient builders had laid green paving blocks in a yellow clay border. They tamped blue clay into the sacred beast's eyes, nose, and mouth (page 228).

The profusion of jade and serpentine axheads showed that the ax was a sacred symbol, and meant as much to La Ven-

Earth Monster Yawns as a native work crew strains to pry his massive monument from deep jungle mud at Tres Zapotes. Turn page sideways to see three stocky figures carved in low relief inside wide-stretched mouth of grotesque animal believed to symbolize the Earth Monster. Scene may represent a wedding, as central figure appears to be a woman facing kneeling figure to her right.

tans as the cross to Christians. Rich burial gifts of semiprecious stones pinpointed La Venta as a ground set apart for the interment of priests and notables.

As yet we had found virtually no human skeletal material, invaluable to the archeologist. Our expedition to Cerro de las Mesas, a village in southern Veracruz, bared the first well-preserved human remains in quantity.

Cutting through an upper mound that enclosed another like onion skin, we came upon five pottery vessels. Each contained the neatly sawed-off face of a human skull.

The lower or primary mound apparently was built to protect the remains of a single individual. The body had been tightly flexed and laid on its side in the exact center of the mound, the head cut off and placed face down in a large, orange-colored marine shell filled with red paint. Buried in the paint were two jade beads and a carved monkey's head.

The skull itself was large and thin; the forehead had been flattened. The

Green Tiger in Tile glares out of deep La Venta pit. Polished stone mosaic, here viewed upside down, represents eyes, nose, and fangs of a jaguar. Tilers set blocks into an asphalt base over a stone platform, bordered them with yellow clay. Four diamond-shaped elements provide decorative fringe.

La Venta art, like Egyptian, eventually became stylized. Natives today fear jaguar, *el tigre*, as did ancient forebears to whom it was sacred.

effect, grotesque to our eyes, probably
was greatly admired by the man's con-
temporaries. The teeth were carefully
and neatly inlaid with circular pieces of
gold-colored pyrite.

Buried with the body were massive
shell beads, a turtle shell containing lustrous Panama seashell rattles and engraved with a plumed serpent. Just
north of the skull lay a highly polished
stone yoke, one of those mystifying
carved works often found in Veracruz.

A curious sandwich arrangement of
buried cement floors at the Cerro de las
Mesas site yielded 52 pottery vessels of
hard red ware. Each cradled the skull of
a young adult with two or three verte-
brae attached, an indication that the
heads had been severed. The 52 skulls
had been artificially flattened during the
owners' lifetime. In many the front teeth
bore chipped notches. The heads probably represented a mass sacrifice performed on a grimly memorable occasion.

Near by we discovered a deep trench
filled with an orderless jumble of human
bones. This find conjured up a picture of
less important victims being shoved over
the ceremonial mound's rear edge from
a blood-stained altar.

Skeletal remains at Cerro de las Mesas
mutely witnessed that the custom of ap-

Treasure-trove at Cerro de las Mesas—782 Pieces of Fine Jade. Held upright is priest with knife in hand. Most prized find is realistic infant at center. Long, dark canoe below figurines has typical La Venta faces carved on flat prow and stern. Beads, found loose, are in many shapes.

230

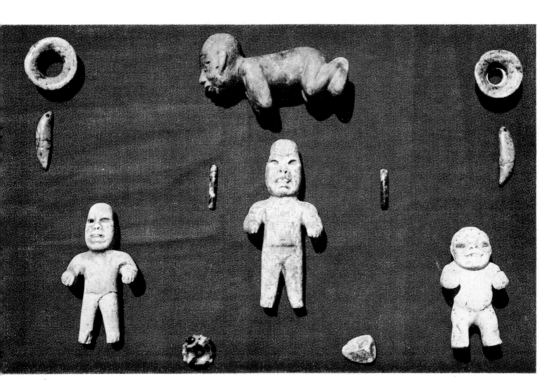

plying skull pads to deform the head in infancy was practiced by the site's later occupants, not its first inhabitants.

The season was running out. One more day, and our work would be through. For reasons known best to himself, Miguel, a Mexican assistant supervising the digging crew, ordered workmen to remove a wedge of earth that had been left as a wheelbarrow ramp in one corner of the trench. They struck a big chunk of cement and fragments of an incense vessel.

Sensing that something important might lie below, Miguel took over with his trowel and eased earth from the top of the pile. He uncovered a red-painted stone monkey, a similar turtle, a thin circular piece of polished jade, then another, and another.

At this point Miguel sent for me.

It was evident he had stumbled onto a discovery of exceptional importance. Apparently the large potsherds, the chunk of cement, and stone figures formed a protective cover.

Carefully we worked around the entire deposit until we had exposed a huge

Stone Figurines and Jade Jewelry from child's tomb at La Venta include small, hollow ear plugs. Pendants below were attached to them. Statuette at left has lost one of its black obsidian eyes. Other two have eyes of fool's gold (iron pyrites). Below: Clay image released from long vigil at Cerro de las Mesas was one of many burial offerings indicating the tomb occupant's prominence. Man's teeth were inlaid with pyrite ornaments.

231

pile of jade. Here and there under the mass of large ear ornaments, beads, and jade tubes we got teasing glimpses of pointed implements, sections of human images, and carved plaques.

Painstaking work the rest of the morning cleared the earth completely from around the pile (page 222). Another half hour was spent taking out all the jade—782 magnificent specimens. This fortune in stones, ranging in color from porcelain white to shades of green and deep blue, was the largest find yet made of the most precious substance known to Mexico's ancient civilizations (page 230). It certainly did not accompany a burial; doubtless it constituted tribal property rather than individual wealth.

The jade may have been an offering at a temple's dedication or the enlargement of a mound. Or perhaps the owners buried the treasure on the approach of an invader, possibly the Aztecs.

We scarcely expected to match that windfall on a subsequent trip to La Venta. But in rich tombs at that sandy, swamp-girt treasure island, we did discover emerald-green masterpieces of Oriental quality. In all, we counted 340 handsomely carved specimens, 300 of them imperial green jade, first of their kind uncovered in the New World.

Rumors of other huge carved stones lured us inland to the San Lorenzo highlands in the 1946 season. There we found a great carved altar almost exactly like the larger one unearthed at La Venta. Still another, almost perfectly preserved, depicted two chubby figures with arms upraised as if to hold the altar's heavy table top.

A surprising new feature of the ancient culture was the mass of hollowed trough-shaped stones we found along with a number of flat rocks in a gully. These stones were apparently part of an ancient aqueduct.

The wide variety of pottery, clay figures and other artifacts we recovered at San Lorenzo demonstrated changes in style and form with the passage of time.

An old Mexican, serving as a guide, led us across a group of typical La Venta mounds to a steep ravine. He pointed to *el Rey*. Lying on the slope, face up, top of the head down, was the colossus of all the colossal heads. The moment we saw it, we knew we were gazing at a La Venta masterwork (page 216). Four other finely preserved heads also came to light at San Lorenzo.

Over the years La Venta Man's trail had taken us beyond Veracruz and Tabasco to the Mexican States of Campeche, Oaxaca, and Chiapas. We traveled on foot, in dugout canoes, on jogging mules, and horses. Further explorations, including Dr. Drucker's 1955 work at La Venta, will continue to shed light upon a civilization that our investigations made known for the first time.

From the great stone monuments and exquisite little artifacts, long buried and ignored, we learned that these interesting people were one of the first to emerge from the simple early agricultural level of Middle America and achieve civilizational stature. In the jungles of Veracruz and Tabasco they erected big ceremonial centers that flourished before the rise of Maya, Zapotec, Toltec, and Totonac cultures. The great earth mounds that loomed from hot leafy jungles were precursors to the soaring stone pyramids of the Aztecs and Maya.

The early dates we found on La Venta monuments suggest that these Olmec people originated the marvelous calendar that subsequently gave the Maya their supreme claim to intellectual fame.

La Venta, or Olmec, people were America's first great artists. Their pure, delicate work in stone contrasts strikingly with gaudy embellishments that characterize most later sculptural art in Middle America. They were apparently the first New World artists to use jade,

Zotzil Indians Wear Sandals Straight from Mayan Monument Art. A stiff leather projection fits around heel and protects ankle. Short pants have no pockets, so these central Chiapas highlanders carry money, packages, lunch, and oddments in net bags with shoulder straps. Pink-tasseled black-and-white scarfs cover noses and mouths on dusty roads. Serapes vary in Zotzil villages from white with pin stripes to pure black. Flat-crowned hats are heavy, double-weave straw.

that beautiful and difficult medium so highly prized in pre-Columbian America.

They even possessed books. In a trench at Cerro de las Mesas we found what was apparently an ancient illustrated volume. Its pages had entirely disappeared, but still remaining were green, red, blue, and purple designs, welded together so tightly that it would be virtually impossible to separate them.

About A.D. 600 these cultural pioneers disappeared, submerged by a people of different physical type and culture who sought to destroy the monumental works of art they found.

La Ventans were not a race of conquerors; they did not even extend their boundaries widely beyond their southern Veracruz and northern Tabasco homeland. But they gave to ancient Mexico its first great cultural impetus. Their effect did not cease until Cortés and his men brought to a sudden end 2,000 years of New World development.

233

MONTE ALBÁN AND MITLA

WILLIAM G. PRESTON; ROBERTO A. TJRNBULL (RIGHT)

The Richest Archeological Find in the Americas came to light on the heights of Monte Albán, near Oaxaca in southern Mexico. There the theocratic Zapotecs reached their height, A.D. 500–1000, then abandoned the metropolis to long-time enemies, the Mixtecs, in turn conquered by the Spaniards. Zapotec and Mixtec cultures long posed tantalizing mysteries. Less than 25 years ago shapeless grass-covered mounds (right) still shrouded the impressive plazas, courts, pyramids, and platforms above.

In 1931 Dr. Alfonso Caso of Mexico's National Museum made archeological history when he discovered sensational tomb treasure in gold, silver, jade, and turquoise; ornaments and utensils in onyx, marble, rock crystal; rare jet and amber; carved jaguar bones; priceless ropes of pearls. Famed Tomb 7, first used by its Zapotec builders, was taken over by Mixtecs who buried the treasure with nine nobles and priests and one woman. More than 150 Monte Albán tombs have now revealed secrets indicating the important Zapotec-Mixtec role in the cultural give and take among the La Venta, Maya, Teotihuacán, Toltec, Aztec, and other civilizations.

WILLIAM G. PRESTON; ALFONSO CASO (TOP RIGHT)

Mitla's Hewers of Stone spared no effort in beautifying the city that enshrined the tombs of Zapotec kings and priests, and served as home of their Great Prophet, a high priest so sacred that any commoner who looked upon him was believed to die. Mitla became leading Zapotec city after the abandonment of near-by Monte Albán to the Mixtecs. "Abode of the Dead," Aztec conquerors called it. A city "prouder and more magnificent" than any they had seen in New Spain, said early Spaniards.

The upper chambers of Mitla's massive rectangular palaces stand on low platforms rising around square central courts. The Hall of Monoliths (above) with its 14-foot columns contrasts in massive simplicity with structures (right) which catch the eye with intricate mosaics that sweep both inner and outer walls—a geometry in stone made up of countless individually carved segments held in place by pressure. Below ground stretch enormous cruciform corridors, the tombs from which souls of the departed wandered into the earth's interior in search of the kingdom of the dead.

In one upper chamber the Great Prophet "sat and slept . . . his throne like a high cushion . . . all of tiger skin, stuffed entirely with delicate feathers or with fine grass," wrote Oaxaca-born Spanish friar Francisco Burgoa (1600–1681). In a special underground sanctuary the prophet consulted images of the gods "with hideous grimaces and writhings . . . which filled all present with fear and terror." Into another "dark and grewsome room" Zapotec priests threw bodies of sacrificial victims and those slain in battle. It led, Burgoa claimed, to a 30-league passageway penetrating the earth's depths. No such tunnel has ever been found.

Food-bearer to the Dead. This funerary urn from a Monte Albán tomb, with serpent's split tongue protruding from its mouth, represents the serpent god Quetzalcoatl. Behind its bold-carved front is a container for food or drink to nourish the tomb's occupant during his journey into the next world.

Such urns were sometimes in human form. Others pictured animal gods, combinations of gods such as the serpent and the jaguar, or people wearing the masks of deities. Quetzalcoatl was a popular symbol. In various guises as creator of the world, god of wind and rain, and patron and bestower of all culture, this snake divinity roams through the mythology of advanced Indian civilizations of Middle America.

On this urn of the classic Zapotec period III (A.D. 500–1000), the god wears a long-eared cap decorated with shells of the same type sculptured beside the undulating feathered snakes of Teotihuacán's Temple of Quetzalcoatl. The similarity forges another link in the long chain of evidence that points to the close relationship among Indian deities, from the Maya long-nosed god Itzamna to the many-featured snake divinities of the La Ventans, Toltecs, Aztecs, and other related cultures.

237

WILLIAM G. PRESTON; ALFONSO CASO (LEFT)

Riddles in Stone stand at the entrance to this Monte Albán pyramid. Dots and bars that show clearly on the largest slab recall the Maya numeral system (page 198). But no other glyphs have been deciphered to link the dates with any specific events. Human figures carved on other slabs are nicknamed "dancers" because of their strange shapes and extravagant gestures. Their unknown creators gave them twisted feet, heads flat or grotesquely elongated. Were they meant to caricature defeated and despised enemies? Or did they portray deformed pilgrims seeking miraculous cures at Monte Albán temples? Archeologists find no answers.

The toothy grin of a skeleton-jaw mask dominates the "jaguar knight" breastpiece (left) found in Monte Albán's fabulously rich Tomb 7. Made of gold parts soldered together, it represents a man wearing a jaguar-head helmet. Serpents decorate the ear plugs; a small bird hangs at the throat. The A-O monogram on the lower right plate identifies the piece as Mixtecan, for this year symbol was used by the Mixtecs, never by Zapotecs.

238

Reminiscent of La Venta Sculpture, these curiously deformed "dancers" decorate many Monte Albán stones. Heavy, infantile features, thick snarling lips, and head coverings like football helmets are distinguishing traits of both art forms—another evidence of the exchange of ideas and techniques that must have taken place among the early coexistent civilizations in this part of the Americas.

Some of the bas-reliefs were imbedded in the walls of Monte Albán's Great Platform, one of whose stairways is being restored by workmen below. The carvings are not characteristic of Zapotec sculpture; and since they were used as construction material apparently taken from an earlier building, scholars assume they were carved by pre-Zapotec people. Among the workmen are descendants of the Zapotec and Mixtec Indians who originally used this massive structure.

WILLIAM G. PRESTON (RIGHT)
ROBERTO A. TURNBULL

239

Feather-decked Aztec Fighter Prays for Victory at altar of his war god, Huitzilopochtli. Lavish ornaments of gold, silver, pearls, and turquoise accent the scowling, teeth-bared visage of Tenochtitlán's chief deity. Deer symbol at center of forehead shows Huitzilopochtli also to be god of hunting. Two humming birds rest on his cuffs. Smoke curls up from incense burner at his side. War club, decorated shield lie at feet of the warrior, whose torso is sheathed in cotton-quilt armor. Feather headdress and bustle, turquoise ear and lip ornaments indicate military order.

240

CHAPTER II

THE AZTECS OF MEXICO

BY FRANK H. H. ROBERTS, JR.

HIGH ON THE TEMPLE PLATFORM atop Tenochtitlán's great pyramid, an Aztec youth awaits his fate.

Within the temple broods the war god Huitzilopochtli, a monstrous idol, "with broad face and terrible eyes," weighted down by gold and jewels. Near by stands his brother, Tezcatlipoca, "God of Hell . . . girt with figures like little devils with snakes' tails."

Their victim lies stretched on his back across the low sacrificial stone, centered stagelike on the open platform. Two black-robed and painted priests hold his feet; three others grip his arms and head. A sixth, dressed in red, bends over the prostrate youth.

Suddenly the red-garbed priest raises his hand. Sunlight glints on the polished stone of the sacrificial knife.

With practiced skill the priest plunges the dagger into the youth's naked breast. From the gaping hole he tears out the still warm and bleeding heart. He offers it to the sun, then places it in the copal-burning censer before the war god.

Such typical rituals of the Aztecs were described by eye-witness soldiers and priests of the Spanish conquest of the 1520's. The barbarous color and brutal drama of human sacrifice characterized life among these fierce, war-making Indians of Mexico's high central valley.

Victims of the heart offerings were captives, criminals, children, or young men and women especially chosen and prepared for the occasion by a series of rites extending over a considerable period of time.

The ceremony was held at the end of every year, and a more elaborate one at the end of every thirteenth year. Other sacrifices were made whenever the gods needed to be propitiated. The longer the period between, the greater the number of victims.

Religion dominated Aztec life. The people spent much time and energy placating a complex group of deities. They believed that failure to honor their divinities with sufficient offerings would bring about the end of the world at the close of the 52-year calendar round, a period that corresponds to our own century.

Besides the ever-demanding war god (opposite) and Tlaloc, god of rain, there were deities associated with flowers, maize, the earth, the sky, drunkenness, the lower regions, birth, and death. Each day, night, week, month, and year had its own particular god or goddess.

Magic and shamanism were widespread, sorcerers and witch doctors on every hand. People consulted fortune-tellers to determine whether the fates were propitious for a journey, a business transaction, or any ordinary feature of their daily life. Certain days were regarded as unlucky and no new undertaking would be started then. A child born on one of these days was doomed to misfortune throughout life.

Prophecy played a major role in the priests' busy routine. Half their duties were nocturnal. Incense of copal and rubber had to be burned before images of the gods four times each day, three times each night. On altars the priests placed such offerings as food, clothing, and flowers.

Blood, however, was the most important offering. Earlier peoples of Middle America, the Maya of Yucatán for example, had such sacrificial rites. But it is with the Aztecs that they are most often associated.

Pigeons or quail were common offerings. Priests poked thorns through their own tongues, cheeks, and ears to obtain blood. Torn and ragged ears characterized a priest (opposite).

Besides the all-important ritual of tearing out the heart, other human victims were drowned, in rites similar to those at the Sacred Cenote at Chichén Itzá by the Maya (page 197), or shot with arrows. Occasionally priests clubbed a victim to death, or sealed him in a cave to starve to death. Some victims died in sacrificial combat.

From the writings of Bernardino de Sahagún—a Franciscan monk who went to live among the Aztecs about 1530—we have a graphic description of the sacrificial fight at the *temalacatl*. This was a stone set on a platform in the center of the great temple enclosure where all could see. Similar to a large millstone, it had a hole in the center to which the victim was tethered by a rope around his waist. The captive could walk around the stone but could move only so far before the rope checked him.

The rite began when a number of priests emerged, each in costume representing a god, from the thatch-roofed temple atop the pyramid. They descended the stone steps in a long line,

followed by four warriors: two "Jaguars" and two "Eagles." Armed with swords and shields, these men advanced in fighting attitude, making motions like fencers.

When the procession reached the foot of the stairway, it advanced to the stone and formed a wide circle around it. The priests seated themselves and began at once to play on their flutes, trumpets, and shell horns, to whistle or to sing.

The victim was dragged forward and given a native liquor, pulque. He raised the bowl to the east, the west, the north, and the south, as if offering it to the cardinal points of the world, then drank the liquid through a hollow cane.

A priest approached with a quail, tore its head off before the captive, took the captive's shield, raised it high above his head, and threw the beheaded quail behind him. The victim was made to take his place on the stone, then tied with the rope by a priest dressed to represent a bear (page 246).

The captive was now handed small clubs and a sword edged not with obsidian blades, but with feathers. The skirmish began. One after another the warriors, armed with real weapons, fought the victim. Sometimes a brave captive wore down the four who sought to kill him. In such cases a fifth, who was left-handed, was sent against him and usually conquered him.

The victim's breast was then torn open and his heart offered to the sun. The body was thrown down the steps, bumping along till it reached bottom. There it was skinned and cut up, and the flesh distributed for cannibalistic ceremonies. A warrior paraded the skin about the streets; everyone who met him presented him with a gift. These gifts were taken to the man who had captured the victim and he distributed them as he saw fit.

The insatiable Aztec gods demanded ever more victims for sacrifice. This provided a ready excuse for war, as did the

Faces and Bodies Painted, Two Priests Plan a Rite. Ragged ears tell of self-inflicted cuts that gushed forth blood offerings to the gods. Bedraggled hair, recalling Medusa's writhing snakes, is matted with sacrificial gore. Yet Aztec ceremonies could be less somber when honoring light-hearted deities. The Flower Prince was god of pleasure, feasting, and frivolity. Priests here dress for the occasion in appropriate bright hues, wearing fringed cotton robes, and head-dress and back ornaments of light basketry, decorated with carvings and topped by quetzal plumes.

243

Visiting Aztec Diplomat Swings Badge of Office—a Fan. Temple guards snap to attention as the ambassador approaches a Tenochtitlán shrine. Boatmen paddle produce-laden canoes along the Venice-like canal. Beyond, a rich chieftain goes in fancy litter, preceded by army of retainers.

PAINTING BY H. M. HERGET

Aztec towns occasionally formed military alliances. The Mexican valley's "Big Three"—Tenochtitlán, Texcoco, and Tacuba—once took to the field together. But normally ties were loose. Even tribute-paying tribes kept political independence. This Aztec lack of unity aided the Spanish conquest.

desire for spoils and tribute. Attacks on Aztec traders traveling to other cities also caused conflict. War was chief occupation and consuming passion of the Aztecs. They felt idle without one.

An Aztec declaration of war was a formal proceeding, decided on in council. Highest in military command was the Chief of Men, assisted by war officers in charge of the city's subdivisions.

These officers, elected on merit, could not be deposed. They were distinguished by the cut of their hair, by lip and nose plugs, by their wide and flowing mantles, and by towering plumes of green feathers. Designs indicating war honors, number of captives taken, or exploits of extreme bravery ornamented their shields.

Below the officers came three classes of meritorious braves: the Jaguars or Beasts of Prey, the Eagles, and the Wandering Arrows. They won their titles by capturing one or more prisoners. They served as scouts and skirmishers in the army's van, led small bodies of men, and on occasion commanded larger subdivisions.

Meritorious braves cropped their hair close over the ears. Their masks or helmets imitated wild-animal heads. Sometimes they wore skins of those animals.

Warriors generally donned armor of quilted cotton,

Armed with Feathers, Near-naked Captive Fights for Life. His opponents, protected by shields and armor, wield weapons edged with sharp obsidian blades. He parries their deadly blows with feather-fringed sword. Spectators watch tensely as priest in black-bear costume referees this unequal ceremonial combat. The victim, a war prisoner, can win freedom by outfighting two "Eagle" warriors, two "Jaguars," and finally the left-handed warrior behind carved, drum-shaped stone. Failure means death in the heart-sacrifice ritual. Rope tethering him to the stone limits his movements. Yet occasionally an exceptional fighter did win against such odds. One winner, offered a high post in Tenochtitlán's army, preferred sacrificial death with its promise of a place in the warrior's special heaven.

Moment of Death Follows Year of Pleasure. To appease their gods, Aztecs sacrificed thousands of men, women, and children each year, their own as well as outsiders. Most died ingloriously. But one special category of victims was feted and worshiped a year before death. The handsomest and most intelligent of youths was chosen. He feasted on delicacies, was taught to play the flute, to walk and talk with royal air. Late in the year he was married to four maidens, reared as goddesses for the honor. In the final ritual, the young man broke his flutes, one after another, as he mounted steps to the sacrificial temple. At the top, priests seized him, tore open his chest, offered the still throbbing heart to the god Tezcatlipoca. The youth's soul then ascended to the highest of all Aztec heavens.

247

PAINTINGS BY H. M. HERGET

three-fourths to an inch and a half thick. (page 240). The Spaniards were quick to adopt this apparel, so effective was its protection against arrows and javelins.

Sometimes the legs were similarly encased and the entire suit covered with feathers and plates of gold or silver. Besides their cushioning effect, feathers also identified military groups. Some uniforms had white and red feathers, some green, some blue and yellow. Others simulated actual birds.

Aztec warriors fought principally with javelins tipped with obsidian or copper. They also used slings and stones, bows and arrows, swords and clubs.

The sword, called *maccuahuitl* or sometimes *macana,* was of wood, about four feet long, four to five inches wide, an inch or so thick. Pieces of obsidian were fastened in grooves along the edges with cement made from the roots of a tree pounded with earth and mixed with the blood of birds and bats.

Warriors defended themselves with small round shields of the parrying type. Made of netted canes interwoven with cotton and covered with painted boards and feathers, they were so strong that only a crossbow shot at close range would penetrate them.

Aztec combat tactics showed good knowledge of military technique. But their expeditions were short and, like American Indians in general, they usually stopped fighting at nightfall. During the conquest, only two engagements took place at night. *Noche triste,* "Sad Night," the Spaniards called one, when Cortés and his men were driven from Montezuma's capital after a furious battle (opposite).

The Aztecs were warlike, and in the thrall of bloodthirsty gods. But they were also a many-sided people, with a complex and advanced culture. Theirs was the last of Mexico's great Indian civilizations. Their featherwork, gold, and wood crafts were unparalleled for their time. Their designs and symbols live on in the architectural ornament of new and old buildings in Mexico City.

Mexico's modern capital rises above the ruins of the Aztec capital, Tenochtitlán, that Cortés conquered. The present-day National Palace stands on the palace site of the Aztec king, Montezuma. The massive Cathedral is rooted in the rubble of the Aztecs' great sacrificial temple.

Practically every excavation for new construction in the city adds its quota of Aztec relics to the extensive collections in Mexico's National Museum. One such lucky find was an awesome statue of Coatlicue, Earth Goddess, wearing a skirt of writhing snakes.

The story of the Aztecs is better

Jagged Blades and carved handles tell grim story of sacrifice. With these knives priests cut out victims' hearts and offered them to insatiable gods. As many as 50,000 persons, mostly war captives, died each year in Aztec rites. Blades were of flintlike stone or obsidian, handles often adorned with delicate turquoise mosaic. Handle of upper knife represents man in eagle costume.

LUIS MARDEN, NATIONAL
GEOGRAPHIC STAFF

Yepeuqyaoyotl ycha mote cuico m á

known than that of many New World peoples, thanks to archeological relics, pictograph manuscripts, and other native and Spanish records. But where the early wandering tribes came from, and when and where they stopped before founding Tenochtitlán are still mysteries that tantalize scholars.

The Aztecs entered the Valley of Mexico early in the 14th century, when Europe was deep in the Middle Ages. Then a crude hunting people, they came into contact with communities of high culture bordering a great lake.

According to some accounts, the newcomers settled near Chapultepec, where they acquired certain cultural traits of

Aztecs Launch Furious Assault on Spaniards

Tenochtitlán, 1519: Bearded Cortés and Marina, his Indian mistress and interpreter, with mounted aide and four Tlaxcalan allies, stand off attack behind smoking cannon in palace courtyard. Aztec warrior (upper right) fires the chapel, indicated by Virgin and crucifix. Montezuma (upper left), hostage of the Spaniards, begs his people to let the dons leave in peace. In answer they hurl stone (shown in motion) that fatally wounds him. Earlier the invaders had entered the Aztec capital unopposed. Then during Cortés's absence, a lieutenant massacred unarmed citizens dancing at a religious festival, and war was on. Cortés rejoined his beleaguered garrison. But all were driven from the city with heavy losses during the Noche Triste, "Sad Night." Eventually the Spaniards, reinforced by Indian allies, returned to conquer. Pictograph was made by a Tlaxcalan Indian artist of that time.

249

the Acolhuacans. Between about 1367 and 1376, the Acolhuacans drove them out, forcing them to take refuge on two small reed-covered mud banks or islands in the center of the lake.

Aztec tradition explains the choice of their future permanent homesite in more picturesque and flattering terms. It had been predicted that they would stop and found their dynasty when they saw an eagle on a cactus eating a serpent.

Upon reaching the borders of a large lake they saw a beautiful island, and the priest who led them beheld a huge eagle with a snake struggling in its talons. The bird came to rest on a cactus plant, killed and devoured the reptile. The Aztecs, overjoyed at the prophecy's fulfillment, at once established their city.

The legend is symbolized today by the eagle, serpent, and cactus in the Mexican coat of arms and flag.

However founded, the island settlements grew into two towns, Tenochtitlán and Tlaltelolco. Though the space between them was little more than a broad canal, they progressed as independent units for more than a hundred years. In the 15th century the sixth ruler of Tenochtitlán conquered Tlaltelolco and united the two.

Meantime the Aztecs were growing to real power in the Valley. Maxtli, skilled general of their fourth ruler, Itzcoatl (1427–1440), conquered many neighboring cities and tribes, exacting rich tribute from them. Tenochtitlán prospered and expanded, until by the time of the

Scepter, Crown, and Cloak of this high priest are lavishly decorated with insignia of gods he serves. Behind him rise Tenochtitlán's great pyramid temples, tier on tier of stone. His power is great in both religious and temporal matters, for he and his subordinate priests direct the elaborate rituals on which all tribal life is based.

They make intricate astronomic calculations that harmonize sacred and solar calendars. They teach youths to read and keep pictograph records. They follow lives of demanding ritual to win success in war and bountiful crops from capricious gods.

PAINTINGS BY H. M. HERGET

Wood Carver Whittles Temple Decoration Amid Busy Market

Around him macaws scream, children chatter, women gossip, merchant and customer bargain. Bernal Díaz del Castillo chronicles: "When we arrived at the great market place, called Tlaltelolco, we were astounded at the number of people and the quantity of merchandise that it contained, and at the good order and control that was maintained. . . . Let us begin with the dealers in gold, silver, and precious stones, feathers, mantles, and embroidered goods. . . . Indian slaves both men and women . . . tied to long poles, with collars round their necks. . . . In another part there were skins of tigers and lions, of otters and jackals, deer and other animals. . . . Let us also mention the fruiterers, and the women who sold cooked food, dough and tripe in their own part of the market; then every sort of pottery made in a thousand different forms from great water jars to little jugs . . . then those who sold honey . . . and yellow ointment and cochineal. . . .

"There are also buildings where three magistrates sit in judgment, and there are executive officers . . . who inspect the merchandise [which was] so numerous . . . and the great market place with its surrounding arcades was so crowded with people, that one would not have been able to see and inquire about it all in two days."

conquest tribute was pouring into the coffers of Montezuma II from all southern Mexico, the Veracruz coastal plain, even from Guatemala.

By all accounts Tenochtitlán in its heyday was a beautiful city. Governmental buildings and houses of the rich were made of cut stone, middle-class homes of adobe blocks. Only dwellings of farmers and the poorer classes were wattle and daub with thatched roofs.

Most larger buildings enclosed cool courtyards and patios. Walls were plastered a gleaming white or colored dull red. Trees dappled the city green, lake and canals sparkled blue. Fruit-and-vegetable-laden canoes, gay splashes of color from gardens and rooftop flower beds, and the bright-hued garments of the populace made an enchanting scene.

Aztec wives busied themselves sweeping rooms and courtyards. They ground maize, or corn, to make meal for the tortillas, even as it is ground today in many parts of Mexico (page 261). There were rich sauces and other foods to prepare, such as *guacamole*, a dish of tomato, alligator pear, and chile. And there were babies to tend.

Older men taught young boys. Teenage boys were schooled for priesthood or military service, or apprenticed to merchants or artisans. Education for girls was not so rigorous. Unless they took vows of chastity and went into a religious order, girls married between the ages of 11 and 18, arrangements being made by parents or priests.

Tenochtitlán's markets (page 250) were as pulsingly alive as those of to-

Daily Life in Aztec Times found man as burden bearer, woman as weaver. Turkeys, parrots, squash, and green vegetables ride to market on farmer's back (left). Then, as now, barefoot men jogged miles, carrying heavy loads by tumpline round the head. American Indians domesticated the turkey long before Columbus sailed. Maize or Indian corn, sweet potatoes, beans, peppers, tomatoes, and cacao or chocolate also swelled the Aztec larder.

Below, mother teaches her daughter the art of basket weaving, using reeds from swamps that once surrounded Tenochtitlán. Her blue basket design is attractively simple, like the red pattern of her dress. Corn grows high between weaver and thatched homes traced against the sky.

253

PAINTINGS BY H. M. HERGET

Stone-and-adobe Igloo in modern-day village descends from the Aztec steam bath. Children (left) watch a resident of Huexoculco, in the Valley of Mexico, fan furnace flames in one of the community's 70-odd sweat baths. Resembling Finnish steam baths, the huts are called *temascales* (from Aztec *tema*, to bathe, and *calli*, house).

Bather enters on hands and knees, plugs the door, pours water on hot stones to produce steam, and swelters in darkness, sometimes for hours, like lobster boiled alive in a pot. Sweat baths, in wide use among North American tribes, were prescribed by Aztec medicine men for many ills. Aztecs bathed often—too often for health, Spanish chroniclers felt. Bernal Díaz del Castillo wrote that Montezuma bathed every afternoon.

JUSTIN LOCKE

Man Shrinks Before Teotihuacán's Mighty Pyramid of the Sun. In ancient days, long lines of pagan celebrants marching up the broad stone steps must have seemed to disappear into the sky! Flattened on top to support the usual temple, the pyramid towers 216 feet above the arid land, dwarfs all other structures along Teotihuacán's "Highway of the Dead," which leads from the Pyramid of the Moon to the serpent-decorated Temple of Quetzalcoatl. Mystery shrouds the sacred city's past. Unknown architects began work here long centuries before the Aztecs arrived. The newcomers, finding the monuments abandoned, created legends ascribing divine origin to the magnificent remains.

day's Mexico City. Merchants and artisans bartered their wares. Feather quills filled with gold dust occasionally served as currency.

Gold and silver workers displayed their art. Wood carvers, workers in stone, creators of intricate turquoise or shell mosaics, featherworkers, pottery makers, bodyguards, and burden-bearers thronged the market place. Spinners and weavers produced cotton cloth; tailors fashioned it into garments. Others made ornate headdresses for officials and warriors. Sandal and weapon makers,

tanners and basketweavers plied their trades. Vendors of honey, herbs, pitch pine for torches thronged the arcades.

The artisan looking up from his work, the merchant at his stall could tell at a glance the rank of the person approaching. Everyday dress for the Aztec man was breechcloth, hipcloth, mantle or cape, and sandals. The mantle and ends of the breechcloth were short and plain for the lower classes, long and embroidered for those of higher station. The elaborateness of a woman's short skirt and sleeveless blouse served to reveal the wearer's position in the social scale.

Village chiefs wore a white mantle, ambassadors carried a fan (page 244). Priests usually dressed in black; even their bodies were stained black. But the robe of the sacrificial priest was red.

Scantily clad farmers (page 253) trudged in from outlying districts carrying fruit, sweet potatoes, tomatoes, squash, beans, peppers, and cacao or chocolate. The maize they brought was a variety developed by the Aztecs; this matured rapidly, an essential quality for the high, arid plateau country. Tobacco, cotton, hemp, rubber, copal resin for religious ceremonies were also on display in the market place. And turkeys, fish, and birds.

Some vegetables came by canoe from floating gardens, or *chinampas,* such as today may be seen at Xochimilco, not far from Mexico City. These chinampas go back to Tenochtitlán's early days when the Aztecs, weak and hemmed in by their foes, subsisted on fish, birds, aquatic plants, and such vegetables as they were able to grow on rafts of reeds and wattlework heaped with mud from the lake.

Through the years the floating islands increased in size and numbers. Plant roots interlaced, eventually anchored at the bottom of the lake, and the islands became a series of rectangular plots separated by canals just wide enough for the passage of canoes.

"New World Venice" Cortés called the Aztec capital. One of the conqueror's soldiers described it as a place of wide and handsome streets, formed half of hard earth like a brick pavement and half of canal, side by side, so that the people traversed them by land or water.

Many boulevards of modern Mexico City follow the course of these main

Aztec Calendar Stone makes striking exhibit in Mexico's National Museum. Dating from 1479, the 24-ton basalt monolith stood at the base of the Aztec religion and way of life. By its weird carvings priests set their rituals and guided farmers' sowing and reaping.

The sun god, feared and revered as Lord of Heaven, glowers fiercely from the stone's center. Four rectangles around his face stand for earth, air, fire, and water, destructive elements believed to have ended the world's previous four ages. In the encircling band march 20 symbols, one for each day of the Aztec month. Beyond, mythology and astronomy symbols represent time, gods, man, and nature.

Eighteen 20-day months made up the Aztec solar year, leaving a five-day period into which the whole year's bad luck was crowded. Major time cycle was 52 years. As its closing night approached, panic deepened, fed by the fearful prediction that the world's end would coincide with the end of one of these cycles. With the new day's dawn, the people celebrated their escape by lighting fresh fires, feasting, making human sacrifice.

CALENDARIO AZTECA O PIEDRA DEL SOL.
EN EL MES DE DICIEMBRE DEL AÑO DE 1790
AL PRACTICARSE LA NIVELACION PARA EL NUEVO
EMPEDRADO DE LA PLAZA MAYOR DE ESTA CAPITAL
FUE DESCUBIERTO ESTE MONOLITO Y COLOCADO
DESPUES AL PIE DE LA TORRE OCCIDENTAL DE LA
CATEDRAL POR EL LADO QUE VE AL PONIENTE
DE CUYO LUGAR SE TRASLADO A ESTE MUSEO
NACIONAL EN AGOSTO DE 1885.

Toluca Valley Family sorts carrots in wooden canoe. Beyond, ripening grain turns fields to gold. Pre-Aztec farmers cultivated this fertile valley watered by the Lerma River. Near-8,800-foot altitude makes winters brisk, but in summer cool nights follow warm days.

At Calixtlahuaca (Aztec for "Plain Dominated by Buildings"), near the valley metropolis of Toluca, the archeologist's shovel has revealed evidences of several Indian cultures. One was the Matlatzinca, linked with ancient Toltecs of the near-by Valley of Mexico. Modern Toluca crafts produced woven skirt and handbag of woman in picture.

256

Floating Gardens at Tlahuac grew food for Tenochtitlán. Tree-bordered fields on opposite shore were once Aztec *chinampas*, plots made by piling lake-floor mud on reed-and-wattle rafts. Gardeners built huts on them, could row their "farms" from place to place. As at Xochimilco, Tlahuac's better-known neighbor, the gardens grew, interlaced, finally took root.

Lakes, ponds, and swamps dotted the high Valley of Mexico in olden days. With hungry tribes competing for farmland, the handy island gardens provided a vital source of strength to the Aztecs. Now this blue and green vale of Tlahuac—10 miles southeast of Mexico City—is a watery oasis in country where dust storms often swirl across dry beds of former lakes. Drainage projects channeled and dried up most of the water that made enchanting scenes of fertility recorded with amazement by 16th century Spaniards. Modern problems are to grow crops and trees to hold down soil; to obtain drinking water to supply huge, industrial Mexico City, and at the same time leave sufficient for near-by farming requirements.

257

canals. People walk today on pavement where the Aztec went in his canoe.

Meeting the problems of their soggy site made the Aztecs exceptional engineers for their time. They erected buildings on piles and constructed great causeways leading from the city to various towns bordering the lakes. The Pan American Highway now runs into the city along one of the ancient causeways.

Aztec skill erected a great dike during the years 1440–1450 to prevent the Lake of Texcoco flooding the city. The work, extending some ten miles from Atzacoalco on the north to the hill called La Estrella on the south, was constructed with a core of clay and stone, crowned with a wall of rubble masonry.

On either side a strong stockade broke the force of the waves. Openings for canoes pierced the dike. Sluice gates controlling the water level opened in summer to let fresh water into the lake depleted by evaporation.

For governing purposes, the Aztecs separated their island home into four quarters, each containing a phratry, or clan, of kindred peoples or those of common descent. Twenty *kins* made up

AZTEC PICTURE WRITING

THE DATE is 10 Rabbit. That year, says the pictograph at left, Chief Ahuitzotl died and Montezuma II succeeded.

The Aztec time symbol (10 dots surrounding the rabbit head) corresponds to our A.D. 1502. The bound mummy represents death, its crown royalty. The attached animal, Aztec symbol for a small water creature, gives deceased chief's name. Crown, throne, and speech scroll at Montezuma's mouth symbolize a monarch: "He who speaks."

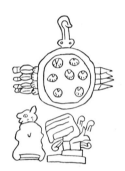

Earlier in the year 10 Rabbit—square at left above—Ahuitzotl took Tehuantepec (cat head on hill at right). The shield denotes war, the flaming temple conquest.

Thus, by fanciful designs and prancing and posing humans and animals, the Aztecs recorded their war-filled history. Interpreters divide pictographs into three groups: those for persons and places, those for dates, and those for events, including natural phenomena and objects like gold, jade, and feathers. Often all three types combine to tell a story.

A place-name example is the cat's head topping a hill in the above picture. In Aztec language "tecuani" meant man-eating cat, possibly a jaguar. "Tepec" stood for hill or town. Hence Tehuantepec for the town that Ahuitzotl conquered.

This uses the rebus principle—a phonetic method of expressing words or syllables by objects whose names sound like the words but whose meaning is different. "I can bear pain" is shown by four pictures—an eye, a can, a bear, a window pane.

a phratry. Each kin elected and deposed its own officers, consisting of a governor and a group of "Elder Brothers," or council. There was also a group of councilors known as "Grandfathers," who qualified by prowess in war, wisdom in council, shrewdness in trade, or courage. Courage alone could not secure it, but was essential, since the honor came only to candidates who underwent cruel ceremonial rites.

At the head of each phratry was a war captain. These four captains served on the great tribal council in company with representatives from each kin, Elder Brothers, and certain temple priests. The great council met every 80 days, sepa-

Some scholars say that the central Mexican highlanders, no innovators despite their many accomplishments, adopted ideas of picture writing from the older and more complex technique of the Maya. Other authorities trace sources to Toltec or related cultures.

Aztec date symbols were taken from their calendar, similar to that of the Maya (page 198), but far less exact. Each of the 20 days of the 18 months in the Aztec solar year bore its own name and number. Each successive year was known by the signs of the day on which it began. But only four names could start the year, because of the chronological order of days and the "lost" five-day period at year's end. Symbols for these were Reed, Flint, House, and Rabbit.

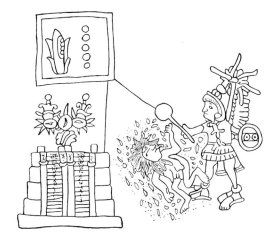

In the picture above, the year 5 Flint or Flint Knife, corresponds to 1484. Linked with it a highly adorned priest brandishes a weapon as he executes a victim, shown weltering in blood.

This gruesome scene depicts the dedication at Tenochtitlán of the great temple of the Aztec war god Huitzilopochtli, traditionally the beginning of human sacrifice by the Aztecs. Gore stains temple stairway. Surmounting pyramid is the hieroglyph for Tenochtitlán—ancient name of Mexico City. It pictures a cactus growing out of a stone.

The sun's disk with a segment cut from it (figure a at top of next column) tells of an eclipse of the sun. This occurred in 5 Rabbit (1510).

In 10 House, three years before Columbus's first voyage of discovery, a comet swept over the Valley of Mexico (figure b). The Aztecs pictured the fiery

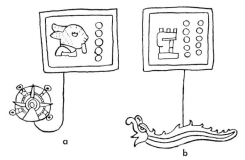

trailing body as a serpent writhing across the heavens. Montezuma regarded it as an evil portent of the fall of his empire. When the fair-skinned Spaniards landed in Mexico in 1519, he felt the end had come. His attitude helped make the conquest possible.

In figure c below, earthquake and volcanic eruption take curiously static forms. Reading the picture from bottom to top, the speckled rectangle is the earth. The Aztec word for movement, a sort of winged eye, indicates the quake. Joined to it are a star and smoke curls, hieroglyph for the eruption's "smoke ascending to the stars." The date was 2 House (1533).

It snowed heavily in Tlachquiahco Province in year 11 Reed (1503), says figure d. Great cloud bank represents snow. H-shaped object pelted with rain signs is combination hieroglyph for province's name.

By such simple symbols, easily understood once the key is learned, Aztecs recorded migrations, famines, defeats, victories, tribute paid by other tribes. Their picture accounts, painted in books of fiber paper or deerskin, lack the detail and flow of written narrative. But skeleton outlines tell the world in spritely fashion much about how this people lived and the degree of civilization they achieved.

rating into two judicial bodies which sat simultaneously and passed on all important affairs. A smaller council, composed of one speaker from each kin, met every 20 days in a directing and judicial capacity. Final power was vested in the Chief of Men and the Snake Woman, actually a man. The Chief of Men was both legislator and executive. Eventually he became king, or emperor.

The Snake Woman was a second emperor. He functioned as secretary of state in charge of intertribal affairs. He kept tally of tribute paid by Aztec-conquered cities, towns, and villages, using pictograph records such as those shown above.

Woman Grinds Corn Beneath Adobe Bins

Thatch-topped bins near Atlatlahuca, in hot country southwest of Mexico City, keep grain safe from rodents. Aztecs used similar granaries— huge clay urns covered with thatch to shed rain; kept hulled corn in house in pottery jars. One early codex shows farmer and wife pouring grain into a tall vessel. Aztecs worshiped corn gods and goddesses. Xilonen, "Young Maize Mother," was linked with still older cults. Stealing maize was punishable by death or slavery.

The woman's grinding stones shown here have remained unchanged in form for thousands of years. Their grist will make tortillas such as the Aztecs ate, except that early cakes—from size of clay griddles found—were much larger than present ones. Discoursing on Indian diet, chronicler Bernal Díaz wrote, "The Indian fig is an agreeable, nutritious fruit; and the tortilla, made of maize flour with a slight infusion of lime—might pass for a very tolerable camp fare."

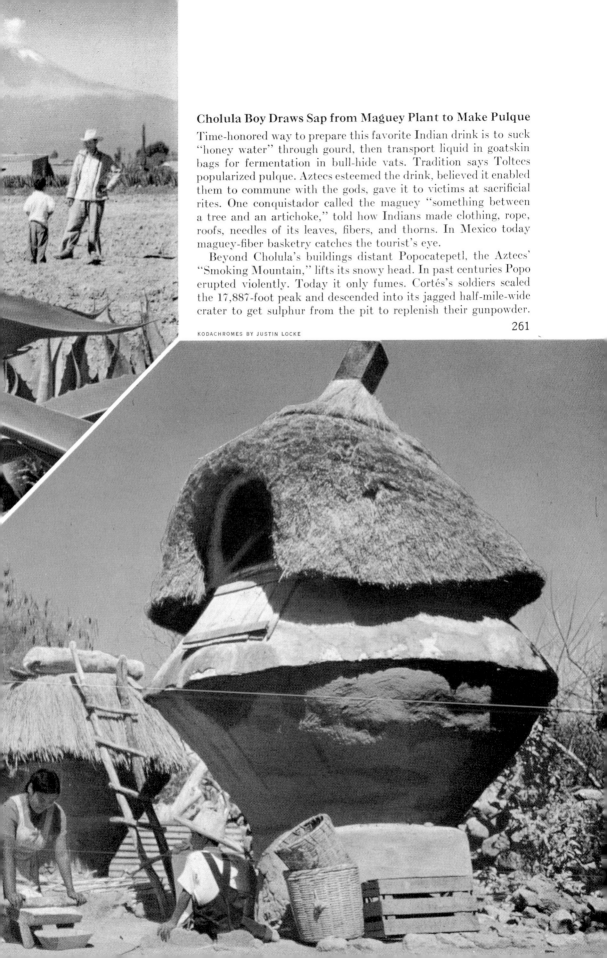

Cholula Boy Draws Sap from Maguey Plant to Make Pulque

Time-honored way to prepare this favorite Indian drink is to suck "honey water" through gourd, then transport liquid in goatskin bags for fermentation in bull-hide vats. Tradition says Toltecs popularized pulque. Aztecs esteemed the drink, believed it enabled them to commune with the gods, gave it to victims at sacrificial rites. One conquistador called the maguey "something between a tree and an artichoke," told how Indians made clothing, rope, roofs, needles of its leaves, fibers, and thorns. In Mexico today maguey-fiber basketry catches the tourist's eye.

Beyond Cholula's buildings distant Popocatepetl, the Aztecs' "Smoking Mountain," lifts its snowy head. In past centuries Popo erupted violently. Today it only fumes. Cortés's soldiers scaled the 17,887-foot peak and descended into its jagged half-mile-wide crater to get sulphur from the pit to replenish their gunpowder.

KODACHROMES BY JUSTIN LOCKE

261

At one time the tribe owned all land in common and chiefs were chosen by the people. Undesirable chiefs were deposed. Then gradually a tendency toward inheritance of office developed. As more tribes and territories were conquered during the rule of the powerful Itzcoatl, social classes based on captured wealth began to appear. For the first time there was distribution of spoils.

The new land went to the warriors, creating a group of rich landowners. Artisans in certain crafts gained special privileges. The priesthood grew stronger, with members in civic as well as religious posts.

Whether the system was a monarchy or a democracy is largely a matter of definition. Even after inheritance of office became common, an Aztec man was nominally elected to his position and when not satisfactory was ousted. Although there was a definite lineal descent of the post of Chief of Men toward the end of Aztec dominance in the Valley, he was voted on in council. The Snake Woman was elected for life, but could be removed for cause.

True, there were slaves, but not in the usual sense. Their labor belonged to another, but their persons did not, and it was possible for a slave to have slaves of his own. His children were born free. The owner of a slave's labor could not sell it without the slave's consent.

Parents sometimes sold a child; an impoverished family would offer one of its members as security on a loan. Lawbreakers, occasionally a war captive spared from sacrifice, became slaves. But many others voluntarily accepted bond-

Magnificent Gardeners, the Aztecs contributed many flowers to the world. Their descendants, still speaking the old Nahuatl tongue, grew these gladiolas, tuberoses, and carnations in Xochimilco's "floating gardens." Vendor's stall sits in Mexico City suburbs before the Shrine of the Virgin of Guadalupe.

Indians in dark shawls and white cottons visit the Guadalupe shrine (opposite). Here in pagan times stood a temple to the Aztecs' "Little Mother," Tonantzin. In the transition to Christianity, the Virgin, protector of the Indians, succeeded the Aztec deity naturally. In 1531 Her vision appeared to a simple Indian. A church was built, and ever since Guadalupe has been Mexico's leading shrine, drawing December pilgrims to the Festival to the Virgin.

KODACHROMES BY JUSTIN LOCKE

age, especially when crops failed. To obtain food, a luckless farmer might become a slave to share the bounty of his more fortunate neighbor, or place himself under the protection of a wealthy merchant or landowner.

The lowliest laborer and the richest noble were accorded equal justice under the laws laid down by the Aztec monarch and the penalties stipulated for violation of his edicts. The accused was heard by the magistrate of his phratry, an official elected for personal ability and integrity.

There were two major divisions of crime among the Aztecs—a crime against one's own group, and an offense against another group. The group to which an offender belonged was obligated to see that he was brought to justice.

Murder was punishable by death. Intemperance, except for those aged 70 or over, or during festivities, was dealt with severely: the young were put to death; middle-aged men had their heads shaved—a shattering disgrace. A priest who broke the laws was put to death. In certain cases the offender paid for his crimes on the stone of ceremonial combat.

Slanderers had their lips cut off. Theft was punished according to the amount or nature of the stolen goods and the number of offenses charged against the individual. Stealing gold or silver was a major crime; offenders were flayed. Lesser crimes brought imprisonment.

263

Great Stone Faces reflect an-cient Toltec glory. Ruined Tol-lan, capital of the Toltecs, stands near modern Tula, about fifty miles north of Mexico City. Its giant figures were sculptured not in one piece but several, put together with mor-tise and tenon. Feet buried in earth, the colossi once support-ed a temple roof with their flat heads. In the 12th century a nomadic tribe took over from the civilized Toltecs, burned their temple, tossed the statues into the rubble.

Below: Teotihuacán's sculp-tured reptiles project from the Temple of Quetzalcoatl, the Plumed Serpent. Tláloc, the spectacled rain god, shares the frieze. The grotesque but mag-nificently carved stone serpent heads once were painted, and had eyes fashioned of glittering volcanic glass.

Ruins of the mysterious cere-monial city northeast of Ten-ochtitlán so impressed the Az-tecs that they, too, made it a religious site, named it Teo-tihuacán, "Place of the Gods."

264

Near This Old Aqueduct Tower at San Bartolo Naucalpan a converted Aztec chief found the lost image of the Virgin of Los Remedios. Enshrined there, it is honored by a colorful September fiesta.

A whole class of outcasts was made up of those driven from their own groups for violating laws, exiles from other tribes, and those who failed to cultivate their gardens or to pay their taxes. The Aztec citizen gave about one-third his wealth in taxes. Each section of the city had great storehouses for food, clothing, animal skins, pottery, gold, silver, feathers, tools, and similar objects paid into the treasury.

To be shorn of one's civil rights and cast out was serious indeed. It cut a man off from the protection and subsistence of his group. He became a solitary, hungry wanderer, to be killed by foes unavenged, to fall prey to wild beasts.

Besides the blood-drenched rites for which they are most remembered, the Aztecs danced and sang in ceremonies where the main offerings were flowers and fruit. Love of flowers and music is one of the traits handed down to present-day descendants (page 262). Aztec music was produced by wooden and pottery flutes, conch shells, rattles, drums, and rasping instruments made from notched bones.

The Aztecs enjoyed all kinds of games, the best known being *tlachtli*. This was played as the Maya played it at Chichén Itzá (page 203).

Tumbling and juggling were popular. Montezuma II, emperor at the time of the conquest, was especially fond of acrobatic performances. Favorite dancers occupied a house near his palace. Dwarfs and midgets also entertained him.

Montezuma's zoo and aviary impressed the Spaniards. They saw animals new to them and were amazed at the variety of species. They were fascinated by the serpents, particularly those "with bells on their tails," the rattlesnakes.

All birds known in Mexico, and some from other areas as well, comprised the aviary collection. Besides eagles, macaws, and quetzals, there were tiny parakeets and many long-legged water birds. They were kept for their feathers, which were plucked from time to time for use in fans, headdresses, and cloaks.

From their world of color and variety, the Aztecs looked forward to a future life provided with many heavens.

Those slain in battle, victims of sacrifice, and women who died in childbirth were promised the highest heaven. Death from storm or lightning sent the soul to a hilltop heaven of plenty. A person prosaically dying in bed from natural causes went below to a place called Mictlan. Death from corruptive diseases sent the spirit even lower.

Funerals of the wealthy were elaborate, with jade, gold, and other offerings placed in the tomb. A poor man was fortunate if an ordinary clay vessel went to the grave with him.

But rich or poor, chief or peasant, each Aztec played his part in shaping an early New World culture that offers one of the most fascinating of studies.

The heart of that civilization, the Tecpan or temple enclosure of Tenochtitlán, has now become Mexico City's Zócalo, the *Plaza de la Constitución*. Could its original scenes be recaptured by some magical picture playback, today's plaza strollers would be enchanted, as were the Spaniards, to see the Aztecs' royal palace rising in splendor, to hear the roars and chatter of Aztec zoo and aviary.

In the open park would loom the massive circular stone of ceremonial combat. Near by would be etched the sinister outlines of the great sacrificial temple and the skull rack on which its victims' heads were impaled.

The ancient buildings are long vanished, their stone fragments tossed into the canals or buried in the foundations of the modern city. But here and there among the Indians thronging the streets the stamp of Aztec lineage still stands out. And in the charm and gaiety of life in the Mexican capital the Aztec love of flowers, dancing, and art lives on.

CHAPTER 12

HUNTING PREHISTORY IN PANAMA JUNGLES

BY MATTHEW W. STIRLING

BREAKERS BOOMED on the desolate northern Panama shore. We steadied our canoe, waiting a chance to ride one in to the beach. Our craft soared high, then sagged deep into the foam-flecked trough of a curling Caribbean roller.

I saw my wife Marion and National Geographic Photographer Dick Stewart shoot shoreward with their canoe-load of baggage. My assistant Bob Rands and I followed right behind. Just as we crossed the bar, the frail vessel veered sideways. Heavy surf smashed aboard. Our crew paddled desperately. We beached just in time.

Soaked to the skin, we stood 130 miles west of the Panama Canal on one of this hemisphere's loneliest and wildest coastal stretches. Inland rose a steep, jungle-clad wall of rain-soaked mountains, dipping their toes in the crashing surf.

Near by, Columbus set up the first Spanish colony on America's mainland. But food dwindled, Indians raided, and the "Admiral of the Ocean Sea" abandoned the site. Later explorers shunned this forbidding land.

Now we were seeking pottery, arrowheads, stone axes, ancient graves, other relics of Indians who lived here during and before the time of Columbus. On this third Panama expedition sponsored jointly by the National Geographic Society and the Smithsonian Institution, we aimed to study links between Indian civilizations in South and Central America. Cultural ideas flowing between Inca and Maya empires must have had impact on the isthmus through which they passed. Our job: find evidences of that ancient Indian "golden age."

We hired a guide and headed up Rio Coclé del Norte, poling and towing our canoes through rushing current. Wild fig trees fringed the riverbanks. Monstrous tarpon churned the water.

That afternoon we reached Canoa, the lonely thatched home of an aged woman who promptly led us on a wild goose chase after a mythical burying ground. Near by we found ruins of Spanish gold mines—collapsed tunnels dug by Indian slaves, millstones sheathed in vines.

So began our life in jungle camps. Rain often drenched us, though this was the "dry" season. While we probed sodden diggings, our guide shot game for the pot. "Painted rabbit," or paca, a 20-pound rodent with porklike flavor, was our favorite dish. Fried tapir steaks, dosed liberally with tenderizer, formed another staple.

Sometimes we shot deer, sometimes curassow, kin to wild turkey. Natives sold us rice, bananas, even eggs and chickens. Palm nuts, and our own dehydrated soups, canned fruit, and cheese filled out menus. At night we curled up in mosquito-proof army jungle hammocks, slung between trees. Howler monkeys, insects, frogs sang us to sleep.

We pushed up tributaries of the Coclé del Norte, first Rio Coclecito, then the Cascajal. To buck Cascajal rapids we lightened canoes, hiring extra craft to carry overflow equipment. The Indian crewmen had pointed teeth, chipped with stones, a mark of beauty and health.

Waterfalls, rapids, fallen trees slowed our passage. One poleman kept the big canoe from falling away downstream, another threw weight on his pole to drive ahead a few feet against the sucking current. Over the side, we manhandled boats past rough stretches.

When the river opened into a deep, calm lake, we thankfully made camp. From our hilltop, dry for once, we could see peaks along the Continental Divide. On two previous expeditions we had ranged along its Pacific slope.

From our riverside camp we set to work collecting pottery fragments and stonework. But rain came on the fourth afternoon. It poured all night and at 5 a.m. we broke camp in darkness and shoved off downstream.

First stop was at a native settlement where we had cached our outboard motor and extra equipment to lighten upstream loads. We retrieved these, hired a small leaky canoe, and two Indian boys to man it. We stowed it with archeological treasures, picks, shovels, and food, until only an inch of freeboard remained. But the boys had a fine time guiding it downstream, fishing as they went. They hooked one 10-pounder.

Seemingly past our worst obstacles, we relaxed, enjoyed the downstream run, and thought back on four years of archeological work in Panama.

I remembered a December afternoon when, shivering in light overcoats, we paced the steamer deck, watching New York's snow-draped skyscrapers fall astern. Two days later we basked in tropical sunshine, the overcoats a nuisance.

That was the start of our first Panama expedition. We probed tombs and burial urns in the hilly Peninsula of Azuero.

Marion Stirling Views Grim Ornament. More than 200 slain enemies furnished the 800 human teeth in this Panama warrior's necklace. Dr. Stirling unearthed it with the skeleton of its owner from a burial urn near Parita. Pre-Columbian Indians took their choicest possessions with them to the grave, leaving clues to their culture for scientists who patiently dig up the past.

NATIONAL GEOGRAPHIC PHOTOGRAPHER
RICHARD H. STEWART

By Dugout and "Eggbeater" the archeologist probes Panama's past. Pushing off from stilt-house villages, the expedition bucks brawling rapids in shallow, rock-strewn rivers, only practical routes into much of Panama's jungle-choked interior. Boatmen pole, paddle, haul canoes from one wilderness campsite to the next. For a change of pace, Dr. Stirling takes to wings (above), hovers over an isolated mound where Indians once lived. Helicopter makes sport of jungles once penetrated only by brawn.

KODACHROMES BY NATIONAL GEOGRAPHIC
PHOTOGRAPHER RICHARD H. STEWART

271

can Highway, we spread blankets in the schoolhouse and slept.

Next day, after five hours on horseback, we came to the rim of a natural bowl in the hills. Below us the festival was in full swing. Floating up came the shouting of 2,000 Indians, the blare of primitive instruments.

"Like Times Square on New Year's Eve," said Marion.

The revelry dinned all night as we tried to sleep half a mile away. Early next morning we moved among dancing, chanting Indians, faces striped red and black. Tall, broad-shouldered men wore long trousers, white or blue shirts, some even neckties. Many sported feather headdresses and draped stuffed animal skins over their backs. Women in Mother Hubbard dresses sat with children in corral-like enclosures of slashed undergrowth, guarding gourds of chicha.

This fermented liquor, made from corn, manioc, fruit, or other plants, didn't strike us as strong—although Spaniards described one ancient variety that tasted like turpentine and did double duty as embalming fluid. But the Guaymi, keyed up for their annual festival, got wondrously drunk by mid-morning. While conch-shell or cattle-horn trumpets

But more vivid are memories of much-alive Southern Guaymi Indians and their spring festival, the *balsería.*

Modern survivors of gold-rich tribesmen who resisted Spain's conquistadores, Guaymi still distrust white men. They often set mantraps along their jungle trails—bows and arrows or loaded guns with trip lines attached.

Few outsiders have watched their strange ceremony. The Guaymi try to conceal both its date and site, informing their own scattered tribes by knots tied in reeds along trails. When we got word of a scheduled three-day balsería we bumped toward the mountains in our truck. At Tolé, north of the Pan Ameri-

Four Years of Exploration in
PANAMA

0 — STATUTE MILES — 50
© National Geographic Map

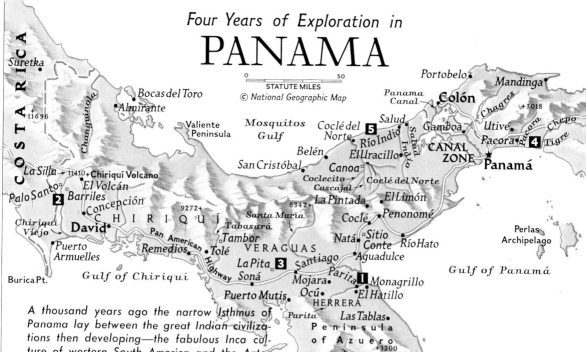

A thousand years ago the narrow Isthmus of Panama lay between the great Indian civilizations then developing—the fabulous Inca culture of western South America and the Aztec and Maya realms of Mexico and Central America. Four National Geographic-Smithsonian expeditions led by Dr. Stirling have sought clues proving relationships between the two.

1 Shell mounds at Monagrillo yielded primitive pottery making this the oldest Panama site so far reported. The designs suggest early pottery types from both Peru and Mexico. Near Parita, man-made mounds revealed urn burials. Sitio Conte to the north proved one of the New World's richest archeological sites.

2 Excavations at foot of Chiriquí volcano disclosed a culture indicating a link between those of Chiriquí-Veraguas and Costa Rica.

3 La Pita tombs yielded pottery, stone, metal relics typical of the rich Veraguas culture.

4 Helicopters, used for the first time in archeological research by the 1949 expedition, helped locate shell mounds along coast and saved weeks in transporting equipment over rugged, trailless country east of Canal Zone.

5 Visiting the wild northwest coast virtually unexplored since Columbus, the 1951 expedition traced ancient Indian cultures up the Coclé del Norte, Salud, and Indio Rivers.

---

blared, and bells and rattles clamored, reeling men seized six-foot balsa logs and began the strange competition for which the balsería is named.

Holding his light log like a billiard cue, a Guaymí would heave it hard, end first, at his opponent's shins. The other man would weave and shuffle enticingly, waiting for the thrust. When it came he would dance nimbly aside or sprawl in the hot dust, feet knocked out from under him. A friend would grab the log, drive it back at someone on the other team. Crowds roared encouragement.

Vicious fist fights erupted every few minutes. Stakes were high—usually the other fellow's wife. Each battle raged until one man was beaten helpless. At the ringside the woman in question awaited the battered victor.

The effect of chicha advanced with the day. The men (they outnumbered us several hundred to one) swarmed around us—not with hostile intent—but with crushing friendliness. It was not trip lines and mantraps we had to fear. It was being killed with affection. At the first chance we rounded up our horses and quietly rode away.

Now, gliding down the Cascajal, I wondered if the Guaymí across the mountains were working out secret plans for this year's balsería.

Rounding a bend, we came to rapids

273

Deep Trenches Unlock Secrets of the Past. Dr. Stirling records each pottery fragment and depth at which found. This Parita site yielded Indian tombs 23 feet down. One held 32 skeletons.

Kitchen, Office, and Workshop Combine in a Jungle Home. Above, Mrs. Stirling cooks while her husband notes archeological finds along Rio Coclé del Norte. Torrential rains, even during Panama's three-month "dry" season, meant pitching camp on high ground to prevent flooding. Archeology is great work for jigsaw-puzzle addicts. At her camp table below, Marion Stirling spent long hours cementing ceramics broken 500 years ago. Figurine with hollow head was worshiped as the jaguar god. Natives often thought the expedition had come to seek gold—as the conquistadores had.

Chocó Men Take Pains with Their Looks. Bangs are carefully brushed. Red and black paint comes from seeds, fruits. Besides aiding beauty, Indians think some designs ward off illness. Chocó wore gold ornaments until Spaniards looted, now weight themselves down with silver or linked coins.

where the river forks to bypass an island. One branch is shallow, one deep and fast with a right-angle turn. Our guide elected to take the larger canoe—"Queen Mary"—through the deep channel.

Hurtling down the flume, we knew we had misjudged the current's force. A great tree loomed in midstream. A sudden eddy caught the vessel broadside, like the crack of a whip swung it against the tree. Dick Stewart and one native were torn from their seats by a limb. They clung to it as the torrent dragged the stern under. The craft capsized.

I clawed at the canoe's bottom, felt my grip weakening, finally let go—to find the water only waist deep. The maelstrom had swept the "Queen Mary" and me to a sand bar. Marion found footing beside me, clutching suitcase and typewriter.

Boxes, bags, cartons bobbed off downstream. Dick's two movie cameras, still cameras, and extra lenses had gone to the bottom. One of our men dived and salvaged them, along with sacks of archeological material. Everything was soaked, much food useless, some film ruined.

We finally reloaded the canoes, ate wet cheese and crackers, and drifted down the Coclé del Norte, reaching its mouth at midnight, drenched as usual.

Next morning we dried equipment, then stared astonished as a U. S. Air Force helicopter whirred down on the beach. Its pilot had come to investigate bones thought to be those of a lost flyer. Dick Stewart hopped a ride to the Canal Zone for new cameras.

The beat of the blades was familiar. On our second Panama expedition we

276

had explored mounds near the Rio Tigre by helicopter. Our two whirlybirds hoisted us over mangrove swamp which would have made tortuous going on foot. We spotted the mounds rising from patches of savanna. Hovering above them, the pilots checked the ground, flattening the seven-foot-high grass with a down-blast from the rotors. We landed, collected bits of pottery, took off to explore more jungle, hung in mid-air to take pictures, returned to base. Five hours did the work of weeks by foot and canoe.

With Dick on his way to civilization and a launch coming for us next day, our troubles seemed over. But when the boat arrived, surf threatened again. Our big canoe twice went through the breakers, carrying bananas out to the bobbing launch. Our own baggage would take two more trips. But the crew had bucked enough combers for one day. They would make only one more trip to the launch.

We stowed everything into the canoe, plus a native passenger, a crate of live chickens, Marion, and myself. At the last minute, Mendoza, owner of the little store at the mouth of the Coclé del Norte, decided to come along. Lucky he did.

Three crew members were aft, two forward, each with a long pole to shove us across the bar, and a paddle for deep water. We cleared the river mouth and hit breakers, smacking through for about 400 yards. But the craft was riding deep, answering sluggishly.

Spotting calmer water, we turned parallel to the surf and drove for it. Immediately a breaker pounded over us. Frothing water flooded aboard.

At that instant Mendoza took command, bellowed orders to the exhausted crew. A second comber swept us, tumbled me from my perch on piled cargo; Marion went half overboard. In the nick of time we hauled her back.

Grabbing plastic army helmet liners, we bailed the foundering dugout. Mendoza kept the crew straining in unison

at the paddles. At last the water level inboard dropped, the half-sunk craft inched painfully ahead through the last line of breakers and out to open sea where the launch waited. We were safe.

All the chickens had drowned.

We repaired water-soaked equipment in the Canal Zone, then pushed off for La Pintada, south of the Continental Divide. There in the uplands we traced ancient cultural connections between the Caribbean lowlands and those of the Pacific coast. We scaled cliffs to locate tombs. We found spectacular petroglyphs—rock carvings—and, moving on to the Peninsula of Azuero, struck a rich site which yielded fine polychrome pottery. Our finds indicated that Panama's pre-Columbian Indian cultures mainly stemmed from South America.

As this third Panama season ended, I felt like a cat which has lost eight of nine lives. Yet, two years later we were back. This most recent trip brought us among the Chocó Indians of Darién.

Since 16th century days when Spaniards plundered and slaughtered the Chocó, few white men have laid eyes on them. But a new, booming trade in bananas has cracked their wall of isolation. Indian banana growers venture downriver from their little-known country. Trader's rum is making inroads. In a few years, we felt, "civilization" would spoil them. Now was the time for a visit.

We hitched a ride on an Army cargo carrier, then transferred to an "African Queen" type vessel, the *Lila*, for the journey up the Sambú River. On board we saw our first Chocó Indians, a pretty 18-year-old girl and her younger brother.

She looked ill at ease in baggy blue cotton dress. But as the *Lila* chugged out of mangrove swamps to nose between high jungle-clad river banks, the girl celebrated homecoming by stripping down to the brief wraparound typical of her people. Self-confidence restored, she and her brother dove neatly from the gunwale and swam ashore as the vessel neared the trading post of Sábelo.

Sleepy Sábelo had boomed with the influx of Colombian Negroes, middlemen of the banana trade. We also saw many Chocó in Sábelo—small, well-built banana planters who had canoed to town with their families. Men zealously guarded their wives, and no wonder. With gleaming black hair and skin as fair as a European's, many women were strikingly handsome.

To guide us into real Chocó country, Ailipio, a shy, wiry five-footer with a smattering of Spanish, offered his services and those of his 24-foot piragua, carved from an espavé log. Finely balanced, the craft never ducked us once.

Ailipio nonchalantly spun the flywheel of his outboard motor and off we went. Somehow we never got used to seeing a near-naked, painted Chocó expertly steering a sputtering outboard.

We stopped at one of the large thatched houses, raised on stilts, which line the riverbank at about half-mile intervals. There we picked up Nicaño, Ailipio's muscular nephew, valuable bow man when we went over the side to nurse the dugout through white water.

Flatlands gave way to mountains. The river's crystal water reflected virgin jungle or arching banana fronds near Chocó houses. Chattering monkeys chased through the canopy of trees. Flocks of parrots rose screaming.

We swung toward shore, landed on a flat rock between two Indian houses— Ailipio's and his mother-in-law's. Why would our guide live so far upstream when his work took him so often to Sábelo? He had a second house downriver, he said, complete with second wife.

We swam in the whirpool at Ailipio's door and watched our host and his two sons spearing fish from small canoes. They would dive under for uneasy minutes, then reappear yards from where we expected, triumphantly waving a fish.

Pushing upstream next morning, we battled increasing current. Once we landed to explore a Chocó burying place. Dishes, spoons, clothing, carved wooden toys covered each grave. One with a concrete slab on it seemed out of keeping. It belonged to a rich Chocó, Ailipio explained, first to buy an outboard motor. The family had debated whether to bury the motor with him, according to custom. They decided it would serve better on the river.

Indian houses grew less frequent. As we passed each one, Ailipio exchanged shouted gossip with its owner until out of earshot. We investigated a fish trap of cane stalks and watched an Indian skillfully finishing his dugout canoe with razor-sharp machete.

Further on, in a new jungle clearing, two men carved decorations on a huge canoe high on the bank. They greeted us and posed with rich silver ornaments and heavy earrings.

Reaching the last house at the head of canoe navigation on this "Main Street" of the Chocó, we had the thrill of knowing that we had probably traveled farther into the fascinating Chocó country than any white man before us.

We would spread our air mattresses on the sleeping platform in a Chocó house and rise at dawn with our hosts to swim before breakfast. Womenfolk folded away sleeping mats and swept with twig brooms until the airy room was spotless. They dropped garbage through wide

Bright Pottery Designs Reveal High Culture

Humanized reptile faces peer from 500-year-old earthenware found in Panama. Crocodile-design cups at top are red, black, and purple on white. To right of turtle plate is a conventionalized king vulture. Such fanciful ware bore food and drink for pre-Columbian Indians, proving they had an eye for beauty as well as utility.

Though breakable, pottery doesn't perish. Color, shape, and style tell the expert when and where each vessel was fashioned, thus helping fill gaps in our knowledge of ancient Indian life.

NATIONAL GEOGRAPHIC PHOTOGRAPHER
RICHARD H. STEWART

spaced palm flooring to hogs waiting under the house. Long-haired Chocó men primp at their facial make-up while women finish house chores.

Then the workday starts, women tilling seasonal crops, men harvesting or loading bananas, hunting, fishing, or clearing land. Men take their make-up kits with them to freshen up the bold black, red, or purple designs on their faces. They are not so concerned about their black body stain, which starts to wear off after a week of swimming half a dozen times a day.

A typical Chocó house is a self-sufficient family community: perhaps an elderly couple, their married daughters, sons-in-law, grandchildren, and of course dogs. While elders work, little girls tend fires and babies at home. Small boys help their fathers. A Chocó five-year-old can pole a canoe expertly.

Work ends at mid-afternoon when women serve the second meal. We tried such Chocó food as roasted green bananas, but preferred our rations. The Indians dabbed at our spaghetti and pretzels, but shied from onions, bacon, ham.

Chocó home life appealed to us. Women weave baskets. Men make or repair spears, blowguns, bows and arrows. We entertained well-mannered, frisky Chocó youngsters with magic tricks until bedtime. Parents raise them with large doses of affection and an unrestraining hand.

When finally it was time to leave Chocó country and get back to archeology, we realized the simple, self-reliant life we had shared with these Indians would make us homesick for them. Ailipio came to see us off.

"When will you return?" he asked.

"Some day, God willing."

"If I am alive, I will come to be with you again. You are my friends."

We felt the same way.

PAINTING BY H. M. HERGET

Noblemen Meet on Road, Swap Yarns of the Inca's Court. "A tribute of lice!" laughingly relates the highland official in vicuña-wool tapestry tunic (center). This humiliating tax was imposed by the late 15th century Inca Tupac Yupanqui on a newly conquered province unable to pay a more substantial levy. The amused listeners are a coastal gentleman in striped cotton robe with gold earplugs and gold-headed staff of office, and a befeathered dweller of eastern Andes slopes.

CHAPTER 13

THE INCAS
EMPIRE BUILDERS OF THE ANDES

BY PHILIP AINSWORTH MEANS

HALF AN HOUR after I descended from the airplane which brought me to Cusco, Peru, its implacable, modernistic roar still sounded in my ears. Consequently, when I strolled into the huge plaza where the Indian market is held every day, I felt chronologically confused. In my ears the 20th century whirred, but before my eyes was a scene that belonged to the 16th century at the latest.

Hundreds of Indians, mostly women, were carrying on a leisurely trade. I saw a few people of Spanish blood in modern dress walking in the arcades along the margins of the plaza, but everyone else in the scene was Indian.

Perhaps the most striking indigenes of all were the llamas, those haughty and beautiful cousins of the camel. With their tall, pointed ears gaily decked with streamers of colored wool, and sometimes even with little bells of copper or of silver, they seemed to tread the earth with scornful pride.

Little by little the airplane roar yielded to the staccato, purring-clicking sibilance of a strange language rising into the thin, cold air around me. Presently I realized that it was Quechua, the ancient general tongue of western South America.

Drawing nearer, I observed the trade going on in the booths. The first I saw was partly modern in aspect. A woman was selling Woolworthian trifles for small coinage. Between customers she busied herself with an up-to-date portable sewing machine.

A few steps farther on, however, I came upon another booth altogether antique in appearance. A sturdy Indian woman was offering a haunch of llama meat, another reluctantly adding a potato at a time to a pile on the ground.

Both women were unhurried, all their emotions concentrated in their faces. The expression of the seller was one of determined avarice; that of the buyer one of increasing hesitancy (page 299).

I could see that very soon the buyer would reach her limit and take her potatoes to some other booth whose mistress had less lordly ideas about the potato value of a haunch of llama.

I was, indeed, witnessing an authentic barter trade such as was universal under the Inca Empire. My mind turned back to olden times when, between about 1100 (the Crusades were then stirring Europe to holy zeal) and the middle of the 15th century (when Gutenberg and his printing press were helping to inaugurate our modern age), the Incas built up a solidly organized realm of amazing size.

I reflected that, in a period equal to that between Columbus's arrival in the

Antilles and our own Mexican War, a family of American Indians had created an empire worthy to be compared with the realms of Alexander, Caesar, Charlemagne, Napoleon; an empire which outshone others because its benevolent and sagacious ruling caste, the Incas, strove successfully to make all their subjects prosperous and happy within the framework of their separate cultures (map, page 287).

The Incas and their subjects were not a whole people as were the Maya. About A.D. 1100, the Incas were a small tribe of Quechua-speaking llama herders dwelling on a lofty plain some leagues southwest of Cusco. Their homeland had the stark, grandiose beauty of the Andes, but it was unfit for agriculture and for shaping an improved mode of life.

Although nothing outwardly distinguished the Incas from hundreds of other little tribes, an inborn genius for growth and organization stirred within them about this time, filling them with a conviction that a "manifest destiny" awaited them.

Their first step toward dynastic grandeur was a tribal migration from their bleak homeland down into the fair and fertile valley of Cusco, rimmed with sublimely soaring, snow-crowned mountains and watered by the headlong torrent of the Huatanay River.

Ancient legends of how it was done are numerous and quaint, but contradictory. The version preserved among the Inca caste itself, and transmitted to us by reliable Spanish chroniclers, is that the Inca tribe, led by Manco Capac and his sister-wife Mama Ocllo, marched upon Cusco.

There they gained dominion over the folk already in the valley by a picturesque and wily appeal to their credulity and superstition.

A beautiful lad named Roca was clad in a garment covered with spangles of burnished gold. Thus arrayed, he appeared at the mouth of a cavern above Cusco where the rays of the sun fell dazzlingly upon him.

Pointing aloft to that radiant figure, which seemed to be a part of the sun fallen to earth, the strategists persuaded the wonder-struck multitude that the shining boy was the Son of the Sun, to whom their entire allegiance was due.

Thus between the years 1100 and 1140, Sinchi Roca (War Chief Roca), the first really historic ruler of the Inca dynasty, was accepted by the dwellers in Cusco as a divine monarch sent to govern and protect them. By gaining their reverence and loyalty, Sinchi Roca formed the nucleus of what was to become a mighty empire.

Of the legends concerning Inca origins, this version seems most nearly authentic. A curious aspect is the incestuous marriage between Manco Capac and his sister, Mama Ocllo. It may have been a custom of the primitive Incas, as this legend implies; or it may be an element inserted into the legend much later when, the Empire having grown great and its rulers proud of their sacred blood, sister-marriage became obligatory.

At any rate, the Incas, from Sinchi Roca down to Pachacutec, the eighth Inca, seem not to have married their sisters; rather, they allied themselves with daughters of powerful chiefs whose friendship they needed. Not until their might became such that this support could no longer enhance it did the historic Incas, beginning with Tupac Yupanqui, revive or initiate the practice of wedding their sisters to preserve the holy purity of their blood.

Only from an airplane high above the majestic mountain panorama can one clearly understand the magnitude of the empire-building accomplished by the Inca dynasty. From this lofty viewpoint one sees endless, tumbled Andean ranges, flanked on the west by a long strip of coastal desert crossed by occasional

PAINTING BY H. M. HERGET

Wildly Swaying Throng Snake-dances Through Cusco's Holy Square, bearing a great woolen rope of many colors. Its pumalike head reaches the imperial carpet before the Inca, who sits on his brilliant throne flanked by high priests and the flexed mummies of his ancestors. These bundled Incas of past glory have been brought out in state from the Temple of the Sun, whose trapezoid-shaped windows overlook the square. During the great January rite, begun with the full moon, llamas and guinea pigs were sacrificed to the creator-god Viracocha in the hope of bountiful crops.

283

green bands of westward-flowing streams, and on the east by a vast jungle world stretching away toward the Atlantic.

The huge area wherein the Incas shaped their empire was one of infinite diversity, severed by all but impassable barriers: deep chasms carved by rushing rivers, leaping ranges of peaks crossed only by difficult passes where the air is thin and piercingly cold, deserts where all things shrivel under the onslaught of the sun.

Left to themselves, the innumerable peoples of highlands and coast would never have coalesced into an empire. Each tribe, ensconced in its compact valley home, would have gone on living on the produce of its fields and llama herds with no thought for the world beyond the mountains. True, sundry chiefs here and there, especially on the coast, formed confederacies and kingdoms of some extent, but none knew how to build an empire on the scale that the Incas achieved.

The Incas began their career in a modest way. At the end of the reign of Sinchi Roca their realm included only Cusco and the country around it. The southern

Great Wall of Peru knifes inland across sharp Andean spurs, plumbs deep valleys, straddles the Santa River north of Chimbote. Fourteen fortresses command hilltop vantage points flanking this Western Hemisphere counterpart of China's ancient wall. One large military post studied from the air appeared to have 15-foot rock breastworks enclosing a 200-by-300-foot area.

The northward course of Inca empire surged past this 40-mile wall built by the Chimus (page 296), who flourished in the centuries immediately preceding the rapid Inca rise to power. Some 25 principal rivers like the Santa tumble from the Andes to Pacific across Peru's barren coast. Before Inca roadbuilding, each isolated river valley tended to develop a culture of its own. Northern valleys outpaced the southern. Beyond the coastal cordillera evolved the highland Tiahuanaco of Lake Titicaca and the Inca, centered along headwaters of Amazon tributaries.

Chart at right shows when notable cultures reached their zenith, often after centuries of development and influence by coexistent groups.

NOTABLE CULTURES IN PERU

Tentative Dates	Cultures	Epochs
1532	Historic	COLONIAL
1480	Inca	IMPERIAL [INCA]
	Chimu	FUSION
1200	Tiahuanaco	FLORESCENT
1000	Nasca Mochica	
500	Salinar Paracas	FORMATIVE
A.D. / B.C.		
	Coastal Chavín	EARLY CERAMIC
	Guanápe	
1000?	Cerro Prieto	PRE-CERAMIC

PAINTING BY H. M. HERGET

High Priest of the Sun, the Villac Umu, holds aloft a golden bowl shaped to focus sun's rays on tinder contents and set it smoldering. With it he will light a ceremonial fire on the altar behind. The cult of sun worship is far older in Peru than in Mexico; this suggests Andean origin. Cusco alone had some 3,000 Virgins of the Sun.

frontier was La Raya Pass, at the headwaters of the Urubamba River, into which, after rushing through Cusco, the Huatanay River flows.

Across this pass in the Vilcanota Range an east-west defensive wall of uncut stones laid in clay was found. Likely it had marked the boundary in pre-Inca times between Quechua-speaking people to the north and Colla-speaking folk of the Titicaca Basin to the south. The wall and rough-stone houses for its defenders may still be seen.

Small though it was, the realm Sinchi Roca left at his death must have been perfectly organized internally. Even then the ruler's chief care was to ensure the well-being of his subjects and thus make them his zealous supporters. To do less would have belied the sacred character to which he pretended.

The second Inca, Lloque Yupanqui (Left-handed One Who Will Be Renowned for Pious Actions), ruled about 1140 to 1195.

Having begun his reign by inspecting all his realm and visiting his vassal *curacas* (chieftains), he passed beyond the Vilcanota wall and came to grips with the Collas (also called Aymarás), a sturdy folk who were creating a state not dissimilar to the Inca's own.

Skillfully combining diplomatic blandishments with martial force, Inca Lloque Yupanqui brought into his realm the northern half of the Titicaca region, then organized it in accordance with Inca policies of merciful rule and justice for all. At his death Incadom was equal in extent to Massachusetts, Connecticut, and Rhode Island.

Mayta Capac (Diligent Great One), who ruled from about 1195 to 1230, continued his father's policies and conquests. On reaching the ruins of Tiahuanaco, near the southern end of Lake Titicaca, Mayta Capac beheld the vestiges of an architectural style far superior to rough stone laid in clay, hitherto the only construction known to the Incas. He saw, as we may see today, superbly cut and carved stones held together when necessary by copper clamps set in sockets (page 292).

The practical lessons to be derived from this superior technology—practiced some centuries before by people of the Tiahuanaco Empire (A.D. 600–900)—were not thrown away upon Inca Mayta Capac, who seems to have had a genius for engineering and architecture. From building methods he studied at the abandoned capital of these mysterious people arose a vastly improved Inca architecture.

Likewise this great engineer was the first Inca to build a suspension bridge of stout aloe cables swung from massive piers of masonry. The fame of this bridge spread far and wide, increasing his already high prestige among the tribes (page 294).

Mayta Capac also was the first Inca to lead his army across the coast range and down to the Pacific. There he had to contend not only with men but with the hot, dry, dense air of the lowlands.

To the large-lunged mountain folk the coast is very trying, so Mayta Capac began to use a system later brought to high perfection by his successors. He divided his large army into sections; each served only a short time on the coast and afterward went back to the mountains to recuperate.

By a characteristic combination of military and diplomatic tactics, Mayta Capac brought part of the southern coast's civilized population into the Empire. Typical was his treatment of wizards in that region. Instead of trying to suppress them and thereby driving them underground, he recognized them as a professional class whom the people might consult freely. Doubtless he argued that their spells might do a little good while not strong enough to do much harm.

In a relatively short reign, from about 1230 to 1250, the fourth Inca, Capac Yupanqui, continued his father's conquests on the coast and so increased the realm that at his death it was equal to New England, New York, and New Jersey combined. He improved the internal organization and in general ruled wisely.

Inca Roca, about 1250 to 1315, wishing to expand his empire north through the highlands, found the way barred by the most formidable foe the Incas had yet encountered.

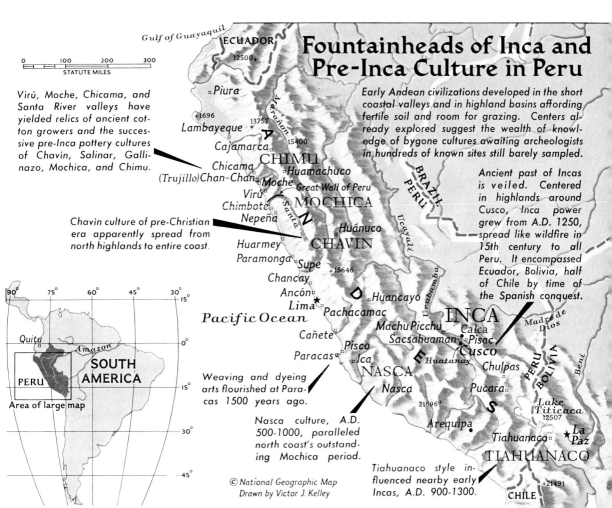

Fountainheads of Inca and Pre-Inca Culture in Peru

Early Andean civilizations developed in the short coastal valleys and in highland basins affording fertile soil and room for grazing. Centers already explored suggest the wealth of knowledge of bygone cultures awaiting archeologists in hundreds of known sites still barely sampled.

Ancient past of Incas is veiled. Centered in highlands around Cusco, Inca power grew from A.D. 1250, spread like wildfire in 15th century to all Peru. It encompassed Ecuador, Bolivia, half of Chile by time of the Spanish conquest.

Virú, Moche, Chicama, and Santa River valleys have yielded relics of ancient cotton growers and the successive pre-Inca pottery cultures of Chavin, Salinar, Gallinazo, Mochica, and Chimu.

Chavin culture of pre-Christian era apparently spread from north highlands to entire coast.

Weaving and dyeing arts flourished at Paracas 1500 years ago.

Nasca culture, A.D. 500-1000, paralleled north coast's outstanding Mochica period.

Tiahuanaco style influenced nearby early Incas, A.D. 900-1300.

© National Geographic Map
Drawn by Victor J. Kelley

STATUTE MILES
0 100 200 300

SOUTH AMERICA
PERU
Area of large map

Gulf of Guayaquil
ECUADOR
Piura
Lambayeque
Cajamarca
Chicama
(Trujillo) Chan-Chan
Moche
Virú
Chimbote
Nepeña
Huarmey
Paramonga
Supe
Chancay
Ancón
Lima
Pachacamac
Cañete
Pisco
Paracas
Ica
Nasca
Arequipa
Tiahuanaco
La Paz

CHIMU
MOCHICA
CHAVIN
Huamachuco
Great Wall of Peru
Huánuco
Huancayo
Machu Picchu
Sacsahuaman
Calca
Pisac
Cusco
Chulpas
Pucara
Lake Titicaca

INCA
NASCA
TIAHUANACO

BRAZIL
PERU
BOLIVIA
CHILE

Pacific Ocean

Quito
Amazon

Up Temple Steps at Pachacamac a High Priest Bears the Sun's Golden Image. Another priest carries two gold cups. Chosen Women of the Sun, soldiers, courtiers, minor priests follow.

Beyond in the courtyard, low-walled at Pacific's edge, the inhabitants lie flat on their faces. The Inca's armies have just taken the holy city. The victors will combine its religion with their own.

289

These were the Chancas, a people of forest-country origin who had come up into the highlands north of Cusco from eastern jungles. They were fierce, ambitious, courageous. Inca Roca was far from successful in his encounters with these implacable foes. Thus the Chancas became a black and menacing cloud on the northern horizon of Incadom.

Nor was his son, Yahuar Huaccac (He Who Weeps Blood), a man fit to confront the grave peril of the Chancas. This, the sixth Inca, who ruled about 1315–1347, seems to have been cursed from his childhood by some malady or evil influence. Modern psychologists would explain him in terms of an inferiority complex because of unfortunate events in his youth. However that may have been, we know that he was the only Inca who was feckless and cowardly, and the Chanca menace increased mightily in his time.

Finally something drastic had to be done. The Chancas were on the march. With hideous yells and frantic brandishing of weapons they moved furiously southward, intent on capturing Cusco. Had they succeeded—and they very nearly did—Incadom would have been utterly crushed and all its hard work undone.

Prince Hatun Tupac, son of the inefficient Inca, was the man sorely needed to oppose so redoubtable an enemy. First receiving in a dream mysterious counsel from a deity who announced himself to be the creator-god Viracocha, the prince assembled the bravest of Inca manhood, adding half-reluctant allies from other parts of the realm. At the head of these forces he marched to the broad plain of Anta and there awaited the enemy.

Presently the Chanca horde came swooping down the pass into the plain, shrieking warlike cries, trumpets and

drums resounding defiantly. Battle was joined. For many hours the lines of struggling warriors swayed back and forth, plying star-headed clubs, javelins, slings, knives of flint or bronze.

Prince Hatun Tupac was in the forefront of combat, exhorting his men, himself slaying many a foeman. At last the tide turned in the Incas' favor. The Chancas began to retreat. Only then did the prince's hesitant allies, who had been waiting to see whom fortune would approve, join in with the Inca troops.

As these new contingents came up, the prince and his men in triumph shouted to the enemy, "Behold! The very bushes and rocks of the plain are becoming soldiers to defend our Father the Sun!"

To the Chancas it seemed truth itself. Their retreat became flight, then headlong rout. Prince Hatun Tupac had saved the day and so assured his dynasty's fu-

Inca Prince Rides to Cusco

Lordly as the surrounding snow-capped Andean peaks, a member of the imperial family approaches the capital in splendor, his litter cushioned on the shoulders of sturdy retainers. Favored nobles bear his feather-adorned canopy. Golden fox heads tip the poles supporting his ornate throne.

Priests follow with their *quipus*, or knotted-cord records; then warriors clad in polished bronze plate armor with javelins, war clubs, painted shields, and handleless battle-axes. Ax motif appears in the prince's headdress. Tapping copper and tin wealth of the Andes, Inca smiths alloyed them to make bronzes to suit varied needs. Weapons and tools were cast in bronze of low tin content and cold-hammered. More tin went into bronze ornaments. Iron and steel were unknown.

PAINTING BY H. M. HERGET

ture. Thereupon in grateful remembrance he took the name of his counselor, the god Viracocha, and by it he is best known in Inca history.

Viracocha's conquest of the Chancas was solemnly celebrated in Cusco. A superb triumphal pageant was held in Coricancha, the Temple of the Sun. Captains of the victorious army, soldiers, and citizenry all took part. In their midst were countless Chanca prisoners and their womenfolk.

Lances bedecked with gay plumes, multicolored shields, massive war clubs with gleaming bronze heads shaped like stars, served as panoplies for the scene. Jubilant music, joyful dancing, and piercing shouts of thanksgiving combined into a paean of praise to the god Viracocha and to his imperial namesake.

Borne in a golden litter, the Inca entered the temple last of all. At his coming the prisoners were forced to throw themselves flat on the ground. Over the pathway formed by their prostrate bodies the Inca and his greatest nobles marched to the altar chanting a verse whose refrain was "My enemies I tread upon."

Here we have a very different aspect of Inca statesmanship from the merciful and generous one to which we are accustomed. There was, however, good reason for it. The Inca Viracocha had just overwhelmed the most formidable enemy his house had ever known. Puma-eyed and proudly vengeful, he thus signalized, for all the Andean world to see, the invincible character of the Inca dynasty.

This was all the more necessary because of the fatal weakness his father had displayed. By this terrible warning the Inca Viracocha foretold the fate that awaited all who opposed the Inca family.

The reign of Viracocha, about 1347–1400, marks the beginning of the great period of Incadom. Conquests were made in the southern highlands down to and including Tucumán (in northwestern Argentina) as well as beyond the Chanca

Moderns Marvel at Sacsahuaman Walls

Superb example of cyclopean masonry, the zigzag ramparts of the great fortress of Sacsahuaman stand imperishable on heights north of Cusco.

Ancient builders, without steel tools, blasting powder, or machinery, quarried enormous blocks, transported them miles across ridges and ravines without draft animals or the wheel, dressed and raised them into position without cranes. Largest stones exceed 25 feet in height, weigh hundreds of tons. Irregular in shape, they fit tight without mortar.

Sheep, first brought in by the Spaniards, graze beside the massive gateway of Tiahuanaco (left) at southern end of Lake Titicaca. In the frieze, 48 man-bird figures face toward the central god or ruler, whose cheeks run with tears. The monolith was carved more than 1,000 years ago by Indians whose culture had impact in the central Andes. Incas found Tiahuanaco in ruins and abandoned.

WALTER HENRICKS HODGE (TOP LEFT);
ROBERT GERSTMANN, BLACK STAR (LEFT)

292

region in the north. Social institutions, also the material aspects of Inca civilization were being improved throughout the realm which, at Viracocha's death, was equal to the sum of New England, New York, New Jersey, Delaware, Maryland, and eastern Virginia.

The Inca Pachacutec (All-Teacher), son of Viracocha, ruled about 1400–1448. He it was who brought the empire to its finest flowering.

Taking to heart the lesson of the Chanca war, he resolved to prevent further incursions into his realm by savage folk dwelling in woodlands east of the Andes. Accordingly, he built a long line of fortresses along the eastern frontier. The most noteworthy is the great citadel of Machu Picchu, excavated and cleared by the National Geographic Society-Yale University expeditions led by Hiram Bingham in 1912–1915 (Chapter 14).

Neither Pachacutec nor any other Inca was merely a brutal conqueror. He fought valiantly when he had to, but preferred pacific methods. Once the submission of a hostile chief was won, the Inca proceeded also to win his devotion. The vanquished was given a high admin-istrative post and his dependent officials were tendered positions equal to those they had previously held.

Whenever possible, each tribe or state was taken into the Inca realm as a going concern, without loss of prestige to anyone who upheld the overlordship of the Sapa Inca, Sole Emperor; and the defeated people were thenceforward protected and encouraged exactly as were all his other subjects.

Characteristic of Inca sagacity was the amazing knowledge of geographic factors applied to colonizing. Either a tribe long accustomed to Inca rule was moved to some newly conquered region, where they taught the inhabitants the ways of the Inca house, or a newly vanquished people was moved en masse to a district whose denizens would be their teachers.

In either case the place to which colonists were to be sent was always as similar as possible to their homeland. To determine this the Incas used relief maps, executed in colored clay, whereon the natural features of each part of the realm were clearly indicated.

As a further means of inwardly strengthening the empire, sons and kins-

293

men of the great vassals were brought to Cusco. There, in company with youths of the imperial caste, they were educated in both military science and the peaceful arts at the House of Teaching.

The supreme authority of the Inca flowed down through many grades of administrative officials, the humblest of whom had supervision over ten families, in a spirit of fatherly guidance. It reached into every household in the land, and saw that all wants were filled, that life, though laborious in just degree, was happy and free from care.

The household was the unit of society. Its head, called *puric,* or full-grown man, performed the heavy labor, aided by his wife and older children. Neither the very young nor the old were called upon for manual toil.

The puric alone paid tribute to the state. Justly apportioned, it took such forms as a part of the family's produce from the fields or as a reasonable stint of work by each puric on roads, irrigation channels, terraces for agriculture, or other public works. Or, if a man were skilled in some handicraft, his output during a certain time was paid into the government's storehouses which

Bridges, Paved Highways Linked the Far-flung Andes Empire

Across a deep ravine from their thatch-roofed home, dark-eyed daughters of an Inca official go down to a mountain spring. In bright cotton dresses embroidered in vicuña wool, they tread wide stairs. Fitted stone also walls cottage and garden terraces below. Massive stone piers anchor stout aloe or liana cables of the suspension bridge on which the girls crossed the gorge.

Llamas bearing tribute of textiles, pottery, and provisions destined for the ruling Inca approach a road supervisor's house and traveler's rest (below). One temperamental beast protests overload in typical llama fashion by ejecting toward the herder "a wounderful stinking water." Also intended for the royal "Son of the Sun" is the jug of chicha on the herder's back.

The remarkable engineering talent of the Incas conquered formidable natural barriers that kept pre-Inca cultures apart despite beeline proximity. Their gift stands convincingly revealed by recent archeological mapping of route remnants over the entire 3,100-mile north-south range of 15th century Inca power. Some 10,000 miles of paved roads ran south from Quito deep into Chile and Argentina. They climbed from seacoast to 15,000 feet, crossed western-slope desert, traversed cliff faces on masonry shelves, descended to fringe the Amazon jungle. Not built for the wheel, roads ascended in steps, slipped through tunnels just wide enough to admit a loaded llama.

The famed Inca bridge spanning the Apurimac River (novelist Thornton Wilder's "Bridge of San Luis Rey") on the Cusco-Lima route linked precipice walls 150 feet apart. Suspension cables 16 inches thick swung high out of range of flash floods. Built around 1350, it finally plunged into the roaring gorge in the 1880's.

PAINTINGS BY H. M. HERGET

Chan-Chan, Ancient Chimu Capital, Has Crumbled Into Dust. Chief Peruvian coastal ruin and one of the world's most extensive archeological sites, Chan-Chan spreads over some 11 square miles adjacent to modern Trujillo. The city may have housed as many as 250,000 at its height. Aerial view shows the remains of one of the central palaces, together with the sunken gardens, homes, shops, avenues, plazas, and temple pyramids that surrounded it. Dark rectangle at center was probably a reservoir. Chan-Chan comprised at least ten major sections like this, each flanked by adobe walls up to 30 feet high. These have disintegrated with passing centuries. From Chan-Chan, Chimu culture spread 600 miles along Peru's coast, then fell to Inca Pachacutec; the great fortress at Paramonga was last to surrender. Conquistadores took rich booty from the abandoned capital.

provided for all the needs of society.

The land flourished. Hundreds of villages held periodic fairs where goods were exchanged. The people knew neither the complications nor benefits of money.

Adjacent to every village were its fields, some on the flat valley floor, others on masonry terraces along the hillsides. Their walls still exist, making beautiful and intricate patterns in the landscape (page 324). Water burbled through carefully made irrigation channels fed by streams or springs, and flowering plants grew along their banks. Hedges of fantastic cactus or of blooming shrubs marked the limits of each tribe's lands.

Here and there a white granite temple gleamed, an altar or a sundial carved from one mighty block of stone upon its summit (page 286). At appropriate places rose the mansions of local officials, bowered in feathery trees and adorned by radiantly colored blossoms (page 294).

The plowing season was solemnly inaugurated every year by the Inca in person, using a golden plow on certain fields of the Sun above Cusco. In the garden of the Temple of the Sun, now the Monastery of Santo Domingo in Cusco (page

301), all food crops, flowers, and shrubs, even insects and butterflies were imitated in delicately wrought gold, as if to encourage Nature herself.

Ordinary farmers used plows of heavy wood, with footrests and handles (page 298). Preparing the furrows was done by human strength alone, for the haughty and intractable llama, though he will carry up to 100 pounds on his back, has never permitted himself to be harnessed as a draft animal. If his load is even a trifle too great to please him, he will, in the words of an old chronicler, "turne round his head and ejecte from his mouthe a wounderful stinking water."

Like their modern descendants, husbandmen of Inca days knew the value of fish heads as fertilizer. Those of the coast also made use of guano brought from the bird islands off the shore. For weeding and tending crops a variety of simple but effective tools was used. Their like may still be seen on many an Indian farm.

This mighty and diversified realm had been created by a development of the relayed-army technique begun by Mayta Capac. It was lashed to the supreme authority of the Sapa Inca by a splendid system of roads, paved, and provided with steps where necessary (page 295).

Conquering Incas Built a Terraced Temple to Outshine Pachacamac's Shrine. South of Lima stand ruins of the pre-Inca temple of Pachacamac (foreground) and the Inca Temple of the Sun. With dramatic effect, the Incas erected their radiant temple overlooking the vast Pacific to divert worship in this ancient pilgrimage center from the creator-god Pachacamac, region's supreme deity, to the Inca creator-god Viracocha (page 288). Viracocha was not bloodthirsty like Aztec deities, but burials of strangled women at Pachacamac show the Incas did make human sacrifices.

Incaland: Home of Potato

Amid terraced farm slopes of the Andes an Indian digs with foot plow; his sister wields a hoe, his wife carries home a bag of potatoes. Many wild species grow in cool highlands of Peru, Bolivia, Ecuador, and Chile. Hundreds, perhaps thousands of years before the Incas, Indians found plants with pea-sized edible tubers. Adept farmers, they cultivated them, improved taste and size through centuries, developed varieties suited to elevations from sea level to 14,000 feet.

Spanish conquerors, bent on finding precious stones and metals, recorded nothing of the potato's origin. Some took plants home to Spain, where the exotic vegetable languished for decades before spreading elsewhere. Ireland became its stronghold; from there it moved to the New England colonies as the "Irish potato." The Orient still slights the white potato, but in the world as a whole it has come to rate as the single most important vegetable.

Over these highways sped *chasquis,* or post-runners. Each ran a distance nicely calculated to permit him to go at top speed from his posthouse to the next, bearing a *quipu* (knotted-string record), an oral message, or even a watertight basket in which fish from the sea swam in salt water until they reached the imperial kitchen.

Over these roads huge armies could be marched quickly. Even the deepest chasm ceased to be a barrier, for marvelous suspension bridges of thick aloe ropes fixed by massive masonry piers on either bank leaped across them.

The Sapa Inca was borne along the roads in his magnificent litter which rested on the shoulders of specially trained bearers, while noblemen proudly carried the poles which upheld the gorgeous canopy (page 290). Whenever the imperial litter halted, the multitude cried aloud: "Most high Lord, child of the Sun, thou art the sole and beloved Lord. The whole earth truly obeys thee."

Naturally enough, the privilege of traveling by litter was reserved to the very highest persons: to the Sapa Inca and his empress, to governors or viceroys of the four grand provinces which made up the Realm of the Four United Parts, as the Empire was officially styled, and to specially favored conquered kings or conspicuously successful generals whom the Inca wished to honor. Everyone else, no matter how high his rank, walked.

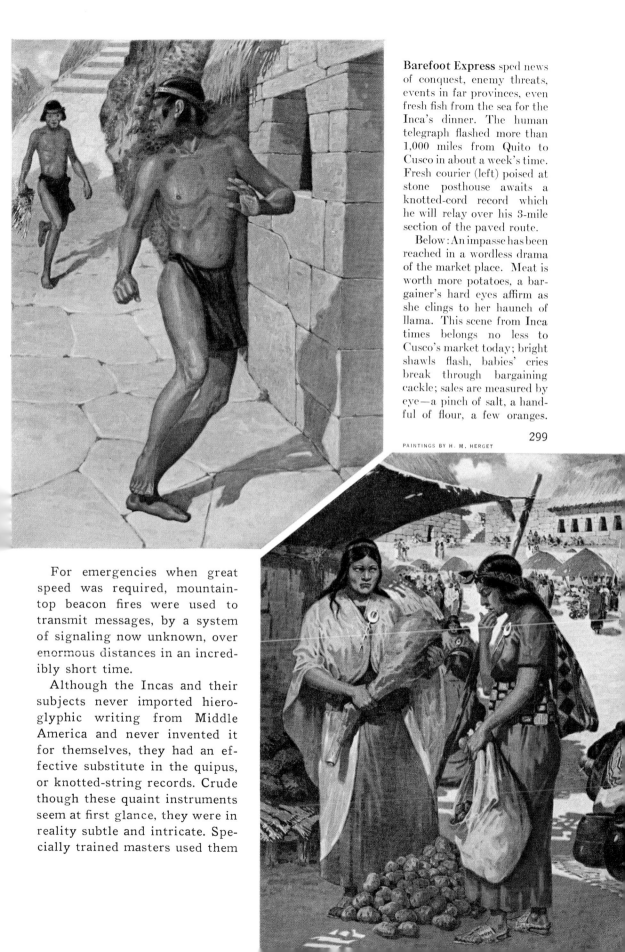

Barefoot Express sped news of conquest, enemy threats, events in far provinces, even fresh fish from the sea for the Inca's dinner. The human telegraph flashed more than 1,000 miles from Quito to Cusco in about a week's time. Fresh courier (left) poised at stone posthouse awaits a knotted-cord record which he will relay over his 3-mile section of the paved route.

Below: An impasse has been reached in a wordless drama of the market place. Meat is worth more potatoes, a bargainer's hard eyes affirm as she clings to her haunch of llama. This scene from Inca times belongs no less to Cusco's market today; bright shawls flash, babies' cries break through bargaining cackle; sales are measured by eye—a pinch of salt, a handful of flour, a few oranges.

299

For emergencies when great speed was required, mountain-top beacon fires were used to transmit messages, by a system of signaling now unknown, over enormous distances in an incredibly short time.

Although the Incas and their subjects never imported hieroglyphic writing from Middle America and never invented it for themselves, they had an effective substitute in the quipus, or knotted-string records. Crude though these quaint instruments seem at first glance, they were in reality subtle and intricate. Specially trained masters used them for arithmetical calculations, and possibly for simple narratives.

Quipu-ology, the study of these knot-records, was a third-year subject in the four-year course at the Teaching House, where ruling caste youths were educated. Even today one sees llama herders counting flocks by means of a simplified survival of the ancient system.

For studying the movements of sun, moon, and stars, and for determining the seasons of the year, the Incas used several methods. One was the sundial, to be found in every temple (page 322). Carved, as a rule, from a large boulder, its upper surface was flat save for a stout column of the same stone, carefully shaped when the dial was made. The shadow cast by this gnomon, besides marking the hours and seasons, was the object of much esoteric learning now lost to us.

Again, groups of towers were used whose shadows told learned men about the equinoxes and solstices and so aided them in appointing days for festivals held throughout the year. Seemingly simple compared with modern calendars and astronomical observatories, the ancient Peruvian techniques enabled the Incas to measure time nearly as accurately as we do.

It is in their architecture, however, that the applied science of the ancient Peruvians may best be seen today. Whether it be in the stupendous megalithic masonry of Fort Sacsahuaman (page 292), above Cusco, or in the beautifully regular courses of the best walls at Machu Picchu and other sites, we see the result of endless patience and of astonishing structural skill.

All building was done, we must remember, with no machines beyond the inclined plane, the crowbar, and perhaps a rudimentary pulley. For the rest, Incaic masons depended on stone or bronze knives, infinite polishing and grinding with sand and water, and concerted pulling of materials along the ground by large numbers of men. It is doubtful that even the crudest form of rollers was used or known.

Yet how impressive the best architecture of ancient Peru! In the early days of rough stones laid in clay, a style which continued to be used in common structures, it was crude enough. But the superior methods of construction Mayta Capac learned at Tiahuanaco formed the basis of continued progress by his successors. Under Pachacutec the present glorious curved walls at Coricancha (the Temple of the Sun in Cusco), at Pisac, at Machu Picchu, and at many other places, marked the final stage of architectural development.

Lacking the carved ornateness of Mexican and Maya buildings, the structures made in the Inca period depend for their effect on balance and proportion. Tapering doorways with monolithic lintels, similar windows and niches, serve to break up surfaces otherwise too plain to be sightly (page 283).

On the coast, where sun-baked clay was the chief building material, stepped pyramids with gaily painted terraces supported the temples and mansions of the great chiefs (page 288). Humbler folk lived in gabled houses of many colors. In both coast and highlands roofs were of thatch; but to judge by a few surviving examples, so exquisitely made as almost to rival the masonry.

Wise men preserved from father to son

Inca Walls Defy Time and Quake, Spanish frosting topples. To erase Inca memory, Spaniards built their Monastery of Santo Domingo on the foundation of the Inca holy of holies, Cusco's Temple of the Sun. What must today's Indians think as they compare their ancestors' mortarless stones with the conqueror's cemented works, here crumpled by 1950's severe earthquake? Although ancient Peruvians never attained the true arch, they showed amazing architectural skill. They ground granite blocks to a mathematically determined arc to build the curving outer walls.

301

PAINTING BY ROJAS PONCE, COURTESY OF COLUMBIA UNIVERSITY

Beneath a Jaguar Headdress Glares the Mochica God of Fertility. This hardwood image with red eyes and long white tusks of shell was unearthed in Peru's Virú Valley in the 1,000-year-old tomb of a warrior-priest regarded as the god in human form. Buried with him was a boy, like the lad here sowing turquoise "seeds" in furrows formed by Ai apaec's digging stick. At lower right is a serpent.

the oral traditions and the knowledge of nature accumulated through many generations. Bards, singers, and dancers graced by their special skills the ceremonial life of the court and festivals of the people.

There were, naturally, contrasts in way of life between the great and the ordinary folk. This becomes apparent when we study the marriage customs. The Inca and all his caste were polygamous. Multiplicity of wives and concubines was regarded as a privilege suitable only to the great.

A part of Yahuar Huaccac's inferiority complex is made manifest by his special addiction to carnal delights: in his enormous harem he could display prowess in this respect if in no other. All the Incas, to be sure, had hundreds of mates, and the Chosen Women (Virgins of the Sun) were accustomed to yield themselves to the Sapa Inca, Son of the Sun, whenever he willed it. The First Wife, however, was *Coya*, or Empress, all her days.

Among the lowly, marriage was not only monogamous but universal. Spinsters and bachelors were practically unknown. Marriage was a civil rather than a religious rite. At stated intervals each village chief assembled before him all youths and maidens who wished to be married. Arranging men in one row and girls in another, he married each couple in turn as they came up to him.

This arbitrary method was not so cold-blooded and mechanical as it may seem at first, for in Incaland as elsewhere love had its way. We may safely assume there was jockeying for position in both masculine and feminine lines of the about-to-be-wed, so that the right couple in each case finally stood before the marrying chief.

Having acquired his wife, the young puric, aged 25 or so, led her to his little stone or adobe house where appropriate ceremonies were held by the kinsfolk of both. Afterward the young wife aided her husband in growing potatoes, maize, and other crops (page 298).

Chicha, a maize beer singularly unpleasant to our refined notions, was, and still is, brewed by being chewed by old women who spat the masticated kernels into a jar of brackish water, where they fermented for eight days. Strained and otherwise treated by the wife, this undainty liquid became a drink of considerable potency and charm, such as even finicky modern folk can swallow, if need be (pages 306, 309).

When children began to be born to the puric and his wife, the always benevolent government allotted additional land for the support of each child. Then as now, the Indian mother merely retired behind a hedge or into her house, there to give birth alone without aid from midwife or physician. Under these conditions infant mortality must have been high; but at least the survivors were uncommonly tough.

Pachacutec's days were passed in the austere majesty of massive masonry palaces at Cusco and other places. Huge courts were thronged with colorfully clad retainers, whose sole ambition was to lay down their lives for him. Flowers, brilliant featherwork, superb tapestries of vicuña wool in lustrous hues, vessels and ornaments of gold, and all that was fairest of his subjects' handicrafts adorned the stately niche-lined apartments where he dwelt when not campaigning at the head of his armies.

Fortunately, many of these things have survived from his day to ours and may be seen in museums in Peru, Ecuador, Bolivia, the United States, and many another country of which Pachacutec never heard.

Aside from all his surrounding splendor, the Emperor Pachacutec was a great soul, a noble philosopher whose heart held charity for his fellow men. Many of his sayings have been preserved for us

Modern Quechua Work, Pray, and Play at the Heart of the Ancient Empire

Near Cusco a somber Inca descendant (above) herds his llamas to safety to let a truck pass on the winding Pisac-Calca road. The beasts seem annoyed. Prized source of hides, meat, wool, and labor, the "camels of the Andes" recognize their master's voice, obey his sharply hissed commands. Right: Staff bearers meet after Sunday Mass to form an escort of honor for the Pisac priest. Ritual was intoned part in Latin, part Spanish, part Quechua. Below: Indian dancer's mask (center) pokes fun at Spanish mustaches. Costumed drummers and dancers at the gayest fiestas frequently wear mournful expressions. Grin (right) is rare.

304

KODACHROMES BY KIP ROSS, NATIONAL GEOGRAPHIC STAFF

by Indian and Spanish chroniclers. Among them are these:

Envy is a worm that gnaws and consumes the entrails of the envious.

It is very just that he who is a thief should be put to death. Adulterers, who destroy the peace and happiness of others, ought to be declared thieves, and condemned to death without mercy.

Judges who secretly receive gifts from litigants ought to be looked upon as thieves, and punished with death as such.

The noble and generous man is known by the patience he shows in adversity.

The physician herbalist who is ignorant of the virtues of herbs, or who, knowing the uses of some, has not at- *tained to a knowledge of all, understands little or nothing. He ought to work until he knows all, as well the useful as the injurious plants, in order to deserve the name to which he pretends.*

Drunkenness, anger, and madness go together: but the first two are voluntary and to be removed, whereas the last is perpetual.

Such words as these, reveal that the Incaic mind was not wont to compromise with wrongdoing.

If vagabonds and other mischievous persons were flogged with a sling for a minor offense and hanged by the feet until dead for a grave one, there was also a strong humanitarian note in the

Chicha on the Rocks

Ancients carved the snakelike channel in this sloping stone near the fortress of Sacsahuaman (page 292). Descendants still use it with gusto on weddings and other festive occasions.

Chicha, maize beer of past and present, is poured into a hollow near the top. As it twists downhill, celebrators lap it directly from stations along the sparkling flow. Their earnest efforts to waste none frequently result in inebriation.

Serpent symbol suggested by the writhing groove is common not only to Andean cultures but to those of Central and North America (pages 66, 116, 237). Incas interpreted good or bad omens from movements of snakes and spiders. To prophesy the fortunes of war, priests paraded stones around a ceremonial fire in Cusco's holy square, bearing painted images of snakes, toads, pumas, and jaguars.

law's differentiation between robbery from malice aforethought, for which the perpetrator was duly punished, and robbery committed to obtain badly needed food. For this, chastisement was inflicted, not on the thief, but upon the official whose duty it was to forestall need so grievous!

The prisons maintained by the Incas for punishing criminals of all classes, especially traitors and nobles who shirked their high duties, were terrible places filled with poisonous snakes and other horrors. But, so the old chroniclers tell us, they were almost always empty of human inmates.

Pachacutec also was a daring original thinker. Before the assembled priests of Inti (the sun) he once reasoned out the existence of a god still higher than the sun. He pointed out how that luminary always follows a set path, performs definite tasks, and keeps certain hours as does a laborer. He showed that the solar radiance can be dimmed by any passing cloud. The sun must, Pachacutec argued, have a master who is master also of all created things.

He ended by proclaiming to the priests the omnipotence of his father's counselor, the Supreme Deity, the creator-god Viracocha. He ordained, however, that the worship of Viracocha be confined to the ruling caste, as being too subtle and sublime for ordinary folk. He commanded the people be taught that Inti was greatest of the gods.

Thenceforward, when addressing the sun, the Incas always spoke to him as to a kinsman. To Viracocha they prayed with the deepest awe and humility.

Beyond question the reign of Pachacutec was the zenith of the Inca Empire. At his death, about 1448, it was equal in extent to the Atlantic States from Maine to South Carolina, inclusive.

From northern Peru down into Bolivia and northwestern Argentina its diversified territory of highlands and coastlands spread, a work of empire-building which can be grasped only if we visualize a Roman Empire consisting of a series of Switzerlands bordered on one side by a long coastal Sahara and on the other by a Congo-like wilderness of tropical forest.

Pachacutec and his generals had conquered all the great coastal kingdoms up to the Gulf of Guayaquil, as well as the wilder and more backward folk, wor-

Andean Artistry models the alpaca (top) and the llama. Lake Titicaca region yielded these hollow silver examples of Inca skill in working the abundant native silver, gold, copper, and lead.

Mochica art on vessel (left) from a young woman's grave in the coastal Virú Valley portrays tippling warriors. Man at right drinks from goblet, holding chicha jar on right arm. Swashbuckling companion waves empty goblet to punctuate his tale. Fired at too great heat, jug warped and broke in the making.

307

Peruvian Styles Change Slowly. Pisac musician (left) plays the flute of his Inca ancestors but departs from their loose robes and wrap-around skirts. Early Spaniards put the Indians in short trousers. The poncho, sleeveless, hand-dyed, and home-spun, came later. Above: Calca townswomen quaffing chicha, the native beer, wear their pie-pan hats "sunny side up"; when it rains they reverse the brims. Age-old formula for chicha: Let corn chewed to a pulp ferment in crock of brackish water.

shipers of the puma, of the dog, and other strange or repellent deities, in the highlands behind the coast.

Nevertheless, when he came to die, he seems to have been filled with melancholy forebodings, and his death chant has a note of sadness in it:

> I was born as a flower of the field;
> As a flower I was cherished in my
> youth.
> I came to my full age; I grew old.
> Now I am withered, and I die.

In the time of the Inca Tupac Yupanqui, about 1448–1482, Incadom was further enlarged by the conquest of most of what is now Ecuador. This Inca, son of the great Pachacutec, began his career in the east, however, rather than in the north. His father had stopped forever invasions from that direction by his series of frontier citadels; now the son determined to invade the eastern wilderness.

During long preparation he assembled a fleet of more than 250 war canoes, gaily adorned with carvings, canopies, and banners. In them he and a great following journeyed down the Amaru Mayo (Serpent River, now the Madre de Dios) as far as its junction with the Beni.

The sylvan savages were poor folk from the Inca's point of view. The only tribute he could wring from them after much desperate fighting was macaws, monkeys, honey, and beeswax. Besides, the climate of their land was noxious in its dampness and heat to men accustomed to the free, thin, cold air of the mountains. Consequently, the Inca contented himself with a merely theoretical conquest in that region.

Later, having conquered and Inca-ized the best parts of the Kingdom of Quitu

Living Sky-high on the Bolivian Altiplano

Festive occasion for Aymará Indians is their annual livestock fair on the wind-swept Andean plateau (left). Many have tramped vast distances to trade highland cows, leather, cheese, frozen potatoes for lowland coca, fruit, bamboo, and factory clothes, dyes, and gadgets. Such fairs have come down from Inca times.

Below: Market-bound Indians enter La Paz by an old llama trail. Saucered amid frosty peaks, this world's highest capital (11,900 feet) tops Lhasa, Tibet, by 80 feet. Most Bolivians live two miles above sea level. A large-lunged few dwell as high as three miles.

Below left: Indian women barter before the church at Laja. Here La Paz was founded in 1548. But the altiplano proved so cold and barren that the city was soon transferred to its sheltered valley. Today, some 6,000,000 Indians live on the bleak altiplano, which extends from Bolivia north through Peru and Ecuador.

311

KODACHROMES BY T. IFOR REES

(Ecuador), and having humorously exacted a tribute of lice from a certain province which seemed to produce nothing else (page 280), the Inca Tupac Yupanqui again took to boats.

He built a great flotilla of rafts of buoyant balsa wood. These pointed craft each had a hut with a hearth in it amidships, and a mast with a square cotton sail near the bow. They could carry a surprising number of fighting men and a considerable cargo of weapons and supplies. Their like may still be seen on the Guayaquil estuary.

The naval expedition of Tupac Yupanqui sailed from Tumbes, in northernmost Peru, and was gone for nearly a year. There is good reason to think it visited the Galapagos Islands.

This maritime excursion is unique in Inca annals. As a rule, neither the Incas nor other folk of ancient Peru were expert on the sea. Coastwise trading ventures on rafts and fishing voyages off the coast in boats of other quaint but cumbersome types were the nearest they ever came to mastering the Pacific Ocean.

The heir of Tupac Yupanqui was the Prince Titu Cusi Hualpa. Better known as Inca Huayna Capac (Young Chief Rich in Virtues), he ruled from 1482 to 1528 or 1529. His reign was largely taken up with struggles to extend his realm south in Chile and north in Ecuador.

The Empire had grown too large to be administered as well as Pachacutec had done. When we consider that it was equal in size to all the Atlantic States combined, and that its territory was far more diverse than is that of those States, we can readily understand the disruptive forces which were beginning to crack the mighty fabric.

That the Inca Huayna Capac himself fearfully realized the overgrowth of his realm is made evident by his last will. He inscribed it in some incipient form of writing upon wooden rods or tablets.

In that document he gave the southern four-fifths of the realm to Prince Inti Cusi Hualpa, better known as Huascar. Huascar, his legitimate heir, was the son of his sister-wife. To his favorite but bastard son, Atahualpa, he gave Quitu. Atahualpa's mother was almost certainly a daughter of the last independent King of Quitu, so there was a certain measure of justice in bequeathing that kingdom to her son.

Filled with dread of the future, partly caused by the first faint rumors of white-faced and bearded strangers who rode on fierce and huge llamas and who commanded the lightning, the Inca Huayna Capac sought what solace he could find in his harem of several thousand women.

At last, sick and affrighted, he died in his palace at Quitu (present-day Quito). His body was taken in state to be buried at Cusco, but his weary heart was laid to rest in his beloved Quitu. This rending of the Inca's corpse is strangely prophetic of what was soon to befall the Empire itself.

As might have been expected, Huascar and Atahualpa speedily went to war with one another to gain supremacy. When, a few years later, Francisco Pizarro led his tiny band of Spanish adventurers into the land, Huascar was prisoner of his half-brother, who was enjoying a usurped and transitory grandeur as Sole Inca.

The story of how Pizarro captured Atahualpa by a trick, wrung from him the promise of a roomful of gold (worth well over $3,000,000) in ransom, and finally condemned him to death after it had been honorably paid, has been graphically told by Prescott and many others.

At length, in 1533, Atahualpa, whom all eye-witnesses describe as a grave and majestic monarch, handsome in person and very proud, was garroted amid the wailing of his women and vassals.

With him died not only the Inca Empire but also an entire and unique po-

litico-social philosophy and a civilization based upon the happiness of all. Money lust and gold hunger entered Peru along with Christianity, and the long struggle began between the just and fair intentions of both the church and the king of Castile and the determination of all too many individuals to wring as much wealth as possible from the Indians in the shortest possible time.

Inca civilization was not, as many suppose, utterly obliterated. Rather, because of the liberal attitude of the Ro-

Graceful Bulrush Boats Ply Lake Titicaca

Early Spaniards, recalling the coast's balsawood rafts, misnamed these cork-light Indian craft *balsas*. The name has endured. Unsinkable hull and sail are made of pithy rushes from marshes that conceal millions of waterfowl. Larger balsas carry a dozen people; some transport llamas. When waterlogged they are pulled ashore to dry. Indians cut the rushes, dry them in cornstalklike shocks, then bind them with grass twine into bundles that form keel, hull, and gunwales to turn back waves.

The versatile rush (*totora*) thatches houses, makes rain capes; its young roots provide tender food. Lake Titicaca, 12,507 feet high, some 50 miles wide, is world's loftiest great lake. Its basin cradled advanced Indian civilizations.

313

man Catholic Church, of the kings of Castile, and of the best men among the conquerors, it was blended with Spanish colonial civilization. The same thing happened wherever Spain ruled—in Central America, in Mexico, in our own Southwest.

Today, in what was Incaland, the descendants of the Incas' subjects still constitute some two-fifths of the total population. Thus in many a remote Andean village, while the soft, opalescent evening is closing in, we may become aware that an Indian concert is in progress in the square.

Drawing near, we see instruments that are pure Inca: flutes, Panpipes, clay trumpets, drums, and rattles. They combine to build a pulsating music at once exciting and contagious, filling the mind with thoughts of bygone times.

Moment by moment knots of Indians come to the dance, until the whole adult population of the village is treading an antique and stately measure under the silverbright radiance of Mama Quilla,

the moon. The insidious lilt of the orchestra commands their every motion.

The fervor mounts and mounts until the square is filled with whirling skirts of women and swaying forms of mantle-draped men. The frenzy lasts until the dancers drop exhausted and the wailing, throbbing melody dies away like a sigh on the cold night wind.

Departing, we realize that we have witnessed something Pachacutec must often have seen in the Golden Age of the Incas, long ago. We can almost convince ourselves that his spirit, brooding and wistful, has been among us.

Dancers and Distaffs Whirl in Aymará Land

Celebrators feast, drink, and dance themselves dizzy at a Bolivian fiesta. Men in Sunday best appear somber next to their barefoot women, who spin like tops, skirts billowing, colors flashing. The more skirts, each a different solid color, the greater a dancer's prestige. If oranges, purples, and reds clash, so much the better.

A squatting mother (opposite) spins yarn, guides it onto her spindle. Highland Indian women spin whenever their hands are free—whether sitting, walking, or dancing. They love bright shawls, voluminous skirts, high-crowned hats. Ignoring the splendor of their rugged mountain scenery, they make colorful dyed cloth compensate for drab homes and Spartan conditions. Since ancient times llama, alpaca, and vicuña have supplied their wool. The vicuña's, finest and rarest, was for rulers and nobles only in Inca days.

Derbied vendor (right) offers a plaster doll representing Ekeko, Aymará god of abundance. His dwarfish figure is commonly adorned with miniature boats, houses, even automobiles, symbols of prosperity. La Paz publishes tiny newspapers in his honor at its January *Alasitas* ("buy") fair.

KODACHROMES BY CARL S. BELL

Swirling Mists Shroud Machu Picchu, lost city of the Incas. High Andean peaks guarded this sanctuary of Virgins of the Sun, last stronghold of a dying empire. The forgotten, jungle-claimed citadel was rediscovered by Hiram Bingham, leader of three National Geographic-Yale expeditions.

CHAPTER 14

DISCOVERING MACHU PICCHU

BY HIRAM BINGHAM

CROSSING THE BRIDGE made me wonder if this jaunt to find an alleged "Inca ruin" wasn't more quixotic than practical. There I was on hands and knees, inching across a half-dozen slender, vine-lashed poles that just cleared the foaming, icy Urubamba River.

Days of rugged travel through magnificent Andes gorges in Peru's southern highlands had brought me with two Yale colleagues to the base of a 10,000-foot mountain called Machu Picchu. The trip had been hard enough without this added excursion on the strength of local rumor. Still, if there really were ruins it was my job to visit them.

I crawled across the bridge and with Arteaga, my guide, attacked the precipitous slope. On all fours, we pulled ourselves up through slippery grass. Arteaga moaned that this was just the place to find a fer-de-lance, that vicious snake reputed to spring after its prey.

Drenched with sweat and gasping for breath, we struggled up jungle-shaded cliffs, digging with fingernails to keep from falling. Directly under us, far below now, the frothing rapids of the Urubamba roared angrily.

Calling on every reserve of strength we clambered through the thinning tangle of jungle. Gradually the ground leveled. At last, on trembling legs we straightened to see a grass hut. Friendly Indians approached with dripping gourds of cold spring water. We drank first, then looked around. We stood in a high clearing on a steep saddle of the mountain.

In the distance, massive summits, some snow-clad, reared wild crests. From far below came the snarl of the rapids, echoing through the dark, misty gorge. I drank in the view between gulps of water and shuddering lungfuls of air, and wondered just what I was doing on such a remote spot, nearly a mile and a half above sea level, on this blazing July day in 1911.

The answer was involved. With my Yale companions, who had decided to spend the day in camp (very wisely, I thought), I had come to Peru to collect geological and geographical data, above all to ferret out the last capital of the Incas.

Spanish accounts tell of the Inca prince whom Pizzaro appointed ruler after Atahualpa's death. Manco II, delighted at the honor, accepted without realizing he was slated to be a puppet. He rebelled and fled from Cusco down the Urubamba Valley with his loyal followers. In a region sealed off from the rest of the world Manco set up a mountaintop community: Vilcapampa.

There, he and his three sons ruled free of Spanish domination. Surrounded by nobles and Chosen Women, virgins dedicated to serving the sun god, these last four Incas held out for 39 years after

Empty Temples Stare Through Thatchless Roofs at a Sun Worshiped by the City's Builders

KODACHROME BY KIP ROSS, NATIONAL GEOGRAPHIC STAFF

From Huayna Picchu's 9,060-foot Peak Looming Above City, Sentries Scanned Distant Gorges

Cusco had fallen to Spain and the power of the Andes empire had been shattered. Spanish troops finally captured and beheaded the last Inca, but his age-old sanctuary, the sacred capital, never knew the tramp of a conquistador's boot. Vilcapampa vanished from the world's memory.

On the trail of this lost city, my colleagues and I had followed clues which led us to the foot of Machu Picchu. We had explored a number of Inca ruins, none of which seemed to fill the bill. We had chased down many a rumor of lost cities and been disappointed. This mad expedition up an almost unclimbable mountain would be, I felt, yet another disappointment.

Our Indian hosts said there were old structures "a little farther on." Possibly some huts, I thought. I gathered strength, stilled quaking legs, and with a boy to guide me, set out along the soaring ridge.

It was easy going at first. The thinner air of 8,000 feet refreshed me. New summits slid into view on the far horizon.

I felt utterly alone except for low, scudding clouds. Then I rounded a knoll and almost staggered at the sight I faced. Tier upon tier of Inca terraces rose like a giant flight of stairs along the steep slope of the saddle. Each terrace, hundreds of feet long, was banked with massive stone walls up to ten feet high. Our Indian friends had cleared many of them, tilling the rich soil as their Inca ancestors had done.

But what group of Incas had needed a hundred such terraces in this lofty wilderness? Enough food could be grown on this mountaintop to feed a city.

Suddenly breathless with excitement, I forgot my fatigue and hurried the length of a wide terrace toward the tangle of jungle forest beyond it. I plunged once more into damp undergrowth matting the ridge's hump, and fought my way forward through vines and foliage.

Then I stopped, heart thumping wildly. A mossy wall loomed before me, half hidden in trees. Huge stone blocks seemed glued together, but without mor-

Up These Stairways Paraded Inca Priests and Chosen Women. Windows piercing massive walls overlook the Grand Canyon of the Urubamba. The hidden refuge had more windows than busy Inca Cusco, 50 miles away, for weather was milder at Machu Picchu's 8,000 feet than at Cusco, two miles high. Masons hewed lintels from single blocks weighing up to three tons. Semicircular Temple of the Sun, center, resembles that at Cusco (page 301). Sacred sundial (page 322) stands on eminence at right.

FRANKLIN L. FISHER

The Discoverer Returns. Hiram Bingham dedicates a new highway leading to the lost city's doorstep, a far cry from the hazardous cliff-climb which first brought him to Machu Picchu in 1911. Inca terraces, such as those spilling down slope in background, gave him his first surprise glimpse of the forgotten refuge.

Until the opening of the new *Carretera Hiram Bingham,* visitors zigzagged up to the ruins from the Urubamba Valley on mule back. Once a network of narrow Inca roads linked the citadel with the outside world. Dr. Bingham's three National Geographic Society-Yale University expeditions, which freed the ruins from the jungle's green grip, traced the moss-grown paving of these trails through forest and landslide rubble.

World War I called him away from his archeological labors; later he became Governor of Connecticut and United States Senator. The 1948 road opening marked his first return to Peru in years.

A. OGDEN PIERROT

tar—the finest Inca construction. Awed, I traced the wall through the shadowy underbrush. It was part of a ruined house. Beyond it stood another, and beyond that I could make out more houses almost encased in twining growth.

Eagerly I searched farther, seeing everywhere the gleam of white granite masonry. Under an overhanging ledge appeared a small cave, its walls lined with niches of the finest cut stone—a royal mausoleum. Above the same ledge rose a semicircular building with gracefully sloping outer wall, like that of Cusco's Temple of the Sun. Its straight courses of curved masonry diminished in size toward the top, the work of master craftsmen. No pin could penetrate between tightly fitted blocks.

Stone steps led to a clearing where two white granite temples stood against the sky. Each had three walls. One temple had never been roofed. I stared at a huge rectangular block along its rear wall and decided I was looking at the throne on which mummies of dead Incas had been placed to receive homage from priests and worshipers.

The clearing was a sacred plaza. Across it was a temple with three great windows looking out over the canyon. Here high priests in gold trappings had worshiped the sun. One gabled compound of beautifully built houses must have sheltered the ruler himself. I could picture its palaces floored with vicuña rugs and soft textiles woven by the Chosen Women.

Down the forest-mantled slope I found houses crowded together in a bewildering array of terraced levels linked by stairways. Here had lived those who worked the fields. Here women filled narrow-necked water jugs at stone basins.

Exploring this vast ruin, I was struck by its defenses. The Urubamba River, far below, tumbles around three sides of this soaring mountain shoulder. On the fourth stands the pinnacle of Machu Picchu, fortified, as we learned later, by a watch tower where a handful of men could

321

To This Massive Sundial Inca Priests "Tied the Sun." They sighted past the upright to mark the sun's course. Winter's lengthening shadows alarmed the populace; their sun god was slipping away. But at the solstice, calendar-wise priests tied their deity so he could go no farther, and must return bringing summer. In one piece weighing many tons, Machu Picchu's granite *intihuatana* was carved from the city hilltop on which it stands. Spaniards took pains to destroy these pagan symbols, but this stone remains intact—further sign no conquistador ever found the hidden city.

withstand the onslaught of thousands. As I well knew, invaders who managed to cross the river would face sheer cliffs. Those who got past observation posts and scaled the height of the ridge would meet an outer wall built along the ends of the farm terraces. Next came a dry moat and inner wall.

I gradually understood, surveying this sacred citadel perched like an eagle's nest on a cliff-ringed mountain saddle, that here indeed was a lost city come to light. Could it be the same Vilcapampa I sought? I now believe it was. In these royal buildings had lived the last of the Incas. This was their sanctuary, their towering fortress which defied all invasion, then lay forgotten for 300 years.

Bursting with news of my discovery, I returned home. Machu Picchu cried for complete archeological exploration. I was greatly pleased when the National Geographic Society joined with Yale University for this purpose.

First tasks facing the new expedition were to bridge the Urubamba and build an improved trail up the saddle. Kenneth C. Heald, our topographer, solved these problems despite snakes, reluctant Indian labor, and a grass fire that chased him over a cliff. As soon as the trail was finished a long line of porters moved up it like ants, each laden with supplies. In the ghost city work hummed.

We felled trees that had sprouted on ancient walls, hacked away bushes, burned debris, scrubbed moss from stones. Gradually axes and machetes chewed away the jungle to reveal the breath-taking details of Machu Picchu. At least 100 stairways coursed through the many-leveled city. One, with some 200 steps, formed "Main Street," splitting the city in two. Along its length, a series of catch basins trapped water from the one slender stone aqueduct. Water must have flowed freely to supply the city's needs. But we found the spring-fed flow only a trickle. Perhaps water failure explains the end of Machu Picchu.

The finest stairway led to a little hill-top commanding the city. Here we discovered a carved *intihuatana*, a stone column where Inca priests worshiped their solar deity (opposite). On festival days, nobles, priests, and Chosen Women ascended these steps in a colorful, solemn parade. Beside their sacred stone, they blew kisses to the sun.

Dwellings vary. Some have carefully matched masonry, others were built quickly with small stones. Many have steep-pitched gables with carved stone rings to which thatched roofing was lashed. Groups of houses have their own characteristics—perhaps a private garden plot of terraces like the court of a modern apartment, a carved granite shrine, or interior niches which might have held mummies. One large house boasted the equivalent of a streamlined kitchen. Built into its floor are concave grinding stones on which the Inca housewife ground maize or crushed frozen potatoes.

Inca stone masons may have used bronze chisels to carve rings and cylinders in granite. But no iron tools or derricks helped them fashion and move massive units that wall their buildings. Some walls at Machu Picchu have keyed blocks, cut to prevent lateral slipping. One choice house near the temples shows what masons could do with a single hewn stone. It forms half the wall, at left of the door. Part of the interior niches and a lower corner of the room were carved from its mass. Spanish writers marveled at a stone with 14 angles in a Cusco palace. This one has 32 angles!

The semicircular temple I had admired when I first saw Machu Picchu seemed to grow in beauty as we cleared away underbrush and moss. Its wall leading to what may have been a priest's house is a masterpiece of masonry. I rate it the finest wall in America. Where it joins the priest's house, stones are keyed, hooking into one another so earthquakes, settling foundations, torrential mountain rains could not spread them.

While Machu Picchu was being freed of smothering jungle, we dug for archeological treasures. Outside the principal buildings we found fragments of pottery, perhaps broken during religious festivals and drunken orgies that followed. Seeking bronze ornaments and utensils, we offered a Peruvian dollar to any workman finding a burial cave.

The bonus offer paid off. Before season's end, we had opened about 100 caves, unearthing the bones of 173 humans. Close to 150 were women, strengthening my belief that Machu Picchu was a sanctuary for the Chosen Women. With some skeletons lay buried objects—jars, dishes, bronze and silver jewelry, stone disks perhaps used as counters.

One day we found the remains of a *mamacuna*, or high priestess, the superior of a convent. Beside her was a concave bronze mirror, used to ignite tinder by focusing the sun's rays—a piece of "magic" which the common worshipers watched with awe from the plaza.

Our excavations yielded only three post-Columbian objects, revealing how completely Machu Picchu had remained sealed off from the world.

Today a narrow gauge railroad carries tourists from Cusco to the base of the mountain. A fine, new highway sweeps up to the old stronghold that withstood the world for so long. Now the world has come to this mountain domain. The humblest traveler can stand on the ramparts and stroll silent stairways of this last citadel of a great empire.

THREE LIONS

Staircase of the Gods at Pisac. Peru's Indians tilling ancient gardens that march with giant strides up Andes slopes little realize that forgotten ancestors toted on their backs every bit of this soil. These "works of enchantment," at U.S. labor rates, would cost as high as $60,000 an acre!

CHAPTER 15

AMERICA'S FIRST FARMERS FOOD GIVERS TO THE WORLD

BY O. F. COOK

AMONG ITS ANCIENT WONDERS the world includes the hanging gardens of Babylon. These have been a tradition for 3,000 years—yet they were little more than a transient toy. Larger, higher, all but imperishable are the hanging gardens of Peru, climbing steep Andes slopes like giant staircases.

No plaything, they once supported multitudes of ancient people. Today's Peruvian Indians, still using these monumental terrace farms, consider them the work of the gods.

Long before Columbus, natives of the Andes grappled with the vast reclamation project of transforming barren desolation into fertile fields. Centuries of toil, engineering skill almost beyond compare turned rocky valley floors and steep canyon walls into rich acres. Tier upon tier of terraces scaled sterile slopes, massive stone retaining walls contrasting with the fragile green of growing crops. Spouting jets and gleaming trickles of water laced downward from step to step. High on the mountainside, small figures bent to their toil.

The hanging gardens of the Andes marked the high point of ancient America's agricultural development.

In its most primitive form, New World farming had been a slash-and-burn affair. The native selected a patch of jungle, felled trees, burned them along with undergrowth, and planted his crops with a sharp stick (page 201). After harvest he moved away, letting the jealous jungle reclaim its own. Some tropical Indians still follow this method, using land, then abandoning it (page 350).

Tillage was the next stage, practiced by farmers who settled on land to use it year after year. Perhaps with a digging stick, the tiller scratched at his top soil, destroying weeds and loosening humus for seeding.

But soil tilled year in and year out must be nourished to continue growing crops. Indians found the answer by spreading manure, dead fish, seaweed, decayed vegetable matter on their land. This practice of fertilization was their next step in learning agriculture's art. Irrigation followed, probably first in regions where streams could easily be diverted to soak into thirsty soil.

All these stages of agriculture must have flourished in ancient Peru. They continue there today. But they pale before that final stage—staircase farms of "made" or transported soil—evolved by settlers in tortuous gorges centuries before the rise of the Incas.

The first terrace builders are a forgotten race without written record or even tradition. They must have achieved their

Stolid Oxen, Gift of the Spaniards, tug a wooden plow through the loam of a central Andean corn-field. Plows, often fashioned from tree limbs, are now tipped with steel but otherwise resemble those that ancient farmers used on wide bottomland terraces. Plowing then was by manpower, since the haughty llama detests harness, spits in the face of anyone foolhardy enough to try to hitch him. On steep hillside fields, today's Quechua farmers till by hand, turning soil with wooden spades to the rhythm of a chant, while women break clods with clubs. Digging sticks, wooden rakes have changed little since Inca days. Steel sickles, machetes, hoes, axes now make Indian's work lighter.

skill gradually, perhaps through millen-niums. In their soaring Andean homeland they faced seemingly impossible diffi-culties. Level land lies only along coast-al deserts or on high plateaus where bitter climate forbids crops. Lower, warmer mountainsides are rock-strewn and water-coursed. A rubble of stones, washed down by torrential rains, chokes valley bottoms.

This soilless land offered its pre-Inca settlers poor prospects for farming, but mouths had to be fed. Clearing away stones, the first farmers found that building them into walls took less space than simply tossing them into mounds. Surplus stones went behind each wall, forming a level bed on which soil could be spread. From this beginning the ter-race idea grew, the technique of build-

ing them became an art. We still cannot imagine the work that went into moving huge rocks, fitting them together with joints so fine that the naked eye has dif-ficulty distinguishing them. Hundreds of people must have strained at some boulders. Patient weeks of grinding made the perfect fit.

Behind each retaining wall, the build-ers tamped down two distinct layers of earth. First they dumped subsoil—small coarse stones and clay packed to within two or three feet of the wall's top. To fill the remaining space, Indians trans-ported topsoil, often from distant sources. Llamas may have helped carry stones and loam. But since most terraces occur below the high altitudes where these beasts of burden work best, it is likely that farmers themselves toted soil on their backs in baskets or mats. Legend says earth for Cusco's Inca Garden came from near Quito, more than a thousand miles away!

Reclaiming the gullied wasteland of valley bottoms, ancient engineers banked fresh, rich soil behind walls sometimes 15 or 20 feet high, forming broad fields. They even narrowed and straightened rivers, hemming them in with successive walls of rock.

Swift mountain streams usually loop back and forth between their valley walls. Peru's rivers, by contrast, often flow arrow straight in channels of constant width. Below Ollantaytambo, the Urubamba River rushes along a canal-like course for nearly five miles. Though little remains of the ancient walls built to confine it, the channel's artificial nature is obvious. Straightening such

streams added a few feet of growing space, a few rows of crops—but labor was abundant, land scarce, and food vital to survival.

Rising from these artificial bottomlands, narrow mountainside terraces climb skyward, sometimes in banks of 50 or more. Most are eight to 15 feet wide, up to several hundred feet long. On the steepest pitches, high walls built with backbreaking labor provide fertile strips as little as a yard wide.

Farmers did not confine cultivation to walled terraces, which usually keep to lower slopes below 11,000 feet, but carried it all the way up. In higher regions there was no need to dispose of rocks in terraces; stones simply rolled down precipitous mountain walls. Wherever soil accumulated, crops were grown. Just below Urcos short ridges climb a narrow

Harvesting the Precious Potato, a Peruvian couple grubs with crude hoes on their Andean plot. Fuel-short highland Indians make one dung-fed fire cook food for two days, usually eat cold boiled potato with parched corn, wheat, barley, or beans. Quinoa cooked in a thick porridgelike mass offers variety. Meat is a rare treat. Natives preserve potatoes by an Inca dehydrating method. They expose tubers to mountain air, letting them alternately freeze and thaw, trampling them barefoot at intervals to drive out juices. Resulting chuño keeps indefinitely. Llama herders carry it in wool sacks, may eat it in soup for breakfast, or mixed with stew for the day's only other meal.

HARRY TSCHOPIK, JR.

path of precious loam squeezed between a break in a cliff wall.

Even today's Quechua Indians till slopes so steep that squashes have to be staked to keep them from tumbling down the mountain, and where potatoes, after being dug, must be picked instead of shaken from the vines. Cool and cloudy, these high shoulders need less irrigation than the valleys far below.

Ancients fashioned narrow transverse ridges of earth along these heights, a few large ridges at intervals with many smaller ridges between. The large ridges, not cultivated but left in grass, trapped the run-off rain water and allowed it to seep down rather than gouge out gulleys and wash away precious soil. This "contour plowing" technique is to-day hailed as a modern, scientific method of preventing erosion on hillside fields!

The areas once farmed in this way are much more extensive than the lands still cultivated in the valleys below. Traveling through valleys whose every upper slope shows signs of former cultivation gives one a feeling that a great age has vanished from these mountains. Its mementos are so widespread the eye can scarcely avoid them even when it glances up to the glaciers and eternal snows. Ancients tilling the misty heights stood against the same icy background.

From these glaciers came water to nourish crops. Aqueducts linked terrace farms with high mountain freshets. A Spanish writer tells of one aqueduct extending 120 leagues, with a depth of 12 feet. Wherever possible, these channels were carved along the very crests of sharp mountain ridges, and today have worn deep grooves. Water crossed cliffs in ditches carved out of the rock face, sometimes tunneled through obstructions, sometimes rode on built-up masonry. From the topmost terrace of a series, water filtered "downstairs." At Machu Picchu it apparently jetted pic-turesquely from one terrace to another, perhaps affording welcome shower baths for field workers.

Gaps or passageways can still be seen cutting across a flight of ruined terraces. Probably these were designed both as paths and as drainage channels to keep heavy rains from cutting away topsoil or undermining walls. Soils hereabouts are tenacious, keeping shape and resisting erosion, a condition that helped the terrace builders.

Many terrace and irrigation works must have been laid out the way modern engineers plan a reclamation project. Had wandering settlers taken what plots they liked, level bottomlands would show signs of having been occupied first. Stones spread fanwise around field boundaries would indicate clearings. Instead, the regular terrace patterns and carefully planned aqueducts show that "blueprints" were drawn and scanned before a stone slid into place.

Ancient Egyptians lavished skilled labor on building pyramid tombs for their sovereigns. Peruvians, concerned with life rather than death, spent their efforts on agricultural structures. They built tombs, too, but modest ones in caves or on high rocky cliffs where farming was impossible.

Peru's staircase farms grew and developed more species of plant foods than any other region in the New World. Some of these food gifts have been of inestimable value. Conquering Spaniards stormed through Peru seeking gold. But the samples of the humble potato they shipped back to Spain proved in the long run to be the Inca's real treasure.

The instinctive prejudice against new food plants kept the potato in the background of European diet for two centuries. People forgot the land of its origin and called it the Irish potato. It didn't begin to be grown as a crop until the French Revolution. Even then it had to be forced on the public by the persistent efforts of the French philanthropist, Parmentier, who demonstrated its food possibilities by establishing a large number of soup kitchens for the poor of Paris. Potato soup still bears the name Parmentier—a homely memorial to the philanthropist.

Today the value of the world's annual potato crop probably far exceeds that of all the gold the Spaniards took from the Incas.

Many other crops that explorers came upon elsewhere in the Americas were cultivated in the Andes: the sweet potato, maize, cassava, pineapple, bottlegourd, cotton, tomato. The lima bean, the peanut, and quinine are of undisputable Andean orgin. Maize is another story. Controversy still smolders over its country of origin—Mexico or Peru.

In Peru, agriculture is a matter of altitude. Geographically you are in the tropics. Agriculturally you may be anywhere between the Equator and the Arctic Circle. From among plantations of

sugar, coca, and cacao at Santa Ana you can see at the other end of the valley some peaks of the cordillera covered with glaciers and perpetual snow. It is like looking from Jamaica to Alaska. Even on foot you can climb in a few hours through the full range of farming possibilities.

The cultivation of cassava, or manioc, characterizes the lowest farm belt, extending in the Urubamba Valley to an altitude of about 6,000 feet. From here to 11,000 feet the potato is the chief crop. Higher still, the land is mostly used for grazing. On some slopes above the Pass of La Raya, between Cusco and Lake Titicaca, potatoes thrive at altitudes above 14,000 feet.

Peru is still a fountainhead for new varieties of this food staple. It boasts many kinds of potatoes of better quality than those we cultivate in the United States. Many have awkward shapes and deep eyes, making them hard to peel, but it should be possible to interbreed and combine their best features.

Market Day at Pisac offers Andes Indians a chance to gossip and display a wide range of crops. These vegetables call to mind that ancient Peruvians domesticated more food and medicinal plants than any other early people. Potatoes, lima beans, peanuts, quinine are four of many contributions.

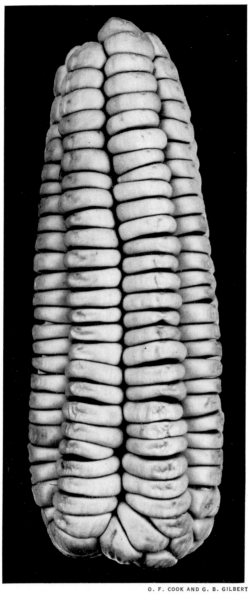

O. F. COOK AND G. B. GILBERT

Indians Eat Cusco Corn Kernels Like Grapes

They squeeze the meat from the thick skin of boiled inch-wide kernels of this unique Peruvian corn of 9,000- to 11,000-foot heights. Pygmy corn grows near Lake Titicaca at nearly 13,000 feet, while in the tropical lowland belt thrives a large-eared variety with normal kernels. Perhaps this latter spread to Central America. Many experts claim Mexican origin for corn. Mexico's teosinte grass crosses readily with maize and was formerly thought to be its ancestral form. Also, maize was more vital to Mexico than Peru because it competed with fewer food crops. But Peru has more kinds of corn than anywhere else.

In the high altitude belt, among their potatoes Indians plant other root crops: the oca, a relative of our sheep sorrel; anu, kin to the flowering nasturtium; and allucu, of the Madeira vine family. Another root crop, the yacon, like the Jerusalem artichoke, grows in the lower altitude of the potato belt. Below 6,000 feet a series of sweet potatolike crops flourishes.

Maize, the chief seed crop, sprang abundantly from the terraces. The Andean variety, Cusco corn, has inch-wide kernels, almost the size of chestnuts, which natives eat a kernel at a time. Above 12,000 feet maize is raised in only a few places, not as a regular food, but as a luxury for making native beer, or chicha. To take the place of maize, the natives of elevated districts use plants closely related to one of our common weeds, called "pigweed" or "lamb's-quarters."

Near the Pass of La Raya, two varieties of pigweed thrive. One, quinoa, growing three or four feet tall, is used for chicha making as well as providing a breakfast cereal somewhat like oatmeal. Cañihua, smaller, has gray seeds which Indians grind into flour—a ration for shepherds on the high plateaus.

Peru's Indians today, looking in awe upon the terraced wonders their far-distant ancestors built, no longer know the secret of their construction. The art has passed from this hemisphere.

It reached its highest point with the early Incas. Theirs are the finest walls with the tightest fit between masonry blocks. Later Inca terraces appear to have been hastier jobs—stones merely bedded in dirt and faced with clay to give a smooth appearance.

But if late Incas lowered construction standards, they also organized agriculture to a high level, assuring bountiful crops to support a great population free from want. Rulers controlled the land and its uses, keeping an eye on every farm activity from planting to harvesting. Public storehouses were maintained, not only in towns and cities, but along highways and in lofty passes between the valleys, to ensure that the surplus from one area speedily made good for crop failure in another.

When the country was devastated by the Spaniards, "the chiefs assembled, the *quipus* [knotted-cord records] were examined and checked, and if one province had lost more than another, that which had suffered less made up the difference; so that the burden was shared equally by all," says the account of Cieza de Leon, written about 1550. "To this day these accounts are kept in each valley, and there are always as many accountants as there are lords, and every four months the accounts are made up and balanced."

Inca religion aimed largely at improving crops. Feeling that prosperity of all depended on the wealth of the Inca, every farmer made sure the royal larder was filled, the regal acres fertile. Even today Peru's rural Indians buy medicinal and aromatic plants at market so they can make burnt offerings—"paying the Incas"—and be assured of good crops and healthy flocks. They bury small images of clay or metal in the ground—models of fields and farmsteads with rows of sheep and cattle.

At the time of the conquest, Peru's farm system had given its people a way to live and let others live. Converted to agriculture as an ideal of existence, they were freer from predatory instincts than Europeans. Looting Spaniards suffered by comparison.

A few realized they were destroying something that could not be replaced. One old conquistador, last of Pizarro's band, wrote a deathbed "confession" to his king, describing the Inca realm, with "neither a thief, nor a vicious man, nor a bad, dishonest woman. . . .

"Crimes were once so little known among them," he continued, "that an Indian with one hundred thousand pieces of gold and silver in his house, left it open, only placing a little stick across the door, as the sign that the master was out, and nobody went in. But when they saw that we placed locks and keys on our doors, they understood that it was from fear of thieves, and when they saw that we had thieves amongst us, they despised us."

Ancient Maya Carved a God Sowing Maize

This Guatemalan stone figure with maize headdress (page 182) symbolizes the importance of corn to ancient civilizations in the New World. Indian corn fed hungry Pilgrim settlers on New England shores; it remains an important American food contribution to the world.

SYLVANUS GRISWOLD MORLEY, CARNEGIE INSTITUTION

PUEBLO BONITO, *"Beautiful Village,"* rises in magnificent relief beneath sandstone walls of *New Mexico's Chaco Canyon. Called the foremost prehistoric ruin in the United States, it stands 100 miles south of Mesa Verde's cliff dwellings, 100 miles north of Zuni towns, 100 miles east of Hopi pueblos. Ancient crossroads, high point of early Pueblo culture, Pueblo Bonito was at last unearthed and fully described by seven National Geographic Society expeditions, 1921-27.*

Smithsonian archeologist NEIL M. JUDD, *who led the work, relates how he reconstructed the life of the forgotten builders of the apartment city. To date the ruin, three other National Geographic expeditions, 1923, 1928, 1929, collected beams from some 40 Indian ruins to extend a "tree ring calendar" back to Pueblo Bonito's time. Astronomer* ANDREW ELLICOTT DOUGLASS *describes finding the key beam that closed the gap in a thousand-year chronology.*

But mysteries still remain in the Southwest. *Giant figures, visible only from the air, sprawl on high mesa tops on the California-Arizona border. National Geographic Society Trustee* GENERAL GEORGE C. MARSHALL *tells of seeing the gravel effigies. At his suggestion the Society sent an expedition to study them, resulting in a fascinating theory of their origin and purpose.*

332

EXPLORING PUEBLO BONITO

BY NEIL M. JUDD

THERE IS IMMEASURABLE JOY in starting work on a gigantic rock pile, the accumulation of fallen walls and centuries of wind-blown sand, and finding a series of ancient dwellings unfolding.

Pueblo Bonito again stands clearly outlined on Chaco Canyon's floor. A hundred thousand tons of earth and stone and sand have been carted away. Summer after summer, from 1921 to 1927, we dug deeper into a maze of empty rooms, repaired broken walls, pieced together the life of an unknown people.

This ruined desert apartment house—a city within itself—is one of the most remarkable Indian achievements in the United States. No other apartment building of comparable size existed in Amer-

Walls Rise Again as Pueblo Bonito emerges from the ruin of centuries. Excavation often found several building eras layered on the same spot. Kiva "Q," by its circular shape, must have been built by the Late Bonitians. Indian belief required it to be at a lower level than dwellings it replaced, for its floor roofed the earlier world from which men ascended to the earth. This kiva is one of more than 30 uncovered at the three-acre site.

National Geographic Society expeditions unearthing Pueblo Bonito devoted much time to repairing or rebuilding walls to protect excavated rooms from weather damage. Mud plaster still clings to some original walls. So skillfully did foreman Jack Lavery imitate the ancient masons' work that Zuni laborers nicknamed him *Enote Nahme*, "Prehistoric Grandfather."

O. C. HAVENS

ica until the Spanish Flats were erected in 1882 at 59th Street and Seventh Avenue in New York City. Its foundations cover as much ground as the United States Capitol. In its heyday it housed perhaps 1,200 people and contained fully 800 rooms, terracing back from two inner courts like giant steps to outer walls four stories high.

Toward the last these walls had neither doors nor windows. A fortress, beleaguered, desperate, Pueblo Bonito could be entered or left only by ladder.

Outside, low earth ridges trapped water flooding down from the mesas after midsummer thunderstorms, irrigating fields of corn, beans, squash. Rainfall

ruled the city's prosperity, just as a thousand years later it governed our excavations. When the rain god smiled, 35 or more Indians, ten white men, and eight or nine horses kept busy in the ruins. But when hot July winds chased clouds beyond the horizon, our labor force shrank and we measured our well twice a day.

Our Navajo neighbors came in with lard buckets, canvas bags, even barrels to complain that their water holes were dry. We shared our meager supply and agreed that the whole country had been drying up ever since the white men arrived. When they returned with all their goats and horses, we clamped on the lid and told them to dig their own wells deeper.

Then there was the mother-in-law problem. I'm sure no previous National Geographic Society expedition was ever thus bedeviled. The Navajo believe that a man goes blind if he looks upon his wife's mother. Whenever the mother-in-law of one of our Navajo workmen passed by, he would abruptly turn his back, drop his shovel, and pull his shirt over his head until she disappeared.

Day by day—from potsherd, fragment of worked stone, charred beam—we filled in the life of this ancient people who left no written records save some unintelligible cliff markings.

Just as Pueblo women still grind a daily ration of Indian corn between two milling stones, so Pueblo Bonito housewives crunched the precious yellow maize kernels, mixed primitive corn meal dough and cooked it over rooftop fires.

They tanned skins and wove blankets, cotton cloth, and fiber sandals. They shaped and polished the most beautiful prehistoric pottery found anywhere in the United States, decorating it with thin black lines against a white surface. Mothers early taught their young, for we found miniature ladles and pitchers imprinted by baby fingers just learning the art of working long ropes of clay into useful and decorative vessels.

Men tilled the fields and hunted game atop the mesas. Whether at work or play, Pueblo Bonito's men and women brightened cheeks with brick-red rouge dug from compacted clay beneath sandstone cliffs.

While men controlled the ceremonial and religious life of the community in their deep, circular kivas, it was the women who headed household life and brooked no interference in domestic matters. Not only did they own their homes, they also built them—a custom that survives in pueblos to this day.

Of course men helped. They cut and carried stone, felled timber, and seated huge roof beams on the walls. Also, male societies apparently built their own kivas. This might explain why kiva masonry is frequently inferior to that of the dwellings: Pueblo Bonito women were better masons than their husbands.

We found Pueblo Bonito's history in its walls. The crudest were more mud than stones. Then builders began rubbing sandstone blocks smooth on the outer face and chinking cracks between with rock chips. Finally, thin stone blocks were fitted tight and true into walls that needed almost no mortar.

Pueblo Bonito shows two distinct eras in building. The first inhabitants, whom we call the Old Bonitians, began a cluster of crudely built houses in the ninth or early tenth century. Then came some near-strangers, the Late Bonitians. Ap-

Master Masonry characterized Pueblo Bonito's golden age, A.D. 1050–1130. Ancient wall builders gave smooth facings to inner cores of stone and adobe rubble, laying shaped stones horizontally, so perfectly fitted they needed no mortar. Many such walls still stand, 800 years later.

parently welcomed in, they at once began rebuilding the pueblo. To these progressive people the great terraced structure owes its final form. Master masons and potters, hewers of wood and stone, they changed, enlarged, strengthened, tore down, and rebuilt with utter disregard for the work involved. What they willed, they did.

These men even had the self-confidence to brace up with puny logs and stones a gigantic cliff, tons of solid rock, that threatened to topple upon their homes. This colossally naïve feat of ancient American engineering gave Pueblo Bonito its Navajo name: *Tse-biya hani ahi,* "Place-of-the-braced-up-cliff."

Such tireless energy made Pueblo Bonito famous. Vendors of brilliant macaws came from Mexico's tropical forests, and native dealers in sea shells from the Pacific coast. They took back with them *chalchihuitl,* turquoise. Then as now Indians of the Southwest prized this stone above all else. Turquoise, symbol of the blue desert sky, spirit of mystic oceans and vaulted heavens!

We felt something of that when we came upon a turquoise treasure (frontispiece). The day my trowel cut away earth to reveal a breathtaking necklace, every Indian on the site, as if by telepathy, dropped his shovel and draped himself over the wall to watch what was going on deep in the room below. They talked in whispers as our tiny brushes swept away the sand. At last the blue-green stones shone out in all their ancient splendor. Reverent murmurs and exclamations rose from the spectators.

Who knows what cost of life and labor went into obtaining the rough, unworked stones; how many hours it took to shape 2,500 beads by rubbing them back and forth across sandstone tablets, to pierce them by drilling each with sharpened flint or other tool!

With such jewels, with corn ripening in the fields or drying on the housetops, Pueblo Bonito was attacked again and again by covetous nomadic tribes. Lone garden workers were slain seeking shelter, boys and young women taken captive and dragged away as slaves. Even the

Tell-tale Beams form a precise Chaco Canyon calendar. A thousand years ago weather left its permanent record in trees that gave Indians these ceiling poles. Their inner rings date this house in Pueblo del Arroyo, unearthed a few hundred feet from Pueblo Bonito, as exactly as if it boasted an engraved cornerstone. The oldest such beam from Pueblo Bonito sprouted as a pine sapling in the year 700. It was 219 years old when it felt the bite of a Bonitian's stone ax.

To Zuni and Navajo workmen, reading tree rings seems as mysterious as foretelling an eclipse of the sun. The ancient builders of canyon towns the workmen unearthed had no written language and left no man-made calendars.

O. C. HAVENS

One Tree Records 1,700 Years of History. Dr. A. E. Douglass, who first dated Southwest ruins by tree rings, points to a mark left in a sequoia by a fire, A.D. 634. Trees add a new layer of wood each year just under the bark. Climate varies the ring width, leaving indelible testimony of rain or drought. Dendrochronology, this astronomer's gift to archeology, now can trace climate back to A.D. 11 in ancient pine and fir beams from Indian ruins. Another calendar runs through California's "Big Trees" back to before 1,000 B.C. This 10-foot tree, born A.D. 211, fell in 1915.

solid outer wall did not always shield these urban farmers. Hand-to-hand struggles must have been waged in the inner plazas; hafted stone axes and wooden war clubs crushed brown bodies; flint-tipped arrows sought out crouching defenders of the terraced city.

Famine thinned the defenders' ranks as long dry years parched the fields. The soil itself became permeated with alkali, making agriculture impossible. Sealed in their canyon by marauders, they could neither cultivate distant farms nor support themselves through barter.

We found burial rooms that tell a mute story of pillage. Skulls tossed aside, arms and legs torn from bodies crushed on their burial mats, burial offerings overturned and trampled. All this happened shortly before, or just after, the city was finally deserted by its builders.

Invariably I am asked, How old is Pueblo Bonito? When was it built? When abandoned? Answers to these questions came with astonishing exactness when Dr. Douglass turned tree rings into a calendar that dated not only Pueblo Bonito but scores of ruins in the Southwest.

TREE RING CALENDARS

BY ANDREW ELLICOTT DOUGLASS

ANCIENT ORAIBI, abandoned, crumbling into ruin, baked under an Arizona noon sun. Like Hopi tribesmen of long ago, we entered a three-story house on its second floor, over a terrace of old rooms now filled with rubbish.

A flat stone lay in the middle of the floor. Lifted away, it revealed a hole into the room below. The sweepings of years from the room above had filled the lower space until there remained only three feet of headroom. I swung down and with a flashlight looked around.

In the center stood an upright post, not more than six inches thick. It held up the floor above, and thus could not be cut. But it seemed stout enough to be bored, so with excitement I watched the tubular core drill bite through at the point of greatest diameter.

That same evening the bit of wood told its story. The post had been cut as early as A.D. 1370; it had supported its ceiling generation after generation for well over 500 years. Before that, its annual growth rings traced clearly the years the tree grew in some long-forgotten pine forest, across unmistakable signs of the Great Drought in the last decades of the preceding century to an earliest recognizable ring from the year 1260.

Our tree ring timetable of the past had reached a new and significant point. We were coming close to the elusive era when Pueblo Bonito was built under the cliffs of Chaco Canyon. But even this new find was not old enough, not as old as we needed.

In the year-by-year growth of ancient trees we had found a key to open the past. Because climate is indelibly recorded in tree rings—scant or abundant rainfall means lean or fat growth rings—certain ring sequences become recognizable, tree to tree, forest to forest, even beyond the range of living trees to the ancient firs and pines felled for beams by the stone axes of prehistoric house-builders.

In 1922, when the National Geographic Society's great work was just beginning in Pueblo Bonito under Neil M. Judd, tree ring dating was also in its earliest stages. Pueblo Bonito was found to be some 40 years older than Aztec Ruin, 65 miles to the north. But this was only relative age; no meaningful dates could be assigned to either.

Mr. Judd felt that enough old timbers could be found to establish a continuous calendar reaching back from living forests to beams in the oldest pueblos. Thus with the single goal of dating Pueblo Bonito, three National Geographic Society expeditions set out over the next seven years to find the needed timbers.

We took hundreds of borings and sec-

Charred Rings of HH39, key to Pueblo Bonito's past. This historic beam section found at Showlow, Arizona, completed the tree ring calendar that solved dating secrets of the Southwest. The ring beneath the arrow grew A.D. 1247; the star (right) shows 1275, beginning of the Great Drought.

How this missing link tied together two separate chronologies is shown in the field charts above. Longer lines represent years of extreme drought, shorter lines less severe years. The upper, "modern" chronology, was anchored in time. Lower chart shows latter part of the "floating" chronology, a record of ancient beams interrelated in time but not specifically tied to a calendar date. The Showlow sequence, reproduced at its right end, matched the oldest part of the modern chronology, groove by groove, year by year!

ANDREW ELLICOTT DOUGLASS

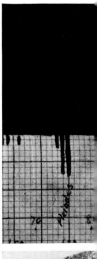

tions from giant tree stumps in old forests, from carved beams Pueblo Indians had salvaged from Spanish missions they destroyed in 1680, from stone-hewn timbers in pueblos still occupied, studied and fitted them into a calendar which, by the end of our 1928 season, reached back to the year 1260.

Meanwhile, from even more ancient Indian sites—Mummy Cave, Wupatki and Citadel, from Mesa Verde, and Chaco Canyon itself—we pieced together a second chronology, one continuous prehistoric sequence 585 years in length.

Nowhere did this earlier calendar appear to overlap with our modern sequence. Reluctantly, we called the new calendar a "floating" chronology. The search began for a link between the two, the bridge from present to past.

We tried very old living pines, even offering a reward for any tree 600 years of age, but without success. We tried to match our floating sequence with the long-lived California sequoia, but no clear correlation could be made.

At Oraibi, oldest continuously inhabited Hopi pueblo, we found some ancient-looking floor planks in a kiva still used for tribal ceremonies. The boards could neither be removed nor cut without offending the gods. With a gasoline lantern I spent seven hours one night lying flat on my stomach with a lens in my eye, nose almost touching the boards, counting and measuring their rings. No avail—they were far too young.

Even to gain access to many beams required high diplomacy. To the Oraibi Chief, Tawa-Guap-Tiwa, I took a present of purple chiffon velvet, so lovely that I was afraid to show it to Mrs. Douglass for fear it would never get to the Indian reservation. Many times we had to appease Indian spirits by placing a piece of turquoise in the hole from which a core was taken, to keep the "spirit of decay" out of the timber.

But it gradually became clear that none of the occupied Hopi pueblos was old enough to link our two chronologies. It was necessary to find the locality

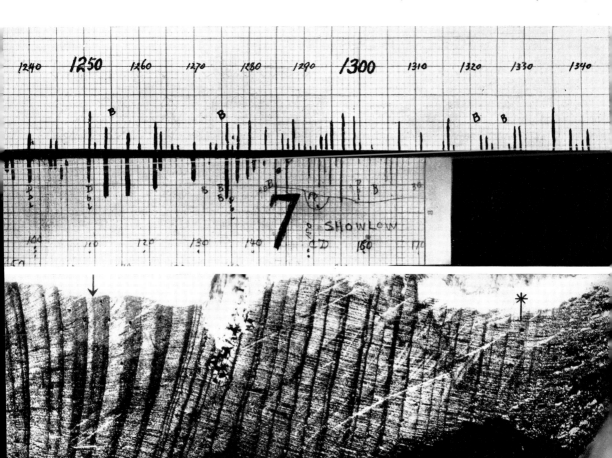

from which the Hopi had last migrated.

Early in 1929 we selected four ruins—Kokopnyama in the Jadito Valley, Kintyel to the southeast, Showlow and Pinedale 100 miles south. Shards of an early orange-colored Hopi pottery had come from each, pointing to the period we wanted.

Showlow, now a thriving Mormon town, takes its name from an early-day cowboy bet. From its buried Indian ruin, pieces of charred wood had been reported—ancient wood!

Charred or half-burned beams were readable to us by that time. We dipped such pieces in paraffin and gasoline, and by delicate handling could study their blackened rings. Even the first charcoal fragments from Showlow seemed, on preliminary examination, to hold tree rings in both the historic and prehistoric sequences.

The day Mr. Judd and I arrived on the site, yet another log was unearthed. We bound it carefully with cotton twine, but even so the timber crumbled almost at touch. Our "solid" log was a mere cone of charcoal with most of the unburned wood decayed away. We numbered it HH39.

Its outermost rings clearly dated to the 1300's, from our fixed chronology. Following the rings inward, we found the unmistakable record—very small rings—that told of hardships the tree had endured in 1299, 1295, the drought years of the 1280's and the 1270's.

Then came the years of the seventh decade of that century. Their rings agreed in every detail with those of the Oraibi beam. But whereas that beam could tell us nothing back of 1260, Showlow's HH39 did not stop there. Here was 1258, a hard year, and 1254, even harder. Likewise, 1251 and 1247 were dry.

Finally, the very core! This charred old stick began life A.D. 1237, just ten years after the Sixth Crusade sailed to battle the Saracens for Jerusalem.

The history within that carbonized bit of ancient beam held us spellbound. We tried to joke about it, but failed miserably. Later that evening we gathered under the spluttering gasoline lamp in the village hotel to determine whether this was really the tie between our new and old chronologies.

From the rings the answer soon came. Year 551 in our "floating" sequence matched perfectly with year 1251 in Beam HH39. And then the surprise! We had no gap to bridge; it had already been closed. Our two chronologies overlapped. But the last rings of the old series were taken from such small fragments that I had never accepted the evidence. HH39 cleared all doubts.

By the time I finally slept, I knew that our calendar reached back now to A.D. 700; that the earliest beam found in Pueblo Bonito was cut from a tree felled in 919; that the Late Bonitians had come probably between 1025 and 1050. I knew that the "Beautiful Village" reached its golden age of construction by 1066, the year William the Conqueror faced Harold the Saxon at Hastings, and that it was still occupied in 1127. By the end of the Great Drought in 1299, Pueblo Bonito almost certainly was empty, sands piling high around its silent walls.

To the American Southwest, Beam HH39 matches Egypt's famous Rosetta Stone. It unlocked the hieroglyphics of the past—in this case the rings of trees.

From it we have been able to date Pueblo Bonito and, more recently, beams reaching back to A.D. 11. Tree rings have given us an accurate chronology of ancient Pueblo culture, a key to the mysterious migrations of these prehistoric peoples. Attacking nomads, drought, and the heavy hand of starvation pushed them on. The pine forests that once grew on the borders of Chaco Canyon died or were cut away; but beams long preserved in dead cities of the Southwest tied together climate and human history.

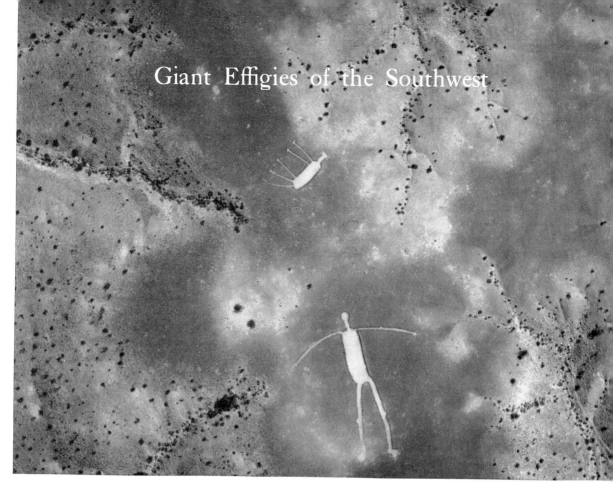

Giant Effigies of the Southwest

BY GENERAL OF THE ARMY GEORGE C. MARSHALL

OUR PLANE DRONED across the southern California desert in 1943. Gen. Henry H. Arnold, then Commanding General of our Army Air Forces, glanced down at the rumpled mesas and turned.

"Have you ever seen the great effigies near Blythe?" he inquired.

I had not even heard of them. He told me then that on a bluff above the small California town of Blythe, a local pilot, George Palmer, had discovered several great figures outlined in the rocky soil. One appeared to represent a man; others depicted animals.

The curious thing about them was this: So huge were they in outline and so shallow in indentation that they were virtually invisible to anyone standing only a few yards away. Nor were there any hills near enough for a full view. In short, not even their creators could ever have glimpsed their handiwork's total design. This would have been plain only to the gods of the mesa, a passing bird—or people in airplanes, surely an unforeseen invention.

"One of our young pilots brought back a startling photograph [above]," General Arnold said. "Would you like to see what that picture showed?"

We changed course, and soon we were scanning the ridges sloping back from the lower Colorado River above Blythe. Then we saw them: gravel sculptures such as few men had ever laid eyes on—simple in outline, childish in form, yet so gigantic as to take one's breath away.

The sight left me a lasting impression. Who made the effigies? What was their purpose? Here lay a riddle for the National Geographic Society and the Smithsonian Institution to solve!

A GIGANTIC FIGURE SPRAWLS ON THE BROAD, BARE MESA above the Colorado River in southern California, its arms and legs outflung as if for some interminable sun bath. Not far away a misshapen four-legged creature, an odd circle, and a scraggly ellipse mark the desert. In 1932 a civilian flyer first saw these strange figures; later, airline pilots reported others. Who made them, and for what forgotten gods of the sky, no one knew.

In 1951 a National Geographic Society-Smithsonian Institution expedition led by Frank M. Setzler, Head Curator of the Smithsonian's Department of Anthropology, went into desert country to find and study these mysterious, lonely figures. The U.S. Air Force lent a patrol plane, helicopter, and radio truck. In some places the shallow desert sculptures proved to be furrows of dark-brown gravel scraped away from the lighter underlying mesa. In others, paths were stamped in the gravel by moccasined feet. Automobile tracks criss-crossed a few figures, but many seemed unchanged since the time they had been shaped.

Could the four-legged figure be the late Pleistocene horse of 10,000 years ago? Probably not. The great Blythe "horses" have no patina, or "desert varnish." This black-brown coating, baked by the desert sun, comes from the action of certain lichens. It takes less than 10,000 years to form. Thus, since the Pleistocene horse was already extinct, and the European horse unknown to the Indians until after the Spanish came in 1540, the figures must have been made since the 16th century.

The huge effigies—one stretches 170 feet—must have been created by a populous, settled society. Nomads would scarcely take such pains on desert images, then wander on. After 1540, the leading sedentary Indians along the lower Colorado River were Yuman-speaking tribes. The "missing link" was found when Yuman mythology was traced backward from a Pima desert effigy known as Hâ-âk, southeast of Phoenix, Arizona. Legend recounts that Hâ-âk, a ferocious child-eating female monster, was slain by the all-powerful "Elder Brother" summoned by panic-stricken Indians. Mr. Setzler's conclusion: Yuma artists shaped the grotesque California figures—a shrine to Hâ-âk and her destroyer, Elder Brother—between 1540 and the mid-1800's.

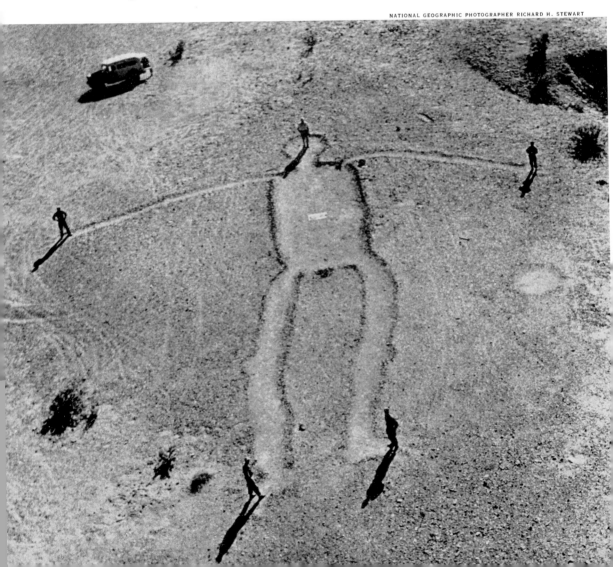

PART III

INDIANS TODAY

FROM AMAZON

TO ARCTIC

KODACHROME BY CLIFFORD EVANS AND BETTY J. MEGGERS

SYMBOL OF A WAY OF LIFE, Yukuma stalks fish from a dugout on the Essequibo in British Guiana. Legs decorated with plant juice, torso touched with red to ward off harmful forest spirits, this Wai Wai bowman weaves his own loincloth, lives in harmony with his surroundings. Civilization calls him "uncivilized," but who knows better the ways of fish, bird, and jungle animal than Yukuma? The white man's beads and knives are welcome—even the white man's God. But Yukuma will keep his own too: the god who created the Wai Wai, and the other god responsible for white men and everything else, including the airplane Yukuma occasionally hears overhead.

Like most tropical forest Indians, Yukuma's hunting-and-fishing people live in small isolated groups, follow a simple, rugged pattern of communal agriculture. Land must be torn from the forest by brute force. Even then the jungle never quite lets go. In two or three years the soil wears out; the natives must move on, hack new clearings, build another settlement. Through the vast Amazon and Orinoco basins, through Panama's narrow waist, and the humid coastal plains of Central America, the rain forest puts a common stamp on Indian life. Highland ways are different. The dweller in arid western Andes is worlds apart from the head-hunting Jivaro of rain-drenched eastern slopes. How strange life among the Chocós of steaming Darién would seem to a Mexican highlander! Yet differences are often of degree rather than kind.

Both Guiana lowlander and Guatemalan highlander farm. Cassava cakes correspond to tortillas. But intensive maize cultivation supports large upland populations. Permanent villages, individual homes, elected officials contrast with scattered extended-family groups living in communal jungle huts. Wai Wai abandon fields and change wives frequently; Guatemala Indians almost never. Primitive cosmology contrasts with organized ritual. Sedentary Guatemalans seem ever treading hairpin roads that rise to 10,000 feet; seminomadic rain forest dwellers seldom journey far, seldom trade. While rudimentary agriculture and pottery making have only reached Essequibo country since the 16th century, the Guatemala Indian draws on 2,000-year-old Maya skills. Handicraft specialization brings trade and the weekly market, leading highland social event.

CHAPTER 17

INDIANS OF SOUTH AND CENTRAL AMERICA

IN SEARCH OF "LIVE" ARCHEOLOGY, a husband and wife team of Smithsonian arche-ologists pushed into southernmost British Guiana, vast, empty homeland of some 60 Wai Wai, the colony's most primitive tribe. CLIFFORD EVANS *and* BETTY J. MEGGERS *describe these festive pyg-my-size people as they found them, sharing their daily rounds. Turning the coin to reveal a con-trasting culture,* LUIS MARDEN, *National Geographic writer-photographer, shows the numerous Indians of Guatemala living for church and market and perpetuating ancient arts and crafts.*

THE WAI WAI OF GUIANA

BY CLIFFORD EVANS and BETTY J. MEGGERS

FAR BENEATH OUR DC-3 British Guiana's dense green jungle unrolled. Skimming above it, we could not help feeling that we were flying backward in time—back to that mysterious age before white men set foot in the New World.

Suddenly our plane lurched to a stop on Gunn's Landing Strip, a dirt runway scratched from the wilderness in the Crown Colony's far south, almost on the Equator. Looking out, we caught our first glimpse of the Indians. They stood by the runway, their light-brown skins glistening with red paint.

Short and stocky, they were as small as Central Africa's pygmies. In their simple breechclouts and aprons, and carrying long bows, they would not have seemed out of place to Columbus save for the strings of glass trade beads gir-dling necks, legs, and arms.

These were the Wai Wai we had trav-eled so far to study. Carib-speaking ab-origines, they are the only uncivilized people left in British Guiana. Beside

them stood two American missionaries, come to welcome us and lend a hand as interpreters. Soon we were pushing through the "big bush," then up the Es-sequibo to the missionary settlement.

At dawn several days later we loaded a dugout and set out on our first explora-tory trip upriver. Our guide was Charlie, a civilized Wapishana Indian from the savanna who had married a Wai Wai. His English words were few, and con-versation was limited.

Charlie was good-natured and willing, but a poor provider. Civilization had robbed him of the art of silently stalk-ing game in the forest. Whenever he went off hunting, distant shots would raise our hopes. Nearly always he re-turned to camp empty-handed.

"What happened?" we would ask.

"Me shoot monkey," he would answer gloomily. "Him stay, hang by tail."

Provisions began to run low, so we looked for a Wai Wai hunter. Yukuma, a young stalwart, took on the job, and

345

we arranged to pick him up at his village. We arrived hours late, but Yukuma had made no preparations. After all, what is time in the jungle?

The delay gave us a chance to visit. A single thatched, cone-shaped hut housed the whole community of ten people. Inside, feather ornaments, gourds of palm oil, and baskets hung everywhere. Cassava cakes and smoked meat were piled on racks. The ceiling itself bristled with dozens of 6-foot arrows.

Lean dogs lay tethered on special platforms along the walls. Later we were amazed to find that Wai Wai often take their pets out on leash, walking them regularly like apartment dwellers.

The hut contained no partitions. Each family occupied the space between two roof posts. Every compartment had its hearth for cooking and night warmth, smoke drifting through a roof opening.

Native hospitality demands that food be offered visitors no matter when they arrive. At Yaka Yaka, a woman dressed in bead apron, necklaces, and arm and leg bands quickly laid a mat for us, first beating it on a dog to shake out loose dirt. Before us she placed a large bowl of cassava starch and palm fruit, another of wine made from *cara* (a potatolike tuber), a steaming pot of pepper broth, and cassava bread.

The broth set our mouths afire. Fortunately, the starch drink quenched the flames, though it was about as appetizing as flour paste. The wine proved mild and sweet, but the bowl's lip curved inward, so the liquid flowed more easily into the nose than the mouth.

We noticed sleeping hammocks draped between the hut's posts. A woman's was always slung beneath her husband's we learned, for it is her duty to

346

Village in the Round

A barking dog challenges visitors to Yewara, in the remote rain forests of British Guiana. Dr. Betty Meggers and her Indian companions pause before the pole-and-thatch hut housing the entire village, one of four in Wai Wai land. Custom prescribes that they wait for a formal invitation to enter. Once inside the communal dwelling, they will immediately be offered food and drink.

On other expeditions the authors found their privacy to resemble that of the proverbial goldfish under the curious stares of primitive peoples. Not so among the Wai Wai. When Drs. Evans and Meggers first hung their hammocks under a lean-to at Mawika, not even the smallest tots came to stand and stare. Jungle etiquette on the upper Essequibo is strict.

KODACHROME BY CLIFFORD EVANS

keep the fire going all night. Among the Wai Wai labor is sharply divided between the sexes. Men build the communal house, hunt and fish, clear land, plant, and sometimes help dig crops. They weave all hammocks, baskets and cloth. Women cook, chop firewood, tend children, fetch water, weave bead aprons, spin cotton, and make cassava graters. The graters are essential, for one of the most important of woman's tasks is processing cassava from its poisonous root state to a kind of bread (page 355).

Eventually Yukuma was ready. He piled the dugout high with cooking pots, bread, sugar cane, his hammock, two bows, stacks of arrows, and shotgun. Yukuma was proud of his gun, earned by working for the missionaries. But ammunition is scarce and gun blasts frighten off the game. For daily use he relied on silent and deadly arrows. No longer did we want for fish or game. Yukuma's bow and arrow seldom missed (page 344). With dawn, when the dripping jungle rang with melodies of waking birds, we would hear him imitate a call, to which a feathered creature replied. Soon he returned with the too-talkative bird for breakfast, and a monkey to add its rich, sweet flavor to the evening stew.

Food problem solved, we rode along the broad river highway through lonely jungle. In all this vast tangle of southern British Guiana there are only the missionaries and 60 Wai Wai. These few natives live in four villages close to the Essequibo, travel by water, and seldom penetrate the jungle except to hunt. Across the Brazilian border, on headwaters of the Mapuera River, live another 60 or 70 Wai Wai of similar ways.

Paddling along, we could see a bright-

347

blue morpho butterfly glimmering overhead. Here a pale-green spider crouched on his web of golden silk. There, high in the trees, we spotted an ant nest, a lavender orchid, an oriole's cocoonlike nest. Bats clustered on the underside of a dead branch. Now and then along the bank appeared a slide where tapirs—largest land animals in the South American jungle—came to drink.

A heron, gleaming white in a universe of green, stood on a granite outcropping, eyeing a little fish skittering over the water's surface. Flights of gaudy macaws scolded incessantly.

Swirling rapids added spice to our journey. Often we wished we understood Wai Wai, or that Charlie knew more English, as we listened to our companions debate each passage. Gestures marked the argument, while the rough stretch loomed closer. Decisions were always reserved for the last moment.

One rapid barred our way three times on a certain trip. We were relieved when first and second tries succeeded. Imagine our horror, the third time, when we found that Charlie and Yukuma had grown bored and sought a new passageway. Again we were off on a tilt with disaster. That we came through safely is a tribute to the Indians' skillful maneuvering, not to their caution.

As we worked our way upstream, we investigated sites of long-abandoned villages the Wai Wai chief recalled from his boyhood. Our pottery finds from some 30 diggings were unspectacular and relatively recent. But this was significant, for it refuted previous theories that the region might be the original source of tropical forest culture like that of the Wai Wai.

Having neither time nor words to teach Charlie and Yukuma archeological technique, we did most of the work. We sent the men hunting; otherwise they waited. At such times the contrast between the Indian who lives off the jungle and one exposed to civilization was

Morning Make-up starts a man's day right. Comb on foot, "vanity case" open before him, this Wai Wai paints shaved eyebrows, draws red designs on cheeks with tiny wooden paddle as a too-young spectator watches.

In the time-consuming daily routine, long jet-black hair must be combed and dressed heavily with palm-nut oil, then fashioned into a tight pigtail and adorned with feathers or encased in a long cane tube that hangs to the hips. Bodies are daubed red; eagle down is sprinkled on bangs. Earrings are never removed.

With white beads for arm bands, blue and white for legs, red for necklaces, the fastidious Wai Wai feels fully clothed. The women pay less attention to daily make-up.

Primitive Artist contrasts pot black and seed red in decorating his canoe paddle. The Wai Wai lavishly smear red on their bodies, implements, and dogs because they believe evil spirits cannot see anything painted that color. For red pigment they use the coating of the urucú seed; for black, soot mixed with cassava starch. The mixing can at the artist's knee was a contribution from civilization—eight days away by foot and canoe. His bracelets are seamed ends of smaller tin cans.

Wai Wai seldom probe the trackless jungle except to hunt. For them the Essequibo is a broad highway despite its menacing rapids. They measure distances in paddling time, or by the number of bends in the river. The Essequibo is also a handy larder. Fish abounding in the river and its backwaters are taken by poisoning, angling with steel hooks, and shooting with arrows. Harpoon heads attached to strong lines are used in the brawling rapids.

striking. Charlie simply sat and watched or wandered about. Yukuma made baskets of palm leaves, sharpened the wooden points of his arrows, cleaned his gun, or practiced bird and animal calls— never at a loss for things to do.

Frequent stops for hunting and fishing delayed us. We became annoyed at what looked like overstocking. But a jungle Indian knows that lean days follow good ones. Yukuma had a special interest in hunting. His consumption of food was enormous. One day we kept record: a large bird, several pounds of smoked fish, half a huge cake of cassava bread, half a monkey, two long sticks of sugar cane, six plantains, and large quantities of pepper-pot broth!

The Wai Wai have a keen sense of hu-mor and even enjoy a joke on themselves. Yukuma was no exception. Late one afternoon we returned to camp to find that a hawk had helped himself to our cache of smoked fish. Our provider doubled up with laughter. What a joke! To think a mere bird had outwitted the great hunter Yukuma!

Often pitching our camp near Wai Wai settlements, we found tribal courtesy shown in many ways. One of the most welcome was the privacy they allowed us. But failure to pry reflected no lack of interest. When the time seemed proper, they delighted in looking us over.

One of our camps was perched on the riverbank. Daily, women trooped by to bathe or fetch water, each carrying on her hip a child or a puppy. Often they

stopped to marvel at our camping equipment. One woman was fascinated by our canvas bucket; every trip she lingered, full of unbelief, to see if it still held water. Our Primus stove captivated another aboriginal housewife. She often appeared at mealtime to watch it perform. Once she brought her husband; from her sound effects we could tell she was describing just how it worked. All the Wai Wai enjoyed looking through the ground-glass focusing plate in our camera. They never tired of seeing people upside down drinking out of a bowl and not spilling a drop.

The Indians were much impressed by our size. One of them cut a straw the length of Cliff's foot and entertained his fellows hugely by comparing it, in clowning fashion, with his own. They were especially amused when we inadvertently copied their customs. Once we were forced by steep terrain and lack of suitable trees to hang our hammocks one above the other, native style. That sent the village into gales of laughter; everyone turned out to see that Betty's hammock was correctly placed at the bottom.

One morning we noticed something under way at a near-by pond. Investigating, we found Wai Wai poisoning fish. The fishermen had gathered quantities of a vine, one of a hundred-odd poisonous plants that South America's Indians know. Beaten to a pulp, the vines were

Jungle Farmers slash and burn to clear land for communal crops. Even with steel axes, felling hardwood trees is heroic work. Men burn off smaller growth, spend days chopping branches from fallen giants. Limbs, dense and wet after drying several months, must be fired repeatedly.

In a stump-strewn field, trunks lie everywhere like giant jackstraws (opposite). Hoe-wielding Indians plant cassava, sugar cane, bananas, pineapples, and tubers helter-skelter among them; further clearing would be waste time and effort, since the land will soon be abandoned. Almost never do Wai Wai return to a previous site.

Perhaps because their tillable land is so hard-won, the Indians can never understand why missionaries bother to grow flowers. The Wai Wai have no words for individual flowers, but can name every animal, bird, and fish.

Upper right: well-dressed Wai Wai's pigtail sports toucan and curassow feathers. Monkey teeth dangle at belt.

placed in a palm-leaf basket and sloshed vigorously through the water, leaving a wake of milky sap. Hardly had the Indian passed with his basket of death when small fish began to pop, gasping, to the pond's surface, for the sap paralyzes gill action. Then the excitement began. If someone tried to grab a fish, it showed sudden vigor and evaded capture. So the Indians set about with machetes and butcher knives, stunning their prey. Charlie muttered, "No good," in typical sportsman's reaction. But the Wai Wai found the tiny fish a welcome addition to their evening pepper pot.

Near our work's end, the village of Yewara, finding itself overstocked with cara, decided to convert the tubers into wine and invited the other three villages and us for a celebration. On the appointed day we heard shouting downriver. Soon dugouts streamed into the Yewara landing. Piling ashore with dogs, children and gear, the visitors set up camp. To our surprise, guests and hosts ignored each other. Yewaras came down to the river and filled their water jars as if the crowded bank were empty. By Wai Wai custom the time had not yet come to greet the guests.

Amid the hanging of hammocks and kindling of cooking fires, men busied themselves weaving long capes of palm leaves and shoulder fringes of yellow fronds. Both sexes applied fresh paint and sprinkled white eagle down on well-oiled bangs. Much testing of bark horns,

351

KODACHROMES BY CLIFFORD EVANS AND BETTY J. MEGGERS

Costumed Wai Wai Hold Marathon Dance

Party finery ranges from palm-frond capes to bright feather headdresses. Pendants in one young man's necklace are Brazilian census tags. Guests from other villages join their Yewara hosts in a festival lasting the better part of three days and nights. A shuffling, circling dance that fills waking hours is punctuated by shrill whistles and howls and frequent pauses for drinking tuber wine.

Like children everywhere, two small boys entering hut (lower left) have fun shrouding themselves in fathers' discarded capes. Heel of one betrays camouflage. Through all the intermittent din of pounding feet and primitive noisemakers, babies sleep in hammocks or in bark slings draped across mothers' shoulders.

KODACHROMES BY CLIFFORD EVANS AND BETTY J. MEGGERS

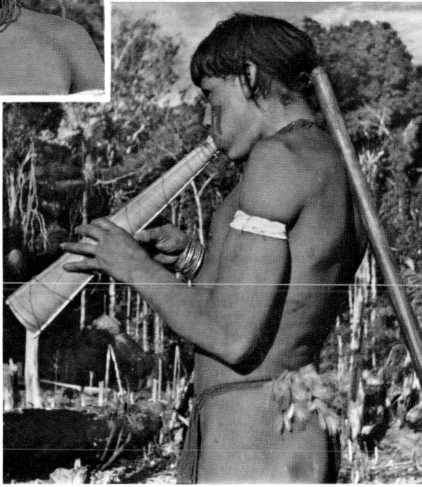

Young Man With a Horn Tunes Up for the Festivities. Shrill reed flutes, rattles, occasionally a harmonica add to the racket.

353

made for the occasion, filled the air with raucous counterpoint.

Dusk fell. Preparations complete, the visitors sallied forth to call on their hosts. Returning in the dark, they donned dance costumes and again climbed the village path. We crouched with them at the edge of the clearing where the men of Yewara, togged in fancy feather headdress, streamers, and leg and arm bands, were already circling single file in the fire's dim light.

Finally came the sign: the dancers stopped in front of the communal hut and stood in a line facing the clearing. Our party filed out in two lines, one for men, one for women, and amid the blaring horns the dance was on. It lasted

Practiced Hands Make Pottery and Graters

Like other American Indians, Wai Wai lack the potter's wheel. They coil Essequibo clay in layers, shape with fingers, smooth with a piece of gourd, and bake it in an open fire.

The woman opposite makes a cassava grater by driving stone chips into a spongy board. Later she will apply a coat of milky latex to hold the chips in. Grating is first step in turning the brown-skinned, poisonous root cassava, or manioc, into food. Stuffing the white pulp into a flexible sausagelike basket hanging from a house pole, the woman stretches the basket down with a long lever, squeezing till the deadly prussic acid juices stream out. The flour is baked on a griddle into thin, crisp cakes.

Cassava is staff of life to the tropical lowland Indian. British Guiana's savanna Indians have lost the art of making graters, so the primitive Wai Wai swap theirs with the "outsiders" for beads, knives, and other trade items.

CLIFFORD EVANS AND BETTY J. MEGGERS

three days, with the big bowl of purple wine passed frequently, and time out only for celebrators to sleep off their exhaustion.

On this festive note we left the Wai Wai to return to Georgetown, capital of British Guiana. We had come to the upper Essequibo in an hour and a half by air. It took us eight days by foot and dugout to reach civilization again. As we ended our excursion into the past, we could still echo the words of English explorer Robert Harcourt, who wrote in 1613: "The naturall inhabitants of that Countrey are a loving, tractable, and gentle people . . . with those bar-barous people we may live in safety, without suspicion of trechery, or dread of danger. . . ."

But what of their future? Are the Wai Wai waging a losing fight against extinction or absorption? Smallpox or measles could wipe them out, as it did their predecessors, the Taruma. And even though they maintain their slim numbers, they can scarcely avoid influences from the outside world. Already the pottery vessel is giving way to white man's enamelware; an oil tin replaces the time-honored earthenware griddle. Few men in years ahead may see the Wai Wai as we saw them.

TO MARKET IN GUATEMALA

BY LUIS MARDEN

IN THE GUATEMALA HIGHLANDS, where dark pines and lichen-covered oaks clothe the hillsides and wet gray mist swirls up from the valleys, I once met an Indian on his way to market. He was bowed under a top-heavy load of bulbous clay pots, but his dignity was unimpaired.

"Señor," he said, pointing to his thick-soled leather sandals, "you see these *caites?* Well, in the pictures, God and all the saints wear the same things. That proves Indians are the children of God."

The speaker was a living symbol of the two main concerns—religion and market —that mold the lives of the "naturals," as Guatemala's Indians call themselves. Their whole existence revolves around the religious calendar, with its feast and saints' days. When they speak to their God, prayers resemble conversation with a friend. In low-voiced monologue they talk to Him of poor crops, of family illness, and other troubles. Sometimes supplicants gesticulate fiercely, as if to say, "God, you make everything come out all right—or else!"

Going to market offers a welcome occasion for social exchange, church visiting, perhaps dancing to the sound of marimbas, besides buying and selling everything from pigs to incense, chickens and chile peppers and skirts to ceremonial masks, flutes, drums—and the inevitable tortillas, corn, and beans.

One woman, asked by a priest whether she would rather go to market or heaven, unhesitatingly chose the market.

Each highland village has its own market day. Most offer a specialty: Momostenango for blankets; Totonicapán for ribbons, belts, and Conquista-dance costumes; Chinautla for pottery. Some market centers are "empty towns"; Indians live in the surrounding countryside and gather there only for market or a fiesta.

Along roads that seem to tilt up into the sky, Indians trot under heavy loads piled on a four-legged wooden frame that hangs from a tumpline around their heads. With a metal-tipped staff to help them set down the load and to rise again, and a rolled-up palm-leaf raincape, rush sleeping mat, tin lamp, and battered coffeepot hanging to the outside, the villagers jog tirelessly along, stopping wherever night overtakes them.

So overdeveloped do bearers' calf muscles become that their short lower legs bulge like inverted brown tenpins. Some are bald from the rubbing of the tumpline. Loads of their produce or their wives' handicrafts sometimes exceed a hundred pounds, and they go 20, 30, even 50 miles to market. But no complaint, for the Guatemalan Indian is first and foremost a trader.

Pure-blooded Indians make up more than half of Guatemala's three million population. Not for them the humid jungle that reaches north to the Mexican border or the hot coastal strips on both sides of the country. Their thatch-roofed villages of stone or adobe perch on the edges of ravines or nestle in valley hollows in the lofty region of cold blue lakes and sleeping volcanoes. From their deep forests comes the tangy smell of resin and charcoal fires.

In the 250-odd villages a race that was old when Cortés came to the New World carries on the traditional Maya pottery

All Saints' Day in Chichicastenango. Firecrackers pop and sizzle as St. James rides a tightrope from the belfry of Santo Tomás church. The effigy wears a necklace of 300-year-old pieces of eight; firecrackers explode in basket under his horse. On the crumbling church steps Indians rest, trade, kneel, and burn the copal incense their Maya ancestors burned to pagan gods.

Law, Ritual, and Craft — Indian Triumvirate

Unlike village religious elders, this man wields temporal power. His staff of office marks him as *alguacil*, or constable. His beat: Todos Santos Cuchumatán. Guatemalan villages usually have two governments: the Indians' and that of the *ladinos*—people of mixed Indian and Spanish blood.

Women of a Palín religious group (upper right) meditate before partaking of a ceremonial meal.

Chichicastenango weaver (lower right) carries on Guatemala's famous art with ancient "hip" loom—two end sticks with warp threads stretched between. One is tied to an immovable object, the other to weaver's waist to permit adjustment of thread tension. Weavers seldom use a pattern; they work symbolic designs into fabric from memory, may weave in their initials as artists sign paintings, and leave a blank to show man's imperfections and so avoid envy of the gods. As 20th century penetrates the highlands, hand-weaving grows scarcer and villages tend to mix designs.

KODACHROMES BY LUIS MARDEN, NATIONAL GEOGRAPHIC STAFF

Antonio Proudly Directs a Rite

Religious ceremony plays a large part in the life of this village elder, whose worship blends ancient beliefs with Roman Catholic teachings. "Our Indians want to be on good terms with God, and on not-too-bad terms with the Devil," a village padre told the author.

"It is true," the priest continued, "that they secretly pay homage to their idols, and pray to their supreme native deity, Nim Ajau, God World. He is all-pervading, everywhere, and he brings good crops and keeps a man from evil.

"Every village has its witch doctor. He pretends to deliver them from the evil designs of Ajau Juyú, the Lord of the Forest."

On a hill above Momostenango the author walked among mounds of smoke-blackened pottery fragments, the burning places or altars of God World. Through blue clouds of incense smoke he saw droning men and women kneeling before flickering flames, observing a holy day in the *tzolkin*, the 260-day Maya calendar. On the day of Eight Thread, or Eight Monkey, some 15,000 Indians come down from the hills to pray and make offerings at the burning places.

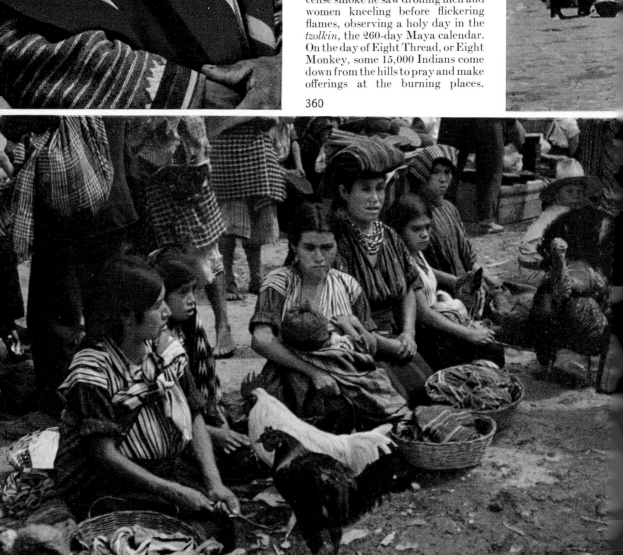

Market Day at Nebaj finds red-skirted women in majority. These Indians have trudged all night under loads of their specialties. Food, pottery, even coffins are sold in open market at this apple-growing center. Bargaining goes on in low tones; no one shouts his wares.

It's "business as usual" during baby's lunchtime in Sololá market (left). Behind nursing mother, men wear Sololá's traditional costume. Roosters and turkeys inspect hand-woven garments in vendors' baskets. Odor of garlic and onions reminds of the region's special produce.

Homeward bound from San Juan Sacatepéquez, women walk in "Indian file" (right). Baby rides mother's back; purchases fill baskets. Guatemalan Indians rarely walk abreast. Men wear sandals; women go barefoot.

KODACHROMES BY LUIS MARDEN,
NATIONAL GEOGRAPHIC STAFF;
GILES GREVILLE HEALEY (ABOVE);
HELEN S. WILLIAMS (LEFT)

making, wood carving, and other handicrafts. Their hand-woven textiles have become world famous. Spaniards introduced the use of wool; before the conquest, Indians had worked only cotton. Dyes are indigo for blue, cochineal for red, brazilwood for purple, mixed chips of campeche and yellow wood for green.

Prominent in the textiles of many villages is the double-headed Hapsburg eagle of Charles V of Spain. Horsemen are represented as centaurlike beings with the man's torso sprouting directly from the horse's back. This practice stems from the early Indian belief that horse and rider were one strange animal.

Old dress remains much the same; colors run through the spectrum from deepest reds through saffron yellow to blue and violet. The woman wears a wraparound saronglike skirt, the *huipil* (a loose blouse), and shawl and headdress. Men's trousers are often striped or plaid, and topped with a gay sash or wraparound knee-length skirt. Each area, sometimes each highland village, has its own colors and costumes, and oldtimers in the Republic can tell where an Indian comes from by the way he dresses.

Members of a Cofradía at San Antonio Palopó appear with their patron saint before Lake Atitlán. Like other *cofradías*, this religious brotherhood cares for the church and stages festivals to honor its saint, whose image is kept in home of the chief *cofrade*. At rites they quaff a pungent ceremonial drink from a gourd, carry the saint's image outside, and dance for him, playing on drums, marimbas, and the thin-voiced *chirimía*, a sort of snake charmer's musette.

Opposite: In the clear waters of volcano-rimmed, mile-high Lake Atitlán, the hand-hewn boat seems suspended in air over vari-colored depths. The fisherman gingerly grasps one of several crabs clinging to the stale-fish bait on his trotline. Tying pincers with green rushes, stringing the crabs on a stalk, he will carry them alive to market across the 1,500-foot-deep lake.

In Guatemala City, most metropolitan of Central American capitals, brightly dressed Indians carrying loads of handicrafts or vegetables to the great mart trot unconcernedly past plate-glass windows displaying products of the machine age; in the highlands, amid the wailing of flutes and thumping of drums, kneeling Indians intone Maya chants. Guatemala today furnishes living proof that white settling of the New World did not inevitably mean extermination of the native Indian and that the two races and cultures can exist side by side in peace.

San Lorenzo Girls Rinse Corn at the Village Fountain, Favorite Tarascan Rendezvous

CHAPTER 18

MEXICO'S TIMELESS INDIANS

MODERN MEXICO THROBS a song of the 20th century. Yet almost within the shadow of the capital's steel-and-glass skyscrapers, the heirs of lost civilizations live out hard, humble lives to the rhythm of an age-old refrain. No one needs a time machine to cut back through the centuries. Writer-photographer JUSTIN LOCKE *turned off the Guadalajara-Mexico City highway to explore remnants of the Tarascan Indians' once-golden empire. He met a proud, friendly people who still hunt with prehistoric throwing sticks, fish from primitive dugouts, and kidnap brides. Entraining to remote Otomí villages northeast of the capital, Swedish anthropologist* HELGA LARSEN, *long a resident of Mexico, witnessed the perilous flying pole dance of pagan days.*

THE TARASCANS OF LAKE PÁTZCUARO

BY JUSTIN LOCKE

THE PAST IS NEVER FAR AWAY in Mexico's Michoacán State, where Tarascan Indians and strange pagan gods ruled supreme before the white man came.

An aged, throbbing bus deposited me on the shore of Lake Pátzcuaro, seat of the golden empire that once stretched to the Pacific Ocean and rivaled in power the Aztec domain in pre-Hispanic Mexico. Today Tarascan country extends a scant 40 to 60 miles between western Sierra highlands, home of the volcano Paricutín, and the lake where I stood.

A hardy, 85-year-old fisherman agreed to take me to Janitzio, one of several islands that loomed through the dawn mist. His primitive, shallow-draft boat snaked through thick grass. Beyond us, a solitary hunter guided his boat toward a thousand tiny dots.

"Gallareta," said the old fisherman, pointing to a drifting flock of coots.

Cautiously the hunter rose. He catapulted his spear in a swift, high arc. Birds whirred into the air, wings flashing in the sun-flecked haze. But the hunter had made his kill. The *atlatl*, his highly effective spear thrower, I recalled, predates the bow.

Our boat nosed now toward Janitzio's shore, along with stragglers of the island's fishing fleet returning from the early morning catch. Misty sunlight washed the tan adobe buildings, the pitched roofs of tile, the balconies overhanging narrow, winding streets.

Big seines were being stretched to dry as I walked down a cobbled path to the home of Salvador Fermín (page 367), a fisherman whom I had met on an earlier visit. Through the open doorway I called into Fermín's terra-cotta kitchen, where bright-colored pottery decorated the red earthen walls.

A young Indian girl flipped tortillas above an open fire. The glare brightened her dark eyes, flashed from her silver earrings, tinted her sparkling yellow blouse. She wore a necklace of coral from the distant sea and a heavy wool skirt that extended to her bare feet.

Island Fires Need Highland Fuel

These Tarascans loading their dug-outs live on Janitzio, a volcanic island denuded of wood. Their Sierra cousins, rich in forest products, catch no fish. Each Sunday forest and lake people meet in Erongarícuaro to exchange wares. Donkeys plod back to the mountains with fish; canoes (lower right) are pushed off to return across Lake Pátzcuaro with a week's firewood. The dugouts themselves are custom-made in the Sierra, borne to the lake by oxcart. Hewed from single pine logs, the flat-bottom craft appear awkward and bulky but can be paddled at surprising speed.

Tarascan women, celebrated for lustrous skin and long dark hair, let braids hang to their knees. They wear hand-loomed black wool skirts or red ones hung in pleats, topping them with aprons and blouses in a rainbow of hues. Drying nets (below) provide a filmy backdrop as Janitzio girls banter on a rocky path. One steps down to the lake front to wash dishes; her friends go to the market.

366

KODACHROMES BY JUSTIN LOCKE

"My father is hanging his nets with his crew, but my mother soon will be back from the store," she said shyly.

I sat by the door to wait. The room contained a wooden chest, nets, water jugs, *petates* or sleeping mats woven of tule just as they were five centuries ago. A far corner of the room shadowed an altar decorated with figurines and pictures of saints. A vase of paper flowers stood beside two receptacles for copal incense. These would be lit at sundown, a simple ritual recalling sacred bonfires pagan Tarascans lighted to their gods.

Tarascan Indians, I knew, had not always lived as humbly and obscurely as my friends, the Fermíns. Displacing or absorbing earlier nomadic and farming tribes in the 14th century, the Tarascans built an empire whose might was felt throughout west-central Mexico. Summoned by high priests in richly feathered capes, the warriors, naked bodies tattooed and painted red and black, sallied forth behind feathered banners, led by officers in jeweled vestments.

Tarascan craftsmen turned out copper tools that were widely sought, multicolored feather "paintings," brilliant gold and lacquer work, and idols carved from stone or molded of *pasta de maiz,* ground pith of cornstalks.

Powerful were the Tarascans until two related twists of fate. Hernán Cortés set foot on Mexican soil, and Tarascan chief Zuangua refused to join the Aztec emperor Montezuma in common cause against the invaders. The Tarascan empire in turn fell to the Spaniards, and the notorious Nuño de Guzmán, avid for gold, sealed its fate forever. The natives fled to the mountains.

While I daydreamed at the cottage door, Fermín's wife came up the street, bearing an earthen jar. From it she drew five glistening white fish, the prized *pescado blanco,* wrapped them in clean, wet grass, and gave them to me.

In following days, I watched Taras-cans catch minnowlike *tiru* with their graceful *mariposa* nets—huge webbed "butterflies." In a bowered patio on Jarácuaro, "island of hatters," I listened to delicate, pensive Tarascan tunes, then boated to Erongarícuaro on the western shore for Sunday market, magnet for Tarascans everywhere.

On Saturday night burro trains laden with firewood thread down through pine forests from Sierra heights. Wrapped in colorful serapes, the foresters bed down beside their stacks of wood to await sunrise when islanders swarm ashore with baskets of fish to barter.

Dust swirls from bare feet in the village square. Laughter mingles with haggling. Wives from near and far inspect chickens, beans, sugar cane; chirimoyas, a tree-grown fruit. Vendors arrive with clay pots, palm-leaf raincoats, twig brooms. Boys sell garlic buds plucked from vegetable necklaces; hatters stack merchandise in tiers on their heads. A merchant from Guadalajara tempts passers-by with jewelry, ribbons, and toys.

Breezes whip men's baggy muslin pants as islanders shove off laden dugouts by noon to avoid late afternoon squalls.

On the opposite shore lies Tzintzuntzan or "Place of the Humming Bird," once-proud capital of the empire, now a sleepy village with 400-year-old olive trees. Tzintzuntzan on fiesta days throngs with satin-clad Tarascans and overalled Spanish-Indian mestizos who clamber to the tops of ancient ruins to enjoy views of village and lake.

Here and elsewhere I heard tales of remote, unexplored ruins. In Tarascan hands I often saw stone idols, copper bells, clay pipes, knives fashioned from tough volcanic glass, and other relics. I heard of the golden cow of Cerro el Zirate; of the dreaded *miringua,* malevolent spirit of the Sierra; and of buried treasure by the ton. I was asked in all seriousness: "Have you heard that the

Amid Drying Nets, Tarascan Fisherman Salvador Fermín Shows Off a Flavorsome Catch

Fish by Sixes, Pots by the Pound . . .

"I offer my last six fish," island girl tells forester, "for another load of your firewood." These choice *pescado blanco* (white fish) share 6,671-foot-high Lake Pátzcuaro with tiny *tiru* caught in the famous butterfly nets, miniatures of which the dark-eyed Janitzio girls sell at lower right. Black bass, introduced into the lake, gobbled up so many tiru that the graceful, winglike nets fell into disuse until the fish made a limited comeback. Tata (father) Domingo, the octogenarian below, is too old to fish but young enough to make nets.

The Tarascan empire's once-great copper industry survives only in Santa Clara (below). Some 30 smiths fashion *casos* (kettles) from flat copper sheets, working with charcoal and antique hand bellows. Sold by weight, the pots are popular throughout Mexico. Tarascans once knew the secret of tempering the metal, legend says. But the conquerors levied a tribute in copper, seized the mines, and sapped the industry that had produced fine axes, hoes, pincers, awls, ornaments.

370

Americanos are draining the lake so as to reach the golden pillars that uphold Janitzio?"

Actual gold I found in the *tierra caliente* (hot country) to the south, once gold-working center of the empire. Goldsmiths still ply their craft in half a dozen villages, one appropriately on the Rio de Oro—River of Gold.

Trekking into the western Sierra on horseback, I climbed to Cherán, a hamlet clinging like lichens to a volcanic slope. The streets were deserted and cold; it was a rainy December day. Clouds scudded toward the valley, an unearthly place where cinder cones rise 800 feet above cultivated fields.

Bare-limbed willow trees framed a group of Cherán *trojes,* those baffling Tarascan log houses of obscure origin.

Masks Off! Pranksters Feast After Fiesta

Tarascans love to dance, not ballroom fashion but in teams at religious festivals, masquerading as saints or devils, hermits or buffoons. A favorite number is *Viejitos* (Little Old Men) in which youths masked as bearded, wrinkled patriarchs burlesque the infirmities of age. The highland swains above danced in disguise at the Fiesta of the Three Kings. Then, like Halloween pranksters, they serenaded girl friends and bearded prospective fathers-in-law. Home again, they shed camouflage, give way to laughter and a hearty meal of beans, tortillas, chile, and atole, a thin corn gruel. Pranks are gleefully recalled. "Did you see her face when I . . .?"

Opposite: The soft pat-pat of tortilla making seldom stops during daylight hours in this Janitzio Island home. As a welcome change for festivals, mother bakes sweetened wheat cakes in the beehive-shaped adobe oven. Content without refrigerator, vacuum cleaner, washer, or table, she loves to ornament walls with her pottery. Copper kettles, baskets, wooden trays come from Tarascan villages specializing in those wares. Bedroom, parlor, shrine, and kitchen share this clean-swept, chimneyless room.

Protruding shake roofs give the dwellings an Oriental look. A group of boys, faces solemn and dreamy, huddled beneath the eaves. Their bright woolen serapes provided the only touch of color.

To my surprise, I found an American couple teaching in Cherán. Mrs. Maxwell D. Lathrop, a linguist like her husband, told me: "Tarascan has no known kinship with any other Indian tongue.

"Written Spanish baffles Tarascan children, though their IQ is high. Learning to read their own language, they assimilate in six months what it takes three years to learn in Spanish."

At the village of San Lorenzo, near the cornfield where Paricutín rose like an evil genie to rain lava and ash on Tarascan lands, I stopped for Christmas.

By the village fountain, maidens washed corn for the holiday dishes (page 364). Guitar sound sparkled in the air. As I lingered, a guide gently chided me. "Be careful," he said. "Wells and public fountains, you know, are the scene of many courtships. Unless you plan to steal a girl to be your bride, let us be on our way."

He had a point. As in the days of the Spanish conquest, Tarascan youths frequently kidnap a mate—with the happy cooperation of the bride-to-be, of course.

After a great hue and cry that is all part of the fun, the marriage is formalized.

About 10 o'clock on Christmas Eve, a confusion of sounds awakened the night. Entering the chapel courtyard, I saw musicians gathered around a small fire tuning their instruments. Tarascan women, faces covered by dark-blue shawls, entered the church to kneel before a portable shrine of the Virgin Mary.

Young girls, dressed as shepherdesses in blue and white and wearing flowered straw hats, shouldered the shrine, bearing it toward a village home honored with safeguarding the Christ Child's image during the year.

The musicians fell in behind and struck up an air. Villagers followed in silent procession. Pine flares began to appear in the darkness. When the Virgin was placed next to the Christ Child, the flickering tongues of fire revealed a strange dance before the sacred images. The shepherdesses sang softly as they glided about. Abruptly, devils in sparkling black-and-red costumes rushed in.

"I guard the Holy Child," shrieked a tiny winged angel and bravely stood her ground. Defiantly claiming their power over man, the demons nonetheless retreated. Masked hermits in conical hats and gray robes jumped upon them and struck them with whips of twine.

Bells summoned the villagers back to church. As the images were carried to the altar, prayers rippled through the church; hundreds of candles seemed to glow at once in the darkness.

To the strum of guitars, eight masked "negrito" dancers approached the center of the nave, clapped and danced. Candlelight shone softly on the bells, mirrors, and beads of their richly embroidered costumes. As the service ended, women sang a muted song, children blew faint whistles to imitate bird song.

In the doorway stood three devils in flashing costumes. Wrapping our blankets tightly about us, we gave them wide berth as we walked into the night.

374

Ghosts of Dead Volcanoes
Knob the Valley of Cherán

In this weird wonderland, not far from mighty
Paricutín, "angry god of the Sierra," a farmer
sowing corn may reap a live volcano. "I heard
a low rumble, as if something had growled,"
said the plowman who witnessed Paricutín's incredible birth in 1943. "I looked; there was
nothing. Then, just behind my furrow, I saw a
spiral of white smoke." His cornfield erupted
that night. Within a week the fiery cone grew
to 500 feet; then to 1,500 feet—9,100 feet above
sea level. Paricutín buried entire Tarascan villages, forcing Indians to flee across black seas of
surging ash.

Mexico's belt of fire, overlying a reservoir of
molten rock, has erected hundreds of cinder
cones in the Tarascan highlands. Trees cover
some ancient piles; other forlornly naked cinder
heaps appear unchanged since their fires died.
Farmers like these climb Juanchan (center) and
till the crater bed.

Playing volcano, below, Tarascan boys start
an eruption by puffing through an embedded
pipe. The toy cone is shaped of ash spewed
from near-by Paricutín, now a sleeping giant.

JUSTIN LOCKE

MEXICAN FLYING POLE DANCE

BY HELGA LARSEN

DEFYING DEATH in a pagan rite, Indians of the eastern Sierra still erect poles as tall as masts and hurtle to earth on long, unwinding ropes. The dangerous dance of the *voladores* (flyers) survives in certain remote hamlets northeast of Mexico City although its symbolism has been almost entirely forgotten in the course of centuries.

Few outsiders have seen this virtually unrecorded spectacle. So when I heard that the Otomi Indians were going to fly at Pahuatlán, I hastened there by train and horse.

When I arrived the flying pole already stood in the bustling plaza, a magnificent spar towering almost 70 feet. A live turkey, candles, chocolates, cigarettes and other offerings had been placed in the deep hole to nourish the pole and make it strong.

Three Indians climbed to the top, finding footholds in a thick vine twisted about the pole. They carried six long ropes and a short tree section hollowed out and smeared with pink soap. They fitted this cylinder over the pole top, like a thimble free to revolve.

The uneven top of the thimble was the "dance floor." It measured exactly 24 inches in diameter! Below it hung a framework of sticks and ropes—the aerial carrousel intended to hold the flyers. Over this frame the Indians passed their six long ropes, wound spoollike around the top of the pole, leaving the ends dangling in air.

The whole structure is so frail a flyer will tell you frankly, "We are helpless if anyone loses his balance." To muster courage, voladores often get drunk. Some villages have banned the dance because of fatal accidents.

Old Spanish chronicles mention four as the number of flyers. Dressed as birds, the men represented the four sacred

376

birds guarding the cardinal points of the compass. The four flyers made 13 rounds before reaching the ground. Thus the rite symbolized the Indian "century"—four 13-year periods making up a 52-year cycle.

Pahuatlán has increased the number of daredevils to six. "Six is more elegant," natives told me.

The Indians climbed down the pole, now ready for the extraordinary dance. Excitement mounted in the plaza. Suddenly someone cried, "Los voladores!" Six gaily dressed flyers paraded into the plaza and approached the pole. The team wore bright red costumes, with two ban-

dannas crossing in the back to suggest wings. All were men. The chief, 63 years old, had flown for 35 years. Five were dressed in breeches, the sixth in billowing skirts. This was Malinche, or Man-Woman, portrayed in nearly all Mexican dances and believed to represent the Indian girl who befriended Cortés.

One by one the flyers climbed up, Malinche hampered by her skirts. They seated themselves in the flimsy frame, bracing feet against the pole. They looked like rag dolls.

Then a volador climbed to the tiny platform and began to dance. The others shook rattles; one played flute and drum.

The music floated down as the tiny figure whirled and leaped. My heart surged into my throat; one false step, one slight loss of balance, and he would plunge to death at my feet.

The other flyers took turns at breath-taking acrobatics. Malinche's dance, to four different tunes, was the most spectacular. Spectators stiffened and gasped when she leaned recklessly from the little perch and enfolded each of the others with a large bandanna. Then she eased back into her place in the frame.

Now the voladores tied the rope ends around their waists. With a piercing cry, they hurled themselves backward into space.

For one breathless moment they dangled from the summit, five flyers head down — only Malinche flies feet first. The ropes started to unwind, slowly at first, then faster and faster as the voladores swung in ever widening circles.

Round and round the mast they flew, slim bodies stretched along taut ropes gripped with their feet—down to the red-tiled roof-tops now, down to the balconies, down to the arcades, coming closer and closer to the sea of tense, upturned brown faces.

The music had changed to a livelier rhythm; hollow instruments throbbed furiously. Even when it seemed the aerialists' heads would scrape the ground, one still played his pipe and drum, the others shook gourd rattles. Suddenly, as the crowd roared and broke like a surging wave around the voladores, the heroes righted themselves gracefully and landed—safe at last—on their feet.

RODNEY GALLOP

379

A Fast-changing World Faces This Eskimo Mother and Her Solemn, Fur-framed Hitchhiker

CHAPTER 19

NORTHLAND LIFE

TRANSPOLAR PLANES DRONE *through Arctic skies, weather and radar stations dot northland shores, yet the Eskimo remains master of a vast top-of-the-world domain. Numbering less than 40,000, this resourceful people draws on a 2,000-year-old culture, survives using ingenious gear adapted to a merciless environment. Central Eskimos have followed a rhythm of migration as unvarying as that of the birds—moving inland to fish and hunt game in summer, back to winter on the ice, realm of sea mammals and polar bears. One group, the Padlermiut, for some reason remained inland. Passing centuries obliterated maritime ties; caribou became focus of their existence.* DONALD B. MARSH, *Anglican Bishop of the Arctic, describes these unique Caribou Eskimos as he knew them in days before the airplane accelerated change in the northland. At Point Hope, Alaska, anthropologist* FROELICH G. RAINEY, *Director of the University Museum in Philadelphia, joins the colorful—and crucial—annual whale hunt of the Eskimo villagers of Tigara.*

CANADA'S CARIBOU ESKIMOS
BY DONALD B. MARSH

THEY CALL themselves Padlermiut, People of the Willow Thicket. White men have dubbed them Caribou Eskimos, and with good reason. Fifty years ago these people depended upon one animal, the caribou, for life itself. Men, women, and children dressed in skins of caribou, which they hunted with bows and arrows. Caribou meat fed them. Caribou bones and antlers were their tools.

Though they lived on Canada's Northern Plains, only slightly west of Hudson Bay, theirs was an inland culture. Unique among Eskimos, they possessed no traditions of the sea. They spoke a language like that of Greenland Eskimos, yet they knew nothing of hunting sea mammals, Greenland's basis of life. Seal, walrus, polar bear were unfamiliar, salt water and tides mysteries. They had no seal-blubber lamps, trade-mark of Eskimos all over the North.

Today the Padlermiut depend as much on traders as on caribou. They hunt with guns instead of bows. Within a lifetime they have emerged from the past; modern times stare them in the face. As a missionary, in summer I have shared their smoky caribou-skin tents; in winter, their freezing crudely built igloos. For 20 years I watched them struggle with the elements and with advancing civilization.

When I first set sail from Churchill, seat of a small Church of England mission, I scarcely knew what to expect at Eskimo Point, 160 miles north. Even then, changes had already overtaken the Padlermiut. For one thing, those I met were camped beside salt water.

As the anchor dropped, I saw against a background of conical skin tents a group of men with long flowing hair and wrinkled, seamed, but smiling faces. All were clad in caribou skins; much of this clothing was so dirty and greasy as to look the color of the earth. They stooped slightly as they walked, so many winters

Padlermiut Life: a Tuft of Moss, a Roof of Snow, and for Dining, an Ax

A village crone (below) returns from day-long rounds scraping snow from clumps of reindeer moss and stunted willows. "People of the Willow Thicket" lack seal or walrus oil, feed cooking fires with twigs. Amid littered furs and equipment (right) she will carry her load down steps to the rock-topped snow bench that forms the family hearth. Smoke drifts from porch and snow chimney. Crudely built, often roofed with caribou hide and raftered with summer's tent poles, these igloos chill to below zero when fires die. Awaiting a feast of cooked meat, tea-drinking men (below right) hack hors d'oeuvres from a frozen caribou carcass.

382

A. W. F. BANFIELD

had they huddled over feeble caribou-fat lamps; yet theirs was the dignity and poise of men who are sure of themselves. The women, hair matted and straggly and skin clothes greasy, also greeted me with friendly smiles. The young men and lads stood off by themselves. Their appearance gave me a shock. Surely these were not Eskimos! Most wore sweaters, many with encircling bands of color. The crowns of their heads were close-cropped, tonsure fashion.

So this was the new mode of the North!

Food dominates the thoughts of the Padlermiut. They often do not know where the next meal is coming from. When they have caribou, they eat one big feast of cooked meat each day. For an appetizer a haunch of frozen raw caribou, together with an ax, is provided. Anyone really hungry may chop off a portion. Most wait for the heaping, steaming pot of boiled meat.

The sight of a fire roaring on a snow bench within snow walls has never failed to astonish me. Smoke swirls, as if feeding on the snow itself. It blackens the cook's face and reddens her eyes, then drifts upward to a snow chimney. Handful by handful, she tosses twigs to the insatiable fire. In two or three hours the meat is done.

Nowadays the meat boils in a gasoline drum or washtub. In old days she would have used a polished stone vessel. For communal meals one woman usually cooks for the men and another for her sisters. Men and women feast separately.

The family dinner platter is a wooden tray four feet long, a foot wide, and two inches thick. Carved from a tree trunk, such a tray is an heirloom to be handed down from generation to generation—or to be buried with its owner for use in the next world.

When dinner is ready, the host invites the guests to fall to, but politeness demands some show of reluctance. Then, eyes lighting up, each man grasps his favorite portion—tongue, fat breast meat, steak. Sinking his teeth in one end, he shears off the remainder with a stroke of a butcher knife, just missing his nose and chin. Sinew, cartilage, fat, or flesh—all are grist for powerful jaws. Boiled head is a prime delicacy, as is rendered back fat stuffed sausagelike into caribou intestines.

No one talks, but silence does not reign! When the meat is devoured, the bones are cracked and the marrow extracted with special bone implements. Horns are sometimes eaten when in the velvet. At one time liver, head, and lungs were taboo, even to the dogs, but now only the lungs go uneaten.

Tea, black, strong, and bitter—and sometimes boiled from re-used leaves—is consumed in enormous quantities. Formerly the meat's cooking water was

Land of the Caribou— and the Caribou Eskimo. In April and May, along the edges of the Arctic tree line, caribou mass for their great migration toward the lichen-rich tundra. First the does, heavy with fawns, then bucks with velveted antlers, emerge from the scrub, mill about on frozen lakes, and head north in mighty herds (left).

At defiles and oft-used crossings, Eskimos and Indians lie in wait with rifles, as their fathers once did with bows. Lookouts give cry. Downwind floats the clicking of the caribou's heel bones, the grunt of the loping herd, and its rank, distinctive odor.

Suddenly the dun-gray horde bursts into sight. Steel-jacketed bullets thud into leaping flesh. Behind the firing line, women and children ravenous for the season's first fresh meat bring kettles to boil. Later they cure the hides for clothing, cache the meat, remove sinews for sewing.

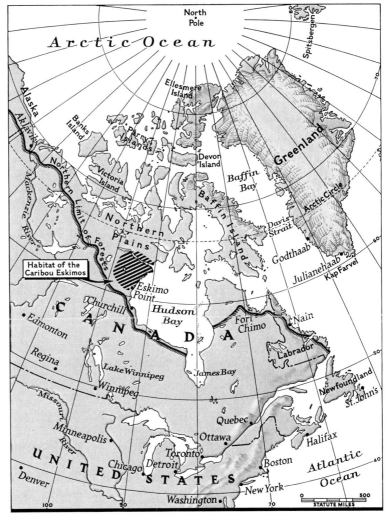

NATIONAL GEOGRAPHIC MAP DRAWN BY THEODORA PRICE AND IRVIN E. ALLEMAN

the standard drink. When I first visited the Padlermiut, they bought tea put up in lead-covered packages, melting down the metal in frying pans to make bullets.

In times of abundance a man may be invited to a succession of caribou banquets. I saw one man stagger out of his fourth en route to his fifth. Not knowing other meals were to follow, he had done his utmost at each to see that nothing was wasted. On a later occasion he had to slit his coat front and back in order to complete his rounds!

In early times, if the camp had meat, no one went hungry. When caribou were scarce, the successful hunter gave away most of his kill, happily boasting, "To me has fallen the privilege of providing for the camp." Today the rule applies only to native food. White man's food obeys white man's laws. Flour, lard, and meat bought at the store with fox pelts are not given away lightly. Men sit all day splitting matches to make them go three times as far.

As a shopper, the Caribou Eskimo cannot understand fixed prices. If his need is great, he is eager to pay more than the trader asks. One man offered three fox pelts for a snow knife, explaining that he was unable to hunt without the knife. Why the trader refused his offer baffled the Eskimo. Another man offered seven pelts for the trader's only razor—but the trader didn't want to grow a beard.

Gifts they undervalue to the point of seeming ingratitude. By their philosophy, if the donor had any use for the object, he wouldn't give it away.

Reading, writing, and arithmetic are comparative newcomers to the Eskimo's curriculum of life. Several decades ago the Reverend E. J. Peck, who spent 40 years among the Baffin Islanders, adapted Cree Indian characters to the Eskimo tongue. Now most Eskimos in the eastern Arctic can read their own language. For history, however, they have never needed the written word. A marvelous

tribal memory serves them faithfully. Across the Arctic the centuries-old folklore is almost word for word the same, even among the most isolated tribes.

Custom rules life in the community. Timeless custom backed by strict taboos. One decrees that no woman in her fertile years may eat eggs. A wolf hunter, having wounded his prey by gunshot, killed it with an ax. In doing so he broke one of the wolf's bones—violation of a rigid taboo. He died soon after—and his fellows knew why!

An *angakok,* or shaman, may be either man or woman. Each has his or her own familiar spirit for consultation. Some witch doctors have performed such unbelievable feats that they have acquired a virtual life or death power over their fellows. Men have committed suicide on orders from an angakok.

Such a powerful wizard lived among inlanders of the Northern Plains. His people swear they saw him grow walrus tusks from his jaws. At his initiation into shamanship, he was reported to have buried himself in a lake freezing over. Three days later he was chopped out, none the worse, the Eskimos said.

Wearing charms comes as naturally to the Eskimo as his belief in shamans. I have seen some so smothered in tokens that they appeared to be in rags. Little bags may contain a fish heart, a piece of sealskin to give strength, weasel skin to impart hunter's cunning, or a cloth strip token from a well-wisher.

Many times I have witnessed the barbaric drum dance of the Caribou Eskimos. Inside a double-size tribal skin tent on an arctic evening, when darkness suspends the taboo against drum beating, a man steps past the outer circle of men into the tight inner ring of women squatting shoulder to shoulder. He taps the rim of his huge one-faced drum with a stubby clublike stick and the sound reverberates like an African tom-tom beat. His body sways rhythmically. He looks up, as if trying to remember his song. Then his knees bend until his caribou-skin coattails sweep the ground. With short steps he hops around the ring. A candle's flickering flame throws his shadow in grotesque shapes and highlights the onlookers' intense faces. Chanting women sway to and fro, closing their eyes as if in a trance.

This same dance they danced in the Stone Age. Yet many of their customs are changing. I remember one old man shaping a block of iron into a harpoon head with a toothless file. His task already had taken two days; he expected to take three more. He was in no hurry; what did time mean in the Arctic? With his new harpoon he would hunt seals so that he might have blubber in which to dip his raw caribou meat next winter. He was learning the ways of shoreline Eskimos.

Alaskan Eskimos Face the Sea

Ukivok village, perched on King Island's rocky southern slope, winters 150 Eskimos oriented to fog-shrouded Bering Sea life. Walrus-hide umiaks, now powered by outboard motors, serve the cliff-dwelling hunters and provide a link with mainland Alaska, 30 miles east (page 154). This fisherwoman chiseled a hole in the ice, kept it clear with long-handled scoop, lured bullheads with bright toothbrush handle. Barbless hooks enable mittened Eskimos to remove catches without exposing fingers to bitter cold. With no level land, boys play baseball on sea ice.

© KODACHROME BY JUAN MUÑOZ

ESKIMO WHALE HUNT

BY FROELICH G. RAINEY

WHEN THE SUN RETURNS in spring to glare down upon the wilderness of pack ice, the wives of the Tigara whaling captains begin preparations for their men to go out to hunt the largest of all living creatures, the great bowhead whale, Agavik.

Up to a generation ago, the Eskimo women prayed to the moon for success. They were not impressed by Sukunuk, the sun, regarded as female, but waited for the male moon, Alignuk, on whom depended their family security and the prestige of their kin.

In March, Alignuk would draw back the trap door in the floor of his house, and a faint silver crescent would appear in the night sky. Then each captain's wife would take her special little wooden bowl and fill it with clean, clear water from a certain lagoon.

After the dogs had quieted for the night, she stole out through the long entrance tunnel of her house and held her bowl up toward the moon, calling: "Alignuk, drop a whale into this pot so that we can kill one this spring!"

If she had obeyed all the rules and if

Red-stained Sea and Ice Spell Full Larders

Shot in mass attacks as they ride north on floating ice pans, walrus provide King Islanders with meat, hides, oil, and ivory. The hunters above have had a good day: they butcher two huge carcasses, have another tethered to the ice, and drag a 200-pound calf from the water.

Below, women pare blubber from a sealskin with broad steel *ulu* blades shaped like pie wedges, as a hungry dog stands watch. Their splitting boards are heirlooms. They will soften the skin by chewing to make supple, water-resistant boots; use the carcass as food; burn the oil in lamps. The women wear cloth covers over caribou-skin parkas. Hunters wear white canvas jackets for camouflage on ice, hunt from October to June. When the last ice goes out, the entire King Island village leaves for Nome, 85 miles distant, for summer jobs or to sell walrus-ivory carvings.

the water was clear, her voice and the glimmer of light in the bowl reached up to Alignuk. He would send a whale.

Tigara clings to the very tip of a long ribbon of sand that curves out into the Arctic Ocean 200 miles north of Bering Strait. A strong northward sea current strikes this spit, known as Point Hope, and swings out toward the northwest. At certain times current and wind combine to force a lead, or opening, in the pack ice. In April, May, and early June, bowhead whales migrate northward along the open lead, heading for Point Barrow and the Arctic Ocean.

The lead along Point Hope usually opens under a north wind and closes under a south wind. The old men watch the weather closely to decide when the boats shall be taken out across the ice to open water. If the bitter male northeast wind blows, the lead will open, but great pans of shore ice may break off and be driven out to sea, carrying with them boats and crews. The ice may be crushed into a seething mass over which a boat cannot be dragged and through which no boat can be driven.

But that spring the day of launching was beautiful, dazzling bright, with only a breath of air from the north. Umigluk's team of nine dogs was hitched to a light sled and a line run from that to the boat sled. Each member of our crew also was in harness. We moved off through the piles of ice and pressure ridges, pulling not only the umiak but also a great pile of extra fur clothing, guns, and all manner of gear to be used on the ice. We would not return to shore until the lead closed, perhaps many days later.

All whaling gear must be clean and, if possible, new. The Eskimos believe the whale cannot easily see bright and shining gear, but if he does, it pleases

him. It promises sharp cutting knives and spades which will not hurt in the butchering. You see, the whale does not die, he only "has his parka removed"—painlessly, if knives are sharp—and returns to sea to report on his treatment by the Eskimos.

Umigluk's father had supervised the refitting of our fragile 20-foot umiak—half the length of the whales we were to attack in it. Old crones of the village, paid in tobacco and meat, had sewn skins of the bearded seal into a new cover for it. Umigluk's mother-in-law had purified it spiritually by an ancient ceremony on the ice.

The crew scraped clean all eight spruce paddles, the harpoon shafts, the great cutting lance shafts, the boat hooks. New sealskin floats were made and tested, new lines made fast. Harpoon bombs were refilled with fresh black powder, fuses reset, caps tested.

I knew from my crew mates, although he never told me himself, that Umigluk had retired the night before to sing his charm song, almost inaudibly, lightly tapping his tiny whaling captain's drum. This song had been taught him by his grand-

Whaling, Eskimo Style!
In paddled boats, with hand harpoons and guns 50 years old, Tigara hunters pursue their Moby Dick, Agavik. Flukes flip skyward (top) as a wounded whale sounds. Sealskin float bobs in foreground. Blubber slab (center) goes to one crew as another (below) hacks gill bone away beneath baleen, the horny material from the mouth. Only the skull, representing the whale's spirit, returns to the sea.

FROELICH G. RAINEY;
MERL LA VOY (BOTTOM)

father, a great medicine man, and no one must hear it.

Our crew, following tradition, had eaten a piece of whale caught the year before—black rubbery skin, yellow blubber, red meat, all raw and ripe. But there had also been an evil portent.

At Easter, in the centuries-old masked whaling dance, Kuwana had spun a wooden top, out of which rose goose feathers arranged like turnip leaves. If it had whirled smoothly and the feathers had sailed off into the air, the whaling would be a success. If it did not, some one present would die.

The top had spun smoothly for a moment, then caught and slid along the stage, scattering its feather plume. There was some laughter and joking when the moment of suspense was over, but I had watched old Nashugruk's drawn face as she sat staring at the top.

Three weeks later Poyuruk, the jovial dancer with the beaming smile, died with pieces of an exploded bronze shoulder gun embedded in his intestines, Kunuknoruk was badly wounded by another explosion, and two other antique guns—bought from American whalers more than 50 years before—had blown up as well.

Now, however, we were just beginning the spring hunt. Only a few minutes after we reached open water, someone shouted "Agavik!" There, half a mile off, a great black hulk surfaced to blow a fine puff of steam from its bow, then submerged.

Half an hour later we heard a harpoon gun fire to the east. Suddenly a boat shot out from behind the ice, then lay still, its crew waiting and watching.

Kunuknoruk rose in the stern of his boat, held out his arms over bowed heads, and prayed in a loud clear voice to Our Father, "Apapta" in Eskimo. In the old days his harpooner would have sung the Avituksiun, a prayer to hold the harpoon fast in the whale.

I asked old Qoqoq later why he prayed to Jehovah instead of to Alignuk, the moon, as he had during much of his life. He said it was not until the missionaries came that he knew Jehovah controlled the whales.

The prayer finished, we headed off toward where Umigluk thought the whale would blow next. After a long, hard pull, we heard the cry, "Avituk!" Again we drove our boat forward, racing the other crews toward a small dark sealskin float (avituk) fastened by 14 fathoms of line to the embedded harpoon iron. When the float appears it is a sign the whale is rising.

Each boat at the scene of a kill gets a portion of the whale, but what part depends upon the order of arrival, hence the race, which has every paddler exerting all his strength. After some two miles of chasing the elusive float most of us had the taste of blood in our mouths.

Ours were all young men; we soon drew into the lead. Suddenly the float broke the surface a hundred yards off our bow. We redoubled the stroke; our boat surged forward like a whale in full flight.

Then beneath us we felt a huge boiling movement of the water; the boat rocked crazily, and directly under the bow rose the great black bulk of the whale. There was a deep and unforgettable blast, something like the exhaust of a locomotive stopping at a station, as the whale blew steam into our faces.

Umigluk at the stern swung us about, and with one terrific stroke of our paddles we drove the boat up the glistening slope of the whale's back. Melik, the harpooner, rose, held the harpoon shaft high above his head, then drove it straight down through three feet of quivering skin, blubber, and flesh.

A mighty shudder passed from the whale through our flexible skin boat. A deep muffled thud followed as the harpoon bomb exploded in that mass of flesh; then came a convulsion that threw the boat off on its side. A cry from Umigluk warned us to clear away the sealskin floats attached to the line, which now was running out with the whale's sounding. In a moment line and floats disappeared. With all my heart-pounding excitement I yet remember the sweat-streaked, beaming faces of the crew, each shouting and laughing.

The nine boats now formed a wide circle. All of us watched for the float. At last it bobbed up, dark and agitated like a female bearded seal rising far out of the water, waving her flippers to lead you away from her pup.

As we closed in, the whale rose, spouting a mist of steam and blood. Kunuknoruk's boat swung in, and young Stephen leaned over the bow, brandishing a ten-foot steel-headed lance. The boat slid up over the whale's flippers until only the stern remained in the water. Stephen thrust downward, then raised himself over the lance like a pole vaulter, forcing it down through probably six feet of flesh.

Two other boats rushed to the kill, other lances searched for vital spots. In a few minutes it was finished. A black hulk floated quietly, with only an oil slick and swirls of bloody water to remind us of its death struggle.

Not until that moment did I realize it was snowing hard. The ice pack was no longer in sight, and the other boats seemed ghostly in the gray light.

As we began to tow the carcass in the blinding snowstorm, the "joy shout" went up, a short repeated barking sound like the cry of a sea lion. The cooks on the ice would hear this, and carry word to the village that the first kill of the spring had been made.

The whale was hauled onto the ice by pulleys, the flukes were cut away and carried to the village at once. They belong to the captain whose crew made the first strike, but are given to the community, symbol of the hunter's relation to supernatural forces, to the village, and to the spirit of the whale himself. Formerly, a piece was borne to the captain's wife on a staff, announcing success. She then came out on the ice with her little ceremonial bowl to give the whale a drink of fresh water. All sea mammals are forever thirsty, the Eskimos say.

Old men marked each boat crew's traditional share by cutting long gashes in the black skin. The last boat wins a "booby prize"—a strip the size of the captain's foot, cut completely around the whale just below the navel.

We worked all day and all night cutting up the whale. Dog teams raced back and forth from the edge of the ice to storage pits ashore, hauling the tons of meat. Sea gulls screamed overhead or dived for titbits in the water. The ice for yards around became slippery with blood and fat. A long, winding red trail marked the course of sleds across the ice to the shore. Clothing was soaked, greasy, but no one cared, for the butchering is a time of joy and feasting.

The hunt continued for many weeks. We waited long days and nights at the edge of the ice, raced through vast fields of drifting floes in pursuit of whales, or sat quietly far out in the lead while herds of white belugas broke the night silence with their puffing.

Once the pack ice began to break up unexpectedly, to grind and crash and move seaward. It was the only time I ever saw Eskimos really terrified. With only eight boats, in an hour of feverish work, more than 100 villagers, including women and children, were ferried across three ice-jammed channels to safety on shore. Later, when the ice reformed, they all went right back out on the pack.

When the sun began to circle the sky without setting, the ice again became restless. Big cracks appeared, pools of water collected on the smooth pans where our boats lay, and we could feel ourselves rising or falling as the ground ice prepared to move north. The season was over. We had struck 13 bowheads, killed five, cached meat from four.

We came off the ice for good one day early in June, dragging our boats across the last of the ice to the sand spit where bumblebees already had found the first spring flowers. It was time for Nalukatuk, the whale feast which begins the day after the boats reach shore and lasts for three days. Now appear such delicacies as raw whale kidneys, tongue, hearts, skin; "ice cream" made from beaten reindeer fat, bits of meat, and berries; and boiled flour-and-seal-oil soup.

Games of strength and endurance, dancing, singing, and drumming renew appetites. But the climax is Nalukatuk, the performance that gives the feast its name. This glorified tossing-in-the-blanket is both a delight and a terror.

From four whale-jaw tripods, a large walrus hide is stretched by ropes three or four feet above

the ground. Forty or fifty people grasp its edge by special rope handgrips, and together toss some courageous victim as high as 15 or 20 feet at each bounce.

Some Eskimos are skilled enough to keep their feet for minutes, "dancing in the air" to drumming and singing.

But the novice has a bad time. He lands just at the wrong moment, his knees buckle, he soon sprawls on his face or back and tumbles through the air amid shouts of laughter, completely at the mercy of the tossers. Such is the Nalukatuk, high spot in the Tigara year!

393

KODACHROMES BY AMOS BURG

Old or Young, Eskimos Grin at Life

Good-natured and self-assured, the Eskimo meets life happily—from a great-grandmother, past 90, weaving a basket of beach grass, to a demure young coquette in hand-me-down dress. "Perhaps they laugh," one writer suggests, "because their parka fur tickles them all the time!"

Looking like a huge necktie rack, split red salmon dry in wind and sun (above) behind boy untangling his fish net. At Point Lay, where the Arctic Circle lies "down south," sod-covered frame house (left) resembles American prairie homes of a century ago. Storage wing needs neither turf overcoat nor glass windows.

395

KODACHROME BY JACK BREED

Ute Mothers Tuck Sleepy Infants in Sunshaded Cradleboards and strap them on their backs. These women belong to the Wiminuche branch, still nomadic, still chary of visitors to their southwestern Colorado reservation. The tribal council voted special permission to make this picture.

396

CHAPTER 20

THE AMERICAN INDIAN CITIZEN AND NEIGHBOR

ONCE MASTER OF THIS LAND, *the Indian is assuming a new role in the United States community. A citizen since 1924, he votes in State and Federal elections, adopts more and more of his white neighbor's ways. The 20th century penetrates even the remote land of the Havasupai, reports* JACK BREED. *The Indian offers his heritage of talents to the Nation.* DOROTHY DUNN, *founder of Santa Fe's School of Indian Painting, tells of a resurgence of native American art— no longer on rocks and buffalo hides but on the easel's paper and canvas—and presents paintings to reveal its vitality and impact. National Geographic staff writer* ROBERT L. CONLY *shows Mohawk daring at work building "Big Town" skyscrapers. But the clash of cultures, the tug of the past still have effect. In the Indian's changing world depicted by* MATTHEW W. STIRLING, *young veterans weigh their hopes of success in white society against tribal security on the reservation*

CONTEMPORARY INDIAN PAINTERS
BY DOROTHY DUNN

NEAR TODAY'S ATOMIC CITY of Los Alamos, an archeological field unit from the Museum of New Mexico was digging in long-abandoned cave dwellings. The year was 1917. Young Crescencio Martinez from San Ildefonso Pueblo was at work as a laborer. One day he overheard archeologists praise pictographs and mural paintings on a cave's blackened walls.

"I can paint, too," he volunteered.

Crescencio got his chance. Given paper and paints, he produced surprising water colors. Soon he was painting dances of his pueblo's summer and winter festivals. With simple reverence he pictured singers, drummers, and dancers of corn, eagle, buffalo, and deer ceremonials. The series was almost complete when he died of influenza in 1918. Others carried on the work. Among them was Crescencio's nephew, Awa Tsireh.

In those days, incredible as it now seems, the Bureau of Indian Affairs banned native painting in Indian schools. Despite official disapproval, three talented youths—Ma-Pe-Wi of Zia Pueblo (page 399) and two Hopi boys, Fred Kabotie and Otis Polelonema, were given supplies by a sympathetic superintendent at the Indian school in Santa Fe and encouraged to paint on their own.

Meantime San Ildefonso was becoming an art center, sparked by a renaissance in pottery making brought about by Maria and Julian Martinez with their now famous matte-on-gloss black ware (page 117). Inspired by the new creative spirit, young men of San Ildefonso and near-by pueblos began painting. Interested Santa Fe people sponsored exhibitions as far as Madrid, Prague, Venice.

In 1932 a change in Indian Bureau policy led to the opening of art classes in the school at Santa Fe. Young people flocked to enroll—Pueblo, Navajo, and Apache from New Mexico and Arizona; Sioux from the Dakotas; Cheyenne, Arapaho, Kiowa from Oklahoma.

Every painter evolved a personal style within the tribal character. One artist specialized in old Plains abstract designs, another in everyday views, others in hunting scenes or the fantasy of tribal mythology. This they have in common: The Indian painter poses no models, follows no color theory, gauges no true perspective. Often he leaves background to imagination. By omitting nonessentials, he produces abstract symbols for plants, animals, earth, and sky. Yet he can convey mood or action with a few lines.

The contemporary movement now has extended to centers in Oklahoma, Utah, and Montana, with frequent exhibitions elsewhere in the country. Some 40 Indian artists today devote substantial time to painting. Three pioneers—Ma-Pe-Wi, Kabotie, and Polelonema—still are painting. Only middle-aged, they are known as the "old masters" of contemporary Indian painting. So spectacular has been this art development that the public sometimes forgets its roots are old.

Painting was already an ancient tribal activity when Spanish conquistadores forded the Rio Grande. For centuries aboriginal artists had expressed reactions to their native land in pictures carved in rock, engraved on bone, painted on hides, wood, pottery, plaster, cloth—even drawn in colored sand. Before white settlers took over the Great Plains, nearly every buffalo-hide tepee, robe, and shield bore vivid figures of horses and men in battles, hunts, and contests (page 53). Such dec-

orations were emblems of prowess. Every man was an artist.

When buffalo herds and tribal lands disappeared, uprooted Indians, longing for self-expression, turned to makeshift materials. Army commissary books, traders' ledgers, lengths of cloth were filled with pencil and crayon drawings, and paintings done with

Ma-Pe-Wi Paints a Buffalo Dance. At home in Santa Fe, an "Old Master" of modern Indian painting gives pointers to his son; his Pueblo wife tends garden. The work on his easel later won high honors at the Santa Fe Fiesta exhibit. The French Government awarded him a medal in 1954 at the Inter-Tribal Indian Ceremonial at Gallup, New Mexico.

WESTERN WAYS FEATURES

brushes and ready-made colors. Subject matter also changed. Art became a nostalgic rendering of childhood reminiscences, youthful exploits, tribal wars of bygone days, and new battles with "long knives," the white men.

Indians in prison won vicarious victories and regained wishful freedom through their paintings. One Cheyenne, escaped from prison, went into battle with his book of drawings strapped to his side. A bullet pierced it, killing him. Later the work turned up in New York's American Museum of Natural History.

This new personal Plains style was the first attempt at art distinct from tribal needs. It recalled the grand days of the buffalo hunt. Religious rites long had

honored the mighty beast that fed, clothed, and sheltered the tented tribes —Sioux, Cheyenne, Crow, Kiowa, and others. Though the earth-shaking herds are gone, they live on in paintings not only of the Plains people, but of Southwest tribes that had little contact with the buffalo (page 404).

"I want to realize the glory of portraying the life of the Indian for the eyes of the people who do not know," says F. Blackbear Bosin, Kiowa-Comanche artist whose "Prairie Fire" retains the spirit and verve of traditional Plains works, though his technique is more naturalistic (page 402).

Unlike the 19th century Plainsmen, the Pueblo Indians and Navajo of the Southwest carried on their native arts as in the past. Tempera paint was made of earth pigments mixed with water or milk, brushes were the chewed ends of yucca leaves, mouths were atomizers. Few artists tried new materials.

One Navajo youth, fascinated by puffing locomotives of the 1880's, made colored-crayon sketches on wrapping paper at a trading post. Later the first known drawings of Navajo ceremonial figures on paper were discovered by an artist-archeologist working at Pueblo Bonito.

As he entered a trading post, he saw some crude but vigorous pictures penciled on cardboard box ends. Their creator, he learned, was Api Begay, who lived in a hogan off toward the horizon.

"What does he do for a living?"

"He don't do anything; he's an artist," someone quipped.

Eventually the archeologist found Api and asked him to do some drawings.

"What will you give me?" asked Api.

"A dollar and this box of colored pencils."

Api was so delighted that he quickly finished several drawings of mythical figures from Navajo rites.

The Navajo are primarily shepherds and horsemen, while the Pueblos live by the soil. Yet contemporary Navajo painters have adopted much in technique from their Pueblo neighbors, whose painting is precisely patterned, rhythmic, and symbolic, the natural expression of a people whose scheme of life is set by the solstices and ordered by the seasons.

In a region of capricious climate, Pueblo painters often express yearning for rain (page 406). Many Navajo paintings reflect the even more brutal water shortage in their barren grazing lands. But Navajo artists also portray cheerful themes as shown in Harrison Begay's girl with sheep (opposite). Charmingly simple, even in subject, is the Pueblo artist Garcia's painting of wild horses going into corral (page 407).

Navajo sand paintings to ward off evil spirits present impressive abstract designs matured through centuries of religious evolution (page 408).

The road traveled by Indian artists has not been easy. Discouragement has plagued many. Punishment and ostracism have been imposed by some communities that frowned on painting shared with outsiders. Indian art is just beginning to be known by the public at large, yet connoisseurs hail it as making valuable and unique contributions. Its influence on non-Indian artists and decorators shows in the striking sand-painting motifs that decorate a lounge of the liner United States.

And to the artist comes an occasional unexpected reward.

Pablita Velarde, outstanding Pueblo painter who has struggled most of her life against poor eyesight, lost her mother when she was three years old.

Recently she received a letter from an English woman who had followed her career. "I think," said this writer, "you may like to have this copy of a photograph I took of your father and mother on their wedding day in 1910."

It was the first photograph of her mother that Pablita had ever seen.

Navajo Girl with Sheep by Harrison Begay. Lovely girl in tribal dress reveals how well her people have treasured flocks introduced by the Spaniards. Idealized sheep, high-spirited horses, well-dressed people typify the decorative, analytic style of this noted Navajo artist, largely self-taught.

Prairie Fire by F. Blackbear Bosin. Searing waves of flame leap into the sky. Antelopes and wolves, their feuds forgotten, join mounted Indians in headlong flight across the drought-stricken Plains. Such is the artist's skill that his animals convey a sense of fright; even the grasses reflect foreboding.

402

Bosin, 34-year-old Kiowa Comanche, reveals the fury of life triumphing in the face of disaster. Speed and action are hallmarks of Plains art, modern and traditional. But in a concisely painted buffalo-robe history of a hundred years ago such an event would have been noted by a single symbol.

403

Creek Ball Game by Noah Deere. Graceful Eastern Woodlands athletes with plumed tailpieces and roached headdresses suggest a procession of youths around a classic Greek vase. But here noses and heads are bloody, for the game is *tokonhon* (stick ball), rough-and-tumble forerunner of lacrosse (page 22). Players may not touch the ball with their hands; they catch and throw it with a racket laced with thongs. Though the immediate object was to drive a stuffed deerskin ball through the opponents' goal post, the long-range aim was to test a man's endurance, honor, team spirit, and potential war valor. Often contests were ceremonial.

Noah Deere was 21 and a student at Bacone College when this painting won him a prize at Tulsa's Philbrook Art Center in 1950.

Buffalo Hunt by Ma-Pe-Wi. Indian hunters, racing under the abstract light of a geometric sun, drive a herd before them in such furious action that hoofbeats fairly pound across the page. The massive bulk of slain and stampeding animals contrasts sharply with the arrow's thin line. Even though they live outside the beasts' former range and lack its hunting tradition, Pueblo Indians cherish memories of bison. Hopi and Rio Grande pueblos still stage buffalo dances. Taos proudly pastures a buffalo herd.

A Pueblo artist who has left his Zia home, Ma-Pe-Wi (Red Bird) here uses ancient symbols of his people. His clouds resemble those on weather charts. His Zia sun, rising above stylized mountains, today rides New Mexico's automobile tags, shines on State flag. Yuccas and piñons, or nut pines, long a source of Indian food, grow between triangular hills. *Buffalo Hunt*, an early work, displays the artist's characteristic grace. Even when portraying impending death, his art pulses with the joy of living.

The horizon detail in both these paintings is unusual in Indian works. Noah Deere (above) stylizes figures against a natural background; Ma-Pe-Wi employs realistic figures in an abstract setting.

PAINTINGS FROM THE COLLECTIONS OF THE PHILBROOK ART CENTER, TULSA, OKLAHOMA (ABOVE) AND THE INDIAN ARTS FUND, SANTA FE, NEW MEXICO

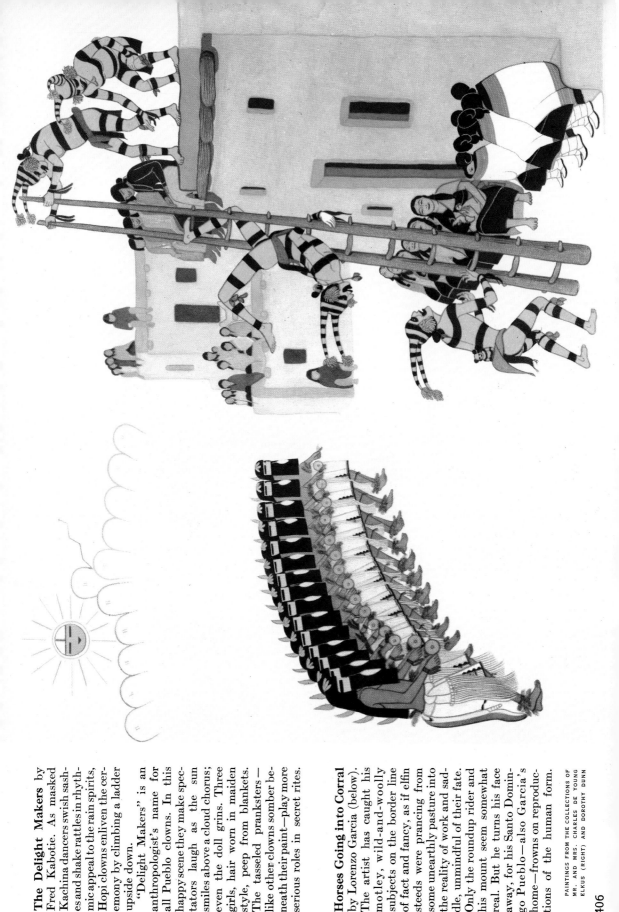

The Delight Makers by Fred Kabotie. As masked Kachina dancers swish sashes and shake rattles in rhythmic appeal to the rain spirits, Hopi clowns enliven the ceremony by climbing a ladder upside down.

"Delight Makers" is an anthropologist's name for all Pueblo clowns. In this happy scene they make spectators laugh as the sun smiles above a cloud chorus; even the doll grins. Three girls, hair worn in maiden style, peep from blankets. The tasseled pranksters — like other clowns somber beneath their paint—play more serious roles in secret rites.

Horses Going into Corral by Lorenzo Garcia (below). The artist has caught his motley, wild-and-woolly subjects on the border line of fact and fancy, as if elfin steeds were prancing from some unearthly pasture into the reality of work and saddle, unmindful of their fate. Only the roundup rider and his mount seem somewhat real. But he turns his face away, for his Santo Domingo Pueblo—also Garcia's home—frowns on reproductions of the human form.

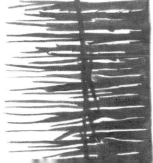
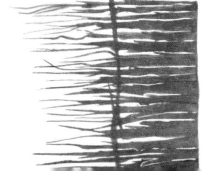

Wind Way by Bennie Tilden. Four long-necked healing spirits, holding snakes marked with deer tracks, derive from Navajo sand painting used in curing rites (pages 112, 119). Taboos forbid tribal artists to copy exactly the design of the original. At ceremony's end it is swept up and cast to the winds.

Bear Hunt by Joe H. Herrera. Tracks of man and bear chart hunt across abstract universe. As if sighting his quarry, hunter finally crouches on all fours. Bear prints cross squint-eyed sun, from which red-tipped clouds unfurl like sails. Horned moon looks down from upper right; ball below is a near-by planet. Symbolic rain falls in dots, mountains zigzag, triangle with seed is fertility symbol. Herrera's modern Pueblo art recalls the ancient forms.

THE HAVASUPAI

BY JACK BREED

AT HAVASU HILLTOP the Topocoba Trail begins a corkscrew descent into the land of the Havasupai, deep in a side gorge off the Grand Canyon of the Colorado. My leathery-faced, whistling Indian guide—"Joe Jones my name!"—casually spurred his horse over the edge and around the first of 29 switchbacks on a thousand-foot slope of slippery rock. As I followed, I did my best to forget his happy retort a few minutes before when I asked why horses rather than mules were used on the dizzy trail.

"You train horse early, he good as mule," Joe said, "but faster."

I swallowed hard and hung on. We dropped seemingly within minutes from the gray and buff limestone of the rim to the brilliant red sandstone of the inner gorge walls. Then we were in a meandering canyon, little more than a dry wash, that was to lead us 12 miles.

For three hours, from the rear, I had ample chance to study my companion. His was no traditional Indian garb; rather he wore sweat shirt, heavy boots, cotton socks, and, to top it all, a baseball cap! His tanned, round face, framing keen brown eyes, reminded me of a Hopi. But his gray hair was neatly cut and parted in barbershop style.

Gradually the red-walled ravine widened. Lush groves of cottonwoods and willows began to appear. Suddenly from the canyon wall came the rush and bubble of Havasu Creek, born of cold-welling springs—water as crystal-clear as any I had ever seen.

We crossed and recrossed the creek, riding between neatly fenced fields. Untethered horses looked up from their munching. Still I had seen neither Indians nor dwellings. Then, from a rise where the dusty trail cut between a boulder outcrop and the canyon wall, I saw, sprawled below, the lovely land of the Havasupai. Fields green with new corn bordered the sparkling stream. Orchards and rich brown, freshly turned earth surrounded quaint hogans and wooden cottages painted yellow, green, and blue.

At this point Havasu Canyon widens to about a quarter mile. Red walls rise hundreds of feet straight up (page 108). Two red pinnacles, ancient gods to the Indians, stand like sentinels. Legend says that when they tumble, doom will come upon the tribe.

Cottonwoods shade Supai village's "main street" leading to a white clapboard schoolhouse, with tiny steeple for the traditional bell, and playground of seesaws and swings—straight out of New England. Indians, busy over crops or chatting around a hogan, paused to wave to Joe, or just to stare at me.

Such is the home of the "People of the Blue-green Water." No automobile enters their hidden valley; the cold war seems far away.

At headquarters of Noble Guthrie, then Indian subagent on this remotest of United States reservations, I found electricity at the flip of a switch, hot and cold running water, refrigerators, innerspring mattresses, a radio transmitter, telephones, and a piano!

"Everything came in by horseback or by drag, down the trail you came," he said. "The old wagon road across the canyon hasn't been usable in years."

Mail comes in twice a week, and with it come cowboy boots, guitars, groceries, and most heavy provisions. It is much cheaper to mail goods to Supai than to hire a private pack horse.

When I was there, 35 Indian families lived in Havasu Canyon. They averaged four children each. Mr. Guthrie told me the reservation can support comfortably few more than 200 persons. A recent census showed 368, but many are away at any one time, working in Grand Canyon tourist centers or in towns near by.

For centuries the entire tribe moved out to gather seeds and track deer, antelope, and rabbit on the canyon rim in winter, farming their valley in summer. This semi-annual migration is now a thing of the past. Required school attendance for children through eighth grade is one obstacle. And few elders really want to leave their Shangri-La valley; they know a good thing when they have it.

No one here works harder than he has to. And since an implement company donated a tractor, packed in disassembled for use by the entire tribe, there's been even more time for horseback gallops along the canyon, rodeos, card games, and festivals. Almost as soon as they can walk, children learn to swim and ride. No elder tells them nay, for Havasupai believe that harsh words or punishment shrivel a child's soul.

If any one worries, it may be the older generation, remembering uneasily the terrible flash floods—the worst in 1911— that have roared down the valley to sweep the village away, while the Indians clung to the cliffsides. Perhaps they deplore, too, the coming of modern ways. Primitive mud and brush hogans, like those of the Navajo, are still common. But many a younger man and his family now live in small wood cottages brought in on mules by the Agency some years ago after a flood.

Joe Jones, I found, had gone halfway. He and his wife still lived in a dark and smelly hogan—their cottage they used as an oversize closet! Inside I saw at least nine pairs of trousers. Joe's previous visitors had left him amply endowed with white man's pants, his pride and joy.

Cooking and much other household life of the canyon still goes on outdoors. I had hoped that hand-shaped pottery and coiled baskets might still be in use, but I was too late. Modern sheepherder stoves, aluminum and porcelained pots and pans have replaced them.

Older women still make fine Supai baskets for sale at the Agency. And I noticed, drying on fences and rooftops, the deer hides for which Havasupai are famous. They tan skins by hand with deer's brains and marrow, working them immaculately white and soft.

Today, as always, Havasupai are outstanding farmers. After each flood they have rebuilt their elaborate irrigation

Heads Up! Bronc Loose! Havasupai scatter before wild hoofs as a thrown rider, in red chaps, scrambles from the dust. Bred to the saddle, the Blue-green Water People hold an all-Indian rodeo and harvest festival each summer in their remote cliff-walled valley. Walapai and Mohave come from the West, Hopi and Navajo from the east, some riding as far as 165 miles to compete.

KODACHROME BY WILLIAM BELKNAP, JR.

dams and ditches, and replanted their 175 acres of rich bottom lands, growing corn, beans, and squash as staple crops. From neat orchards come peaches, apricots, melons, and figs.

After hot work in the fields, the amazing Havasupai like to get even hotter, relaxing in steam baths. They parboil themselves in low tarpaulin-covered sweat lodges, half in and half out of the ground, by pouring water over fire-hot stones. Between periods of steaming—usually as long as it takes to sing four songs—they let sand dry on their bodies. They do this four times, then leap into the cold creek.

Havasupai still have a medicine man to shake his rattles over the sick. But they have a volunteer nurse who sees that seriously ill patients receive more modern treatment as well.

The populace turns out en masse for the movies shown in the schoolhouse.

Western pictures are top favorites. Cheers and boos reverberate; next day youthful braves gallop through the valley, playing "cowboys and Indians."

Superb horsemen, the Havasupai leap on a mount even to go next door, rather than walk. It is a common sight to see four or five Havasupai on one horse, a father in the saddle and his youngsters hanging on tightly fore and aft.

Reluctantly I climbed on a horse myself one morning and started back up the 14-mile trail to Hilltop. Joe Jones whistled and shouted to move his pack horses along. At parting I asked him, "Is there anything you'd like me to send you, Joe? Something you need?"

"I like your pants, thank you very much," said Joe, eyeing my Navy khakis.

He was shouting happily at his horses again as I watched him disappear down the trail, my trousers *and* shirt tied neatly to the back of his saddle!

THE INDIAN'S CHANGING WORLD

BY MATTHEW W. STIRLING

A BATTERED PICKUP TRUCK rattles away from South Dakota's Pine Ridge Indian Reservation. John Red Dog, full-blooded Dakota, drives to work for a rancher—a step toward answering his urge "to live like a white man."

Born in a meager frame house, Red Dog heard old men's wistful tales of buffalo hunts and battles with cavalry. Placed on the reservation, Red Dog's grandfather had scorned the plow offered him and remained bewildered by a life he had never known. The boy's father, lacking incentive, loafed about.

School meant little to Red Dog. Why study? His few ventures off the reservation taught him the bitter lesson of intolerance. He feared white men, was happy to return to strong family ties.

World War II's draft plunged Red Dog into a violent world. Gone was the warm security of his clan. In barracks no one cared. But gradually he learned self reliance, found he could make friends with white soldiers. He grew proud of his infantry unit, and of himself. A crack shot, he earned respect overseas on night patrols probing German positions. On furlough he saw London, Paris, Cannes. Shipped home, he spent a week visiting a white buddy in New York.

Return to the reservation after four years jolted him. Houses looked ramshackle, tribal leaders were sad old men clutching dreams. He found the ceremonies silly, snapped angrily at an elder who chided him. His family was hurt, but he didn't care. Listlessly, he worked his family's protected, tax-free acres. The scrawny cattle, the poverty depressed him. He talked with other Indian veterans, many bitter, more often drunk than sober. "Nuts," he would say in GI jargon, "I'm going over the hill."

Instead he married and raised a son.

He managed to keep his family in food and clothing, and saw that his son studied hard at the Government school. Red Dog's wife, placid, contented, couldn't understand his restlessness. She had her man, her child, her home and chores. What else was there?

Red Dog pictured his son facing the same drab, pointless life. Letters from army friends in Los Angeles and Chicago made him grumble with envy.

The agent found him a job outside— if he could supply a truck. To get money, he asked the council's permission to sell tribal cattle. No law kept him on the reservation; as citizen he could come and go. But cattle rate as lengthy a harangue as tribal uranium deposits.

Red Dog got his truck, and his family soon joined him off the reservation. Some 225,000 United States Indians have taken Red Dog's way to assimilation in the white man's world. The remaining 275,000 dwell on 205 Federal reservations —a home the Indian can always return to. They too face change.

Ojibwa in Minnesota and Michigan woodlands act as guides to city sportsmen. Eastern Cherokees live the mountaineer-farmer lives of their North Carolina neighbors. Tradition-proud Pueblos see their young men take jobs with atom scientists. Navajo elders debated hiring a professional rainmaker complete with airplane and dry ice. Apaches have prospered farming good New Mexico land; one group bids for tourists with a motel. Oklahoma tribesmen hold public office, enter professions, often drive up in Cadillacs to inspect tribal oil wells.

Common to all areas is the impact of 25,000 World War II Indian veterans, hastening the change. Still, tradition shows in timeless ceremonies and crafts, as the following pages illustrate.

Girded with Jingling Bells, a Plumed Teen-ager Performs a Ritual Dance at Taos Pueblo

KODACHROMES BY JUSTIN LOCKE

Pueblo Ceremonies Strike an Old Refrain, but the furniture is Grand Rapids. With rattles and sacred wand, San Ildefonso Indians seek rain for crops of corn. Mellowed adobe walls at Taos (left) recall pagan doorless days when ladders were drawn up to bar invaders. In the Cochiti apartment above, a crucifix looks upon a family supping on the linoleum, washing down tortillas with coffee from an enamel pot.

Navajo Summer in the Open. Amid
towering sandstone pillars of mile-high
Monument Valley, athwart the Arizo-
na-Utah line, this family has quit winter's log-and-mud hogan for an arbor
open to the breezes. Mother weaves a
rug on a loom such as her people borrowed from ancient Pueblos.

Carding raw wool from flocks watched
by son on donkey, she twists it into
yarn on wooden spindle at her left, colors it with aniline dyes. Opening the
warp threads on her upright loom with
a stick, she inserts the colored weft
threads, packs them down with toothed
batten. A borderless geometrical pattern emerges; she seldom pictures men
or animals. Left: Milking a balky
Navajo goat is a fore-and-aft job!

ALFRED M. BAILEY AND FRED G. BRANDENBURG

416

Birth of a Buckle. Prize-winning silversmith Tom Burnsides finishes a shiny belt buckle at Arizona's Pine Springs Trading Post, center of Navajo silver casters. He cut his mold, entirely from imagination, in chalky volcanic tuff hacked from a desert outcrop. Here he chisels away excess silver from the cast, and files it smooth before polishing. All scrap goes into later melts.

The finished buckle (lower right) has center post and tongue soldered on. Just above, as it came from the mold, the cast still has branching channels and extra crossbars for even flow of molten silver from the pouring hole. Needles shooting out from edges indicate small passages punched in the mold to allow air to escape.

The artist adapted his bracelet from the leather bow guard of old-time Navajo archers. He wears a belt of silver concha disks, as does the woman weaver opposite, and turquoise ring and necklace. From boyhood, Navajo males wear bright headbands.

417

Youthful Grins Tell a Success Story in Apache Town. Bylas, a town straddling U.S. Highway 70, is home to 700 Apaches of Arizona's San Carlos Indian Reservation. Fathers of these children own radios, their mothers run powered washing machines. Neat frame houses replace brush wickiups of nomad days, pickup trucks supplant old buckboards. The neighboring town—Geronimo—recalls the fierce tribal reputation (page 115). Geronimo's raiding Chiricahua band, finally rounded up in 1886, were "prisoners of war" until 1913; recalcitrant young-'uns were carted to school, feet bound to prevent their leaping from wagons. But Apaches, like other Indian groups, now value education. These Bylas youngsters enjoy classes, sports, play trophy-winning basketball.

Most young Indians attend regular public schools. The U.S. Indian Service also maintains 222 day schools on reservations, as well as 85 boarding schools, mostly for the increasing Navajo. A Government fund aids college training. Many graduates enter the Indian Service as teachers, stenographers, may rise to become school or agency superintendents. Others have discovered the tourist-attracting value of traditional dances like that at right. When afternoon shadows deepen in Grand Canyon, Indians from the near-by Hopi reservation perform their feather dance on the canyon rim.

WESTERN WAYS FEATURES; JUSTIN LOCKE (OPPOSITE)

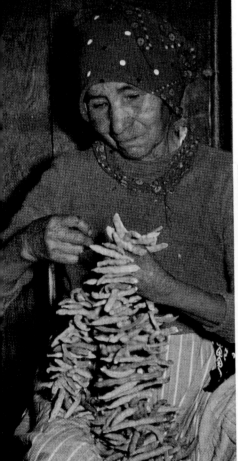

Sewing Machines Conquer Where Soldiers Failed. Seminole seamstress, helped by youngsters, descends from warriors who never surrendered, hung on in Florida after troops moved other Seminoles to Oklahoma (pages 68–71). Self-reliant Florida Indians cherish old ways, but accept white man's inventions and schooling, as earnest young faces show below. Seminole hunt and raise cattle on two reservations near Lake Okeechobee, or make livings outside, farming, lumbering, selling handicrafts.

Some Cherokees, too, resisted transfer west, stayed in North Carolina. Woman, left, one of the State's 3,000 Cherokees, strings green beans for winter fare. Dried, they are "leather britches."

420

NATIONAL GEOGRAPHIC PHOTOGRAPHERS
WILLARD R. CULVER AND ROBERT F. SISSON

MOHAWKS SCRAPE THE SKY

BY ROBERT L. CONLY

THE LAST PLACE you'd expect to meet a Mohawk Indian is atop the towering steel skeleton of a New York City skyscraper. Yet many a Mohawk earns a living 500 to 1,000 feet in the air, where one misstep means death. I saw them catfooting along narrow girders, and wondered at this modern tribal occupation, more perilous than any warpath.

Mohawks helped build the lofty UN buildings, the Metropolitan Life Tower, Woolworth Building, RCA Building, and, outreaching all, the quarter-mile-high Empire State Building.

Tom Lahache, tall, dignified, with typical high Indian cheekbones and deep-set eyes, got his first job in "high iron" some 30 years ago when he was 17.

"You don't pay much attention to how tall a building is," he said. "If you slip, 50 feet is as bad as 500 feet."

With Tom in the riveting gang I watched were Tom Jacobs, Mike Tarbell, and Mickey Snow, all Mohawks, all veteran iron workers. Munching sandwiches and swigging soda pop, they explained how they operate; lunch over, they demonstrated.

Mickey heated rivets in a stove on the girders, then tossed each red-hot rivet to Mike, who caught it in a bucket, and with tongs thrust it into place. Lahache held it firm with a dolly bar while Tom Jacobs flattened the end with a rivet gun. Simple—as long as nobody stepped back into empty air.

These men are among some 400 Mohawks living in an old section of Brooklyn. A few own houses; the rest rent walk-up apartments. Some have cars; most have television sets on which they favor Western programs—about Indians.

Their migration to Brooklyn dates from the late 1920's. The origin of their hazardous talent goes back further still.

After the American Revolution, the exiled Mohawks (page 26) settled in Canada on reservations like Caughnawaga on the St. Lawrence River. For nearly a century they farmed, trapped, piloted fur-laden canoes through the rapids. Then in the '80's a bridge company spanning the river from Caughnawaga to Lachine promised Mohawks jobs as laborers in return for use of their land.

As fast as the bridge went up, so did the Mohawks, swarming out on its narrow beams. Hardened riveters, working on the span's dizziest heights, would find Indians peering curiously over their shoulders to see what was going on.

Impressed, an engineer taught some to rivet. Men willing to crawl around girders were hard to find in those days. When the builders moved on, full-fledged Mohawk ironworkers went too— with brothers, cousins, and friends.

Why did Mohawks take so eagerly to this spine-chilling work? In 1714, John Lawson, surveyor and traveler, noted a puzzling Indian characteristic: "They will walk over deep Brooks, and Creeks, on the smallest Poles, and that without any Fear or Concern. Nay, an Indian will walk on the Ridge of a Barn or House and look down the Gable-end, and spit upon the Ground, as unconcerned, as if he was walking on Terra firma."

Joining construction gangs all over Canada, Mohawks followed jobs into the United States. Manhattan of the 1920's, its skyscrapers sprouting like beanstalks, was a happy hunting ground. Early to settle in Brooklyn was Tom Jacobs. His first job was almost his last.

"I was working on a corner 200, maybe 300, feet up," he told me. "My foot slipped, and all of a sudden there was nothing under me but the ground, so far away I could hardly see it. When I felt

With the Greatest of Ease sure-footed Mohawks tread soaring beams, catch glowing rivets tossed from high-perched stoves. At home in Brooklyn, Mike Tarbell, below, relaxes like any father. Clannish Mohawks live close together, patronize one restaurant so often it's called the Wigwam.

422

Standing on Air, 1,472 dizzy feet above New York's 34th Street, Mohawk riveters erect the 222-foot television tower atop the Empire State Building, which they also helped build. For this breath-taking work, Indians collected $3.25 an hour. "Whatever they get," said an onlooker, "it isn't enough!"

NATIONAL GEOGRAPHIC PHOTOGRAPHER **423**
B. ANTHONY STEWART

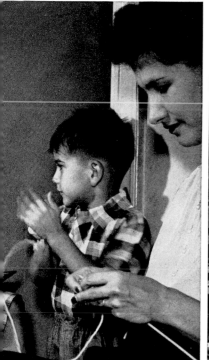

Brooklyn Born Is Linda "Holding an Apple," but Blood of Mohawk Warriors Runs in Her Veins

myself falling, I stuck out my arm, and it caught a beam. I just hung there, swinging in the wind. The other men shouted, 'Tom, what are you going to do?' What a question!

"I chinned myself on that beam, got a leg over it, and climbed up. I sat there for a while to get my breath, then went back to work."

Mohawks have adapted themselves well to Brooklyn, though elders frown on marriages between Indians and non-Indians (which happen anyway). Most

are bilingual. Children go to public schools. Boys play baseball in streets and parks.

At Cuyler Presbyterian Church, where services are held once a month in Mohawk, families sing such old stand-bys as *Ni-io ta-tia-ta-nons-tat* ("Rock of Ages"). And after an "Indian show," complete with tepees, tomahawks, and a "campfire" made of sticks around a light bulb, they give hearty voice to their favorite song, *Ka-na-wa-ke te-tsi-te-we*— "Let's Go Back to Caughnawaga."

For Additional Reference •

The more than 700 issues of the *National Geographic Magazine* provide a treasury of information. Since 1899 The Magazine has published scores of authoritative articles on Indian life in North, Central, and South America—ranging from Aleuts to Zapotecs, Blackfeet to Yahgans, from acorns as Indian food resource to the Snake Dance of the Hopi. Refer to the NATIONAL GEOGRAPHIC MAGAZINE CUMULATIVE INDEX.

Other National Geographic publications include the following:

EVERYDAY LIFE IN ANCIENT TIMES • *215 illustrations*
        120 full-color paintings by H. M. Herget • 356 pages $6.00

THE BOOK OF FISHES *edited by John Oliver La Gorce*
        377 illustrations • 207 in full color • 340 pages $7.00

THE WORLD IN YOUR GARDEN • *145 illustrations*
        80 full-color paintings by Else Bostelmann • 248 pages .. $6.50

THE NATIONAL GEOGRAPHIC BOOK OF DOGS
        342 illustrations • 189 in full color • 432 pages $9.85

Prices postpaid. Write for publications brochure to The Society's headquarters, Washington 6, D.C.